It's comforting to know who you can rely on

The 4000 Chair

The Abbey Lectern

The Kelso Stacking Chair

Our customers have the peace of mind in knowing that we are renowned for our commitment to only using the best raw materials and the highest standards of production in our furniture. Quality of service and product has been our priority since James Chase & Son was established in 1931.

ASK FOR OUR BROCHURE NOW
0845 7125488
Calls charged at local rate

We have over thirty years experience as Church Furnishings specialists, so you will be in good hands. Our chairs are in over 5,000 places of worship throughout the UK, so you will be in good company too. If you do need someone to rely on, call us and we will be delighted to discuss your requirements.

OUR RANGE INCLUDES

CHAIRS • TABLES • PULPITS • ALTARS • KNEELERS
SILVERWARE • VESTMENTS

JAMES CHASE
& SON (FURNISHINGS) LTD

191 Thornton Rd, Bradford BD1 2JT. Telephone: 01274 738282 Fax: 01274 737836
e-mail: sales@james-chase.co.uk website: www.james-chase.co.uk

Local people

supported by a unique, caring organisation.
That's what
makes us different.

Your local Funeral Home is part of the nationwide Co-operative Movement.

A Movement owned by local people like you.

The Co-op is founded on strong principles of caring for others and concern for the community.

Those traditions are as strong today as they have ever been.

As part of the local community, we can offer you a genuinely local funeral service backed

by the strength and reassurance of a unique, caring national organisation.

PLAN AHEAD. For all of us, it is sensible and practical to plan
ahead. The Co-operative Funeral Bond allows you to tailor-make
your own plan and pay for your funeral at today's prices. There are
no hidden extras, no medical is required and there is no age limit.

For an Information Pack simply call us free on
0800 289 120 or contact your local branch.

FUNERALS

We understand

CALL FUNERALCARE FREE ON 0800 44 66 96.
Head Office: 119 Paisley Road, Glasgow G5 8RL. Tel: 0141 429 4433.
Branches throughout Scotland.

Viscount Organs

VISCOUNT continues to develop their unique range of digital (sampled sound) organs and to provide quality instruments for churches and homes at attractive prices – portable instruments from £675, two and 3 manual organs from £2250 rising to £13500 including VAT. There are fifteen models at price points to suit most budgets and specification needs. Unique to VISCOUNT is the opportunity for the organist to choose a "voicing set" (English or baroque) which he can regulate to suit the accoustics and/or to match the repertoire. The tracker feel keyboard with (optional) wooden keynotes, provides a most comfortable instrument to play. Although their organs have a predetermined Stoplist (which achieves their 'low prices') it is possible to 'customise' instruments for personal preferences. Several international recitalists now play their organs for home practice. Their church installation adviser will visit their church to provide a competitive quotation for an installation to include an external speaker system if appropriate. 'In Church' demonstrations can be arranged.

Viscount Prestige V Organ
£7500 Incl VAT
(with 32 Radiating Concave Pedalboard)

Wm M. McIntosh
EDINBURGH ORGAN STUDIO
98 Canongate, The Royal Mile
Edinburgh EH8 8DD
Tel: 0131 556 3004   Fax: 0131 556 8445
e-mail: eos@breathemail.net
Website: WWW.organstudio.co.uk

The Right Reverend John B. Cairns LTh LLB

MODERATOR

The Church of Scotland
YEAR BOOK
—— 1999/2000 ——

Interim Editor
Rev. A. Gordon McGillivray
MA BD STM

Published on behalf of
THE CHURCH OF SCOTLAND
BOARD OF COMMUNICATION
by SAINT ANDREW PRESS
121 George Street, Edinburgh EH2 4YN

THE OFFICES OF THE CHURCH

121 George Street
Edinburgh EH2 4YN

Tel: 0131 225 5722
Fax: 0131 220 3113
Internet: http://www.cofs.org.uk/

Office Hours:
Office Manager:

Monday–Friday 9.00 am–5.00 pm
Mr Robert Simpson

PARISH EDUCATION
Annie Small House   18 Inverleith Terrace, Edinburgh EH3 5NS   Tel: 0131 332 0343

SOCIAL RESPONSIBILITY
Charis House   47 Milton Road East, Edinburgh EH15 2SR   Tel: 0131 657 2000
[e-mail: info@charis.org.uk]   Fax: 0131 657 5000

NATIONAL MISSION
Glasgow Office   59 Elmbank Street, Glasgow G2 4PQ   Tel: 0141 333 1948
Kirkcaldy Office   St Brycedale Church Centre,
St Brycedale Avenue, Kirkcaldy KY1 1ET   Tel/Fax: 01592 646406

(Youth Adviser: Presbytery of Glasgow)
168 Bath Street, Glasgow G2 4TQ   Tel: 0141 333 9374

QUICK DIRECTORY

A.C.T.S. 01786   823588
Badenoch Centre 01540   651373
Board of Communication 0131   240 2236
Bridgeton, St Francis-in-the-East Church House 0141   554 8045
Carberry 0131   665 3135/7604
Christian Aid Scotland 0131   220 1254
Christian Aid London 0171   620 4444
Lodging House Mission 0141   552 0285
Netherbow 0131   556 9579/2647
Pathway Productions 0131   447 3531
Press Office 0131   226 2243
Society, Religion and Technology Project 0131   556 2953
St Ninian's Crieff 01764   653766

First published in 1999 by SAINT ANDREW PRESS, 121 George Street, Edinburgh EH2 4YN on behalf of the BOARD of COMMUNICATION of the CHURCH of SCOTLAND

Copyright © The BOARD of COMMUNICATION of the CHURCH of SCOTLAND 1999

ISBN 0 86153 287 2

British Library Cataloguing in Publication Data
A catalogue record for this book
is available from the British Library.
ISBN 0861532872

Printed and bound by Bell and Bain Ltd, Glasgow.

CONTENTS

All correspondence regarding the Year Book should be sent to
The Editor, *Church of Scotland Year Book*,
Saint Andrew Press, 121 George Street, Edinburgh EH2 4YN
Fax: 0131 220 3113
[e-mail: cofs.standrew@dial.pipex.com]

GENERAL ASSEMBLY OF 2000
The General Assembly of 2000 will convene on
Saturday, 20th May 2000.

FROM THE MODERATOR

TO commend the *Year Book* to ministers should be unnecessary. It ought to be as much stating the obvious as telling someone in a drought that water is good for them. The information contained in the *Year Book* probably does exist elsewhere, but cannot be unearthed without considerable expenditure of time and effort. The facts, names, addresses, regulations and suggestions are only available in this concise form because of the diligence of the Editor, the Rev. Gordon McGillivray, and all those folk in Presbyteries and Church Offices who supply the appropriate updated information year by year. Our thanks are due to them all.

I am the world's least enthusiastic form-filler, largely because so many of them lead to no practical advantage. This is different. There are practical applications to be made of all that is contained herein! Trust Fund addresses, identification of the mandarins at "121" who are always ready with advice and sometimes money, up-to-date information on parishes to be used not only when dreaming of a change of Charge, but also in finding names and contact numbers of ministers for those who are moving house, Hospital Chaplains, Forces Chaplains, and so much more.

It seems quite surprising that there appear to be ministers and congregations who do not need any of this, or are satisfied with out-of-date information. Don't risk being a millennium out-of-date! Read the new edition each year!

John B. Cairns
JULY 1999

FROM THE INTERIM EDITOR

THIS issue of the annual *Year Book* contains no dramatic alterations in format from last year's issue, despite its moving into a new millennium. One sign of the times is the increased number of e.mail addresses both for ministers and for the various Boards and Committees of the Church.

Particular attention is drawn to
- the Dates of Board and Committee Meetings to be found at the beginning of Section 1;
- the alphabetising of Societies and Associations in Section 2;
- the Digest of Assembly Decisions in Section 4;
- the explanation of the Symbols used in the Presbytery Lists in Section 5;
- the inclusion of TA and Army Cadet Force Chaplains in Section 6;
- the Notes at the beginning of Section 7 dealing with Congregational Statistics.

Again I am indebted to Sandy Gemmell, Deputy General Treasurer, for keying in the figures relating to congregational membership, the eldership, congregational income, and Mission and Aid, and also to Ruth Lawrie, Publicity and Design, for resolving my many keyboard problems.

Without the help of Presbytery Clerks, the Secretaries of Boards and Committees, the staff of Saint Andrew Press, Bell and Bain, Glasgow (the Printers), and Contact Publicity (Advertising Agency), the production of the *Year Book* would be a much more difficult and far less pleasurable undertaking.

Please let me know where corrections are necessary.

A. Gordon McGillivray
AUGUST 1999

SECTION 1

Assembly Boards
and Committees

MEETINGS OF BOARDS AND COMMITTEES

ARTISTIC MATTERS
1999	September 2, October 7, November 4, December 9
2000	February 3, March 2, April 6, May 4, June 1, July 6, (August 3), September 7

ASSEMBLY COUNCIL
Meets as required

CHURCH AND NATION
1999	September 6-7, November 4, December 9
2000	January 26-27, February 22, June (to be confirmed)

CHURCH OF SCOTLAND TRUST
1999	September 23
2000	(to be confirmed)

DOCTRINE
1999	December 1
2000	February 2, June 7

ECUMENICAL RELATIONS
1999	September 23
2000	January 27, March 23, June 22

EDUCATION
1999	September 15, November 17
2000	February 9, June 14, September 20, November 15

GENERAL TRUSTEES
(A) General Trustees
1999	September 28, October 26, November 23, December 21
2000	January 25, February 22, March 21, April 25, May 30, July 4, September 26

(B) Fabric and Chairman's
1999	September 7, October 12, November 9, December 7
2000	January 11, February 8, March 7, April 4, May 16, June 13, July 25, Sept 5

(C) Glebes
1999	September 8, October 13, November 10, December 8
2000	January 12, February 9, March 8, April 5, May 17, June 14, July 26, Sept 6

GUILD
(A) National Executive
1999	September 21, November 2
2000	February 8, March 29

(B) Finance and General Purposes
1999	October 5
2000	February 1

(C) Marketing and Publicity
1999	October 18
2000	January 27, March 23

(D) PROGRAMMES AND RESOURCES
  1999   OCTOBER 14, NOVEMBER 11
  2000   MARCH 9
(E) PROJECTS AND TOPICS
  1999   OCTOBER 26
  2000   JANUARY 25, MARCH 14
(F) MATTERS CONCERNING YOUNGER WOMEN
  1999   OCTOBER 6
  2000   JANUARY 19, MARCH 15
  JOINT CONFERENCE
  1999   SEPTEMBER 21-22 (CARBERRY)

INVESTORS TRUST
  1999   OCTOBER 26
  2000   FEBRUARY 22, APRIL 25, JULY 25

MINISTRY
(A) BOARD
  1999   SEPTEMBER 9-10, DECEMBER 8
  2000   FEBRUARY 9, JUNE 14, SEPTEMBER 20-21
(B) MINISTRY SUPPORT
  1999   OCTOBER 14, NOVEMBER 11
  2000   JANUARY 13, MARCH 9, APRIL 13, AUGUST 31, OCTOBER 12
(C) VOCATIONAL GUIDANCE
  1999   OCTOBER 13, NOVEMBER 10
  2000   JANUARY 12, MARCH 8, APRIL 12, AUGUST 30, OCTOBER 11
(D) EDUCATION AND TRAINING
  1999   OCTOBER 13, NOVEMBER 10
  2000   JANUARY 12, MARCH 8, APRIL 12, AUGUST 30,.OCTOBER 11
(E) MINISTRY DEVELOPMENT
  1999   OCTOBER 14, NOVEMBER 11
  2000   JANUARY 13, MARCH 9, APRIL 13, AUGUST 31, OCTOBER 12
(F) HOUSING AND LOAN TRUSTEES
  1999   SEPTEMBER 21, NOVEMBER 16
  2000   JANUARY 18, MARCH 21, APRIL 18, JUNE 20, SEPTEMBER 19, DECEMBER 12

NATIONAL MISSION
(A) BOARD
  1999   SEPTEMBER 1, DECEMBER 1
  2000   FEBRUARY 2, JUNE 7, SEPTEMBER 6
(B) CHAPLAINCIES
  1999   JUNE 9, NOVEMBER 3
  2000   JANUARY 26, JUNE 14, NOVEMBER 1
(C) CHURCH AND INDUSTRY
  1999   SEPTEMBER 15, NOVEMBER 17
  2000   JANUARY 19, APRIL 19, JUNE 21, SEPTEMBER 20
(D) HOSPITALS AND UNIVERSITIES
  1999   SEPTEMBER 28, NOVEMBER 23
  2000   JANUARY 18, MARCH 14, MAY 23, SEPTEMBER 26
(E) PRISON
  1999   OCTOBER 6
  2000   JANUARY 12, MAY 31, OCTOBER 4

(F) MISSION AND EVANGELISM RESOURCES
 1999 SEPTEMBER 14-15, OCTOBER 28
 2000 JANUARY 20, MARCH 16, JUNE 1, SEPTEMBER 12-13

(G) NEW CHARGE DEVELOPMENT
 1999 SEPTEMBER 15, NOVEMBER 17
 2000 JANUARY 19, MARCH 22, JUNE 21, SEPTEMBER 20

(H) PARISH ASSISTANCE
 1999 SEPTEMBER 29, NOVEMBER 24
 2000 JANUARY 19, JUNE 14, SEPTEMBER 27

(I) PARISH REAPPRAISAL
 1999 SEPTEMBER 21, OCTOBER 19, NOVEMBER 16, DECEMBER 21
 2000 FEBRUARY 15, MARCH 21, APRIL 18, JUNE 20, SEPTEMBER 19

(J) IONA COMMUNITY BOARD
 1999 OCTOBER 21
 2000 FEBRUARY 17

(K) JOINT PRISON CHAPLAINCIES BOARD
 1999 SEPTEMBER 10, OCTOBER 8, NOVEMBER 12, DECEMBER 10
 2000 JANUARY 14, FEBRUARY 18, MARCH 24, APRIL 21, MAY 26, JUNE 23, SEPTEMBER 8, OCTOBER 6

(L) PRIORITY AREAS FUND
 1999 OCTOBER 25
 2000 JANUARY 31, APRIL 24, AUGUST 28, OCTOBER 23

NOMINATION OF MODERATOR OF ASSEMBLY
 1999 AUGUST 31, OCTOBER 19

PARISH EDUCATION
 2000 FEBRUARY 18, JUNE 15

PENSION TRUSTEES
 1999 NOVEMBER 2
 2000 MARCH 14, MAY 2, AUGUST 1, NOVEMBER 7

PERSONNEL
 1999 SEPTEMBER 2, DECEMBER 2
 2000 FEBRUARY 17, APRIL 13

PRACTICE AND PROCEDURE
 1999 SEPTEMBER 21, NOVEMBER 16
 2000 JANUARY 18, FEBRUARY 15, MARCH 14, APRIL 18

STEWARDSHIP AND FINANCE
 1999 NOVEMBER 10-11
 2000 FEBRUARY 23, MARCH 22, JUNE 21

WORLD MISSION
(A) BOARD
 1999 OCTOBER 6, DECEMBER 8
 2000 FEBRUARY 16, APRIL 12

(B) EUROPE
 1999 SEPTEMBER 24

(C) FINANCE
    1999   SEPTEMBER 21
(D) FURLOUGH HOUSES
    1999   SEPTEMBER 10
(E) HEALTHCARE ADVISORY GROUP
    1999   SEPTEMBER 21
(F) LOCAL INVOLVEMENT
    1999   SEPTEMBER 23
(G) OVERSEAS PARTNERSHIP
    1999   SEPTEMBER 16, NOVEMBER 11
    2000   JANUARY 27, MARCH 16
(H) WORLD CHURCH IN SCOTLAND
    1999   SEPTEMBER 14; NOVEMBER 9
    2000   JANUARY 25, MARCH 14

WORSHIP
    1999   SEPTEMBER 16, NOVEMBER 11
    2000   FEBRUARY 24, JUNE 8, SEPTEMBER 14

[NOTE: Years, where given, indicate the year of appointment.]

(1) GENERAL ADMINISTRATION
(PRACTICE AND PROCEDURE)

MEMBERSHIP
BOARD OF PRACTICE AND PROCEDURE
(38 members: 32 appointed by the Assembly, plus Moderator, Moderator Designate, Clerks, Procurator and Law Agent *ex officiis*)
Convener: Mrs Ann McCarter (1996)
Vice Convener: Rev. William C. Hewitt BD
Secretary: The Principal Clerk

COMMITTEE TO NOMINATE THE MODERATOR
(54 members: 3 surviving immediate past Moderators, 3 elders appointed through the Nomination Committee and 1 member from each UK Presbytery and the Presbytery of Europe)
Convener: The latest serving former Moderator present and willing to act.
Secretary: The Principal Clerk

JUDICIAL COMMISSION OF THE GENERAL ASSEMBLY
Chairman: Sheriff J. Douglas Allan
Vice Chairman: Rev. Alistair G.C. McGregor QC BD
Secretaries: The Clerks of Assembly

STAFF
Principal Clerk: Rev. Finlay A.J. Macdonald MA BD PhD
Depute Clerk: Rev. Marjory A. MacLean LLB BD
Administrative Officer: Miss Chris Brown MBE BA

REMIT: BOARD OF PRACTICE AND PROCEDURE
(a) To advise the General Assembly on questions of Church Law and of Constitutional Law affecting the relationship between Church and State.
(b) To advise and assist Committees of the General Assembly in the preparation of proposed legislation and on questions of interpretation, including interpretation of and proposed changes to their remits.
(c) To make all necessary arrangements for the General Assembly each year.
(d) To advise the Moderator anent his or her official duties, if so required.
(e) To be responsible to the General Assembly for the care and maintenance of all Assembly buildings and its other property.
(f) To compile the statistics of the Church, except Youth and Finance; and to supervise on behalf of the General Assembly all arrangements for care of Church Records and for Quinquennial Visitations.
(g) To attend to the general interests of the Church in matters which are not covered by the remit of any other Committee; and to perform such other duties as may be assigned to it by Act or Deliverance of the General Assembly.
(h) To deal with urgent issues arising between meetings of the General Assembly or the Commission of Assembly which do not fall within the remit of any Board, provided that
  (a)   it shall not be competent for the Board to take or authorise an action which is

(i)   of such a nature that it would have been *ultra vires* of the Commission of Assembly, or

(ii) of a legislative or judicial nature, or

(iii) an order or instruction to any Court or Courts of the Church;

(b) any action taken in terms of this Clause shall be reported by the Board to the next meeting of the General Assembly or the Commission of Assembly, whichever is the sooner.

---

(2) GENERAL TRUSTEES

MEMBERSHIP
(New Trustees are appointed, as required, by the General Assembly, on the recommendation of the General Trustees)

Chairman:	Mr William S. Carswell MA LLB (1999)
Vice Chairman:	Rev. James H. Simpson BD LLB (1999)
Secretary and Clerk:	Mr Alan W. Cowe MA LLB (Tel: 0131 225 5722)
Depute Secretary and Clerk:	Mr T.R.W. Parker LLB

COMMITTEES – FABRIC COMMITTEE
Convener: Rev. James H. Simpson BD LLB (1994)

CHAIRMAN'S COMMITTEE
Convener: Mr William S. Carswell MA LLB (1999)

GLEBES COMMITTEE
Convener: Mr A.S. Chalmers FRICS (1988)

FINANCE COMMITTEE
Convener: Mr R.G. Burnett BComm CA FCMA (1999)

LAW COMMITTEE
Convener: Mr William S. Carswell MA LLB (1990)

STAFF

Secretary and Clerk:	Mr Alan W. Cowe MA LLB
Depute Secretary and Clerk:	Mr T.R.W. Parker LLB
Assistants:	Miss P.M. Burnside LLB (Glebes)
	Mr David D. Robertson LLB NP (Ecclesiastical Buildings)
Treasurer:	Mr D.F. Ross MA CA
Deputy Treasurer:	Mr W.J. McKean BAcc CA

REMIT
The General Trustees are a Property Corporation created and incorporated under the Church of Scotland (General Trustees) Order Confirmation Act 1921. Their duties, powers and responsibilities were greatly extended by the Church of Scotland (Property & Endowments) Acts and Orders 1925 to 1995, and they are also charged with the administration of the Central Fabric Fund (see below) and the Consolidated Fabric Fund and the Consolidated Stipend Fund in which monies held centrally for the benefit of individual congregations are lodged.

The scope of the work of the Trustees is broad, covering all facets of property administration, but particular reference is made to the following matters:

1.   **ECCLESIASTICAL BUILDINGS.** The Trustees' Fabric Committee considers proposals for work at buildings, regardless of how they are vested, and plans of new buildings. Details of all such projects should be submitted to the Committee before work is commenced. The Committee also deals with applications for the release of fabric monies held by the General Trustees for individual congregations, and considers applications for assistance from the Central Fabric Fund from which grants and/or loans may be given to assist congregations faced with expenditure on fabric. Application forms relating to consents for work and possible financial assistance from the Central Fabric Fund are available from the Secretary of the Trustees and require to be submitted through Presbytery with its approval.

The Committee normally meets on the first or second Tuesday of each month, apart from July when it meets on the last Tuesday and August when there is no meeting.

2.   **SALE, PURCHASE AND LETTING OF PROPERTIES.** All sales or lets of properties vested in the General Trustees fall to be carried out by them in consultation with the Financial Board of the congregation concerned, and no steps should be taken towards any sale or let without prior consultation with the Secretary of the Trustees. Where property to be purchased is to be vested in the General Trustees it is essential that contact be made at the earliest possible stage with the Solicitor to the Trustees who is responsible for the lodging of offers for such properties and all subsequent legal procedure.

3.   **GLEBES.** The Trustees are responsible for the administration of Glebes vested in their ownership. All lets fall to be granted by them in consultation with the Minister concerned. It should be noted that neither Ministers nor Kirk Sessions may grant lets of Glebe land vested in the General Trustees. As part of their Glebe administration the Trustees review regularly all Glebe rents.

4.   **INSURANCE.** Properties vested in the General Trustees must be insured with the Church of Scotland Insurance Co. Ltd, a company wholly owned by the Church of Scotland whose profits are applied for Church purposes. Insurance enquiries should be sent directly to the Company at 67 George Street, Edinburgh EH2 2JG.
(Tel: 0131 220 4119 Fax: 0131 220 4120)

(3) NOMINATION

MEMBERSHIP – NOMINATION COMMITTEE
(44 members)
Convener: Rev. Fraser R. Aitken MA BD (1999)
Vice-Convener: Rev. Keith F. Hall BD
Secretary: The Principal Clerk

REMIT
To bring before the General Assembly names of persons to serve on the Boards and Standing Committees of the General Assembly.

(4) CHURCH OF SCOTLAND INVESTORS TRUST

MEMBERSHIP
(Trustees are appointed by the General Assembly, on the nomination of the Investors Trust)
Chairman: Prof. R.G. Burnett BCom CA FCMA
Vice Chairman: Mr J.B.M. Dick ACIB
Treasurer: Mr D.F. Ross MA CA
Secretary: Mr J.L. Henderson MCIBS

REMIT
The Church of Scotland Investors Trust, established in 1994 by Act of Parliament, offers to Boards, Committees and congregations of the Church a simple and economical medium for the investment of their funds. Investors are at liberty to invest in the Church of Scotland Investors Trust to an unlimited extent and it is felt that the facilities afforded thereby are preferable to the powers of investment offered by the Trustee Investments Act 1961, with all the attendant restrictions and conditions. The Church of Scotland Investors Trust provides three Funds for Church investors:

(a) THE DEPOSIT FUND is intended for short term money and deposits are repayable on demand. Interest is calculated quarterly, but paid gross, half yearly on 15th May and 15th November. The Fund is invested in short term loans to Banks, Building Societies and Licensed Deposit-Taking Institutions. There is no capital appreciation in the Deposit Fund and hence there is no protection for capital against inflation. The Deposit Fund is professionally managed by Noble Grossart Limited, Edinburgh.

(b) THE GROWTH FUND previously known as the "General Investment Fund" is an equity-based Fund, intended for long-term investment. The Fund, which is operated on a unitised basis, is designed to provide capital growth whilst maintaining a steady growth in income distribution. Units can be purchased or sold monthly. Income is distributed gross, half-yearly on 15th May and 15th November. The Growth Fund is professionally managed by Murray Johnstone Ltd, Glasgow.

(c) THE INCOME FUND is intended for medium term investment of capital on which it is essential to obtain an immediate and consistent high yield. The Fund is invested predominantly in fixed interest securities. It offers little protection against inflation for income or capital. The Income Fund is operated on a unitised basis and units can be purchased or sold monthly. Income is distributed gross, half-yearly, on 15th March and 15th September. The Income Fund is professionally managed by Baillie Gifford & Co., Edinburgh.

Application Forms for investment and further information may be had from the Secretary of the Church of Scotland Investors Trust, 121 George Street, Edinburgh EH2 4YN.

(5) STEWARDSHIP AND FINANCE

MEMBERSHIP
BOARD OF STEWARDSHIP AND FINANCE
(73 Members: 26 appointed by the Assembly, plus Convener and Vice-Convener, and 47 from Presbyteries who attend three meetings of the Board at which they have full rights of Board members)

Convener:	Mr Leon M. Marshall CA (1997)
Vice Convener:	Rev. Colin Caskie BA BD (1998)

STAFF

Secretary:	Mr William J. Farrell
General Treasurer:	Mr Donald F. Ross MA CA
Deputy General Treasurers:	Mr Alexander F. Gemmill BAcc CA
	Mr John S. Steven CA
	Mr William J. McKean BAcc CA
Assistant Treasurer	Mrs Anne Macintosh BA CA
Deputy Secretary:	Mr Crawford Conochie
Stewardship Consultants:	Mr Thomas Kinvig
	Mrs Gillian Paterson
	Mr John Gray

REMIT
1. To promote teaching and understanding of Christian Stewardship throughout the Church. To provide programmes to assist congregations in visiting members, making known the work of the Church and promoting Christian giving.
   To help congregations through the service of its Stewardship Consultants in running conferences, advising office-bearers and training visitors.
2. To prepare a Co-ordinated Budget for the costs of Local Mission, the Ministry and the Mission and Aid Fund and submit it to the General Assembly each year for approval.
3. To be responsible with the Ministry Department and Presbyteries for allocating among congregations the Co-ordinated Budget approved by the General Assembly and to seek to ensure that congregations meet their obligations by transmitting regularly throughout the year to the General Treasurer of the Church contributions towards their allocations.
4. To provide financial, administrative and accounting services for the General Assembly, the Boards and Committees of the Church.
   The Board has a duty to report annually to the General Assembly on the general financial position of the Church and powers to examine the financial and statistical information of such Boards and Committees of the General Assembly as the Board shall consider appropriate.
   The Board exercises control of the General Treasurer's Department and the Stewardship Department and maintains a close liaison with the Church of Scotland Investors Trust, which is serviced by officials of the Board.

DEEDS OF COVENANT
A Deed of Covenant is a legal document obliging the donor to pay a specified amount annually for a period exceeding three years to a specified donee. In practice therefore most Covenants are granted for a period of FOUR years or until death, whichever is the shorter period.

The Church of Scotland as a charity is exempt from income tax. Thus the Church of Scotland is entitled to recover basic rate tax deducted from annual payments made by the donor of a Deed of Covenant which has been correctly executed. Deeds must be signed before any payment is made by the donor.

Transferable Deeds (T) are granted in favour of the Church of Scotland; Congregational Deeds (C) are to a particular congregation. The annual payments are made in both cases to the local Church Treasurer. Claims for recovery of tax on (T) Deeds are made through the General Treasurer's Department, Church of Scotland, 121 George Street, Edinburgh EH2 4YN; and on (C) Deeds directly to the Inland Revenue, FICO (Scotland), Trinity Park House, South Trinity Road, Edinburgh EH5 3SD. All claims must be listed on Schedule R68(A), supported by the Treasurer's/Covenant Convener's declaration in the case of (T) claims or Form R68 for (C) claims.

The funds of the Church benefit considerably under the Deed of Covenant Scheme as an additional 30% of the net annual payments can be reclaimed from the Inland Revenue, being the income tax deducted from the annual payments.

Annual payments need not necessarily be made in one contribution; they may be made by instalments: for example, under the Weekly Freewill Offering Scheme or by monthly Banker's Order.

Forms of Deeds of Covenant and other information may be obtained from the General Treasurer's Department, Church of Scotland, 121 George Street, Edinburgh EH2 4YN.

GIFT AID

The Gift Aid Scheme allows single cash gifts to charities by individuals or limited companies resident in the United Kingdom to qualify for tax relief provided such payments are made out of income which is taxed at the basic rate. The minimum limit is £250, net of basic rate income tax.

Cash gifts include payments by cheque and bank transfer.

Each congregation is responsible for keeping proper records of the payments, for obtaining the appropriate Certificates from the donors and for making repayment claims to the Inland Revenue. Special Forms must be used: R190(SD) for individuals and R240(SD) for companies. Congregational Treasurers will claim tax back on the Form R68, accompanied by Schedule R68(G) (Individuals) and/or Schedule R68(G) (Companies). The Inland Revenue have issued a booklet (IR 113) which explains the scheme in detail. The booklet and necessary claims forms are available from Inland Revenue FICO (Scotland), Trinity Park House, South Trinity Road, Edinburgh EH5 3SD.

The Inland Revenue wish to encourage the use of Gift Aid relief especially where this can replace donations which would otherwise have been made under Deeds of Covenant. Unlike Deeds of Covenant the donation may be accepted and the paperwork completed later.

GIVING WITH A WILL

Making a will is part of good stewardship, a sensitive but wise decision.

This can show our love and concern for our families and friends. It can also provide us with an opportunity to give help to good causes.

For Christians there is one good cause above all others.

The Church is called to make Jesus Christ known, so that men and women may come through the Spirit

- to believe in God
- to know his love
- to receive his forgiveness and help
- to serve him in this world and in the world to come.

There is no greater cause to serve and no message more relevant to the needs of the world and people today.

The Church acknowledges with gratitude the many legacies it has received over the years and the kind and generous thoughts which have been their inspiration. Such giving is encouraged by the State. Gifts of money to the Church are exempt from Inheritance Tax without limit.
The General Treasurer or the Solicitor of the Church of Scotland will always be ready to give information about the work of the Church to members, and their solicitors, interested in providing a legacy.

(6) CHURCH OF SCOTLAND PENSION TRUSTEES

Chairman:	Mr W.D.B. Cameron CA
Vice Chairman:	Mr W.J. McCafferty ACII ASFA CIP
Secretary:	Mrs Sirkka Dennison BA

STAFF

Pensions Manager:	Mrs Sirkka Dennison BA
Assistant Pensions	Mrs M. Marshall
Administrators:	Mr N. Hannam

REMIT

The body acts as Trustees for the Church of Scotland's three pension schemes:
(a)   The Church of Scotland Pension Scheme for Ministers and Overseas Missionaries;
(b)   The Church of Scotland Pension Scheme for Staff;
(c)   The Church of Scotland Pension Scheme for Board of National Mission Field Staff.

The Trustees have wide-ranging duties and powers detailed in the Trust Law, Pension Acts and other regulations, but in short the Trustees are responsible for the running of the pension schemes and for the investment of the scheme funds. Six Trustees are appointed by the General Assembly, and members nominate up to three Trustees for each scheme.

The investment of the funds is delegated to external Investment Managers under the guidelines and investment principles set by the Trustees: Baillie Gifford for the Ministers Scheme and National Mission Scheme; and Tilney Fund Management and Scottish Value Management for the Staff Scheme.

The benefits provided by the three pension schemes differ in detail, but all provide a pension to the Scheme member and dependants on death of the member, and a lump sum death benefit on death in service. Scheme members also have the option to improve their benefits by paying additional voluntary contributions (AVCs) to arrangements set up by the Trustees with leading Insurance Companies. Ministers' benefits can also be increased by additional contributions by their congregations.

Further information on any of the Church of Scotland pension schemes or on individual benefits can be obtained from the Pensions Manager, Mrs S. Dennison, at the Church Offices, 121 George Street, Edinburgh EH2 4YN.

(7) PERSONNEL

MEMBERSHIP
PERSONNEL COMMITTEE
(14 Members: 6 appointed by the Assembly)
Convener: Mr David D. Fotheringham FFA
Vice-Convener: Mr Graham Charters MBE FCIS
Secretary: Mr George B.B. Eadie BA

STAFF
Personnel Manager: Mr George B.B. Eadie BA
Personnel Officers: Miss Maria Carena
                             Miss Angela Brady MIPD
Personnel Assistant: Mrs Dorothy Menzies

REMIT
This body was set up in 1978 on the Report of the Advisory Council to determine salaries, length of service and conditions generally for Secretaries and Members of Office Staff. In 1991, and again in 1996, the General Assembly made certain minor adjustments to the remit, including a requirement that the Personnel Committee should conduct an annual salary review of those members of staff for which it is the employing agency.

In recognition of the aim that the Personnel Committee may in time operate as the co-ordinating body for the Church in respect of the salaries and conditions of employment of all persons employed by the five employing agencies, the other four employing agencies are required to provide all information on such matters as requested by the Personnel Committee.

---

(8) THE CHURCH OF SCOTLAND GUILD

NATIONAL OFFICE-BEARERS AND EXECUTIVE STAFF
Convener: Mrs Helen Longmuir BA MCSP DipTP
Vice-Convener: Mrs Elva A.M. Carlisle MA
General Secretary: Mrs Alison Twaddle MA JP
                             [e-mail: atwaddle@cofscotland.org.uk]
Information Officer   Mrs Fiona J. Lange
                             [e-mail: fjlange@cofscotland.org.uk]
                             (Tel: 0131 225 5722 ext 317; 0131 240 2217)

The Church of Scotland Guild is a movement within the Church of Scotland, whose aim is **"to invite and encourage all women to commit their lives to Jesus Christ and to enable them to express their faith in worship, prayer, and action"**.

Membership of the Guild is open to all who subscribe to that aim. At 31st December 1998 there were 47,682 members in 1525 affiliated groups throughout Scotland and beyond. The new 1997 Constitution opens the way for other groups at congregational level – fellowship groups, prayer and study groups, single issue groups – to affiliate to the movement.

Groups at congregational level are free to organise themselves under the authority of the Kirk Session, as best suits their own local needs and circumstances. Large groups with frequent meetings and activities continue to operate with a committee or leadership team, while other, smaller groups simply share whatever tasks need to be done amongst the membership as a whole. Similarly, at Presbyterial Council level, frequency and style of meetings vary according to local needs, as do leadership patterns. Each Council may nominate one person to serve at national level, where six committees made up of these representatives take forward the work of the Guild in accordance with the stated aim. These Committees are:

- Executive
- Finance and General Purposes
- Projects and Topics
- Programmes and Resources
- Marketing and Publicity
- Matters Concerning Younger Women

There has always been a close relationship between the Boards and Committees of the Church and the Guild, latterly through a system of delegates. Many departments of the Church have since set up a link system, and the Guild is delighted that many former delegates have become congregational links to the major Boards of the Church. In addition the Guild continues to relate to the wider work of the Church through the Project Partnership Scheme .

This scheme affords groups at congregational level the opportunity to select a project, or projects, from a range of up to six, selected by the Projects and Topics Committee from submissions by a wide range of Church departments and other Church-related bodies. A project partner in each group seeks ways of promoting the project locally, increasing awareness of the issues raised by it, and encouraging support of a financial and practical nature. She is helped in these tasks by the Project Co-ordinator at Council level and by the Information Officer based at the Guild Office.

The Guild is very aware of the importance of good communication in any large organisation, and regularly sends mailings to its branches to pass on information and resources to the members. In addition the Newsletter, sent to members three times per session, is a useful communication tool. It is a means of sharing both local news and experiences, and of communicating some-thing of the wider interest and influence of the Guild, which is represented on other national bodies such as ACTS Network of Ecumenical Women in Scotland and the Women's National Commission.

Each year the Guild has a Theme and produces a resources pack covering worship and study material. In recent years there has also been a Discussion Topic with supporting material and background information. The theme, topic and projects all relate to a common three year strategy which, for 1997-2000, addresses the issues of **"Riches and Poverty"**. Each of the six current projects – from National Mission, World Mission (2), Social Responsibility, the Iona Community, and the National Bible Society – reflects some aspect of riches and poverty. The 1999-2000 Theme is **"Hold Out the Word of Life"** and Guilds are invited to explore this in a variety of ways to individuals and communities in need, as witnesses and as neighbours. The related Discussion Topic is **"Here is the News"** which addresses the issues of modern information technology and the media – their uses and abuses, and the need to ensure that the Good News is proclaimed to today's world.

(9) ASSEMBLY COUNCIL

MEMBERSHIP
(12 members appointed by the Assembly)
Convener: Mrs Helen M. McLeod, Forfar (1999)
Vice Convener: Rev. Duncan E. McClements MA BD MTh, Falkirk (1999)

[The Principal Clerk attends in an advisory capacity, but without the right to vote.]

STAFF
Research & Development Officer: Mrs Sophia Marriage   (Tel: 0131 225 5722)

REMIT
The revised remit of the Assembly Council, as determined by the General Assembly of 1999, is as follows:

> In ongoing consultation with *inter alia* Presbyteries, Boards, Committees, congregations, other denominations, and appropriate ecumenical bodies, and in collaboration with the Co-ordinating Forum, to assess the changing needs, challenges, and responsibilities of the Church, to identify priority areas and tasks, and to make recommendations to the General Assembly.

---

(10) CHURCH AND NATION

MEMBERSHIP
CHURCH AND NATION COMMITTEE
(48 members: 32 appointed by the Assembly; 16 appointed by Presbyteries)
Convener: Dr Alison Elliot (1996)
Vice Convener: Rev. Erik M. Cramb LTh (1999)
Secretary: Rev. David I. Sinclair BSc BD PhD Dip SW

REMIT
The remit of the Church and Nation Committee as defined by the Assembly is:

> "to watch over developments of the Nation's life in which moral and spiritual considerations specially arise, and to consider what action the Church from time to time may be advised to take to further the highest interests of the people."

There are five Sub-Committees:
- International Interests
- Economic and Industrial Interests
- Social Interests
- Media Interests
- Constitutional Issues

(11) PANEL ON DOCTRINE

MEMBERSHIP
(21 members: 14 appointed by the Assembly, and including representatives from the four University Faculties/Departments of Divinity), with the Principal Clerk, the Procurator, and the Convener of the Board of Practice and Procedure *ex officiis.*)
Convener: Rev. John McPake BA BD PhD (1999)
Vice Convener: Mrs Katharina Nimmo (1999)

STAFF
Administrative Secretary: Rev. Douglas Galbraith MA BD BMus MPhil ARSCM

REMIT
The responsibilities of the Panel on Doctrine include: the fulfilling of remits from the General Assembly on matters concerning doctrine; drawing the attention of the General Assembly to matters inside the Church of Scotland or elsewhere which might have significant doctrinal implications, with recommendations for action; being available for consultation by other Committees of the General Assembly on any matter which might be of doctrinal significance; communicating and consulting in an ecumenical context on matters involving doctrine.

(12) PANEL ON WORSHIP

MEMBERSHIP
(30 members: all appointed by the Assembly)
Convener: Very Rev. Gilleasbuig I. Macmillan CVO MA BD Drhc (1999)
Vice Convener: Rev. Colin Renwick BMus BD (1998)

STAFF
Administrative Secretary: Rev. Douglas Galbraith MA BD BMus MPhil ARSCM

REMIT
The Panel on Worship exists to witness to the importance of worship as a primary function of the Church. It has three major committees:
- The Prayer and Devotion Committee is responsible for *Pray Now* and for courses and retreats to promote spiritual growth.
- The Music Committee encourages new developments in church music, the training of musicians, and the publication of relevant materials.
- The Liturgical Committee is concerned with the provision of worship materials for public use and is responsible, among other things, for the production of *Common Order*.

The Panel is engaged also in providing materials for worship in Gaelic and is involved in the compilation of new hymn books and supplements. From time to time, it publishes occasional papers on aspects of the practice of Public Worship.

(13) COMMITTEE ON ARTISTIC MATTERS

MEMBERSHIP
(27 members, including 1 appointed by and from the General Trustees and 2 appointed by and from the Committee on New Charge Development, plus up to 5 co-opted specialists)
Convener: Mr Douglas Lair RIBA FRIAS (1999)
Vice Convener: Rev. Roy Wilson DA ARIBA ARIAS (1998)

STAFF
Administrative Secretary: Rev. Douglas Galbraith MA BD BMus MPhil ARSCM

REMIT
The Committee advises congregations and Presbyteries regarding the most appropriate way of carrying out renovations, alterations and re-ordering of interiors, having regard to the architectural quality of Church buildings. It also advises on the installation of stained glass, tapestries, memorials, furniture and furnishings, and keeps a list of accredited artists and craftsworkers.

Any alteration to the exterior or interior of a Church building which affects its appearance must be referred to the Committee for approval, which is given on behalf of the General Trustees. Congregations contemplating alterations are urged to consult the Committee at an early stage.

Members of the Committee and of its local area panels are prepared, when necessary, to visit churches and meet office-bearers. The Committee's services are given free.

In recent years the General Assembly has conferred these additional duties on the Committee:
(a)   preparation of reports on the architectural, historical and aesthetic merit of the buildings of congregations involved in questions of readjustment;
(b)   verification of the propriety of repair and renovation work forming the basis of grant applications to Historic Scotland;
(c)   the offering of advice on the maintenance and installation of organs;
(d)   facilitating the transfer of unwanted furnishings etc. from one church to another through the quarterly *Exchange and Transfer*;
(e)   the compilation of a Register of Churches;
(f)   the processing of applications from congregations for permission to dispose of surplus communion plate.

(14) DEPARTMENT OF MINISTRY

BOARD OF MINISTRY
Convener   Rev. George J. Whyte BSc BD
General Secretary: Very Rev. Alexander McDonald
                                  BA CMIWSc DUniv
Depute General Secretary: Rev. John P. Chalmers BD
Director of Educational Services: Rev. Nigel J. Robb MA BD ThM MTh
Accountant   Mrs Pauline Willder MA PgDipIS

COMMITTEES

MINISTRY SUPPORT (25 members)
Convener: Rev. Shaw J. Paterson BSc BD
Secretary: Very Rev. Alexander McDonald BA CMIWSC DUniv

VOCATIONAL GUIDANCE (25 members)
Convener: Rev. Christine M. Goldie LLB BD
Secretary: Rev. John P. Chalmers BD

EDUCATION AND TRAINING (25 members)
Convener: Rev. William F. Storrar MA BD PhD
Secretary: Rev. Nigel J. Robb MA BD ThM MTh

MINISTRY DEVELOPMENT (25 members)
Convener: Mr William Greenock MA
Secretary: Rev. Nigel J. Robb MA BD MTh ThM

TRUSTEES OF HOUSING AND LOAN FUND (10 members)
Chairman: Mr William McVicar CA
Secretary: Mr Ronald C. Mather

CHAPLAINS TO HM FORCES (20 members)
Convener: Rev. Professor Iain R. Torrance TD MA BD DPhil (1998)
Vice Convener: Professor Herbert A. Kerrigan QC
Secretary: Mr Douglas M. Hunter WS
                         19 Ainslie Place, Edinburgh EH3 6AU (Tel: 0131 226 6881)

STAFF
General Secretary: Very Rev. Alexander McDonald
                                   BA CMIWSc DUniv
Deputy General Secretary: Rev. John P. Chalmers BD
Director of Educational Services: Rev. Nigel J. Robb MA BD MTh ThM
Assistant Secretary: Mr Ronald C. Mather
Education and
  Development Officers: Rev. Robert S.T. Allan LLB DipLP BD
                                 Rev. Angus R. Mathieson MA BD
                                 Mrs Yvonne Teague DCS
Vocational Guidance Officer: Mrs Elizabeth Chalmers
Accountant: Mrs Pauline Willder MA PgDipIS

REMIT

The Board of Ministry is responsible for all aspects of the recruitment, education, training, in-service training and support of ministers, auxiliary ministers and deacons as well as making the financial provision for that work. To enable the Board to discharge these responsibilities and fulfil its remit, the Board shall determine from time to time what constituent Committees are required. The exceptions to this will be in respect of the Housing and Loan Fund for Retired Ministers and Widows and Widowers of Ministers and the Committee on Chaplains to Her Majesty's Forces, the Trustees and members respectively of which continue to be appointed as at present and report separately to the General Assembly.

The work of the Board is under the care of the following Committees:

A.   MINISTRY SUPPORT

The responsibilities of the Committee are:
(a)   To determine and declare the Minimum Stipend.
(b)   To advise the Church in matters relating to stipend levels and arrangements.
(c)   To deal with appropriate matters relating to endowments.
(d)   To deal with appropriate matters relating to allowances, expenses, loans and the like for which those engaged in ministry in the Church and their families are, or may be eligible.
(e)   The pastoral care of all in the Ministry, insofar as centralised co-ordination and support are desired or required.

The Ministry
The Church of Scotland is a National Church and has the responsibility of providing the ministry of Word and Sacrament to all the people of Scotland on a territorial basis. This is achieved through the parish ministry, which is supported by the Board of Ministry.

Consolidated Stipend Endowment Fund
The General Assembly of 1981 approved the creation of the Consolidated Stipend Endowment Fund. The creation of this Fund, which meets all the requirements of the Church of Scotland (Property and Endowments) Act 1925, has greatly facilitated the administration of stipend endowments. The Fund is administered by the Church of Scotland General Trustees and is invested through the medium of the Church of Scotland Trust.

Each congregation which had endowment income for stipend purposes in 1981 was given a proportionate share in the Fund. While income from Glebe Rents does not form part of the Consolidated Stipend Endowment Fund, the net sale proceeds of Glebe land constitutes new capital for the Fund and this is used to purchase shares in the Fund.

Endowment Grants
The Ministry Support Committee makes provision for a stipend endowment when a Church Extension Charge attains full status. The Committee also makes grants to allow congregations to improve their endowment income for stipend purposes through the Grants for Further Endowment Scheme. Information about the availability of endowment grants and the terms and conditions on which they are made can be obtained from Mr Ronald C. Mather, Assistant Secretary, at the Church Offices.

Stipend and Aid
The Ministry Support Committee has the responsibility of exercising the delegated authority of the General Assembly in the matter of the declaration of the Minimum Stipend. The actual level of the Minimum Stipend from year to year depends on various factors, but the most important factor is the continuing response of members and adherents through their offerings. Stipends above the level of the Minimum Stipend are determined by Presbyteries and the Committee acting together.

Congregations without sufficient resources to meet the full stipend have an agreed level of Aid granted to them from the Fund, to assist in meeting the stipend. The level of aid to be received is determined in advance by the Committee and the Presbytery acting together. The amount of stipend provision to Aid Receiving congregations forms the major requirement on the Fund.

MISCELLANEOUS PROVISIONS FROM THE FUND

Centralised Payment of Travelling Expenses
The General Assembly in 1990 approved the introduction of the Centralised payment of Travelling Expenses. At the Board of Ministry meeting in June 1999 it was agreed that from January 2000 the payment of a minister's travelling expenses would be based on actual miles travelled, thus meeting the regulations contained in current fiscal policy.

A minister providing a car for pastoral travel will receive an agreed lump sum paid to him in twelve equal parts along with the stipend. This is intended to assist with capital costs in car provision and does not require a separate claim. In addition, travelling expenses at the current level will be reimbursed through the payroll on receipt of the travelling expense claim. The Board reclaims these expenses from congregations.

Rates for Year 2000:

Lump Sum:	£960	
Pastoral Travel:	First 4000 miles	40p per mile
	Remaining Miles	22.5p per mile.

Pulpit Supply
A minister is entitled annually to six Sunday's Pulpit Supply in respect of holidays and to one Sunday's Pulpit Supply when he or she is a Commissioner to the General Assembly. Presbyteries have had responsibility for this provision since 1st January 1998. Those wishing to give or to receive supply should contact their local Presbytery.

Supply Fee and Expenses
The General Assembly of 1996 approved new regulations governing the amount of Supply Fee and Expenses. They are as follows:

In charges where there is only one diet of worship, the Pulpit Supply Fee shall be a standard Fee of £40 (or as from time to time agreed by the Ministry Support Committee).

In charges where there are additional diets of worship on a Sunday, the person fulfilling the Supply shall be paid £10 for each additional Service.

Where the person is unwilling to conduct more than one diet of worship on a given Sunday, he or she shall receive a pro-rata payment based on the total available Fee shared on the basis of the number of Services conducted.

The Fee thus calculated shall be payable in the case of all persons permitted to conduct Services under Act II 1986.

In all cases Travelling Expenses shall be paid. Where there is no convenient public conveyance, the use of a private car shall be paid for at the special Pulpit Supply rate of 20p per mile. In exceptional circumstances, to be approved in advance, the cost of hiring a car may be met.

Where weekend board and lodging are agreed as necessary, these may be claimed for the weekend at a maximum rate of that allowed when attending the General Assembly. The Fee and Expenses should be paid to the person providing the Supply before he or she leaves on the Sunday.

Provision of Cars
The current Terms and Conditions of the Car Provision Scheme are available from the Department of Ministry.

Pre-Retirement Course
The Board of Ministry arranges Pre-Retirement Courses for ministers and spouses. The courses, which are residential, include sessions on such topics as Finance in Retirement, Health in Retirement, and Leisure in Retirement, and will be a charge on the Fund.

Study Leave Scheme

The General Assembly of 1997 approved the introduction of a Study Leave Scheme for ministers, provided they have five years' qualifying service, have completed any compulsory Ministry Development Courses, and are not within five years of anticipated retirement. Those qualifying may take two weeks' study leave annually, or they may save up their entitlement to a maximum of seven years and take it in blocks to a maximum of fourteen weeks at any one time. For every two weeks of leave taken, a minister may claim funding from central funds up to £250. An Education and Development Officer has been appointed to promote and oversee the Scheme. The use to be made of the period of leave will require the approval of the Ministry Development Committee.

B.   VOCATIONAL GUIDANCE

The Vocational Guidance Committee has responsibility for all aspects of Recruitment, Assessment and Selection, and Admissions and Readmissions.

C.   EDUCATION AND TRAINING

The Education and Training Committee has responsibility for all aspects of the Education and Training of the Ministry.

D.   MINISTRY DEVELOPMENT

The Ministry Development Committee is responsible for maintaining present courses and promoting all aspects of Ministry Development.

E.   THE HOUSING AND LOAN FUND

The Church of Scotland Housing and Loan Fund for Retired Ministers and Widows and Widowers of Ministers endeavours, wherever possible, to assist with their retirement housing ministers who are about to retire and surviving widows or widowers of ministers, by way of a house to rent or a house purchase loan. The main source from which the Trustees obtain funds for the purchase of houses or the granting of loans is the levy, at present 2% of stipend, made on all congregations for this specific Fund.

The Trustees may grant the tenancy on advantageous terms of one of their existing houses or, if necessary, they will purchase a house for renting. Alternatively, the Trustees may grant a house purchase loan up to a normal maximum of £59,500 or 70% of the house purchase price whichever is lower, at favourable rates of interest.

It would be helpful to the Trustees if ministers, who wish to be considered for possible help in the future, could submit their applications about ten years before their proposed date of retirement, so that the Trustees have an indication of their possible future commitment, and give the applicant a place on their waiting list.

The Trustees are prepared to consider assisting those who are already housed, but are seeking to move to more suitable accommodation.

Further information may be obtained from the Secretary: Mr Ronald C. Mather, 121 George Street, Edinburgh EH2 4YN. (Home Tel: 0131 334 1085)

F.   CHAPLAINS TO H M FORCES

Recruitment
The Chaplains' Committee is entrusted with the task of recruitment of Chaplains for the Regular, Reserve and Auxiliary Forces. Vacancies occur periodically and the Committee is happy to receive enquiries from all interested Ministers.

Communications between Parish Ministers and Chaplains
Parish Ministers are asked to inform Chaplains when young men and women who have had any contact, however tenuous, with their Congregations, join any of the three Services. The General Assembly of 1989 approved proposals to improve communications, and Parish Ministers are encouraged to complete the "Contact Cards" which will be issued annually by the Board of Ministry.

Forces Registers
The Committee maintains a Register of all those who have been baptised and/or admitted to Communicant Membership by Service Chaplains.

At the present time registers are being meticulously prepared and maintained. Parish Ministers are asked to take advantage of the facilities by applying for Certificates from the Secretary of the Committee.

Full information may be obtained from the Honorary Secretary, Mr Douglas M. Hunter WS, 19 Ainslie Place, Edinburgh EH3 6AU. (Tel: 0131 226 6881)

A list of Chaplains may be found in List B in Section 6.

---

(15) NATIONAL MISSION

MEMBERSHIP –
BOARD OF NATIONAL MISSION (34 members)
Convener: Rev. W. Alexander Cairns BD (1996)
Vice Conveners: Rev. David Randall MA BD ThM (1998)
                                Mrs Tricia Kingston (1997)

PARISH REAPPRAISAL (52 members)
Convener: Rev. Arthur P. Barrie LTh (1999)
Vice Convener: Mr Noel Glen (1999)

NEW CHARGE DEVELOPMENT (23 members)
Convener: Rev. Andrew Ritchie BD DipMin (1999)
Vice Convener: Rev. Fred G. Drummond BD (1999)

PARISH ASSISTANCE (16 Members)
Convener: Dr Andrew Prentice (1996)
Vice-Convener: Rev. Stanley A. Brook BD (1999)

MISSION AND EVANGELISM RESOURCES (30 members)
Convener: Rev. Colin A.M. Sinclair BA BD (1999)
Vice Conveners: Mrs Nina Dinnes (1998)
                                Rev. Graham Houston BSc BD MTh PhD (1997)

CHAPLAINCIES (25 members)
Convener:	Rev. I. Max Homewood MSc BD (1998)
Vice-Conveners:	Mr J. Greig (1999)
	Rev. T. Stewart McGregor MBE MA BD (1999))
	Rev. William R. Taylor MA BD (1999)

IONA COMMUNITY BOARD
Convener:	Rev. M Leith Fisher MA BD (1997)

COMMITTEE ON THE PRIORITY AREAS FUND (17 members)
Convener:	Rev. H. Martin J. Johnstone MA BD (1999)
Vice-Convener:	Mrs Sandra Carter

JOINT PRISON CHAPLAINCIES BOARD
Convener:	Rev. Kenneth McCaffrey (1996)

STAFF
General Secretary:	Rev. Douglas A.O. Nicol MA BD
Secretary Depute (Parish Staffing):	Mrs Norma Henderson
Secretary Depute (Parish Resourcing):	Rev. Frank D. Bardgett MA BD PhD
Accountant:	Miss Elizabeth Orr BSc CA
Property Administrator:	Mr Colin Wallace
Chaplaincies Administrator:	Mr John K. Thomson
Congregational Links Administrator:	Mrs Georgina Payne

REMIT

1.   THE BOARD OF NATIONAL MISSION

Established on 1st January 1990 the Board, with its constituent committees, has the responsibility for planning and co-ordinating the Church's strategy and provision for the fulfilment of its mission as the National Church.

Subject to the enactments of the General Assembly, the Board's remit is as follows:

(a)   Development of Policy:
Aided by reflecting on the deliberations of a regular National Mission Conference, the Board will develop its policy which will be communicated to, and pursued by, the five Constituent Committees.

(b)   Finance:
The agreement of the annual budget and the monitoring of income and expenditure will be the responsibility of the Board.

(c)   New Work:
Constituent Committees will refer to the Board new work and work which is likely to exceed the budget of the Committee. The Board will consider such referrals and grant permission if agreed.

(d)   Property:
The Board will have responsibility for the acquisition and disposal of properties and for the proper maintenance of all its properties.

(e)   Presbytery Representatives:
The Board will have the responsibility of resolving on which Constituent Committees Presbytery representatives will serve.

(f)   General Assembly Report:
The Board will have the responsibility for the approval of the Report to the General Assembly on the work of the Board and the five Constituent Committees.

In addition the Board receives reports from the following:
(i)   Congregational Link Group: This group has the responsibility of communicating the whole range of the Board's work directly with congregations through congregational links appointed by Kirk Sessions.
(ii)   AD 2000 Working Party: This Working Party has been entrusted with assisting the whole Church to prepare for the Millennium.
(iii) Project Rejoice Group: This ecumenical group produces materials for use by congregations for mission and evangelism during the key Christian Festivals.

2.   THE COMMITTEE ON PARISH REAPPRAISAL

In accordance with the overall policy of the Board, the Committee on Parish Reappraisal:
–   Will undertake full responsibilities and rights in connection with the implementation of Act IV 1984;
–   Will be responsible for dealing with all matters coming from Presbyteries regarding planning and vacancies;
–   Will deal with proposals for the staffing needs of parishes in respect of ministers and parish assistance;
–   Will, in consultation with the Presbyteries concerned, and following detailed discussion with the Committee on New Charge Development, determine where new charges shall be established or where, as a result of population growth in an existing charge, an alternative location for the place of worship is deemed desirable;
–   Will be available, when requested, to assist and advise Presbyteries in regard to their own forward and readjustment planning.

The Committee has responsibility for 9 Associate Ministers and 9 Community Ministers appointed under "New Forms of Parish Ministry" and students employed through the Summer Appointment Scheme.

3.   THE COMMITTEE ON NEW CHARGE DEVELOPMENT

In accordance with the overall policy of the Board, the Committee on New Charge Development, without prejudice to any other body, such as the Parish Reappraisal Committee, *etc*, which may have prior rights or jurisdiction, will be responsible for the following areas of work:
1.   Following the instructions of the Committee on Parish Reappraisal, to facilitate the creation of new charges. The Committee, in co-operation with other bodies, including Boards, Committees and Presbyteries, will enable a new charge to begin its mission in the new parish area, and will be responsible for:
    (a)   The development of the Charge;
    (b)   The appointment of the Minister;
    (c)   The provision of a suitable building as the place of worship which may be a new church funded and erected by the Committee, or an existing location within a community which would be suitable for the purpose of worship.
2.   In the case of established charges, where significant population growth is being established by the construction of new housing, the Committee on New Charge Development will, on the instruction of the Committee on Parish Reappraisal, enter into discussion

with Presbyteries and appropriate Committees to determine the needs of the area with respect to the provision of a place of witness.

3. Will be responsible for facilitating and supporting the mission of new charges and those not yet in full status, in co-operation with other Committees or Boards as deemed necessary

4. (a) Will be responsible for advising on and, within the limitations of its budget, assisting with major problems and expenditure associated with ongoing necessary maintenance of buildings where there are building debts outstanding on the part of the congregations concerned, or where the congregation concerned is not yet in full status.

   (b) The responsibility of the Committee on New Charge Development for the purchase of land and the purchase or erection, maintenance, and disposal of buildings pertaining to the work of that Committee are the express responsibility of the Committee.

5. Will provide arbiters to make choice of buildings to be retained in a readjustment situation.

The Committee is responsible for 14 existing new charges, and has a further 6 under development. There are prospective developments in 7 locations.

4.   THE COMMITTEE ON PARISH ASSISTANCE

In accordance with the overall policy of the Board and to meet the staffing needs of parishes as determined by Presbyteries with the approval of the Committee on Parish Re-appraisal, the Committee will:

(a) Be responsible for establishing how the determined need is met;

(b) Be responsible for departmental matters relating to the selection, recruitment, training, personal development, employment, deployment and support of such staff.

The Committee has responsibility for over 70 Parish Assistants and Project Workers, of whom the majority are commissioned Deacons. Staff members undergo a period of training usually extending over a period of two years, followed by a year's Probationary Period in a parish. They may then be commissioned to the office of Deacon by the Presbytery under whose jurisdiction they are serving.

   Most staff serve in parish appointments in the large housing areas of our towns and cities where the number of ordained ministers is low in relation to the population, and some serve in rural or island parishes.

5.   THE COMMITTEE ON MISSION AND EVANGELISM RESOURCES

In accordance with the overall policy of the Board, the Committee on Mission and Evangelism Resources will be responsible for:

–   Developing vision for the work of mission and evangelism in Scotland;

–   Encouraging mission and evangelism in Presbyteries and parishes through congregations of the Church of Scotland by means of research, development and training;

–   Ensuring that the personnel and Centres under the Committee's direction are serving the missionary and evangelistic purposes of the Church to the best advantage;

–   Identifying, originating and supporting projects which are advancing mission and evangelism in key areas of life in Scotland.

The Committee is responsible for the work of a team of Advisers in Mission and Evangelism. Their task is to encourage and resource Presbyteries and congregations in mission and evangelism.

A full list of Advisers will be found in List J in Section 6.

The Committee is responsible for the following Residential Centres:

(a) BADENOCH CHRISTIAN CENTRE. Situated at Kincraig in Strathspey, the Badenoch Christian Centre offers individuals, families and groups the opportunity of enjoying the many outdoor pursuits of the area from a base of Christian fellowship. Opened in 1976, the Centre is residential and mainly self-catering. Full information can be obtained from the Centre Manager, Mrs Diana Lamb (Tel: 01540 651373).

(b) ST NINIAN'S CENTRE, CRIEFF. The special concern of St Ninian's, Crieff, is the advancement of the Church's mission and the renewal of its life and it seeks to serve the Church as a training and resource centre through courses offered and programmes specifically prepared for incoming groups. Its comfortable accommodation and extensive facilities are available for self-programming groups, and guests are welcomed for holiday refreshment as bookings allow. The Director of Training is happy to respond to requests from congregations for advice and help in the planning and provision of local training events and in the preparation of outreach programmes. Full information may be obtained from the Director, the Rev. Dr Adrian Varwell (Tel: 01764 653766; Fax: 01764 655824).

The Committee is also responsible for a number of Projects:

(c) THE NETHERBOW AND JOHN KNOX HOUSE. The integrated facilities of the Netherbow Theatre and the John Knox House Museum provide an important cultural and visitor centre and an international point of enquiry for those concerned with the past, present and future of the Church of Scotland. In addition to a busy "on site" arts and education programme, the Netherbow plays a full part in the life of historic central Edinburgh and provides advice and assistance in the use of the arts in mission, education and worship nationally. The Director of the Netherbow is Dr Donald Smith (Tel: 0131 556 9579/2647).

(d) SOCIETY, RELIGION AND TECHNOLOGY PROJECT. This unique project, initiated in 1970, studies the impact of new technologies on society and helps the Church to form its response in ways which are practical and prophetic. The Project is a forum for all those wishing to shape the Church's response to some of the most pressing issues of our time. The Director of the Project is Dr Donald Bruce, John Knox House, 45 High Street, Edinburgh EH1 1SR (Tel: 0131 556 2953) [e-mail: srtscot@servelan.co.uk]

(e) SUMMER MISSIONS. Each year over 600 volunteers take part in Summer Mission Teams at varied centres throughout Scotland. Details can be obtained from the Rev. Paul Beautyman, Missions Co-ordinator, at 59 Elmbank Street, Glasgow G2 4PQ (Tel: 0141 352 6946).

(f) GLASGOW LODGING HOUSE MISSION. This work is based in the Institute in East Campbell Street, Glasgow, and its object is to care for the thousands of homeless in Scotland's industrial capital. Oversight of the work is given by a Management Committee appointed by the Presbytery of Glasgow (Tel: 0141 552 0285).

(g) BRIDGETON, ST FRANCIS-IN-THE-EAST CHURCH HOUSE. For more than thirty years the Committee has provided financial support for the activities of this Centre in Bridgeton, Glasgow, which provides club facilities for young and old who have little or no church connection.

A Club Leader and Girls' Leader are in charge of the work under a Committee of Management whose Chairman is the minister of the Parish (Tel: 0141 554 8045).

(h) ETHNIC COMMUNITY WORK. A Community Worker serves the ethnic community of Glasgow. Miss Catriona Forbes is based at "The Well", Asian Information and Advice Centre, 40/50 Albert Road, Glasgow G42 8DN (Tel: 0141 424 4523).

(i) OTHER WORK. The Committee also supports Ministry to Deaf People, and encourages congregations to sponsor Playgroups, Mother and Toddler Groups and After School Clubs. Further details of these areas of work can be obtained from the Church Offices.

6. THE COMMITTEE ON CHAPLAINCIES

In accordance with the overall policy of the Board, the Committee on Chaplaincies will be responsible, through its sub-committees on Hospitals and Universities, Church and Industry, and Prisons, for the encouragement, development, support and, where appropriate, review of chaplaincies in Hospitals, Universities, Industry, and Prisons.

HOSPITAL CHAPLAINCIES. The Committee administers the scheme by which, under the 1947 National Health Act, ministers are appointed as Chaplains in all hospitals in Scotland. There are over 30 full-time and around 300 part-time Chaplains. Appointments of Chaplains are made by the General Secretary of the Board as the "appointing authority" on the nomination of the Presbytery of the bounds after consultation with the appropriate Hospital Authority. Presbyteries are responsible for the oversight of Chaplains' work. The Committee also employs five full-time chaplains assistants.

A list of Hospital Chaplains will be found in List C in Section 6.

CHURCH AND INDUSTRY. The aim of Industrial Mission is threefold:
(a)   to provide pastoral care and witness to the Gospel for men and women in all branches of industry in their place of work;
(b)   to assess in the interest of the Gospel the nature of the influence which industry exerts both on individuals and on society;
(c)   to promote the desire for just relationships and understanding at all levels of our industrial society. The work, which is fully ecumenical in character, is now involved in most key industrial sectors. There are some 100 part-time Industrial Chaplains and 8 full-time Industrial Chaplains. The co-ordinator of Scottish Churches Industrial Mission is the Rev. Erik M. Cramb (Tel: 01382 458764).

A list of Industrial Chaplains will be found in List D in Section 6.

PRISON CHAPLAINCIES. The Committee takes an interest in all matters relating to Church of Scotland Prison Chaplains appointed by the Joint Prison Chaplaincies Board.

A list of Church of Scotland Prison Chaplains will be found in List E in Section 6.

UNIVERSITIES AND COLLEGES. The Committee takes an interest in all matters relating to the appointment and support of Chaplains to Universities and Colleges.

A list of University Chaplains will be found in List F in Section 6.

7.   IONA COMMUNITY BOARD

The Iona Community Board is the body through which the Iona Community reports to the General Assembly. It is made up of Members of the Community, and members of the Church appointed by the Assembly. It meets twice yearly, to hear reports of the community's work both on Iona and Mull and on the mainland, and to assist and guide the Community in its task of seeking "new ways to touch the hearts of all".

8.   COMMITTEE ON THE PRIORITY AREAS FUND

This Committee is an associated committee of the Department and reports directly to the General Assembly The Fund is a Grants scheme set up by the General Assembly of 1995, with the involvement of other Scottish churches and agencies. It supports local churches in partnership with other community groups in an effort to bring renewal within disadvantaged urban and rural areas. The Fund seeks to promote spiritual, social and economic welfare and development. It offers financial and practical support, training and advice to local church and community projects in urban priority areas and rural parishes.

The Development and Training Officer for the Fund is Mr Iain Johnston who can be contacted in the Church of Scotland Offices (Tel: 0131 225 5722 ext 352).

9.   JOINT PRISON CHAPLAINCIES BOARD

The General Assembly of 1989 set up a Joint Prison Chaplaincies Board with representatives from the Church of Scotland, the Roman Catholic Church and the Episcopal Church in Scotland. This Board is responsible for advising the Scottish Prison Service regarding the appointment and terms of service of all ministers and priests acting as Chaplains in prisons.

---

(16) SOCIAL RESPONSIBILITY
Charis House, 47 Milton Road East, Edinburgh EH15 2SR
Tel: 0131 657 2000   Fax: 0131 657 5000
[e-mail: info@charis.org.uk]

BOARD OF SOCIAL RESPONSIBILITY
The Board of Social Responsibility engages in social care as part of the Christian witness of the Church to the people of Scotland. In addition, the Board offers guidance to the Church and the media about social, moral and ethical issues.

MEMBERSHIP
(96 Members: 44 appointed by the Assembly plus Convener and 2 Vice Conveners; 47 from Presbyteries; a representative of the Church of Scotland Guild; and a representative from the

Committee on Church and Nation. They attend 3 meetings of the Board per year, in February, June and October, and may be asked to serve on one of the five committees.)
Convener: Mrs Ann Allen (1997)
Vice-Conveners: Rev. James M. Cowie (1997)
                             Rev. David J.C. Easton (1997)

COMMITTEES –
EXECUTIVE
Convener: Mrs Ann Allen

CENTRAL SERVICES
Convener: Rev. Gilbert C. Nisbet

OPERATIONS
Convener: Rev. David L. Court

PLANNING AND DEVELOPMENT
Convener: Mr Ronald C. Lavalette

SOCIAL INTERESTS
Convener: Mrs Ann Allen

STAFF
Director of Social Work: Mr Ian D. Baillie CBE
Deputy Director (Central Services):   Mr James Maguire
Deputy Director (Operations):   Mr David J. Kellock
Deputy Director (Planning and Development): Mrs Joyce M. Buchanan

REMIT

The Board of Social Responsibility is Scotland's largest social work agency in the voluntary sector employing 1600 people. The range and breadth of its work is ever-increasing, but the purpose of the Board of Social Responsibility could be broadly defined as follows:
1.   To offer care and help through the varied establishments and projects it operates, and to encourage and enable caring work at parish level;
2.   To offer to the Church informed opinion on contemporary social, moral and ethical issues;
3.   To encourage balanced judgements on these issues in the light of the Christian faith, and to put forward these judgements at all levels of influence.

DIVISIONAL STRUCTURE

Operationally, the Board's work is split into five geographical areas which cover Scotland. Each of these areas is administered by a Divisional Manager and Assistant Divisional Managers. They are physically located in their own Division, and manage and develop services at a local level. The general administration of the Board, which includes finance, publicity, training,and fundraising is carried out by staff based at the Board's offices in Charis House, Edinburgh. (Tel: 0131 657 2000).

DIVISION 1   CITY OF GLASGOW, EAST DUMBARTONSHIRE,
              NORTH LANARKSHIRE

Divisional Office: Tom Allan Centre, 23 Elmbank Street, Glasgow G2 4PD
                      (Tel: 0141 243 2897   Fax: 0141 229 0423)

Divisional Manager: Paul Robinson
A.D.M. (Planning and Development):   Graham Lumb
A.D.M. (Operations):   Marlene Smith

Services for Older People
Baxter House, 8-10 Lowther Terrace, Glasgow G12 0RN
        (Tel: 0141 334 1231   Fax: 0141 334 3965)
Queen Mary House, 52 Queen Mary Avenue, Crosshill, Glasgow G42 8DT
        (Tel: 0141 423 2736   Fax: 0141 424 1820)
Tollcross Mansionhouse, 601-641 Tollcross Road, Glasgow G32 8TF
        (Tel: 0141 778 5406   Fax: 0141 778 5406)

Drug Dependency
Rainbow, 1 Belhaven Terrace, Glasgow G12 0TF
        (Tel: 0141 339 2691   Fax: 0141 337 1656)

Alcohol/Drug Dependency
Victoria View, 21 Westland Drive, Glasgow G14 9NY
        (Tel: 0141 959 1679   Fax: 0141 954 2572)

Counselling and Support
Tom Allan Centre, Counselling Service, 23 Elmbank Street, Glasgow G2 4PD
        (Tel: 0141 221 1535   Fax: 0141 248 8452)

Learning Disabilities
Florentine, 33 Queen Mary Avenue, Glasgow G42 8DS
        (Tel: 0141 423 0279   Fax: 0141 423 0635)
Saltmarket Project, Flat 1/2, 85 Saltmarket, Glasgow G1 5LE
        (Tel: 0141 552 3207   Fax: 0141 552 5096)

Learning Disabilities (Children)
9 Cairnhill Place, Rosshall, Glasgow G52 3NR
        (Tel: 0141 401 8037   Fax: 0141 401 8037)
The Mallard, 100 Morrin Street, Springburn, Glasgow G21 1AW
        (Tel: 0141 558 7575   Fax: 0141 558 3883)

Mental Illness
Allarton, 32 Laurel Street, Glasgow G11 7QR
        (Tel: 0141 339 1383   Fax: 0141 339 1314)

Offenders
Dick Stewart Hostels:
40 Circus Drive, Glasgow G31 2JE
        (Tel: 0141 554 0277   Fax: 0141 554 6646)
2 Westercraigs, Dennistoun, Glasgow G31 2HZ
        (Tel: 0141 554 0212)

Single Homeless
Kirkhaven Project, 107 Summerfield Street, Dalmarnock, Glasgow G40 4QT
(Tel: 0141 550 4889   Fax: 0141 556 2932)

Supported Accommodation
Whiteinch Project, 13 Victoria Park Drive South, Whiteinch, Glasgow G14 9RN
(Tel: 0141 959 5069   Fax: 0141 950 1991)

DIVISION 2   CENTRAL AND SOUTH WEST SCOTLAND

Divisional Office: Adams House, 136 Auchenlodment Road, Elderslie, Johnstone,
Renfrewshire PA5 9NX
(Tel: 01505 337303   Fax: 01505 382022)

Divisional Manager: Archie Henderson
A.D.M. (Planning and Development):   David Clark
A.D.M. (Operations):   John McShane

Epilepsy
Westhaven, 2 Upper Bourtree Drive, High Burnside, Rutherglen G73 4EH
(Tel: 0141 634 4563   Fax: 0141 634 0599)

Services for Older People
Auchinlee, Campbeltown, Argyll PA28 6EN
(Tel: 01586 552568   Fax: 01586 553241)
Clyde View, 12 East Montrose Street, Helensburgh G84 7HP
(Tel: 01436 674529   Fax: 01436 674529)
Cumnor Hall, 18 Racecourse View, Ayr KA7 2TY
(Tel: 01292 266450   Fax: 01292 886740)
Devorgilla House, 33 George Street, Dumfries DG1 1ED
(Tel: 01387 254007   Fax: 01387 254642)
Dunselma, 55 Main Road, Fenwick, Kilmarnock KA3 6DR
(Tel: 01560 600218   Fax: 01560 600644)
Eastwoodhill, 238 Fenwick Road, Giffnock, Glasgow G46 6UU
(Tel: 0141 638 5127   Fax: 0141 638 8505)
Invereck, Sandbank, Dunoon, Argyll PA23 8QS
(Tel: 01369 706231   Fax: 01369 702423)
South Beach House, 7 South Crescent Road, Ardrossan KA22 8DU
(Tel: 01294 468234   Fax: 01294 604223)
Well Hall, 60 Wellhall Road, Hamilton ML3 9DL
(Tel: 01698 286151   Fax: 01698 286476)

Dementia
Adams House, 136 Auchenlodment Road, Elderslie, Johnstone, Renfrewshire PA5 9NX
(Tel: 01505 337322   Fax: 01505 337872)
Williamwood House, Strathtay Avenue, Netherlee, Glasgow G44 3YA
(Tel: 0141 637 1168   Fax: 0141 637 6398)

Holiday Home/Conference Centre
Crosbie Tower, South Beach Road, Troon KA25 6EH
(Tel: 01292 313696   Fax: 01292 311454)

Alcohol/Drug Dependency
Ronachan, Clachan, By Tarbet, Argyll PA29 6XW
     (Tel: 01880 740252   Fax: 01880 740616)

Learning Disabilities
Cornerstone Project, 15 Mill Road, Hamilton ML3 8AA
     (Tel: 01698 282377   Fax: 01698 283122)
Kilpatrick House, 3 Bridge Street, Alexandria, Dumbartonshire G83 0TA
     (Tel: 01389 752085   Fax: 01389 751679)
Threshold, Well Hall, 60 Wellhall Road, Hamilton ML3 9DL
     (Tel: 01698 423335   Fax: 01698 423398)

Mental Illness
Morven Centre, Ardbeg Avenue, Kilmarnock KA3 2AR
     (Tel: 01563 572459   Fax: 01563 571086)

Residential Schools
Ballikinrain School, Balfron, Stirlingshire G63 0LL
     (Tel: 01360 440244   Fax: 01360 440946)
Geilsland School, Beith, Ayrshire KA15 1HD
     (Tel: 01505 504044   Fax: 01505 502635)

DIVISION 3   **EDINBURGH AND SOUTH EAST SCOTLAND**

Divisional Office: Gate Lodge, 27 Milton Road East, Edinburgh EH15 2NL
     (Tel: 0131 669 9576   Fax: 0131 669 5185)

Divisional Manager: Jeannette S. Deacon
A.D.M. (Planning and Development):
A.D.M. (Operations):   Jennifer Spiers

Services for Older People
Mayburn House, 2 Hawthorn Gardens, Loanhead EH20 9EE
     (Tel: 0131 440 0299   Fax: 0131 440 3448)
Morlich House, 11 Church Hill, Edinburgh EH10 4BG
     (Tel: 0131 447 3239   Fax: 0131 447 2512)
Queen's Bay, 49 Milton Road East, Edinburgh EH15 2NN
     (Tel: 0131 669 2828   Fax: 0131 669 6407)
St Andrew's Residential Home, 34 High Street, Dunbar EH42 1JH
     (Tel: 01368 862474   Fax: 01368 862471)
St Andrew's Centre, 9 Bayswell Road, Dunbar EH42 1AB
     (Tel: 01368 862961   Fax: 01368 863066)
The Elms, 148 Whitehouse Loan, Edinburgh EH9 2EZ
     (Tel: 0131 447 4924   Fax: 0131 447 9051)

Alcohol/Drug Dependency
Malta House, 1 Malta Terrace, Edinburgh EH4 1HR
     (Tel: 0131 332 3217   Fax: 0131 315 2313)
Rankeillor Initiative, 140 The Pleasance, Edinburgh EH8 9RR
     (Tel: 0131 662 0322   Fax: 0131 662 8293)

Counselling and Support
Connections Counselling Service, St Andrew's Centre, 9 Bayswell Road, Dunbar EH42 1AB
    (Tel: 01368 865218   Fax: 01368 863066)
Elderly Persons Project, Wallace House, 3 Boswell Road, Edinburgh EH5 3RJ
    (Tel: 0131 552 8901   Fax: 0131 552 2319)
National Counselling Service, Wallace House, 3 Boswell Road, Edinburgh EH5 3RJ
    (Tel: 0131 552 8901   Fax: 0131 552 2319)
Number 21 Counselling Service, 21 Rutland Square, Edinburgh EH1 2BB
    (Tel: 0131 221 9377   Fax: 0131 221 9399)
Post Natal Depression Project, Wallace House, 3 Boswell Road, Edinburgh EH5 3RJ
    (Tel: 0131 538 7288   Fax: 0131 552 2319)
Simpson House, Drugs Counselling and Related Services, 52 Queen Street, Edinburgh EH2 3NS
    (Tel: 0131 225 6028   Fax: 0131 220 0064)

Learning Disabilities
Dunforth, 46 Park Road, Newhaven, Edinburgh EH6 4LD
    (Tel: 0131 552 3767   Fax: 0131 552 9101)
Eskmills Project, The Old Engine House, Eskmills Business Park, Station Road,
    Musselburgh EH21 7PQ
    (Tel: 0131 665 1966   Fax: 0131 665 1966)
Gorgie Park, 21 Gorgie Park Close, Edinburgh EH14 1NQ
    (Tel: 0131 443 6844   Fax: 0131 443 7569)
Wolfson House, 95 Milton Road East, Edinburgh EH15 2NL
    (Tel: 0131 669 1216   Fax: 0131 669 1323)

Mental Illness
Tynepark Resource and Day Centre, Poldrate, Haddington EH41 4DA
    (Tel: 01620 822444   Fax: 01620 822977)

Homelessness
Cunningham House, 205 Cowgate, Edinburgh EH1 1JH
    (Tel: 0131 225 4795   Fax: 0131 220 1354)
McGregor House, 35 Spring Gardens, Edinburgh EH8 8HR
    (Tel: 0131 661 6359)

DIVISION 4   FORTH VALLEY AND NORTH EAST SCOTLAND

Divisional Office: Leslie House, Leslie, Fife KY6 3EP
        (Tel: 01592 741343   Fax: 01592 743624)

Divisional Manager: John Wyllie
A.D.M. (Planning and Development):   Clark Bremner

Services for Older People
Ashley Lodge, 253 Great Western Road, Aberdeen AB10 6PP
    (Tel: 01224 585558   Fax: 01224 591429)
Balmedie House, Balmedie, Aberdeen AB33 8XU
    (Tel: 01358 742244   Fax: 01358 742382)
Bellfield, 1 Dee Street, Banchory AB31 5XS
    (Tel: 01330 822692   Fax: 01330 822633)

Belmont Castle, Meigle, Perthshire PH12 8TH
    (Tel: 01828 640244   Fax: 01828 640249)
Chequers, 12 Atholl Road, Pitlochry PH16 5DH
    (Tel: 01796 472521   Fax: 01796 472381)
Clashfarquhar, 23 Robert Street, Stonehaven AB39 2DJ
    (Tel: 01569 762438   Fax: 01569 762438)
Duneaves, 7 Claypotts Road, Broughty Ferry, Dundee DD5 1BX
    (Tel: 01382 738559   Fax: 01382 775728)
Kinloch Day Care and Support Services, 10A Newburgh Road, Auchtermuchty,
  Fife KY14 7BS
    (Tel: 01337 827242   Fax: 01337 828515)
Leslie House, Leslie, Fife KY6 3EP
    (Tel: 01592 741228   Fax: 01592 743432)
Rubislaw Park, Rubislaw Park Road, Aberdeen AB1 8DA
    (Tel: 01224 310641   Fax: 01224 323882)
Tryst Day Care Centre, Church Road, Pitlochry PH16 5EB
    (Tel: 01796 472160)

Dementia
St. Margaret's, St Margaret's Crescent, Polmont, Falkirk FK2 0UP
    (Tel: 01324 716149   Fax: 01324 716070)

Alcohol/Drug Dependency
Deeford, 59 Riverside Drive, Aberdeen AB10 7LE
    (Tel: 01224 585453   Fax: 01224 582626)

Counselling and Support
Dundee Women and Children Project, 11 Dock Street, Dundee DD1 4BT
    (Tel: 01382 201854   Fax: 01382 201854)

Learning Disabilities (Children)
Keith Lodge, Cameron Street, Stonehaven AB39 2HS
    (Tel: 01569 762213   Fax: 01569 764161)

Mental Illness
Gaberston House, 82 Whins Road, Alloa FK10 3SB
    (Tel: 01259 722402   Fax: 01259 725930)

DIVISION 5   **HIGHLANDS AND ISLANDS**

Divisional Office: Cameron House, Culduthel Road, Inverness IV2 4YG
                     (Tel: 01463 236136   Fax: 01463 236247)

Divisional Manager: Margaret Wilkinson
A.D.M. (Planning and Development):   Gerald Robson

Services for Older People
Achvarasdal, Reay, Thurso KW14 7RR
    (Tel: 01847 811226   Fax: 01847 811570)
Budhmor House, Portree, Isle of Skye IV51 9DJ
    (Tel: 01478 612012   Fax: 01478 613580)

The Walter & Joan Gray, Main Street, Scalloway, Shetland ZE1 0XJ
(Tel: 01595 880691   Fax: 01595 880908)
Oversteps, Earls Cross Road, Dornoch IV25 3PJ
(Tel: 01862 810393   Fax: 01862 810136)
Whinnieknowe, Mill Road, Nairn IV12 5EN
(Tel: 01667 452387   Fax: 01667 451190)

Dementia
Cameron House, Culduthel Road, Inverness IV2 4YG
(Tel: 01463 243241   Fax: 01463 235808)

Alcohol/Drug Dependency
Beechwood House, 69/71 Old Perth Road, Inverness IV1 3JH
(Tel: 01463 711355/711335   Fax: 01463 711544)
Lifestyle Centre, Town Hall, Francis Street, Stornoway, Isle of Lewis HS1 2XS
(Tel: 01851 701010   Fax: 01851 704209)

Homelessness
Beechwood House, 73/79 Old Perth Road, Inverness IV1 3JH
(Tel: 01463 716206   Fax: 01463 711544)
Cale House, Flat 1, Millburn Road, Inverness IV1 3PX
(Tel: 01463 718616   Fax: 01463 718616)

Supported Accommodation
Lewis Street Flat 3/5, 6 Lewis Street, Stornoway, Isle of Lewis HS1 2JF
(Tel: 01851 706888   Fax: 01851 706376)

HOME SUPPORT
The Board is continuing to develop its Home Support Service which is available in many parts
of the country. This innovative service is designed to provide whatever kind of help a person
might need, from ironing to doing shopping, or even just providing companionship. Home
Support can help anyone, from babies to older people, and is available for as little as an hour, or
a whole day or night. For more details about the service, telephone the Home Support Hotline
FREE on 0800 389 7557. A video *"Home Support – The Gift of Care"* is available for hire.

SOCIAL INTERESTS
Social Interests Officer: Kristine Gibbs [e-mail: kristine@charis.org.uk]
The remit of the Board of Social Responsibility instructs it "to study and present essential
Christian judgements on social and moral issues arising within the area of its concern". It does
this through Study Groups, which present their findings to the Board of Social Responsibility.
The Board then reports to the General Assembly. Some of the recent issues reported upon have
been: Family Matters; Euthanasia; Human Sexuality; Human Genetics; Human Fertilisation
and Embryology; Decriminilisation of Drugs; and Prostitution.

PRESS AND PUBLIC RELATIONS
Public Relations Officer: Hugh Brown [e-mail: hbrown@charis.org.uk]
The Board takes every opportunity to publicise the caring work of the Church, through *Life &
Work,* newspapers, and articles in the Press. The Public Relations Officer co-ordinates contact
with the various media, and is responsible for Press statements (in consultation with the
Church's Press Office). *Circle of Care* Calendar, which is produced each year, highlights some
of the Board's services, and sells 30,000 copies through the channels of the Guild and Church

members; 45,000 copies of *Circle of Care* newspaper are distributed three times a year with the latest news about the Board. Leaflets, brochures and videos are available to explain the Board's work. Some of the Board's reports to the General Assembly (*The Future of the Family, Euthanasia, Human Genetics, Human Fertilisation and Embryology, Health and Healing*) have been published as books by Saint Andrew Press. There are 'user-friendly' packs on various topics: HIV/AIDS Resource Pack, Marriage PLUS – A Study Pack for Couples, and a Day Care Pack.

CONGREGATIONAL LIAISON
Congregational Liaison Officer: Marilyn Davie [e-mail: mdavie@charis.org.uk]
The post of Congregational Liaison Officer links the social care managed and developed by the Board of Social Responsibility at a national level with the social work of the church initiated at parish level. The tasks of the Congregational Liaison Officer fall into three main categories:
1.   To encourage and enable local congregations to identify and meet the needs of local people.
2.   To ensure and enable local congregations to have knowledge and understanding of the Board's work.
3.   To maintain a database of projects which can be shared with other congregations wishing support and ideas.

CONGREGATIONAL CONTACTS
The Board has a network of Congregational Contacts around Scotland. Every parish was invited to nominate someone to be their contact with the Board, and to receive and distribute information about the Board's work. Over 1100 congregations responded positively to this exciting initiative, and it is hoped that this will continue to increase awarenenss of the Board's work at local level.

FINANCIAL DEVELOPMENT
Central Fundraising: Maurice Houston [e-mail: mhouston@charis.org.uk]
This post exists to inform people who want to participate in the mission of Social Responsibility and to enable them to help us in our work with some of the most needy people in Scotland. We invite anyone who is interested to pray with us about the day-to-day running of Social Responsibility projects, to volunteer their time to help carry out essential tasks of all kinds and to give money to support our charitable work. If you want to know more, please get in touch with Maurice Houston on 0131 657 2000.

DEPUTATION WORK
Members of staff and of the Board will gladly visit congregations and other church organisations to speak about the work of the Board. To request a speaker and details of expenses, please write to the Congregational Liaison Officer at Charis House, 47 Milton Road East, Edinburgh EH15 2SR.

(17) WORLD MISSION
Tel: 0131 225 5722   Fax: 0131 226 6121
Update: 0131 226 4121   Ansaphone: 0131 225 1216
[e-mail: world@cofscotland.org.uk]

MEMBERSHIP
BOARD OF WORLD MISSION
(27 members: 12 from Presbyteries, 12 nominated by the General Assembly, Convener and 2 Vice-Conveners)

Convener:	Rev. John M. Spiers LTh MTh, Giffnock (1996)
Vice-Conveners:	Miss Sandra McInnes, Renfrew (1997)
	Rev. Alan Greig BSc BD (1999)

DEPARTMENTAL STAFF

General Secretary:	Rev. Prof. Kenneth R. Ross BA BD PhD
Sub-Saharan Africa:	Mr Walter T. Dunlop ARICS
Faithshare:	Miss Celeste Geddes MA
Partnership in Scotland:	Mrs Catherine Laidlaw ALA
Finance:	Mr MacLeod Robertson
Personnel:	Miss Sheila Ballantyne MA PgDipPM
Overseas Partnership:	Rev. Ian W. Alexander BA BD STM
Asia:	Ms Jill Hughes BA MTh
World Exchange (seconded):	Rev. Robert S. Anderson MA BD

REMIT
The purpose of the Board is to enable the membership of the Church of Scotland at local, Presbytery and national levels, to experience and enjoy being part of the worldwide Church of Jesus Christ, sharing in the mission of God, as partners with other churches in the work of seeking God's kingdom on earth.

The Board carries on its work through the following constituent committees:

Overseas Partnership:	Convener: Rev. Alan Greig, BSc BD (1999)
World Church in Scotland:	Convener: Miss Sandra McInnes (1996)
Europe:	Convener: Rev. Norman Hutcheson MA BD (1998)
Israel Institutes:	Convener: Rev. John Renton BA LTh (1995)
Overseas Charges:	Convener: Rev. Malcolm Cuthbertson BA BD, Glasgow (1997)

WORLD MISSION AND WORLD RESOURCES

Sharing in the mission of God worldwide requires a continuing commitment to sharing the Church of Scotland's resources of people and money for mission in six continents as contemporary evidence that it is "labouring for the advancement of the Kingdom of God throughout the world" (First Article Declaratory). Such resource sharing remains an urgent matter because most of our overseas work is in the so-called "Third World," or "South", in nations where the effects of the widening gap between rich and poor is *the* major issue for the Church. Our partner churches in Africa, most of Asia, in the Caribbean. South and Central

America are desperately short of financial and technical resources which we can to some extent meet with personnel and grants. However, they are more than willing to share the resources of their Christian Faith with us, including things which the Church in the West often lacks: enthusiasm in worship, hospitality and evangelism, and a readiness to suffer and struggle for righteousness, and in many areas a readiness to sink denominational differences. Mutual sharing in the World Church witnesses to its international nature, and has much to offer a divided world, not least in Scotland.

VACANCIES OVERSEAS. The Board welcomes enquiries from men and women interested in serving in the Church overseas. This is usually with indigenous denominations and related organisations with which we are in partnership overseas, in Church of Scotland congregations mostly in Europe, or our work in Israel. Those interested in more information are invited to write to the Staffing Secretary in the first instance.

CHRISTIAN AID SCOTLAND. Christian Aid is an official relief development agency of churches in Britain and Ireland. Christian Aid's mandate is to challenge and enable us to fulfil our responsibilities to the poor of the world. Half a million volunteers and collectors and nearly 200 paid staff make this possible, with money given by millions of supporters. The Church of Scotland marks its commitment as a church to this vital part of its mission through an annual grant from the Mission and Aid Fund, transmitted through World Mission, which keeps in close touch with Christian Aid and its work.

Up-to-date information about projects and current emergency relief work can be obtained from the National Secretary, Rev. John Wylie, Christian Aid Scotland, 41 George IV Bridge, Edinburgh EH1 1EL (Tel: 0131 220 1254); the three area co-ordinators, Ms Eildon Dyer and Mrs Ailsa Henderson, Glasgow Office, 759a Argyle Street G3 8DS (Tel: 0141 221 7475), Miss Marjorie Clark, Perth Office, Room 4b, The Gateway, Perth Volunteer Centre, North Methven Street, Perth PH1 5PP (Tel: 01738 643982); or the Director, Dr Daleep Mukarji, Christian Aid Office, PO Box 100, London SE1 7RT (Tel: 0171 620 4444).

ACCOMMODATION IN ISRAEL. The Church of Scotland has two Christian Guest Houses in Israel which provide comfortable accommodation for pilgrims and visitors to the Holy Land. Further information is available from the St Andrew's Hospice, PO Box 8619, Jerusalem (Tel: 0097226732401; Fax: 0097226731711; e-mail: standjer@netvision.net il), and the Sea of Galilee Centre, PO Box 104, Tiberias (Tel: 0097266721165; Fax: 0097226790145; e-mail: scottie@rannet.com).

A list of Overseas Appointments will be found in List K in Section 6.

A World Mission Year Book is available with more details of our partner churches and of people currently serving abroad, including those with ecumenical bodies and para-church bodies.

A list of Retired Missionaries will be found in List M in Section 6.

(18) ECUMENICAL RELATIONS

MEMBERSHIP – COMMITTEE ON ECUMENICAL RELATIONS
(27 members: 12 nominated by the General Assembly, 13 appointed by the main Boards and Committees of the Church, plus 5 Corresponding Members – the General Secretary of ACTS, one from the Roman Catholic Church in Scotland and 3 on a rotating basis from the Congregational Union of Scotland, the Scottish Episcopal Church, the Synod of the Methodist Church in Scotland, the Salvation Army, the Religious Society of Friends, the United Free Church of Scotland, the United Reformed Church, and the Baptist Union of Scotland: Convener and Vice-Convener.)

Convener: Rev. Thomas Macintyre MA BD, Paisley (1998)
Secretary: Rev. Sheilagh M. Kesting BA BD

REMIT
The purpose of the Committee is to enable the Church of Scotland, at local, Presbytery and national levels, increasingly to maximise opportunities and resources for worship, witness and service together with other churches and related organisations in this country and overseas, working wherever possible through existing Boards and Committees of the Church.

In fulfilment of this Remit the Committee will:

(i)   be the body within the Church of Scotland through which WCC, ACTS, CCBI and, as appropriate, the other Ecumenical Instruments in Britain and Ireland relate;

(ii)   call together for planning, briefing and the exchanging of information, the Church of Scotland's representatives on WCC, ACTS (Central Council, Commissions and Committees), CCBI(the Assembly and the Church Representatives Meetings) and the like;

(iii) bring to the General Assembly for the approval of the General Assembly the names of those who might serve for the following year (or appropriate term) on ACTS, on CCBI and, as appropriate, on Committees, Commissions and the like of these bodies;

(iv) following consultation with the Board of World Mission, bring to the General Assembly for the approval of the General Assembly the names of those who might serve for the following year (or appropriate term) on such Bodies as the World Alliance of Reformed Churches, the Conference of European Churches and the World Council of Churches;

(v)   bring to the General Assembly for the approval of the General Assembly the names of those who might be invited to represent the Church of Scotland at the Assemblies or Synods of other Churches in Britain and at Conferences and Gatherings organised on an ecumenical basis at which official Church of Scotland representation is appropriate;

(vi) (a)   call for and receive reports from representatives of the Church of Scotland attending the Assemblies or Synods of other Churches and those ecumenical Conferences and Gatherings which are from time to time held;

(b)   ensure that appropriate parts of such reports are made available to relevant Boards and Committees.

(vii) (a) be informed of, assist centrally where appropriate, and report to the General Assembly on the Local Ecumenical Projects/Parishes which already exist in Scotland and which may in the future come to exist;

(b)   in consultation with the Board of Practice and Procedure (where matters of Church Law and Practice are involved), advise congregations and Presbyteries seeking to establish new Ecumenical Projects/Parishes or to amend existing Projects/Parishes.

(viii) be the Committee through which reports are submitted to the General Assembly from Groups appointed to take part on behalf of the Church of Scotland in formal conversations and doctrinal dialogues with other Church and ecumenical bodies.

INTERCHURCH ORGANISATIONS

WORLD COUNCIL OF CHURCHES
The Church of Scotland is a founder-member of the World Council of Churches formed in 1948. As its basis declares, it is "a fellowship of Churches which confess the Lord Jesus Christ as God and Saviour according to the Scriptures, and therefore seek to fulfil their common calling to the Glory of the one God, Father, Son and Holy Spirit". Its member Churches, which number over three hundred, are drawn from all continents and include all the major traditions (except the Roman Catholic) – Eastern and Oriental Orthodox, Reformed, Lutheran, Anglican, Baptist, Disciples, Methodist, Moravian, Friends, Pentecostalist, and others. Its Eighth Assembly was.held in Harare, Zimbabwe from 3-14th December 1998. This Assembly marked the 50th. Anniversary of the World Council with an act of recommitment by the member churches. The theme was:"Turn to God: Rejoice in Hope". The Council is once again restructuring to form a more flexible working pattern among the staff..

The General Secretary is Rev. Dr Konrad Raiser, 150 route de Ferney, 1211 Geneva 2, Switzerland (Tel: 010 41 22 791 61 11   Fax: 010 41 22 791 03 61).

WORLD ALLIANCE OF REFORMED CHURCHES
The Church of Scotland is a founder member of the World Alliance of Reformed Churches, which began in 1875 as "The Alliance of the Reformed Churches Throughout the World Holding the Presbyterian System" and which now includes also Churches of the Congregational tradition. Today it is composed of nearly 200. Churches in nearly 100 countries, with an increasing number in Asia. It brings together for mutual help and common action large Churches which enjoy majority status and small minority Churches. It engages in theological dialogue with other Christian traditions – Orthodox, Roman Catholic, Lutheran, Methodist, Baptist, *etc*. It is organised in three main departments – Co-operation with Witness, Theology, and Partnership.

The General Secretary is Rev. Dr Milan Opocensky, 150 route de Ferney, 1211 Geneva 2, Switzerland (Tel: 010 41 22 791 62 38   Fax: 010 41 22 791 65 05).

CONFERENCE OF EUROPEAN CHURCHES
The Church of Scotland is a founder member of the Conference of European Churches, formed in 1959 and until recently the only body which involved in common membership representatives of every European country (except Albania) from the Atlantic to the Urals. More than a hundred Churches, Orthodox and Protestant, are members. Although the Roman Catholic Church is not a member there is very close co-operation with the Council of European Catholic Bishops' Conferences. With the removal of the long-standing political barriers in Europe the Conference has now opportunities and responsibilities to assist the Church throughout the continent to offer united witness and service.

Its General Secretary is Rev Keith Clements, 150 route de Ferney, 1211 Geneva 2, Switzerland (Tel: 010 41 22 791 61 11   Fax: 010 41 22 791 03 61).

CEC: CHURCH AND SOCIETY COMMISSION
The Church of Scotland is a founder member of the European Commission for Church and Society. EECCS owes its origins to the Christian concern and vision of a group of ministers and European civil servants about the future of Europe. It was established in 1973 by churches recognising the importance of this venture. Membership includes churches and ecumenical bodies from the European Union. The process of integration with CEC is now complete, and the name, Church and Society Commission (CSC), established.In Brussels CSC monitors Community activity, maintains contact with MEPs and promotes dialogue between the churches and the institutions. It plays an educational role and encourages the churches' social and ethical responsibility in European affairs. It has a General Secretary, a study secretary and an executive secretary.

The General Secretary is Keith Jenkins, Ecumenical Centre, 174 rue Joseph II, 1040 Brussels, Belgium (Tel: 010 32 2 230 17 32; Fax: 010 32 2 231 14 13).

COUNCIL OF CHURCHES FOR BRITAIN AND IRELAND (CCBI)
and ACTION OF CHURCHES TOGETHER IN SCOTLAND (ACTS)

In September 1990 Churches throughout Britain and Ireland solemnly committed themselves to one another, promising to one another to do everything possible together. To provide frameworks for this commitment to joint action, the Churches established CCBI for the United Kingdom and Ireland, and for Scotland, ACTS, with sister organisations for Wales and for England.

CCBI has a large Assembly meeting every second year, a Church Representative Meeting held two or three times a year, and a Steering Committee five times a year. It has commissions on Mission, Racial Justice and Interfaith Relations. It is staffed by a General Secretary and Co-ordinating Secretaries for Church Life, Church and Society, and International Affairs.

The General Secretary of CCBI is Dr. David R. Goodbourn, Inter-Church House, 35-41 Lower Marsh, London SE1 7RL (Tel: 0171 620 4444   Fax: 0171 928 0010).

ACTS has a Central Council and three Commissions – on Unity, Faith and Order; on Mission, Evangelism and Education; and on Justice, Peace, and Social and Moral Issues. It has five Committees – on Local and Regional Unity, on Communications, on Youth Action, on Women's Participation (entitled Network of Ecumenical Women in Scotland) and on Scottish Churches House. All meet regularly. Every second year it calls a one thousand strong Scottish Christian Gathering. It is staffed by a General Secretary, a Director of Scottish Churches House, and two Associate Secretaries.

At local level there are corresponding arrangements and a continuation of the face-to-face inter-Church groups which came into being or were strengthened in the 1980s.

These structures facilitate more regular consultation and more intensive co-operation among those who frame the policies and deploy the resources of the Churches in Scotland and throughout Britain and Ireland; at the same time they afford greater opportunity for a wide range of members of different Churches to meet in common prayer and study.

The General Secretary of ACTS is Rev. Dr. Kevin Franz, Scottish Churches House, Dunblane FK15 OAJ (Tel: 01786 823588   Fax: 01786 825844

---

(19) PARISH EDUCATION
Annie Small House, 18 Inverleith Terrace
Edinburgh EH3 5NS
Tel: 0131 332 0343

MEMBERSHIP
BOARD OF PARISH EDUCATION
(Convener, Vice-Convener, 50 members elected by General Assembly, 1 representative from The Guild)

Convener:	Rev. G. Stewart Smith, Glasgow (1997)
Vice-Convener:	Rev. J.H.A. Dick, Aberdeen (1997)
Director and General Secretary:	Mr Iain W. Whyte BA DCE DMS

STAFF

Librarian:	Mr Michael Buck
National Adult Adviser:	Ms Lisa Clark
Youth Ministry Development Worker:	Mr Stewart Cutler
Tutor Organiser, Spirituality Programme:	Rev Kenneth Lawson
Counselling Course Leader:	Mrs Mary Lawson
Team Leader, Ministries Training:	Rev Donald MacAskill
Team Leader, Congregational Support:	Mr Steven Mallon
Associate Counselling Course Leader:	Ms Martha Mount
TLS Regional Organiser:	Mrs Judy Page
National Adviser, Children's Ministry:	Miss Ionwen Roberts
National Adviser, Elder Training:	Mrs Sheilah Steven
TLS Regional Organiser:	Mrs Mary Stobo
Tutor Organiser, Full-time Training:	Rev. Ian Walker
Glasgow Presbytery Youth Adviser:	Dr Kathleen Rankin
National Adviser, Child Protection:	Mrs Gillian Scott

REMIT

Based at Annie Small House in Edinburgh, the Board of Parish Education's remit is to oversee the development of an education and leadership training service for the Church of Scotland and, through the Scottish Churches Open College, for members of other denominations.

The Board's provision covers a wide spectrum of courses and events catering for all ages and abilities. This involves training for Children's workers, youth workers and elders, and reaches through to degree and higher degree level courses.

In addition, the Board's courses provide training for the Readership, Parish Assistants employed by the Board of National Mission, and the Diaconate.

COMMITTEES

The Board itself meets twice annually, in February and June, with its committees meeting 4 or 5 times per annum. The committees are organised to reflect the Board's commitment to learning for all, and to developing the concept of Faith Community.

---

(20) DEPARTMENT OF EDUCATION

MEMBERSHIP

The Education Committee (operating as the Department of Education)
(20 members together with Convener and Vice-Convener)

Convener:	Rev. John J. Laidlaw (1999)
Vice-Convener:	Mr William T. Weatherspoon (1999)

STAFF

General Secretary:	Rev. John Stevenson MA BD

REMIT

The Committee on Education is the oldest continuing Committee of the General Assembly (it was formed in 1825) and has a long and historic connection with Scottish Education. It takes an active interest in all that happens at every level and acts for the General Assembly on matters of education in schools, colleges and universities. It is the Committee which is usually approached by HM Government for submission of evidence and for responses to consultation documents on educational issues.It participates in the work of the Scottish Joint Committee on Religious and Moral Education and is represented on the Christian Education Movement (Scotland) and the Association of Teachers of Religious Education in Scotland, and together with these bodies endeavours to promote Religious and Moral Education in schools. As instructed by the General Assembly it seeks to support chaplains in schools and chaplaincy in Further Education Colleges and to co-operate with Presbyteries and Local Authorities in undertaking the training of chaplains. It has established useful and practical links with the Roman Catholic Church through its Education Commission and it has a good record of liaison with the Educational Institute of Scotland and other unions in the educational field. It is represented by one member on the General Teaching Council.

On behalf of the General Assembly it appoints a representative to the committees which deal with education on each of Scotland's 32 local authorities.

(21) COMMUNICATION

MEMBERSHIP
BOARD OF COMMUNICATION

(18 Members: Assembly appointed)

Convener:	Rev. Jean Montgomerie (1999)
Vice Convener:	Rev. W. Peter Graham (1999)
Secretary:	Mr Brian McGlynn

STAFF

Secretary and Director:	Mr Brian McGlynn
Management Accountant:	Mr Steve Murray
Press Office:	Mrs Pat Holdgate, Head of Media
	Mr Brian McGuire, Senior Press Officer
Design Services:	Mr Peter J.F. Forrest, Head of Design
Life & Work:	Editor
	Miss Alison Buckley, Deputy Editor
Saint Andrew Press:	Mrs Lesley A. Taylor, Publishing Manager
	Mr Derek Auld, Sales and Production Manager
Pathway Productions:	Mr Laurence P. Wareing, Director
(22 Colinton Rd)	Mr John P. Williams, Deputy Director
Ministers' Forum:	Rev. John Ferguson (Editor)
Year Book:	Rev. A. Gordon McGillivray (Editor)

REMIT

Under a revised constitution approved by the General Assembly in 1995, the Board is responsible for providing the Church with professional communication services and, *inter alia*, promoting effective communication within the Church and to the outside world. The Board's services are as follows:

1.   THE PRESS OFFICE
(Tel: 0131 225 5722/0131 240 2243; Fax: 0131 225 6475; e-mail: cofsmedia@ dial.pipex.com) The Press Office provides a news and information service to Press, Radio and Television and welcomes the opportunity to assist members, ministers and Presbyteries seeking to spread the Good News through the Media.

2.   DESIGN SERVICES
(Tel: 0131 225 5722/0131 240 2224; Fax: 0131 220 5407; e-mail: cofs.design@dial.pipex.com) This part of the Board's work is concerned with the design and production of a wide range of literature, display materials and exhibitions. Members of staff are pleased to advise congregations and Presbyteries on their particular communications needs.

A mailing list is maintained to provide parish magazine editors with suitable material and resources for their publications. Anyone wishing to be added to this list should provide their name and address to the Department.

3.   PATHWAY PRODUCTIONS – the Church's audio-visual production unit
(Tel: 0131 447 3531; Fax: 0131 452 8745; e-mail: Pathway@dial.pipex.com) From its premises at 22 Colinton Road, Edinburgh, the Unit produces and markets videos, tape-slide sets and audio cassettes. Short training courses in television, radio and video are also held here. The Unit has pioneered church production and use of video as a means of Christian communication. It also produces occasional programmes for broadcast television. In conjunction with the Press Office, the Unit supports religious output on Independent Local Radio.

Videos and audio cassettes may be hired or bought from Wesley Owen Bookshops in Scotland or bought through Pathway's distributor, Saint Andrew Press.

4.   LIFE & WORK
(Tel: 0131 225 5722; Fax: 0131 240 2207; e-mail: lifework@dial.pipex.com) *Life & Work* is the Church of Scotland's monthly magazine. Its purpose is to keep the Church informed about events in church life at home and abroad and to provide a forum for Christian opinion and debate on a variety of topics. It has an independent editorial policy. Contributions which are relevant to any aspect of the Christian faith are welcome.

The price of *Life & Work* this year is 90 pence. With a circulation of some 70,000 it also offers advertisers a first-class opportunity to reach a discerning readership in all parts of Scotland.

5.   SAINT ANDREW PRESS
(Tel: 0131 225 5722; Fax: 0131 220 3113; e-mail: cofs.standrew@dial.pipex.com) Since its creation in 1954 Saint Andrew Press has been responsible for a great number of publications, many of which have made a major contribution to Christian literature. The world-renowned series of New Testament commentaries by the late Professor William Barclay, *The Daily Study Bible,* continues to provide a large share of the sales of the Press. Saint Andrew Press has also published the bestselling *Glasgow Gospel* by Jamie Stuart, the critically acclaimed *Common Order* on behalf of the Church of Scotland Panel on Worship, and more recently the ecumenical songbook *Common Ground.*

Saint Andrew Press also acts as distributor for Wild Goose Publications, Pathway Productions and Church of Scotland Stationery.

All manuscripts should be sent to the Publishing Manager. The staff are always willing to offer professional help and advice.

LOCAL BROADCASTING.
The Board of Communication encourages the work of a number of ecumenical groups assisting local radio stations with their religious broadcasting. Enquiries about local religious broadcasting should be made to the Press Office (see above).

CHURCHES ADVISORY COMMITTEE FOR LOCAL BROADCASTING (CACLB)
CACLB was formed in 1967 to provide an advisory body to the Churches and to the broadcasters. Membership of the Committee is drawn from members of ACTS, the Roman Catholic Church and the Evangelical Alliance, with representatives of the BBC and ILR, together with two members co-opted from the Association of Christians in Local Broadcasting (see below).

Present Officers
President: Bishop Nigel McCulloch
Chairman: Rev. Dr. Leslie Griffiths
General Secretary: Jeff Bonser, PO Box 124, Westcliffe-on-Sea, Essex SS0 0QY
                            (Tel: 01702 348369   Fax: 01702 305121)

ASSOCIATION OF CHRISTIANS IN LOCAL BROADCASTING (ACLB)
ACLB was formed at a CACLB Conference in 1980 to meet the evident need for an association to provide "mutual support, help and comfort" for Christians involved in local radio, in whatever role. Membership is also open to those who, though not directly involved in local radio, appreciate its importance and wish to keep in touch with its problems and development.

For further information about membership consult Jeff Bonser: PO Box 124, Westcliff-on-Sea, Essex SS0 0QY (Tel: 01702 348369   Fax: 01702 305121)

---

(22) THE LAW DEPARTMENT

STAFF
Solicitor of the Church
  and of the General Trustees: Mrs J.S. Wilson LLB NP
Depute Solicitor: Miss M.E. Macleod LLB NP
Assistant Solicitors: Mr I.K. Johnstone MA LLB
                                  Mrs E.M. Kemp MA LLB
                                  Mrs J.M. Hamilton BA NP
                                  Mrs Elspeth Annan LLB NP
                                  Miss Susan Killean LLB NP

The Law Department of the Church was created in 1937/38. The Department acts in legal matters for the Church and all of its Courts, Boards, Committees, the Church of Scotland General Trustees, the Church of Scotland Trust and the Church of Scotland Investors Trust. It also acts for individual Congregations and is available to give advice on any legal matter arising.

The Department is under the charge of the Solicitor of the Church, a post created at the same time as the formation of the Department and a post which is now customarily held along with the traditional posts of Law Agent of the General Assembly and the Custodier of former United Free Church titles.

(23) CHURCH OF SCOTLAND TRUST

MEMBERSHIP
(Members are appointed by the General Assembly, on the Nomination of the Trust)
Chairman: Mr D.F. Stewart WS
Vice-Chairman: Mr J.M. Hodge WS
Treasurer: Mr D.F. Ross MA CA
Secretary: Mrs J.M. Hamilton BA

REMIT
The Church of Scotland Trust was established by Act of Parliament in 1932. The Trust's function since 1st January 1995 has been to hold properties outwith Scotland and to act as Trustee in a number of third party trusts.

Further information can be obtained from the Secretary of the Church of Scotland Trust, 121 George Street, Edinburgh EH2 4YN.

SECTION 2

General Information

(1) OTHER CHURCHES IN THE UNITED KINGDOM

THE ASSOCIATED PRESBYTERIAN CHURCHES
Synod Clerk: Mr David Laing, 224 Queens Road, Aberdeen AB1 8DN (Tel: 01224 317250).

THE REFORMED PRESBYTERIAN CHURCH OF SCOTLAND
Stated Clerk: Rev. A. Sinclair Horne, Magdalene Chapel, 41 Cowgate, Edinburgh EH1 1JR
(Tel: 0131 220 1450).

THE FREE CHURCH OF SCOTLAND
Principal Clerk: The Mound, Edinburgh EH1 2LS (Tel: 0131 226 4978/5286).

THE FREE PRESBYTERIAN CHURCH OF SCOTLAND
Synod Clerk: Napier House, 8 Colinton Road, Edinburgh EH10 5DS (Tel: 0131 447 1920).

THE UNITED FREE CHURCH OF SCOTLAND
Principal Clerk: Rev. John Fulton, United Free Church Offices, 11 Newton Place, Glasgow
G3 7PR (Tel: 0141 332 3435).

THE PRESBYTERIAN CHURCH IN IRELAND
Clerk of the General Assembly and General Secretary: Very Rev. Samuel Hutchinson BA
BD MTH DD, Church House, Belfast BT1 6DW (Tel: 01232 322284).

THE PRESBYTERIAN CHURCHES OF WALES
Gen. Secretary: Rev. Gareth Edwards, 53 Richmond Road, Cardiff CF2 3UP (Tel: 01222 494913;
Fax: 01222 464293; e-mail: ebcpcw@aol.com).

THE UNITED REFORMED CHURCH IN THE UNITED KINGDOM
General Secretary: Rev. Anthony Burnham, United Reformed Church House, 86 Tavistock
Place, London WC1H 9RT (Tel: 0171 916 2020; Fax: 0171 916 2021).

BAPTIST UNION OF SCOTLAND
Secretary: Rev. William Slack, 14 Aytoun Road, Glasgow G41 5RT (Tel: 0141 423 6169).

THE SCOTTISH CONGREGATIONAL CHURCH
General Secretary: Rev. John Arthur MA, Church House, PO Box 189, Glasgow G1 2BX
(Tel: 0141 332 7667).

RELIGIOUS SOCIETY OF FRIENDS
Clerk of the General Meeting: Mrs. Margaret Peacock, 16 Drumlin Drive, Milngavie G62 6LN.

ROMAN CATHOLIC CHURCH
Rt. Rev. Mgr. Henry Docherty, General Secretariat, Bishops' Conference for Scotland, 64 Aitken
Street, Airdrie ML6 6LT.

SALVATION ARMY
Scotland Secretary: Major Norman Armistead, Scotland Secretariat, 30 Rutland Square,
Edinburgh EH1 2BW (Tel: 0131 221 9699).

SCOTTISH EPISCOPAL CHURCH
General Secretary: John F. Stuart, 21 Grosvenor Crescent, Edinburgh EH12 5EE (Tel: 0131
225 6357).

THE SYNOD OF METHODIST CHURCH IN SCOTLAND
Secretary: Rev. David Cooper, 10 Braid Avenue, Edinburgh EH10 6DR Tel: 0131 447 6359

GENERAL SYNOD OF THE CHURCH OF ENGLAND
Secretary General: Mr Philip Mawer, Church House, Great Smith Street, London SW1P 3NZ.
Tel: 0171 222 9011

(2) OVERSEAS CHURCHES

PRESBYTERIAN CHURCH IN CANADA
Clerk of Assembly: 50 Wynford Drive, North York, Ontario M3C 1J7, Canada.

UNITED CHURCH OF CANADA
General Secretary: 3250 Bloor Street West, Etobicoke, Ontario M8K 2Y4, Canada.

PRESBYTERIAN CHURCH (USA)
Stated Clerk: 100 Witherspoon Street, Louisville KY 40202-1396, USA.

REFORMED PRESBYTERIAN CHURCH IN NORTH AMERICA
General Synod: 1818 Missouri Avenue, Las Cruces, New Mexico, USA.

CUMBERLAND PRESBYTERIAN CHURCH
General Secretary: Box 5535, Memphis 4, Tennessee, USA.

REFORMED CHURCH IN AMERICA
General Secretary: 475 Riverside Drive NY 10115, USA.

UNITED CHURCH OF CHRIST
General Secretary: 297 Park Avenue South, New York 10, USA.

UNITING CHURCH IN AUSTRALIA
General Secretary: PO Box A2266, Sydney South, New South Wales 2000, Australia.

PRESBYTERIAN CHURCH OF AUSTRALIA
Clerk of Assembly: GPO Box 100, Sydney, New South Wales 2001, Australia.

PRESBYTERIAN CHURCH OF AOTEOROA NEW ZEALAND
Executive Secretary: PO Box 9049, Wellington, New Zealand.

EVANGELICAL PRESBYTERIAN CHURCH, GHANA
Synod Clerk: PO Box 18, Ho, Volta Region, Ghana.

PRESBYTERIAN CHURCH OF GHANA
Synod Clerk: PO Box 1800, Accra, Ghana.

PRESBYTERIAN CHURCH OF EAST AFRICA
Secretary General: PO Box 48268, Nairobi, Kenya.

CHURCH OF CENTRAL AFRICA PRESBYTERIAN
Senior Clerk of General Synod: PO Box 30398, Lilongwe, Malawi.

General Secretary of Blantyre Synod: PO Box 413, Blantyre, Malawi.
General Secretary of Livingstonia Synod: PO Box112, Mzuzu, Malawi.

IGREJA EVANGELICA DE CRISTO EM MOCAMIQUE
General Secretary: Cx. Postale 284, Nampula 70100, Mozambique.

PRESBYTERIAN CHURCH OF NIGERIA
Principal Clerk: PO Box 2635, Aba, Abia State, Nigeria.

REFORMED PRESBYTERIAN CHURCH IN SOUTHERN AFRICA
General Secretary: PO Box 144, Umtata 5100, Eastern Cape, South Africa.

PRESBYTERIAN CHURCH OF SOUTHERN AFRICA
General Secretary: PO Box 96188, Brixton 2019, South Africa.

PRESBYTERIAN CHURCH OF SUDAN (A)
General Secretary: PO Box 66168, Nairobi, Kenya.

PRESBYTERIAN CHURCH OF SUDAN (M)
General Secretary: PO Box 3421, Khartoum, Sudan.

UNITED CHURCH OF ZAMBIA
General Secretary: PO Box 50122, 15101 Ridgeway, Lusaka, Zambia.

CHURCH OF BANGLADESH
Bishop: Diocesan Office, 54 Johnson Road, Dhaka 1100, Bangladesh.

CHURCH OF NORTH INDIA
General Secretary:16 Pandit Pant Marg, New Delhi, 110 001, North India.

CHURCH OF SOUTH INDIA
General Secretary: Synod Office, 5 White's Road, Royapettah, Chennai 600 114, India.

PRESBYTERIAN CHURCH OF KOREA
General Secretary: CPO Box 1125, Seoul 110 611, Korea.

PRESBYTERIAN CHURCH IN THE REPUBLIC OF KOREA
General Secretary: 1501 The Korean Ecumenical Building, 136-56 Yunchi-Dong, Chongno-
    Ku, Seoul, Korea.

THE UNITED MISSION TO NEPAL
Executive Director: PO Box 126, Kathmandu, Nepal.

CHURCH OF PAKISTAN
General Secretary: 27 Liaquat Road, Civil Lines, Hyderabad 71000, Sindh, Pakistan.

PRESBYTERY OF LANKA
Moderator: 127/1 D S Senanayake Veedyan, Kandy, Sri Lanka.

PRESBYTERIAN CHURCH IN TAIWAN
General Secretary: 3 Lane 269 Roosevelt Road, Sec. 3, Taipei, Taiwan 10763, ROC.

CHURCH OF CHRIST IN THAILAND
General Secretary: 109 CCT (13th Floor), Surawong Road, Khet Bangrak, Bangkok 10500,
    Thailand.

PRESBYTERY OF GUYANA
Moderator: 81 Croall Street, PO Box 10151, Georgetown, Guyana.

NATIONAL PRESBYTERIAN CHURCH OF GUATEMALA
Executive Secretary: Av Simeon Canas 7-13, Zona 2, Aptdo 655, Guatemala City, Guatemala.

UNITED CHURCH IN JAMAICA AND THE CAYMAN ISLANDS
General Secretary: 12 Carlton Crescent, PO Box 359, Kingston 10, Jamaica.

PRESBYTERIAN CHURCH IN TRINIDAD AND TOBAGO
General Secretary: Box 92, Paradise Hill, San Fernando, Trinidad.

BELGIAN PROTESTANT CHURCH
Rue de Champ de Mars 5, B - 1050 Bruxelles, Belgium.

REFORMED CHRISTIAN CHURCH IN CROATIA
Bishop's Office: Vladimira Nazora 31, HR - 32101 Vinkovci, Croatia.

EVANGELICAL CHURCH OF THE CZECH BRETHREN
Moderator: Jungmannova 9, Post Pr 466, CZ 111 21 Praha 1, Czech Republic.

EGLISE REFORMEE DE FRANCE
General Secretary: 47, rue de Clichy, F - 75311, Paris, France.

HUNGARIAN REFORMED CHURCH
General Secretary: Abonyi utca 21, PO Box 5, H - 1146 Budapest, Hungary.

WALDENSIAN CHURCH
Moderator: Via Firenze 38, 00184, Rome, Italy.

NETHERLANDS REFORMED CHURCH
Overgoo 11, PO Box 405, NL - 2260, AK Leidschendam, Netherlands.

REFORMED CHURCH IN ROMANIA
Bishop's Office: Str IC Bratianu No. 51, R - 3400, Cluj-Napoca, Romania.

REFORMED CHURCH IN YUGOSLAVIA
Bishop's Office: Pap Pavla, YU - 21000 Novi Sad, Yugoslavia.

COPTIC EVANGELICAL CHURCH
General Secretary: Synod of the Nile of the Evangelical Church, PO Box 1248, Cairo, Egypt.

SYNOD OF THE NILE OF THE EVANGELICAL CHURCH
Moderator: PO Box 1248, Cairo, Egypt.

DIOCESE OF THE EPISCOPAL CHURCH IN JERUSALEM AND THE MIDDLE EAST
Bishop's Office: PO Box 19122, Jerusalem 91191, via Israel.

NATIONAL EVANGELICAL SYNOD OF SYRIA AND LEBANON
General Secretary: PO Box 70890, Antelias, Lebanon

[Full information on churches overseas may be obtained from the Board of World Mission.]

(3) SCOTTISH DIVINITY FACULTIES

[˙denotes a Minister of the Church of Scotland]
[(R) Reader   (SL) Senior Lecturer   (L) Lecturer]

ABERDEEN

(University Faculty of Arts and Divinity and Christ's College)
King's College, Old Aberdeen AB9 2UB
(Tel: 01224 272380   Fax: 01224 273750
e-mail: <divinity@abdn.ac.uk>)

Master of Christ's College: TheVery Rev. Prof. Alan Main˙ TD MA BD STM PhD

**Head of Department
of Divinity with
Religious Studies:**   The Rev. Prof. W. Johnstone˙ MA BD DLitt (Hebrew)

Professors: Rev. D.A.S. Fergusson˙ MA BD DPhil (Systematic Theology)
Rev. W. Johnstone˙ MA BD DLitt (Hebrew)
The Very Rev. A. Main˙ TD MA BD STM PhD
(Practical Theology)
J.A. Thrower BA MA BLitt PhD FRAS (History of Religions)
I.R. Torrance˙ TD MA BD DPhil
(Systematic Theology/Practical Theology)
F.B. Watson BA DPhil (New Testament)

Lecturers:
K.T. Aitken BD PhD (Hebrew)
H.K. Bond MTheol PhD (New Testament)
A.D. Clarke BA MA PhD (New Testament)
Rev. J.W. Drane MA PhD (SL) (Practical Theology)
S. Kuen BA PhD (History of Religions)
Rev. Ian A. McFarland BA MDiv ThM MPhil PhD (Systematic Theology)
F.A. Murphy BA MA PhD (Systematic Theology)
B.S Rosner BA ThM PhD (New Testament)
Rev. J. Swinton˙ BD PhD RNM (Practical Theology)
C.R. Trueman MA PhD (Church History).

ST ANDREWS

(University College of St Mary)
St Mary's College, St Andrews, Fife KY16 9JU
(Tel: 01334 462850/1   Fax: 01334 462852)

Principal: R.A. Piper BA BD PhD
Dean of the Faculty: R.J. Bauckham BA MA PhD FBA

Chairs: R.J. Bauckham BA MA PhD FBA (New Testament Studies)
T.A. Hart BA PhD (Divinity)
P.F. Esler BA LLB LLM DPhil (Biblical Criticism)
B. Lang DipTheol Dr Theol Dr Theol Habil (Old Testament)

R.A. Piper BA BD PhD (Christian Origins)
C.R.Seitz AB MTS STM MA PhD
(Old Testament and Theological Studies))
A.J. Torrance* MA BD DrTheol (Divinity)

Readerships, Senior Lectureships, Lectureships:

M.I. Aguilar MA STB PhD (Religion and Contextual Theology)
J.S. Alexander* MA BD BA PhD (Church History)
I.C. Bradley* MA BD DPhil (SL) (Practical Theology)
J.R. Davila BA MA PhD (Early Jewish Studies)
M.D. Hampson BA DPhil ThM ThD MA (R) (Divinity)
B.W. Longnecker BA MRel PhD (New Testament)
D.W. Lovegrove MA BD PhD (Church History)
E.D. Reed BA PhD (Theology and Ethics)
R.B. Salters* MA BD PhD (SL) (Old Testament Language and Literature)

EDINBURGH
(Faculty of Divinity and New College)
New College, Mound Place, Edinburgh EH1 2LX
(Tel: 0131 650 8900   Fax: 0131 650 6579   e-mail: Divinity.faculty@ed.ac.uk)

Dean of Faculty: Rev. Prof. Duncan B. Forrester* MA BD DPhil DD
Principal of New College: Rev. David Lyall* BSc BD STM PhD

Chairs: Rev. A. Graeme Auld* MA BD PhD DLitt FSAScot
                               (Hebrew Bible)
                               Stewart J. Brown BA MA PhD FR Hist S
                               (Ecclesiastical History)
                               Rev. Duncan B. Forrester* MA BD DPhil DD
                               (Christian Ethics and Practical Theology)
                               Larry W Hurtado BA MA PhD
                               (New Testament Language, Literature and Theology)
                               A. Alistair Kee MA BD STM PhD DPhil (Religious Studies)
                               David Kerr MA BA DPhil
                               (Christianity in the Non-Western World)
                               Sir Stewart Sutherland MA FBA (Philosophy of Religion)
                               David F. Wright MA FRHistS DD
                               (Patristics and Reformed Christianity)

Readers, Senior Lecturers and Lecturers:
Hebrew and Old Testament: A. Peter Hayman BA PhD (SL)
                               Timothy Lim BA MPhil DPhil (R)
                               David J. Reimer BTh BA MA DPhil (L)
New Testament Language, Literature and Theology:
                               David L. Mealand MA MLitt PhD (SL)
                               Douglas A. Templeton BA BD PhD (SL)
Christian Ethics and Practical Theology:
                               David Lyall* BSc BD STM PhD (SL)
                               Jolyon Mitchell BA MA (L)

Christian Ethics and Practical Theology (cont'd):
Michael S. Northcott MA PhD (SL)
Murray Chalmers* MA (Part-time L)
Derek B. Murray MA BD PhD (Part-time L)
Ewan Kelly* MB ChB BD (Part-time L)
Theology and Religious Studies:
Ruth Page* MA BD DPhil (SL)
Nicholas Wyatt BA BD MTh PhD (R)
Ecclesiastical History:
Jane E.A. Dawson BA PhD DipEd (L)
Centre for Christianity in the Non-Western World:
Marcella Althaus-Reid BTh PhD (L)
Jack Thompson BA PhD (SL)
Moonjang Lee BA MTh MDiv PhD (L)
Fulton Lecturer in Speech and Communication:
Richard Ellis BSc MEd LGSM

GLASGOW
(Faculty of Divinity and Trinity College)
4 The Square, University of Glasgow, Glasgow G12 8QQ
(Tel: 0141 330 6526   Fax: 0141 330 4943   e-mail: M.Paton@divinity.gla.ac.uk)

Dean of Faculty: Rev. Professor David Jasper MA PhD BD
Principal of Trinity College
and Vice-Dean of Faculty: Rev. Douglas M. Murray* MA BD PhD

Chairs: Robert P. Carroll MA PhD (Hebrew Bible & Semitic Studies)
Rev. David Jasper MA PhD BD (Literature and Theology)
Rev. George M. Newlands* MA BD PhD (Divinity)
Rev. John K. Riches MA (Divinity and Biblical Criticism)
H.E. Cardinal Thomas J. Winning STL DCL DD DUniv LLD
   (Honorary Professor)
Rev. Donald Macleod MA (Visiting Professor)

Readers, Senior Lecturers and Lecturers –
Theology and Religious Studies:
John M.G. Barclay MA PhD (SL)
W. Ian P. Hazlett BA BD DrTheol (SL)
Joseph Houston MA BD DPhil (SL)
Rev. Alastair G. Hunter* MSc BD (SL)
Rev. James MacNeil PhB STD (L)
Rev. Thomas F. Magill PhB LSS PhD (L part-time)
Rev. Douglas M. Murray* MA BD PhD (L)
Lloyd V.J. Ridgeon BA MA PhD (L)
Mona Siddiqui MA MLL PhD (L)
Rev. William F. Storrar* MA BD PhD (SL)
Kiyoshi Tsuchiya MA PhD (L)
Heather E. Walton BA MA(Econ) PhD(L)

Centre for Study of Literature, Theology and the Arts:
Director: Rev. Professor George M. Newlands* MA BD PhD
Assistant Director: Kyoshi Tsuchiya MA PhD

(4) SOCIETIES AND ASSOCIATIONS

The undernoted list shows the name of the Association, along with the name and address of the Secretary.

INTER-CHURCH ASSOCIATIONS

THE FELLOWSHIP OF ST ANDREW: Rev. Donald Reid, St John's Rectory, 21 Swinton Road, Glasgow G69 6DS.

THE FELLOWSHIP OF ST THOMAS: Promotes informed interest in Churches of Indian sub-continent. Contact: Rev. Margaret S. MacGregor, MA BD DipEd, 16 Learmonth Court, Edinburgh EH4 1PB (Tel. 0131 332 1089).

THE SCOTTISH ORDER OF CHRISTIAN UNITY: Secretary: Rev. William D. Brown MA, 121 Dalkeith Road, Edinburgh EH16 5AJ (Tel/Fax: 0131 667 1124 e-mail: wdbrown@conventus.co.uk).

CHURCH PASTORAL AID SOCIETY (CPAS): Consultant for Scotland: Rev. Richard W. Higginbottom, 2 Highfield Place, Bankfoot, Perth PH1 4AX (Tel: 01738 787429).

FRONTIER YOUTH TRUST: Encourages and resources those engaged in youth work, particularly with disadvantaged young people. Co-ordinator: Feri Salvesen, c/o Anderson/ Kelvingrove Church, 759b Argyle Street, Glasgow G3 8DS (Tel: 0141 204 4800).

IONA COMMUNITY: Leader: Rev. Norman Shanks, Pearce Institute, 840 Govan Road, Glasgow G51 3UU (Tel: 0141 445 4561); Warden: Rev. Peter Millar, Iona Abbey, Isle of Iona, Argyll PA76 6SN (Tel: 01681 700404).

SCOTTISH CHRISTIAN YOUTH ASSEMBLY: Chairperson: Mr Eric Whitten, 41 Kingston Avenue, Glasgow G14 0EB.

SCOTTISH CHURCHES WORLD EXCHANGE: Arranges Overseas placements for 30-40 volunteers annually. Placements are for 1-2 years. Director: Rev. Robert Anderson, 121 George Street, Edinburgh EH2 4YN (Tel: 0131 225 8115).

SCOTTISH JOINT COMMITTEE ON RELIGIOUS EDUCATION: Rev. John Stevenson MA BD and Mr Frederick L. Forrester MA DipEd MBIM FEIS, 46 Moray Place, Edinburgh EH3 6BH (Tel: 0131 225 6244).

SCOTTISH NATIONAL COUNCIL OF YMCAs: 11 Rutland Street, Edinburgh EH1 2AE (Tel: 0131 228 1464)

SCOTTISH SUNDAY SCHOOL UNION FOR CHRISTIAN EDUCATION: Offers financial assistance by way of grant or loan to help fund training and provide resources in the promotion of Christian Education for children in Scotland. General Secretary: Mrs Lynne Collingham, 2 Fraser Avenue, Newton Mearns, Glasgow G77 6HW (Tel: 0141 571 7359).

SCOTTISH TEMPERANCE ALLIANCE: Mr John Livingstone, The Gean House, Alloa FK10 2EL (Tel: 01592 2443).

SCRIPTURE UNION: Secretary: 9 Canal Street, Glasgow G4 OAB. (Tel: 0141 332 1162).

STUDENT CHRISTIAN MOVEMENT: Mr Nick Davies, 1 Bristo Square, Edinburgh EH8 (Tel: 0131 667 4321).

UNIVERSITIES AND COLLEGES CHRISTIAN FELLOWSHIP: Freepost, Leicester LE1 7ZL.

WORLD DAY OF PRAYER: SCOTTISH COMMITTEE: Convener: Mrs Jenny Easson; Secretary: Mrs Margaret A. Broster, St Columba's Manse, Kilbirnie KA25 7JU (Tel: 01505 683342 Fax 01505 684024).

CHURCH OF SCOTLAND SOCIETIES

ASSOCIATION OF GENERAL ASSEMBLY AND PRESBYTERY CLERKS: Rev. R.A. Baigrie MA, 32 Inchcolm Terrace, South Queensferry EH30 9NA (Tel: 0131 331 4311).

ASSOCIATION OF RETURNED OVERSEAS STAFF: Mrs Lesley D. Wilson, 37 Kings Avenue, Longniddry EH32 0QN (Tel: 01875 852898).

CHURCH OF SCOTLAND TOTAL ABSTAINERS ASSOCIATION: Honorary Treasurer: R.J.M. Hart, 5 St Vincent Place, Glasgow G1 2HT (Tel: 0141 248 6820).

SCOTTISH CHURCH SOCIETY: Secretary: Rev. Matthew Z. Ross LLB BD, The Manse, Ceres, Cupar, Fife KY15 5NQ (Tel. 01334 828233).

SCOTTISH CHURCH THEOLOGY SOCIETY: Rev. William D. Brown MA, 121 Dalkeith Road, Edinburgh EH16 5AJ (Tel: 0131 667 1124).

SOCIETY OF FRIENDS OF ST ANDREW'S JERUSALEM: Hon. Secretary: Major D.J. McMicking LVO, 10 Albert Terrace, Edinburgh EH10 5EA (Tel. 0131 447 6192); Hon. Treasurer: A.J. McGregor CA, Arden, 8c Merchiston Park, Edinburgh EH10 4PN.

THE CHURCH OF SCOTLAND CHAPLAINS' ASSOCIATION: Rev. W. Scott Reid MA DipPS BD PhD, 14/37 Ethel Terrace, Edinburgh EH10 5NA (Tel: 0131 447 7642).

THE CHURCH OF SCOTLAND RETIRED MINISTERS' ASSOCIATION: Hon. Secretary: Rev. James L. Hepburn MA BD, 16 Marchmont Road, Edinburgh EH9 1HZ (Tel: 0131 229 6170).

THE CHURCH SERVICE SOCIETY. Secretary: Rev. Rachel J.W. Dobie, The Manse, Broughton, Biggar ML12 6HQ (Tel: 01899 830331).

THE IRISH MINISTERS' FRATERNAL: Secretary: Rev. Colin R. Williamson LLB BD, Manse of Aberdalgie, Perth PH2 0QD (Tel: 01738 2585).

THE NATIONAL CHURCH ASSOCIATION: Secretary: Miss Margaret P. Milne, 10 Balfron Crescent, Hamilton ML3 9UH.

THE NATIONAL COUNCIL OF YOUTH FELLOWSHIPS: General Secretary: c/o Board of Parish Education, Annie Small House, 18 Inverleith Terrace, Edinburgh EH3 5NS (Tel: 0131 332 0343).

BIBLE SOCIETIES

NATIONAL BIBLE SOCIETY OF SCOTLAND: Rev. Graham R. Houston BSc BD MTh, 7 Hampton Terrace, Edinburgh EH12 5XU (Tel: 0131 337 9701).

WEST OF SCOTLAND BIBLE SOCIETY: Rev. Alexander Macdonald MA BD, Manse of Neilston, Glasgow G78 3NP (Tel: 0141 881 1958).

GENERAL

THE BOYS' BRIGADE: Scottish Headquarters, Carronvale House, Carronvale Road, Larbert FK5 3LH (Tel: 01324 562008).

THE GIRLS' BRIGADE: Scottish Headquarters, Boys' Brigade House, 168 Bath Street, Glasgow G2 4TQ (Tel: 0141 332 1765).

THE GIRL GUIDES: Scottish Headquarters, 16 Coates Crescent, Edinburgh EH3 7AH (Tel: 0131 226 4511); Glasgow Headquarters, 15 Elmbank Street, Glasgow G2.

THE SCOUT ASSOCIATION: Scottish Headquarters, Fordell Firs, Hillend, Dunfermline KY11 5HQ (Tel: 01383 419073).

BOYS' AND GIRLS CLUBS OF SCOTLAND: 88 Giles Street, Edinburgh EH6 6BZ (Tel: 0131 555 1729).

YOUTH CLUBS (SCOTLAND): 17 Bonnington Grove, Edinburgh EH6 (Tel: 0131 554 2561).

CHRISTIAN AID SCOTLAND: National Secretary: Rev. John Wyllie, 41 George IV Bridge, Edinburgh EH1 1EL (Tel: 0131 220 1254   Fax: 0131 225 8861).

FEED THE MINDS: Scottish Secretary, Miss Dorothy Armstrong, 41 George IV Bridge, Edinburgh EH1 1EL (Tel: 0131 226 5254).

LADIES' GAELIC SCHOOLS AND HIGHLAND BURSARY ASSOCIATION: Rev. John Campbell MA, 15 Foulden Place, Dunfermline KY12 7CQ (Tel: 01383 .738055).

MARRIAGE COUNSELLING SCOTLAND: Mrs Frances Love, Director, 105 Hanover Street, Edinburgh EH2 1DJ (Tel: 0131 225 5006 Fax: 0131 220 0639).

RUTHERFORD HOUSE: Warden: Rev. David C. Searle MA, 17 Claremont Park, Edinburgh EH6 7PJ (Tel: 0131 554 1206   Fax: 0131 555 1002).

SCOTTISH CHURCH HISTORY SOCIETY: Rev. Peter H. Donald MA PhD BD, 39 Southside Road, Inverness IV2 4XA (Tel: 01463 .231140).

SCOTTISH EVANGELICAL THEOLOGY SOCIETY: Secretary: Rev. Robert D. Higham BD, Abbeyfield House, 4 School Road, East Linton EH42 1JP.

SCOTTISH NATIONAL CHRISTIAN ENDEAVOUR UNION: Secretary: Headquarters, 134 Wellington Street, Glasgow G2 2XL (Tel: 0141 332 1105).

TEAR FUND: 100 Church Road, Teddington TW11 8QE (Tel: 0181 977 9144). Scottish Secretary: Peter Chirnside, Tear Fund Scotland, Challenge House, Canal Street, Glasgow G4 0AD (Tel: 0141 332 3621).

THE AFRICA EVANGELICAL FELLOWSHIP: Mrs R Mackay, 280 St Vincent Street, Glasgow G2 5RT (Tel: 0141 248 5630).

THE LEPROSY MISSION: 89 Barnton Street, Stirling FK8 1HJ (Tel/Fax: 01786 449266). Area Organisers: Rev. J G M'Connell, 24 Craigmount Avenue North, Edinburgh EH12 8DF; and Rev. A H Swanson, 72 Mulben Crescent, Glasgow G53 7EH.

THE LORD'S DAY OBSERVANCE SOCIETY: Rev. A. Hanna, 2 The Gallolee, Edinburgh EH13 9QJ (Tel: 0131 441 3116).

THE MONTHLY VISITOR TRACT SOCIETY: 122 Thirlestane Road, Edinburgh EH9 1AN.

THE SCOTTISH REFORMATION SOCIETY: The Society, The Magdalene Chapel, 41 Cowgate, Edinburgh EH1 1JR (Tel: 0131 220 1450).

THE SOCIETY IN SCOTLAND FOR PROPAGATING CHRISTIAN KNOWLEDGE: David McLetchie, Esq., Tods, Murray WS, 66 Queen Street, Edinburgh: EH2 4NE (Tel: 0131 226 4771).

THE WALDENSIAN MISSIONS AID SOCIETY FOR WORK IN ITALY: David A Lamb, Esq. LLB, 36 Liberton Drive, Edinburgh EH16 6NN (Tel: 0131 664 3059).

YOUNG WOMEN'S CHRISTIAN ASSOCIATION OF GREAT BRITAIN, SCOTTISH COUNCIL: Miss Isobel Carr, 7 Randolph Crescent, Edinburgh EH3 7TH (Tel: 0131 225 7592).

---

(5) TRUSTS AND FUNDS

THE SOCIETY FOR THE BENEFIT OF THE SONS AND DAUGHTERS OF THE CLERGY OF THE CHURCH OF SCOTLAND

Chairman: The Hon. Lord Davidson
Secretary and Treasurer: R. Graeme Thom FCA
                                 17 Melville Street
                                 Edinburgh EH3 7PH (Tel: 0131 473 3500)

Annual grants are made to assist in the education of the children (normally between the ages of 12-25 years) of ministers of the Church of Scotland. The Society also gives grants to aged and infirm daughters of ministers and ministers' unmarried daughters and sisters who are in need. Applications to be lodged by 31st May in each year.

THE GLASGOW SOCIETY OF SONS OF MINISTERS
OF THE CHURCH OF SCOTLAND

President: Rev. I.M.P. Davidson MBE MA BD
Hon. Secretary and Treasurer: R. Graeme Thom FCA
                                 17 Melville Street
                                 Edinburgh EH3 7PH (Tel: 0131 473 3500)

The Society's primary purpose is to grant financial assistance to children (no matter what age) of deceased ministers of the Church of Scotland. Applications to be submitted by 1 February each year. To the extent that funds are available, grants are also given for the children of ministers or retired ministers, but such grants are normally restricted to students. These latter grants are considered in conjunction with the Edinburgh based Society. Limited funds are also available for individual application for special needs or projects. Applications to be submitted by 31st May each year.

Emergency applications can be dealt with at any time when need arises. Application forms may be obtained from the Hon. Secretary.

SOCIETY OF SONS OF MINISTERS OF THE UNITED PRESBYTERIAN CHURCH

This Society was dissolved in 1971 and the funds transferred to the Church of Scotland to be administered according to the aims of the former Society Annual grants are made to widows and children of deceased ministers of the United Presbyterian Church.

Applications should be lodged by 31st March in each year and forms can be obtained from the Secretaries of the Department of Ministry, 121 George Street, Edinburgh EH2 4YN.

HOLIDAYS FOR MINISTERS

The undernoted hotels provide special terms for ministers and their families Fuller information may be obtained from the establishments:

CRIEFF HYDRO: The William Meikle Fund and Paton Fund make provision whereby active ministers and their spouses, members of the Diaconate and other full time Church workers may enjoy the amenities of the Hydro in the off-peak periods at greatly reduced rates. Chalets are also available for families. Enquiries to the Resident Manager, The Hydro, Crieff PH7 3LQ (Tel: 01764 655555).

THE CINTRA BEQUEST: The Trust provides financial assistance towards the cost of accommodation in Scotland for Missionaries on leave, or for Ministers on temporary holiday, or on rest. Applications should be made to Mrs J.S. Wilson, Solicitor, 121 George Street, Edinburgh EH2 4YN.

THE LYALL BEQUEST: on behoof of the Ministers of the Church of Scotland makes available the following benefits:
1.   A payment towards the cost of holiday accommodation at any hotel or boarding house in St Andrews will be paid to any Minister and to his wife at the rate of £10 per day each for a minimum stay of three days and a maximum stay of one week. Due to the number of applications which the Trustees now receive, an applicant will not be considered to be eligible if he or she has received a grant from the Bequest during the three years prior to the holiday for which application is made. Applications, prior to the holiday, should be made to the Secretaries.
2.   Grants towards costs of sickness and convalescence so far as not covered by the National Health Service or otherwise may be available to applicants, who should apply to the Secretaries giving relevant details.

All communications should be addressed to Messrs Pagan Osborne, Solicitors, Secretaries to the Lyall Bequest, 106 South Street, St Andrews KY16 9QD. (Tel: 01334 475001).

MARGARET AND JOHN ROSS TRAVELLING FUND: Offers grants to Ministers and their spouses for travelling and other expenses for trips to the Holy Land where the purpose is recuperation or relaxation. Applications should be made initially to the Church of Scotland Law Department, 121 George Street, Edinburgh EH2 4YN.

SUMMER SCHOOL AT ST ANDREWS: A School of Theology for Ministers, organised by the Staff of St Mary's College, St Andrews, is held each year, generally in the third week of June. Full information may be obtained from the Principal, St Mary's College, St Andrews.

The undernoted represents a list of the more important trusts available for ministers, students, congregations. A brief indication is given of the trust purposes, but application should be made in each case to the person named for full particulars and forms of application.

THE ABERNETHY TRUST: Offers residential outdoor courses for Youth Fellowships, Church family week-ends, Bible Classes, *etc* at four outdoor centres. Further details from: The Executive Director, Abernethy Trust, Nethybridge PH25 3ED (Tel/Fax: 01479 821279).

THE ARROL TRUST: The object of the Trust is "to promote the benefit and advance the education of young people between the ages of 16 and 25 years of age who are physically or mentally disadvantaged or are in necessitous circumstances by assisting such persons gain experience through education and training for their future careers through travel within or without the United Kingdom". Further details and forms of application can be obtained from: C.S. Kennedy WS, Lindsays WS, 11 Atholl Crescent, Edinburgh EH3 8HE (Tel: 0131 229 1212).

THE BAIRD TRUST: Assists in the building and repair of Churches and Halls, endows Parishes and generally assists the work of the Church of Scotland. Apply: Ronald D. Oakes CA AC MA, 182 Bath Street, Glasgow G2 4HG (Tel: 0141 332 0476 Fax: 0141 331 0874).

THE REV. ALEXANDER BARCLAY BEQUEST: Assists mother, daughter, sister or niece of deceased Minister of the Church of Scotland who at the time of his death was acting as his housekeeper and who is in needy circumstances. Apply: W.N. Pomphrey DL JP LLB, 2 Belhaven Terrace, Wishaw.

BELLAHOUSTON BEQUEST FUND: Gives grants to Protestant evangelical denominations in the City of Glasgow and certain areas within five miles of city boundary for building and repairing Churches and Halls and the promotion of religion. Apply: Mitchells Roberton, 36 North Hanover Street, Glasgow G1.

BEQUEST FUND FOR MINISTERS: Assists Ministers in outlying parts. Apply: A. Linda Parkhill CA, 60 Wellington Street, Glasgow G2 6HJ.

MRS BUTLER'S TRUST: Makes annual grants to widows or dependent relatives of Ministers of the Church. Apply to Clerk to the Presbytery of Edinburgh, 10 Palmerston Place, Edinburgh EH12 5AA.

CARNEGIE TRUST: In cases of hardship the Carnegie Trust is prepared to consider applications by students of Scottish birth, extraction, or schooling for financial assistance with the payment of their fees at the Scottish Universities. If the applicant is in receipt of a Student's Allowance or a Local Education Authority award which includes payment of fees in full, he will not be eligible for assistance from the Trust for this purpose. For further details students should apply to the Secretary, Carnegie Trust, The Merchants' Hall, 22 Hanover Street, Edinburgh EH2 2EN.

CHURCH OF SCOTLAND INSURANCE CO. LTD: Undertakes Insurance of Church property and pays surplus profits to Church schemes. At 67 George Street, Edinburgh EH2 2JG (Tel: 0131 220 4119   Fax: 0131 220 4120).

THE REV. JOHN CLARK FUND: Provides annuities (1) for blind persons and (2) for orphan or fatherless children of ministers and missionaries of Church of Scotland. Apply: Fyfe, Ireland & Co. WS, 27 Melville Street, Edinburgh EH3 7PE.

CRAIGCROOK MORTIFICATION:
Chairman: G.A. Henry WS
Clerk and Factor: R. Graeme Thom FCA
                                   17 Melville Street
                                   Edinburgh EH3 7PH (Tel: 0131 473 3500)
Pensions are paid to poor men and women over 60 years old, born in Scotland or who have resided in Scotland for not less than 10 years. At present pensions amount to £480 p.a.
      Ministers are invited to notify the Clerk and Factor of deserving persons and should be prepared to act as a referee on the application form.

THE ALASTAIR CRERAR TRUST FOR SINGLE POOR: Provides Churches, Christian Organisations and individual Christians with grants to help single adults, who live on low incomes and have little capital, to improve their quality of life. Apply to the Secretary: Michael I.D. Sturrock, 58 Frederick Street, Edinburgh EH2 1LS (Tel: 0131 200 1200).

CROMBIE SCHOLARSHIP: Provides grants of £100 after competitive examination at St Mary's College, St Andrews, to MA Students of Divinity. Apply: Anderson Strathern WS, 48 Castle Street, Edinburgh EH2 3LX.

MRS DOBIE'S TRUST: Makes annual grants to widows or orphans of Ministers of the Church. Apply to Clerk to the Presbytery of Edinburgh, 10 Palmerston Place, Edinburgh EH12 5AA.

THE DRUMMOND TRUST: Makes grants towards the cost of publication of books of "sound Christian doctrine and evangelical purpose". Applications for interest-free loans for similar purposes may also be considered. The Trustees are willing to receive grant requests towards the cost of audio-visual programme material, but not equipment. Requests for application forms should be made to the Secretary, c/o Hill and Robb, 3 Pitt Terrace, Stirling FK8 2EY. Manuscripts should *not* be sent.

THE DUNCAN TRUST: Makes grants annually to students for the Ministry in the Faculties of Arts and Divinity. Preference is given to those born or educated within the bounds of the former Presbytery of Arbroath. Applications not later than 31st October to: G.J.M. Dunlop, Brothockbank House, Arbroath DD11 1NJ; or Rev. J. Colin Caskie, 44 Terrace Road, Carnoustie, Angus DD7 7AR.

ESDAILE TRUST: Assists education and advancement of daughters of Ministers, Missionaries, and Widowed Deaconesses of Church of Scotland between 12 and 25 years of age Applications to: R. Graeme Thom FCA, Clerk and Treasurer to the Governors, 17 Melville Street, Edinburgh EH3 7PH.

FERGUSON BEQUEST FUND: For the maintenance and promotion of religious ordinances and education and missionary operations in the first instance in the Counties of Ayr, Kirkcudbright,

Wigtown, Lanark, Renfrew and Dunbarton. Apply Ronald D. Oakes CA AC MA, 182 Bath Street, Glasgow G2 4HG (Tel: 0141 332 0476 Fax: 0141 331 0874).

GEIKIE BEQUEST: Makes small grants to students for the Ministry, including students studying for entry to the University, preference being given to those not eligible for SED awards Apply to the Secretary, Department of Ministry, 121 George Street, Edinburgh EH2 4YN.

JAMES GILLAN'S BURSARY FUND: Bursaries are available for students for the ministry who were born or whose parents or parent have resided and had their home for not less than three years continually in the old counties (not Districts) of Moray or Nairn. Apply: R. and R Urquhart, 121 High Street, Forres IV36 OAB.

HALDANE TRUST FUND: Provides grants to Ministers of the Church of Scotland on their first induction, towards the purchase of theological books. Apply: A C Bennett and Robertsons WS, 21/25 George IV Bridge, Edinburgh EH1 1EP.

JAMES HAMILTON'S TRUST: Grants bursaries to students at New College and makes grants to Ministers or sons of Ministers training for the Ministry, as are considered most in need of assistance. Apply: The Principal, New College, Mound Place, Edinburgh EH1 2LU.

MARTIN HARCUS BEQUEST: Makes grants to poor youths resident within the City of Edinburgh desirous of entering the Ministry of the Church. Apply: Rev. W. Peter Graham MA BD, 10 Palmerston Place, Edinburgh EH12 5AA.

THE HOGARTH FUND: Provides annuities to orphan or fatherless children of Ministers and Missionaries of the Church of Scotland. Apply Fyfe, Ireland & Co., WS, 27 Melville Street, Edinburgh EH3 7PE.

THE HOPE TRUST: Gives some support to organisations involved in combating drink and drugs, and has as its main purpose the promotion of the Reformed Faith throughout the world. There is also a Scholarship programme for Post-graduate Theology Study in Scotland. Apply Miss Carole Hope LLB, 31 Moray Place, Edinburgh EH3 6BY (Tel: 0131 226 5151).

IONA TRUST: Objects are the preservation of the Abbey buildings and others at Iona and the making of these available for public worship. Secretaries: Anderson Strathern WS, 48 Castle Street, Edinburgh EH2 3LX.

GILLIAN MACLAINE BURSARY FUND: Open to candidates for the Ministry of the Church of Scotland of Scottish or Canadian nationality. Preference is given to Gaelic speakers. Bursaries are awarded after an examination which is held annually in November. Information and application forms from the Secretary, Synod of Argyll Trusts Committee, The Manse of Glenorchy, Dalmally, Argyll PA33 1AS (Tel: 01838. 200227).

THE MISSES ANN AND MARGARET McMILLAN'S BEQUEST: Makes grants to Ministers of the Free and United Free Churches, and of the Church of Scotland, in charges within the Synod of Argyll, with income not exceeding the Minimum Stipend of the Church of Scotland. Apply by 30th June each year to Mr J. Porter, Royal Bank, 37 Victoria Street, Rothesay, Isle of Bute PA20 OAP.

THE MANSE AUXILIARY: Convener: Mrs Jean Baigrie, 32 Inchcolm Terrace, South Queensferry EH30 9NA (Tel: 0131 331 4311). Collects and distributes slightly used clothing, soft furnishings, household linen, *etc,* to Manses on small stipends, Missionaries, Ministers' Widows, and others, especially those in remote areas. Enquiries to the Convener or to the Secretary, Miss Joan McNeel-Caird, 2/26 Goldenacre Terrace, Edinburgh EH3 5RD (Tel: 0131 551 2720).

MORGAN BURSARY FUND: Makes grants to students for the Ministry in Arts and Divinity at the University of Glasgow. Apply: Rev. Alexander Cunningham MA BD, 260 Bath Street, Glasgow G2 4JP.

NOVUM TRUST: Provides small short-term grants to initiate projects in Christian research and action which cannot readily be financed from other sources. Special consideration is given to proposals aimed at the welfare of young people, the training of lay people, and new ways of communicating the faith. Applications to Rev. Dr. Frank D. Bardgett, 121 George Street Edinburgh EH2 4YN.

PATON TRUST: Assists Ministers in ill health to have recuperative holiday outwith, and free from the cares of their parishes. Apply: Iain A.T. Mowat, Esq., CA, Alexander Sloan & Co, 144 West George Street, Glasgow G2 2HG.

JOHN PRINGLE OF ELGIN, ROBINA PRINGLE OF ELGIN AND EDITH EVELYN CRESSY PRINGLE ANNUITANT FUNDS: Makes grants respectively to retired Ministers or Ministers Emeriti, to the widows of such and to the orphan daughters of such, in each case in poor circumstances. Apply: D.F. Ross MA CA, General Treasurer, 121 George Street, Edinburgh EH2 4YN.

RENFIELD STREET TRUST: Assists in the building and repair of Churches and Halls. Apply Ronald D. Oakes CA AC ACMA, 182 Bath Street, Glasgow G2 4HG (Tel: 0141 332 0476 Fax 0141 331 0874).

SCOTTISH CHURCHES ARCHITECTURAL HERITAGE TRUST: Assists congregations of any denomination in the preservation of churches regularly used for public worship and of architectural value and historic interest. Apply to the Secretary, 15 North Bank Street, The Mound, Edinburgh EH1 2LP.

SMIETON FUND. Enables a few Ministers to have a holiday at Crieff. Applications to the Secretary, Department of Ministry, 121 George Street, Edinburgh EH2 4YN.

MARY DAVIDSON SMITH CLERICAL AND EDUCATIONAL FUND FOR ABERDEEN-SHIRE: Assists Ministers in Aberdeenshire and the North to purchase books, or to travel for educational purposes, and assists their families with scholarships for further education or vocational training. Apply: Alan J. Innes Esq., LLB, 100 Union Street, Aberdeen AB10 1QR.

LORD MOUNT STEPHEN TRUSTS: Assists with stipends of Ministers of certain parishes in former Presbyteries of Strathbogie and Fordyce, Abernethy and Elgin. Factor, Secretary of the Department of Ministry, 121 George Street, Edinburgh EH2 4YN.

THE NAN STEVENSON CHARITABLE TRUST FOR RETIRED MINISTERS: Provides houses, or loans to purchase houses for retired ministers or missionaries on similar terms to the Housing and Loan Fund, with preference given to those with a North Ayrshire connection. Secretary: Rev. David Broster, Manse of St Columba's, Kilbirnie KA25 7JU.

SYNOD OF ARGYLL BURSARY FUND: Provides book grants for Candidates for the Ministry of the Church of Scotland who are native to or have strong connections within the bounds of the former Synod of Argyll (ie the Presbyteries of Dunoon, Lorn and Mull and South Argyll).

Applications should be made by 31st October to the Secretary, Synod of Argyll Trusts Committee, the Manse of Glenorchy, Dalmally, Argyll PA33 1AS (Tel: 01838 200227).

SYNOD OF GRAMPIAN CHILDREN OF THE CLERGY FUND: Makes annual grants to children of deceased ministers. Apply to Rev. Iain U. Thomson, Clerk and Treasurer, The Manse, Skene, Westhill Aberdeenshire AB32 6XX.

SYNOD OF GRAMPIAN WIDOWS FUND: Makes annual grants (currently £200 p.a.) to widows of deceased ministers who have served in a charge in the former Synod. Apply to Rev. Iain U. Thomson, Clerk and Treasurer, The Manse, Skene, Westhill, Aberdeenshire AB32 6XX.

YOUNG MINISTERS' FURNISHING LOAN FUND: Makes loans (of £500) to young Ministers in first charge where stipend minimum to assist with furnishing manse. Apply: The Secretary, Department of Ministry, 121 George Street, Edinburgh EH2 4YN.

(6) RECENT LORD HIGH COMMISSIONERS TO THE GENERAL ASSEMBLY

1965/66	The Hon Lord Birsay CBE QC TD
1967/68	The Right Hon Lord Reith of Stonehaven GCVO GBE CB TD
1969	Her Majesty the Queen attended in person
1970	The Right Hon Margaret Herbison PC
1971/72	The Right Hon Lord Clydesmuir of Braidwood CB MBE TD
1973/74	The Right Hon Lord Ballantrae of Auchairne and the Bay of Islands GCMG GCVO DSO OBE
1975/76	Sir Hector MacLennan KT FRCPGLAS FRCOG
1977	Francis David Charteris, Earl of Wemyss and March KT LLD
1978/79	The Right Hon William Ross MBE LLD
1980/81	Andrew Douglas Alexander Thomas Bruce, Earl of Elgin and Kincardine KT DL JP
1982/83	Colonel Sir John Edward Gilmour BT DSO TD
1984/85	Charles Hector Fitzroy Maclean, Baron Maclean of Duart and Morvern KT GCVO KBE
1986/87	John Campbell Arbuthnott, Viscount of Arbuthnott CBE DSC FRSE FRSA
1988/89	Sir Iain Mark Tennant KT FRSA
1990/91	The Right Hon Donald MacArthur Ross FRSE
1992/93	The Right Hon Lord Macfarlane of Bearsden
1994/95	Lady Marion Fraser
1996	Her Royal Highness The Princess Royal LG GCVO
1997	The Right Hon Lord Macfarlane of Bearsden
1998/99	The Right Hon Lord Hogg of Cumbernauld

(7) RECENT MODERATORS
OF THE GENERAL ASSEMBLY

1965	Archibald Watt STM DD, Edzell and Lethnot
1966	R. Leonard Small OBE DD, Edinburgh St Cuthbert's
1967	W. Roy Sanderson DD, Stenton with Whittingehame
1968	J.B. Longmuir TD DD, Principal Clerk of Assembly
1969	T.M. Murchison MA DD, Glasgow St Columba Summertown
1970	Hugh O. Douglas CBE DD LLD, Dundee St Mary's
1971	Andrew Herron MA BD LLB, Clerk to the Presbytery of Glasgow
1972	R.W.V. Selby Wright JP CVO TD DD FRSE, Edinburgh Canongate
1973	George T.H. Reid MC MA BD DD, Aberdeen Langstane
1974	David Steel MA BD DD, Linlithgow St Michael's
1975	James G. Matheson MA BD DD, Portree
1976	Thomas F. Torrance MBE DLitt DD FRSE, University of Edinburgh
1977	John R. Gray VRD MA BD ThM, Dunblane Cathedral
1978	Peter P. Brodie MA BD LLB DD, Alloa St Mungo's
1979	Robert A.S. Barbour MA BD STM DD, University of Aberdeen
1980	William B. Johnston MA BD DD, Edinburgh Colinton
1981	Andrew B. Doig BD STM DD, National Bible Society of Scotland
1982	John McIntyre CVO DD DLitt FRSE, University of Edinburgh
1983	J. Fraser McLuskey MC DD, London St Columba's
1984	John M.K. Paterson MA ACII BD, Milngavie St Paul's
1985	David M.B.A. Smith MA BD DUniv, Logie
1986	Robert Craig CBE DLitt LLD DD, Emeritus of Jerusalem
1987	Duncan Shaw *Bundesverdienstkreuz* JP PhD ThDr, Edinburgh Craigentinny St Christopher's
1988	James A. Whyte MA LLD, University of St Andrews
1989	William J.G. McDonald MA BD DD, Edinburgh Mayfield
1990	Robert Davidson MA BD DD FRSE, University of Glasgow
1991	William B.R. Macmillan MA BD LLD DD, Dundee St Mary's
1992	Hugh R. Wyllie MA MCIBS DD, Hamilton Old Parish Church
1993	James L. Weatherhead MA LLB DD, Principal Clerk of Assembly
1994	James A. Simpson BSc BD STM DD, Dornoch Cathedral
1995	James Harkness CB OBE MA, Chaplain General (Emeritus)
1996	John H. McIndoe MA BD STM, London: St Columba's linked with Newcastle: St Andrew's
1997	Alexander McDonald BA CMIWSc, General Secretary, Department of Ministry
1998	Alan Main TD MA BD STM PhD, Professor of Practical Theology at Christ's College, University of Aberdeen
1999	John B. Cairns LTh LlB, Dumbarton Riverside

MATTER OF PRECEDENCE

The Lord High Commissioner to the General Assembly of the Church of Scotland (while the Assembly is sitting) ranks next to the Sovereign, the Duke of Edinburgh and the Duke of Rothesay, and before the rest of the Royal Family.

The Moderator of the General Assembly of the Church of Scotland ranks next to the Lord Chancellor of Great Britain and before the Prime Minister and the Dukes.

(8) HER MAJESTY'S HOUSEHOLD IN SCOTLAND ECCLESIASTICAL

Dean of the Chapel Royal:	Very Rev. James Harkness CB OBE MA
Dean of the Order of the Thistle:	Very Rev. Gilleasbuig I. Macmillan MA BD Drhc
Domestic Chaplain:	Rev. Robert P. Sloan MA BD

Chaplains in Ordinary:

Very Rev. Gilleasbuig I. Macmillan
  CVO MA BD Drhc
Rev. Maxwell D. Craig MA BD ThM
Very Rev. James L. Weatherhead MA LLB DD
Rev. Charles Robertson MA
Rev. James A. Simpson BSc STM DD
Rev. Norman W. Drummond MA BD
Rev. John L. Paterson MA BD STM
Rev. Alastair H. Symington MA BD
Rev. John B. Cairns LTh LLB

Extra Chaplains:

Very Rev. W. Roy Sanderson DD
Very Rev. Prof. John McIntyre CVO DD DLitt
Rev. H.W.M. Cant MA BD STM
Rev. Kenneth MacVicar MBE DFC TD MA
Very Rev. Prof. Robert A.S. Barbour KCVO MC DD
Rev. Alwyn Macfarlane MA
Very Rev. William B. Johnston DD DLitt
Rev. Colin Forrester-Paton MA BD
Rev. Mary I. Levison BA BD DD
Rev. J.A. Keith Angus LVO TD MA
Very Rev. William J. Morris KCVO LLD DD
Rev. John MacLeod MA
Rev. A. Stewart Todd MA BD DD
Very Rev. William B.R. Macmillan LLD DD

(9) LONG SERVICE CERTIFICATES

Long Service Certificates, signed by the Moderator, are available for presentation to Elders and others in respect of not less than 30 years of service. It should be noted that the period is years of *service,* not *eg* years of ordination in the case of an Elder.

In the case of Sunday School teachers and Bible Class leaders the qualifying period is 21 years of service.

Certificates are not issued posthumously, nor is it possible to make exceptions to the rules, *eg* by recognising quality of service in order to reduce the qualifying period, or by reducing the qualifying period on compassionate grounds, such as serious illness.

Applications for Long Service Certificates should be made in writing to the Principal Clerk at 121 George Street, Edinburgh EH2 4YN by the Parish Minister, or by the Session Clerk on behalf of the Kirk Session. Certificates are not issued from this office to the individual recipients, nor should individuals make application themselves.

(10) LIBRARIES OF THE CHURCH

GENERAL ASSEMBLY LIBRARY AND RECORD ROOM
Most of the books contained in the General Assembly Library have been transferred to the New College Library. Records of the General Assembly, Synods, Presbyteries and Kirk Sessions are now in H M Register House, Edinburgh. All records more than fifty years old and not in current use should be sent to the Principal Clerk.

CHURCH MUSIC
The Library of New College contains a selection of works on Church music.

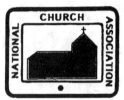

The Church of Scotland

HOUSING & LOAN FUND

FOR MINISTERS AND WIDOWS AND WIDOWERS OF MINISTERS

Many Ministers and their widow(er)s need help to secure a home for their retirement. They live in manses during their years of service, but as these are tied houses, the manse families must move and put down new roots.

The Church of Scotland Housing and Loan Fund purchases houses for renting, or gives loans, which make it possible for the manse family to secure retirement housing.

The Fund can also assist Retired Ministers and their widow(er)s by helping them move to more suitable accommodation.

Such services are rarely available to retired people on the open market and over the years, this service has been greatly valued. Ministers and others remember our fund in their wills and gifts enable our work to continue into the future and are welcome at any time.

Donations, Covenants and Legacies will be gratefully received by The Secretary, Ronald C Mather, The Church of Scotland Housing and Loan Fund for Retired Ministers and Widows and Widowers of Ministers, 121 George Street, Edinburgh EH2 4YN; to whom also applications for assistance should be directed.

THE CHURCH OF SCOTLAND

CHARITY No. Sc 015273

SECTION 3

Church Procedure

(1) THE MINISTER AND BAPTISM

The administration of Baptism to infants is governed by Act XVII (1963). The Statement on the Doctrine of Baptism may be found in the 1991 "Blue Book", page 224.
The Act itself is as follows:

1. Baptism may be administered to a child:
    (1)   whose parents, one or both, have themselves been baptised, are in full communion with the Church, and undertake the Christian upbringing of the child;
    (2)   whose parents, one or both, having been baptised, but not in full communion, are such that the Kirk Session is satisfied that he or she is an adherent, permanently connected with the congregation and supporting the work and worship of the Church and will undertake the Christian upbringing of the child;
    (3)   whose parents, one or both, have themselves been baptised, profess the Christian faith, undertake to ensure that such child grows up in the life and worship of the Church and express the desire to seek admission to full membership of the Church. In such cases the Kirk Session shall appoint an Elder of the District in which the parents reside, or some other person, to shepherd them into full communion and to exercise pastoral care of the child concerned;
    (4)   who, being of unknown parentage, or otherwise separated from his or her parents, is in the view of the Kirk Session, under Christian care and guardianship.
2. Baptism may be administered only by Ministers authorised by the General Assembly to dispense the Sacrament of the Lord's Supper.
3. Baptism may be administered only after the parents or guardians have received such instruction in its meaning as the Minister shall deem necessary.
4. No Minister shall baptise a child resident outwith his own parish, whose parents are not members or adherents of his congregation, without consent of the Minister of that parish or of the Presbytery.
5. Without the consent of the Presbytery, no Minister may administer Baptism in a case where to his knowledge another Minister has declined to do so.
6. Baptism shall normally be administered at a diet of public worship of the congregation of which the parents or guardians are members or adherents, or of the congregation of the parish in which they normally reside. In exceptional circumstances, Baptism may be administered elsewhere (*eg* at home, in hospitals or institutions). In every case, an entry shall be made in the Register of Baptism kept by the Kirk Session of the congregation of which the parents or guardians are members or adherents, or in that of the parish in which they normally reside, as the case may be.
7. Baptism shall be administered in the Name of the Father, and of the Son, and of the Holy Ghost, with water, by sprinkling, pouring, or immersion. Other elements may not be used.
8. In all cases, a Certificate of Baptism shall be given by the Minister.
9. Nothing in this Act shall be taken to mean that the Church of Scotland rejects Baptism in the name of the Father and of the Son and of the Holy Ghost duly administered in accordance with the law and discipline of other churches.

(2) THE MINISTER AND MARRIAGE

1. BACKGROUND

Prior to 1939 every marriage in Scotland fell into one or other of two classes; regular or irregular. The former was marriage by a minister of religion after due notice of intention had been given; the latter could be effected in one of three ways: (a) declaration *de presenti*, (b) by promise *subsequente copula*, or (c) by habit and repute.

The Marriage (Scotland) Act of 1939 put an end to (a) and (b) and provided for a new classification of marriage as either religious or civil. Religious marriage, conducted by a minister of religion, might be contracted in any place at any time after due intimation. Civil marriage could take place only in the office of a Registrar, again after due intimation.

The law of marriage as it was thus established in 1939 had two important limitations to the celebration of marriage: (1) certain preliminaries had to be observed; and (2) in respect of religious marriage, the service had to be conducted according to the forms of either the Christian or the Jewish faith.

2. THE MARRIAGE (SCOTLAND) ACT 1977

These two conditions were radically altered by the Marriage (Scotland) Act 1977.

Since 1st January 1978, in conformity with the demands of a multi-racial society, the benefits of religious marriage have been extended to adherents of other faiths, the only requirements being the observance of monogamy and the satisfaction of the authorities with the forms of the vows imposed.

Since 1978 the calling of banns has also been discontinued. The couple themselves must each complete a Marriage Notice form and return this to the District Registrar for the area in which they are to be married, irrespective of where they live, at least fifteen days before the ceremony is due to take place. The papers required with the form are detailed thereon.

If everything is in order the District Registrar will issue, not more than seven days before the date of the ceremony, a Marriage Schedule. This must be in the hands of the Minister officiating at the marriage ceremony before the service begins. Under no circumstances must the minister deviate from this rule. To do so is an offence under the Act.

Ministers should note the advice given by the Procurator of the Church in 1962, that they should not officiate at any marriage until at least one day after the sixteenth birthday of the younger party.

3. PROCLAMATION OF BANNS

Proclamation of banns is no longer required in Scotland but in the Church of England marriage is governed by the provisions of the Marriage Act 1949, which requires that the parties shall have been proclaimed and which provides that in the case of a party residing in Scotland a Certificate of Proclamation given according to the law or custom prevailing in Scotland shall be sufficient for the purpose. Should a minister be requested to call banns for a person resident within the Registration District wherein his church is situated he should accede, making the proclamation only on one Sunday, if the parties are known to him and he has reason to believe that there is no impediment to the marriage; otherwise on two Sundays.

Proclamation should be made at the principal service of worship in this form:

There is a purpose of marriage between AB (Bachelor/Widower/Divorced, residing at .... in this Registration District and CD, Spinster/Widow/Divorced residing at .... in the Registration District of .... of which proclamation is hereby made for the first and only (second and last) time.

Immediately after the second reading, or not less than 48 hours after the first and only reading, a Certificate of Proclamation signed by either the Minister or the Session Clerk should be issued in the following terms:

At .... the ...... day of ...... 19 ....
It is hereby certified that AB, residing at .... and CD, residing at .... have been duly proclaimed in order to marriage in the Church of .... according to the custom of the Church of Scotland, and that no objections have been offered.
Signed .... Minister or
Signed .... Session Clerk

4. MARRIAGE OF FOREIGNERS
Marriages in Scotland of foreigners, or of foreigners with British subjects, are, if they satisfy the requirements of Scots Law, valid throughout Her Majesty's dominions; but they will not necessarily be valid in the country to which the foreigner belongs. This will be so only if the requirements of the law of his or her country have also been complied with. It is therefore most important that, before the marriage, steps should be taken to obtain from the Consul, or other diplomatic representative of the country concerned, a satisfactory assurance that the marriage will be accepted as valid in the country concerned.

5. REMARRIAGE OF DIVORCED PERSONS
By virtue of Act XXVI (1959) a Minister of the Church of Scotland may lawfully solemnise the marriage of a person whose former marriage has been dissolved on divorce and whose former spouse is still alive. The Minister however must carefully adhere to the requirements of the Act which, as slightly altered in 1985 are briefly as follows:
1. The Minister should not accede as a matter of routine to a request to solemnise such a marriage. To enable him to make his decision he should take all reasonable steps to obtain relevant information, which should normally include the following:
   (a) Adequate information concerning the life and character of the parties. The Act enjoins the greatest caution in cases where no pastoral relationship exists between the Minister and either or both of the parties concerned.
   (b) The grounds and circumstances of the divorce case.
   (c) Facts bearing upon the future well being of any children concerned.
   (d) Whether any other Minister has declined to solemnise the proposed marriage.
   (e) The denomination to which the parties belong. The Act enjoins that special care should be taken where one or more parties belong to a denomination whose discipline in this matter may differ from that of the Church of Scotland.
2. The Minister should consider whether there is danger of scandal arising if he should solemnise the re-marriage, at the same time taking into careful consideration before refusing to do so the moral and spiritual effect of his refusal on the parties concerned.
3. As a determinative factor, the Minister should do all he can to assure himself that there has been sincere repentance where guilt has existed on the part of any divorced person seeking remarriage. He should also give instruction, where needed, in the nature and requirements of a Christian marriage.
4. A Minister is not required to solemnise a re-marriage against his conscience. Every Presbytery is required to appoint certain individuals with one of whom Ministers in doubt as to the correct course of action may consult is they so desire. The final decision however rests with the Minister who has been asked to officiate.

(3) CONDUCT OF MARRIAGE SERVICES
(CODE OF GOOD PRACTICE)

1. *Marriage in the Church of Scotland is solemnised by an ordained minister in a religious ceremony wherein, before God, and in the presence of the minister and at least two competent witnesses, the parties covenant together to take each other as husband and wife as long as they both shall live and the minister declares the parties to be husband and wife. Before solemnising a marriage a minister must be assured that the necessary legal requirements are being complied with and that the parties know of no legal impediment to their marriage and he or she must afterwards ensure that the Marriage Schedule is duly completed.* (Act I 1977)

2. Any ordained minister of the Church of Scotland who is a member of Presbytery or who holds a current Ministerial Certificate may officiate at a marriage service (see Act II 1987).

3. While the marriage service should normally take place in church, a minister may, at his or her discretion, officiate at a marriage service outwith church premises. Wherever conducted the ceremony will be such as to reflect appropriately both the joy and the solemnity of the occasion. In particular a minister shall ensure that nothing is done which would bring the Church and its teaching into disrepute.

4. A minister agreeing to conduct a wedding should endeavour to establish a pastoral relationship with the couple within which adequate pre-marriage preparation and subsequent pastoral care may be given.

5. "A minister should not refuse to perform ministerial functions for a person who is resident in his or her parish without sufficient reason" (Cox, *Practice and Procedure in the Church of Scotland*, sixth edition, page 55). Where either party to the proposed marriage has been divorced and the former spouse is still alive, the minister invited to officiate may solemnise such a marriage, having regard to the guidelines in the Act anent the Re-marriage of Divorced Persons (Act XXVI 1959 as amended by Act II 1985).

6. A minister is acting as an agent of the National Church which is committed to bringing the ordinances of religion to the people of Scotland through a territorial ministry. As such he or she shall not be entitled to charge a fee or allow a fee to be charged for conducting a marriage service. When a gift is spontaneously offered to a minister as a token of appreciation, the above consideration should not be taken to mean that he or she should not accept such an unsolicited gift. The Financial Board of a congregation is at liberty to set fees to cover such costs as heat and light and in addition Organists and Church Officers are entitled to a fee in respect of their services at weddings.

7. A minister should not allow his or her name to be associated with any commercial enterprise that provides facilities for weddings.

8. A minister is not at liberty to enter the bounds of another minister's parish to perform ministerial functions without the previous consent of the minister of that parish. In terms of Act VIII 1933 a minister may "officiate at a marriage or funeral by private invitation", but, for the avoidance of doubt, an invitation conveyed through a commercial enterprise shall not be regarded as a "private invitation" within the meaning of that Act.

9. A minister invited to officiate at a Marriage Service where neither party is a member of his or her congregation or is resident within his or her own parish or has any connection with the parish within which the service is to take place should observe the following courtesies:
    (a) he or she should ascertain from the parties whether either of them has a Church of Scotland connection or has approached the appropriate parish minister(s);
    (b) if it transpires that a ministerial colleague has declined to officiate then he or she (the invited minister) should ascertain the reasons therefor and shall take these, and all other relevant factors into account in deciding whether or not to officiate.

(4) THE MINISTER AND WILLS

The Requirements of Writing (Scotland) Act of 1995, which came into force on 1st August 1995, has removed the power of a Minister to execute wills notarially. Further clarification, if required, may be obtained from the Solicitor of the Church.

---

(5) PROCEDURE IN A VACANCY
(as currently applicable)

This topic is regulated by Act V 1984 (as amended). The text of the Act in its current form is given here for general information. Not printed are the Schedules of Intimation referred to in the Act. These may be obtained in a separate booklet "Intimations in a Vacancy" obtainable from the Department of National Mission, 121 George Street, Edinburgh EH2 4YN.

[NOTE: Throughout this Act all masculine pronouns and titles imply the feminine equivalent.]

APPOINTMENT OF INTERIM MODERATOR
1. At the first convenient opportunity after the death or deposition of a minister the Presbytery shall appoint an Interim Moderator to act in the vacancy; at the same meeting at which it agrees to a minister's translation, accepts his demission of office as minister of a parish, or determines (or is instructed) to dissolve a pastoral tie, the Presbytery shall appoint an Interim Moderator to act in the anticipated vacancy; the person so appointed shall be a ministerial member of the Presbytery and shall not be a member of the vacant congregation. The name of the Interim Moderator shall forthwith be forwarded to the Secretaries of the Department of Ministry.

DUTIES OF INTERIM MODERATOR
2.(1)   It shall be the duty of the Interim Moderator to preside at all meetings of the Kirk Session (or of the Kirk Sessions in the case if a linked charge) and to preside at all congregational meetings in connection with the vacancy, or at which the minister would have presided had the charge been full. In the case of a congregational meeting called by the Presbytery in connection with readjustment the Interim Moderator, having constituted the meeting, shall relinquish the chair in favour of the representative of the Presbytery, but he shall be at liberty to speak at such a meeting. In consultation with the Kirk Session and the Financial Court he shall make arrangements for the supply of the vacant pulpit.

(2)   It shall be the duty of the Interim Moderator to have the charge declared vacant on the first convenient Sunday after it has actually become vacant, that is to say:
  (a)   the day of the death of the minister
  (b)   the day when the minister's demission of office takes effect, as agreed by the Presbytery;
  (c)   the day when the minister is inducted to another charge;
  (d)   the day appointed by the Presbytery or by a superior court for the minister's deposition or for the dissolution of the pastoral tie.
  When the charge consists of more than one congregation this declaration, which shall be made in terms of Schedule A hereto, shall be read in face of each congregation, and shall be duly attested.

(3)   The Interim Moderator appointed in a prospective vacancy may call and preside at meetings of the Kirk Session and of the congregation only for the transaction of business relating to the said prospective vacancy. He shall be associated with the minister until the date of the vacancy (as above defined) and after that date he shall take full charge.

QUESTION OF READJUSTMENT

3.(1)   When an Interim Moderator has been appointed in a vacancy or a prospective vacancy, the question of readjustment shall be deemed to have been raised at that point, whereupon;

(a)   the Presbytery Clerk shall inform the Secretary of the Assembly's Committee on Parish Reappraisal of the vacancy or prospective vacancy; and

(b)   the Presbytery shall ascertain whether the charge has current or accumulated shortfalls in contributions to central funds, and shall determine whether, and to what extent any shortfalls which exist are justified.

(2)   If the vacancy is in a charge in which

(a)   the Presbytery has ascertained that there are no shortfalls, or

(b)   the Presbytery has determined that such shortfalls as exist are justified,

the Presbytery shall without delay consider whether in its opinion the question of readjustment should be pursued, conferring, if thought fitting with the office-bearers of the vacant congregation. If the Presbytery resolves that the question of readjustment should be pursued it shall take appropriate action to this end and shall inform the Assembly's Committee of its decision. If the Presbytery resolves that the question of readjustment should not be pursued it shall record this decision in its minute and shall go on to grant permission, subject to the concurrence of the Assembly's Committee on Parish Reappraisal, for the congregation to call a minister without restriction, informing the said Committee accordingly. If the Assembly's Committee is not prepared to concur this shall have the effect of sisting procedure and the question shall be further pursued notwithstanding the Presbytery's decision. In so pursuing the question in such a case the Presbytery shall seek from the outset the active participation of representatives of the Assembly's Committee. Any decision to pursue the question of readjustment at this early stage shall be without prejudice to the possibility that, at a subsequent point in the negotiations, the congregation may be granted permission to call a minister without restriction. When in any case it is agreed that the question of readjustment is to be pursued the Presbytery shall direct that no steps be taken towards filling the vacancy beyond that of preparing the Electoral Register.

(3)   If the vacancy is in a charge in which the Presbytery has determined that shortfalls are to any extent unjustified, it shall pursue the question of readjustment, provided that it may not resolve to allow a call of any kind until either;

(a)   the shortfalls have been met to the extent to which the Presbytery determined that they were unjustified; or

(b)   the congregation has been linked to or united with another congregation or other congregations.

(4)   The Presbytery shall inform the Committee on the Maintenance of the Ministry and the Board of Stewardship and Finance of its decisions in terms of this Section.

(5)   Any appeal or dissent and complaint against any judgement made in terms of this Section shall not sist procedure in the pursuit of the question of readjustment and shall be competent only in accordance with the provisions of Act IV 1984.

PERMISSION TO CALL

4.   At the meeting of Presbytery at which it is reported that a vacancy has to be filled because the Presbytery and the Assembly's Committee on Parish Reappraisal have reached agreement, or because it has been ordained by a superior court:

(a)   that the charge is to be allowed to call a minister (with or without restriction); or

(b)   that some form of union or linking has been or is about to be effected resulting in the emergence of a vacant charge which is to have permission to call a minister (with or without restriction); or

(c)   that some form of deferred union or deferred linking has been agreed which provides for the congregations involved electing a minister who will ultimately be minister of the united or linked charge but who will immediately become minister of the vacant charge; or

(d)   that an appointment is to be made under Terminable Tenure; or

(e)   that an Associate Minister is to be appointed –

the Presbytery shall appoint an *ad hoc* committee of three (of whom at least one shall be an elder) – to be known as the "Presbytery Advisory Committee" – with which the Kirk Session of the vacant charge (or the Kirk Sessions jointly in the case of a linking or of an impending union or linking or of a deferred union or linking) shall be under obligation to meet, to consider together in the light of the whole circumstances of the parish or parishes what kind of ministry would be best suited to their needs.

VACANCY SCHEDULE

5.(1)   As soon as agreement has been reached between the Presbytery and the Assembly's Committee on Parish Reappraisal as in Section 4 above there shall be issued by the Assembly's Committee on the Maintenance of the Ministry a Schedule or Schedules for completion by the responsible Financial Court of the vacant congregation (or courts of the congregations involved) in consultation with representatives of the Presbytery, setting forth the proposed arrangements for stipend and payment of ministerial expenses and for provision of a manse, and showing the amount of Aid to be given to, or to be received from, the Minimum Stipend Fund.

(2)   This Schedule (or these Schedules) shall be considered by the Presbytery and thereafter transmitted to the Assembly's Committee. The Presbytery shall not sustain an appointment and call until this Schedule has (or these Schedules have) been approved both by the Presbytery and by the Assembly's Committee.

(3)   A copy of the relevant minute of the Assembly's Committee approving the Schedule or Schedules shall be delivered by the Presbytery Clerk to the minister at the time of his induction (see section 25 (6) hereunder).

PREPARATION OF ELECTORAL REGISTER

6.   It shall be the duty of the Kirk Session of the vacant congregation, notwithstanding that the question of readjustment is being pursued, to proceed to make up the Electoral Register of the congregation. This shall contain (1) as communicants the names of those persons (a) whose names are on the communion roll of the congregation as at that date and who are not under Church discipline, (b) whose names have been added or restored to the communion roll on revision by the Kirk Session subsequently to the occurrence of the vacancy, and (c) who have given in valid Certificates of Transference by the date specified in terms of Schedule B hereto; and (2) as adherents the names of those persons who, being parishioners or regular worshippers in the congregation at the date when the vacancy occurred, being at least 18 years of age, and not being members of any other congregation in Scotland, have claimed (in writing in the form prescribed in Schedule C and within the time specified in Schedule B hereto) to be placed on the Electoral Register, the Kirk Session being satisfied that they desire to be permanently connected with the congregation and knowing of no adequate reason why they should not be admitted as communicants should they so apply.

HEARING OF CLAIMS

7.   At a meeting to be held not later than fourteen days after intimation has been made in terms of Schedule B hereto, the Kirk Session shall decide on the claims of persons to be placed on the Electoral Register, such claims to be sent to the Session Clerk before the meeting. At this meeting the Kirk Session may hear parties claiming to have an interest. The Kirk Session shall thereupon

prepare the lists of names and addresses of communicants and of adherents which it is proposed shall be the Electoral Register of the congregation, the names being arranged in alphabetical order and numbered consecutively throughout. the decision of the Kirk Session in respect of any matter affecting the preparation of the Electoral Register shall be final.

INSPECTION AND FINAL ADJUSTMENT OF ELECTORAL REGISTER

8.(1)   The proposed Electoral Register having been prepared, the Interim Moderator shall cause intimation to be made on the first convenient Sunday in terms of Schedule D hereto that on that day an opportunity will be given for inspecting the Register after service, and that it will lie for inspection at such times and such places as the Kirk Session shall have determined; and further shall specify a day when the Kirk Session will meet to hear parties claiming an interest and will finally revise and adjust the Register. At this meeting, or at an adjourned meeting held later, the list having been revised and adjusted shall, on the authority of the court, be attested by the Interim Moderator and the Clerk as the Electoral Register of the congregation.

(2)   This Register, along with a duplicate copy, shall without delay be transmitted to the Presbytery Clerk who, in name of the Presbytery, shall attest and return the principal copy, retaining the duplicate copy in his own possession. For all purposes connected with the following regulations, and for all purposes connected with parish reappraisal, the congregation shall be deemed to be those persons whose names are on the Electoral Register, and no other.

(3)   If after the attestation of the Register any communicant is given a Certificate of Transference the Session Clerk shall intimate the fact to the Interim Moderator who shall delete the name from the Register and initial the deletion. Such a Certificate shall be granted only when application for it has been made in writing, and the said written application shall be retained until the vacancy is ended.

(4)   When a period of more than six months has elapsed between the Electoral Register being attested and the congregation being given permission to call, the Kirk Session shall have power, if it so desires, to revise and update the Electoral Register. Intimation of this intention shall be given in terms of Schedule E hereto. Additional names shall be added to the Register in the form of an Addendum which shall also contain authority for the deletions which have been made, and a copy of this, duly attested, shall be lodged with the Presbytery Clerk.

APPOINTMENT OF VACANCY COMMITTEE

9.   When permission to call has been given steps shall be taken to appoint a Vacancy Committee. A congregation not yet vacant may appeal to the Presbytery for permission for its Vacancy Committee to proceed with the search for a nominee, and, if satisfied that this is in the best interest of the congregation, the Presbytery may grant such permission. But such action shall not be taken without the specific approval of the Presbytery, and in no case shall a nomination be reported to the Kirk Session in terms of section 14 hereunder until the charge is actually vacant. With a view to the appointment of a Vacancy Committee the Interim Moderator shall cause intimation to be made in terms of Schedule F that a meeting of the congregation is to be held (a) to appoint a committee of its own number for the purpose of nominating one or more persons to the congregation with a view to the election and appointment of a minister and (b) to determine whether the election shall be by ballot or by open vote. On one of the two Sundays when this intimation is made there shall also be read an exhortation impressing upon the congregation the importance of their responsibilities in the election and throughout the period of the vacancy. The Interim Moderator shall preside at this meeting, and the Session Clerk, or in his absence a person appointed by the meeting, shall act as Clerk. The procedure shall be as follows:

(a) The meeting shall first determine the maximum number to serve on the Vacancy Committee. The following scale is recommended:

Committee not to exceed
13 when the number on the Electoral Register is under 500
19 when the number on the Electoral Register is under 1000

25 when the number on the Electoral Register amounts to 1000 or more

When the vacancy is in a linked charge, or when a union or linking of congregations has been agreed but not yet effected, or when there is agreement to a deferred union or a deferred linking, the Presbytery shall determine the number who will act on the Vacancy Committee and how that number will be allocated among the congregations involved, unless provision for this has already been made in the Basis of Union or Basis of Linking as the case may be.

(b) The Interim Moderator shall then call for nominations. To constitute a valid nomination the name of a person on the Electoral Register has to be proposed and seconded. Only one nomination shall be made at a time. Anyone proposing the name of a person who is not present must be able to say that that person is prepared to act on the Committee. The Clerk shall take a note of all nominations in the order in which they are made.

(c) When it appears to the Interim Moderator that the nominations are complete he shall read to the meeting the list of the persons nominated. He shall then ask, first whether there are any further nominations, and, second, whether there are any withdrawals. After making any necessary adjustments he shall declare the list complete.

(d) If the number of persons nominated does not exceed the maximum, fixed in terms of sub-section (a) above there is no need for a vote, and the Interim Moderator shall declare that these persons constitute the Vacancy Committee. If the number exceeds the maximum the Interim Moderator shall submit the names one by one as they appear on the list to the vote of the congregation, each member having the right to vote for up to the maximum number fixed for the Committee, and voting being by standing up. In the event of a tie for the last place a vote shall be taken between those tying.

(e) The meeting shall then determine by standing up whether the election of a minister shall be by ballot or by open vote. In cases where the vacant charge consists of two or more congregations or where agreement has been reached on deferred union or deferred linking, the method of voting shall necessarily be by ballot.

(f) After intimating to the meeting the names of the persons elected to the Vacancy Committee, and announcing to the latter when they are to meet to appoint office-bearers (possibly immediately on the close of the congregational meeting) the Interim Moderator shall close the meeting with prayer.

The Interim Moderator shall act as an assessor to the Vacancy Committee, being available to offer guidance and advice. If the Committee so desire he may act as their Convener, but in no case shall he have a vote, either deliberative or casting.

FIRST MEETING OF VACANCY COMMITTEE

10. It shall be the duty of the Interim Moderator to summon and preside at the first meeting of the Vacancy Committee, which may be held at the close of the congregational meeting at which it is appointed. At this meeting a Convener, Vice-Convener, and Clerk shall be appointed. The Clerk, who need not be a member of the Committee, shall keep regular minutes of all proceedings. The Convener shall have both a casting and a deliberative vote (unless he be the Interim Moderator). If the Clerk is not a member of the Committee he shall have no vote.

MEETING WITH PRESBYTERY ADVISORY COMMITTEE

11.(1) The Interim Moderator shall arrange that the first regular meeting of the Vacancy Committee shall be attended by the Presbytery Advisory Committee which shall continue with the Vacancy Committee the discussion begun earlier with the Kirk Session or Sessions regarding the type of minister who could serve to greatest advantage in the situation, and the best way of proceeding in their search for such a minister.

(2) In the case of island and other remote charges it will be regarded as adequate if the Interim Moderator (accompanied, preferably, by a member of the Vacancy Committee) meets with the Presbytery Advisory Committee, or at least with its Convener, to carry on these discussions.

PROCEDURE OF VACANCY COMMITTEE

12.(1) The Vacancy Committee being charged with the duty of nominating one or more persons to the congregation with a view to the election and appointment of a minister, may proceed in any of the two ways outlined hereunder.

    (a)   They may decide as a result of advertisement, recommendation, enquiry, and in other ways upon a list of candidates from which they shall in due course select one or more names for submission to the congregation.

    (b)   They may decide to propose to the congregation (or congregations) that, in respect of the present vacancy only, they should restrict their right of call to the extent of electing and calling, for a period of three years only, a minister of a Church furth of Scotland which is a member of the World Alliance of Reformed Churches, or of the Church of South India, or of the Church of Pakistan. If they so decide the procedure shall be as follows:

    (i) The Interim Moderator shall cause intimation to be made on two Sundays in terms of Schedule GG that a meeting of the congregation is (or that meetings of the congregations are) to be held to determine whether they are in favour of restricting the choice of minister as proposed by the Vacancy Committee.

    (ii) If the congregation (or either or any of the congregations) vote by a majority against the proposal it shall be regarded as having fallen and the Vacancy Committee shall proceed in accordance with the other method open to them as in (a) above.

    (iii) If the congregation votes (or both or all the congregations vote) in favour of the proposal the Interim Moderator shall consult with the General Secretary of the Board of World Mission with a view to the submission of the names of not more than three ministers eligible in terms of Section 13 (11) hereunder. If none of these is accepted by the Vacancy Committee as suitable for nomination, application may be made to the Secretary of the Board for a further list of three names. Should the Vacancy Committee still be unable to recommend a sole nominee the proposal shall be regarded as having fallen and they shall proceed in accordance with the other method open to them as in (a) above.

    (iv) If the Vacancy Committee accepts one of the names for nomination procedure thereafter shall be as hereunder.

    (2) If the Vacancy Committee resolve not to have a sole nominee but to submit more than one nomination (a leet) to the congregation to be voted upon by them the Presbytery Advisory Committee shall have the right to add names up to the number submitted by the Vacancy Committee, and these too shall be heard and voted upon by the congregation.

ELIGIBILITY FOR ELECTION

13. The following categories of persons, and no others, are eligible to be nominated, elected, and called as ministers of parishes in the Church of Scotland:

    (1) A minister of a parish of the Church, a minister holding some other appointment that entitles him to a seat in Presbytery, or a minister holding a current Ministerial Certificate in terms of Sections 5-19 of Act II 1987. This is subject to the reservation that a Presbytery is not entitled to sustain a call to a minister in his first charge of a church and parish of the Church of Scotland until the expiry of at least five years from the date of his induction to that charge unless, before his nomination, a Certificate in one of the forms of Schedule G has been obtained from the Presbytery of which he is a member to the effect that there are exceptional circumstances to justify such a translation. The Interim Moderator shall be responsible for procuring this Certificate and he shall lodge it with the clerk of his own Presbytery before the nomination is reported by him to the Kirk Session in terms of section 14 (4) hereunder.

    (2) A minister of the Church of Scotland who has retired from a parish or appointment as above, provided he has not reached his seventieth birthday.

    (3) (a) A licentiate of the Church of Scotland who has satisfactorily completed, or has been granted exemption from, his period of probationary service;

(b) a graduate candidate in terms of Act V 1998, Sections 26 and 27.

(4)   A minister or licentiate or graduate candidate of the Church of Scotland who, with the approval of the Board of World Mission, has entered the courts of an indigenous Church as a full member, provided he has ceased to be such a member and has obtained from the Committee on Probationers and Transference and Admission of Ministers or its Executive a Certificate of Eligibility.

(5)   A minister or licentiate or graduate candidate of another denomination who has been admitted on petition by the General Assembly to the status of a minister or licentiate of the Church of Scotland, and who holds an extract minute of the General Assembly to that effect.

(6)   A minister or licentiate or graduate candidate of the Church of Scotland who has neither relinquished nor been judicially deprived of the status he possessed and who has become an accredited minister of the United Reformed Church in the United Kingdom, or of the Presbyterian Church in Ireland, provided he produces a Certificate from the Clerk to the General Assembly of his Church as to his status, record and character.

(7)   A minister or licentiate of the Church of Scotland who has neither relinquished nor been judicially deprived of the status he possessed and who has served, or is serving, furth of Scotland in any Church which is a member of the World Alliance of Reformed Churches, provided that prior to such nomination and call he has obtained from the Committee on Probationers and Transference and Admission of Ministers or its Executive a Certificate of Eligibility, having satisfied that body as to his status, record, and character.

(8)   A minister or licentiate of the Church of Scotland who has neither relinquished nor been judicially deprived of the status he possessed and who has undertaken employment which is not subject to the jurisdiction of any Church, provided that prior to such nomination and call (a) he has obtained from the Committee on Probationers and Transference and Admission of Ministers or its Executive a Certificate of Eligibility, having satisfied that body as to his status, record, and character, and (b) he has given a written assurance that before being admitted to a charge he shall have ceased to be so employed.

(9)   A minister of the Presbyterian Church in Ireland, provided he produces a Certificate from the Clerk to the General Assembly of that Church to the effect (a) that he was ordained by that Church, and (b) that throughout a period of not less than five years he has held one or more charges or appointments under the jurisdiction of that Church.

(10)   A minister of any regularly constituted Presbyterian Church in the United Kingdom unless eligible in terms of (9) above, of the United Reformed Church in the United Kingdom, or of any Church furth of the United Kingdom which is a member of the World Alliance of Reformed Churches, provided he holds a Certificate of Eligibility obtained from the Committee on Probationers and Transference and Admission of Ministers or its Executive, that Committee having satisfied itself (a) that he is a minister in full standing within his own Church and that throughout a period of not less than five years he has held one or more charges or appointments in that Church, (b) that he has completed a University and/or College course acceptable to the Committee on Education for the Ministry as being in accordance with the regulations of the Committee for the time being, (c) that his character and conduct are in keeping with his profession, and (d) that he is not subject to the provision of Act III 1995 Section 8 (2) (c).

(11)   A minister of a Church furth of Scotland which is a member of the World Alliance of Reformed Churches, or of the Church of South India, or of the Church of Pakistan, provided he holds a Certificate of Eligibility obtained from the Committee on Probationers and Transference and Admission of Ministers or its Executive, that Committee having satisfied itself (a) that he has fulfilled the educational requirements of his own Church, (b) that he has been ordained by that Church, (c) that he is a minister in full standing therein and has served for at least three years in a charge or appointment under its jurisdiction, and (d) that his character and conduct are in keeping with his profession. A minister in this category may be elected and called only in terms of section 12 (1) (b) above, and that for a period not exceeding three years in the first

instance. With the concurrence of the Presbytery and of the Board of World Mission this period may, at the request of the congregation, be extended for one period of not more than three years.

For purposes of interpretation of Act III of 1972 it is hereby declared that ministers and licentiates in categories (6) to (10) above shall, on election to a charge, be regarded as ministers of the Church of Scotland, and, in common with those in categories (1) to (5) shall not be admitted or inducted *ad vitam aut culpam.*

NOMINATION

14.(1) The Vacancy Committee may resolve to nominate one person only for election (a sole nominee) or they may resolve to nominate more persons than one (a leet). In the latter case they shall be subject to the provision in section 12 (2) above that the Presbytery Advisory Committee may add names to the leet. Before being asked to accept nomination a candidate shall be given adequate opportunity to see the church, the halls and the manse, and if the congregation is one where the temporal affairs are administered in accordance with a constitution peculiar to that congregation he shall be supplied with a copy of the said constitution. Before any nomination is reported in terms of subsection (4) hereunder the Secretary of the Vacancy Committee shall have secured the consent in writing of the person concerned.

(2) Before any nomination is intimated to the Kirk Session in terms of subsection (4) hereunder it shall be the duty of the Interim Moderator to have secured and lodged with his Presbytery Clerk whichever documents are appropriate, *viz.* – in the case of:

- (a) a probationer as in Category (3) of Section 13 – a Certificate from the Committee on the Supervision of Probationers to the effect that he has satisfactorily completed, or has been exempted from, his Probationary Period;
- (b) a graduate candidate – a Certificate from the Clerk of the Presbytery within whose bounds is the congregation of which the nominee is a member to the effect that a current Exit Certificate or Graduate's Certificate exists for him in terms of Act V 1998, Sections 26 and 27;
- (c) a minister in Category (1) of Section 13 who has not completed five years in his first charge – a Certificate from the releasing Presbytery in one of the forms of Schedule G;
- (d) a minister in one of the Categories (4), (7), and (10) of Section 13 – a Certificate of Eligibility;
- (e) a minister or licentiate in Category (5) of Section 13 – an extract minute of General Assembly relative to his admission to the Church of Scotland;
- (f) a minister in Category (8) of Section 13 – a Certificate of Eligibility along with a letter from the minister giving assurance that before induction (if elected) he shall have relinquished his other employment;
- (g) a minister in Categories (6) and (9) – a Certificate from the Clerk to the General Assembly of his Church giving the assurances required in the relevant subsection;
- (h) a minister in Category (1) of Section 13 – a Certificate of Eligibility and an extract minute of the congregational meeting at which it was agreed to operate in terms of Section 12 (1) (b) above.

If the vacant charge is on the General Assembly List of Gaelic-speaking Churches a certificate of competency to preach in Gaelic should also be secured and lodged.

(3) The Presbytery Advisory Committee shall be informed when a sole nomination or a leet is finally approved.

(4) Immediately a final decision on nomination has been reached the Kirk Session shall be informed through intimation made to the Interim Moderator in terms of Schedule H hereto.

PREACHING BY NOMINEES

15.(1) The Interim Moderator, on receiving notice of the Committee's nomination or nominations, shall, if it be a sole nominee, arrange that the nominee conduct public worship in the vacant church or churches on the first convenient Sunday, or, if there be a leet, that the several nominees conduct public worship in the vacant church or churches on a series of Sundays, which should if at all possible be consecutive Sundays, as soon as may conveniently be arranged. He shall then determine a day when a meeting will be held for an open vote, or, if the election is to be by ballot, for a ballot to be taken, and in so doing he shall have regard to the convenience of the electors. When a ballot is involved, time for voting shall be allowed during the day as well as in the evening, and it may be appropriate that more than one voting station be provided even when only one congregation is involved, but if there be more than one voting-station for one congregation, voting at these shall not take place concurrently.

(2) The Interim Moderator shall thereupon cause intimation to be made on two Sundays regarding the arrangements made in connection with the preaching by the nominee or nominees concerned, and setting forth the time and place of the meeting to vote, or the details regarding the ballot, as the case may be – all in terms of Schedule 1 hereto.

THE INTERIM MODERATOR AND THE ELECTION

16.(1) The Interim Moderator shall normally preside at all congregational meetings connected with the election and shall be in charge of the ballot if such there be. In the case of unavoidable absence from any meeting he may authorise a ministerial member of Presbytery (not being a member of the vacant congregation) to act in his place. Such authorisation shall be in writing and shall clearly specify the occasion on which the deputy is to act.

(2) The Interim Moderator may invite one or more persons (not being persons whose names are on the Electoral Register of the vacant congregation) to assist him in the conduct of a ballot vote when he judges this desirable.

(3) When a linking or a deferred union or deferred linking is involved the Interim Moderator shall consult and reach agreement with the minister or Interim Moderator of the other congregation regarding the arrangements for the conduct of public worship in these congregations by the candidate or candidates as in section 15 above. When a ballot is involved the Interim Moderator shall in writing appoint a ministerial member of Presbytery to take full charge of the ballot vote for the other congregation. In the case of a deferred union or deferred linking the minister of the charge which is full shall not be so appointed, nor shall he be in any way involved in the conduct of the election.

ELECTION BY OPEN VOTE

17.(1) If the congregation have determined that the method of election is to be by open vote this will be carried through at a congregational meeting held for the purpose and presided over by the Interim Moderator. When only one person has been nominated the meeting to elect may be held at the close of the service conducted by him, and should certainly be held not later than seven days after he has preached. The question shall be put from the chair "Elect Mr X or not?" and the votes shall be counted and the result recorded. The votes For should be counted even if there are no votes Against. The Interim Moderator shall complete and attest a declaration of the result in one of the forms of Schedule J.

(2) When more than one person has been nominated the meeting to elect shall be held not earlier than the Sunday next after that on which the last nominee preached. In this case the names shall be put and voted upon consecutively in the order in which the nominees have preached, the name having fewest votes being dropped and a fresh vote taken, and so on until only one name remains, or until one name commands more than half of the total votes cast. The Interim Moderator shall then put the question, "Elect Mr X or not?" The voting on the motion to elect or not shall be counted and the result recorded. If there is a clear majority in favour the Interim Moderator shall declare Mr X elected subject to the judgment of the courts of the Church and he shall complete and attest a declaration of the result in one of the forms of Schedule J.

(3) If the outcome of the voting is a resolution not to elect – this is to say, if the sole nominee be rejected, or if no nominee on the leet be accepted, by the meeting – the Interim Moderator shall declare in terms of Schedule J that there has been failure to elect. Thereafter procedure shall be as in section 21 hereunder.

ELECTION BY BALLOT

18.(1) If the congregation have determined that the method of voting shall be by ballot, or if the vacancy is in a linked charge, or in a charge where agreement has been reached on deferred union or on deferred linking the following procedure shall be followed. The Kirk Session shall arrange to have available at the time of election a sufficient supply of voting papers printed in the form of Schedule K hereto, and these shall be put into the custody of the Interim Moderator who shall preside at the election, assisted as in section 16 above. He shall issue on request to any person whose name is on the Electoral Register a voting-paper, noting on the Register that this has been done. Facilities shall be provided whereby the voter may mark the paper in secrecy, and a ballot-box shall be available wherein the paper is to be deposited when marked. The Interim Moderator may assist any person who asks for help in respect of completing the voting-paper, but no other person whatever shall communicate with the voter at this stage. The Interim Moderator, or the deputy appointed by him, shall be responsible for the safe custody of ballot-box, papers and Electoral Register.

(2) As soon as Practicable, and at latest within twenty-four hours after the close of the voting, the Interim Moderator shall constitute the Kirk Session, or the Joint Kirk Sessions when more than one congregation is involved, and in presence of the Kirk Session shall proceed with the counting of the votes, in which he may be assisted as provided in section 16 above. When more than one ballot-box has been used and when the votes of more than one congregation are involved all ballot-boxes shall be emptied and the voting-papers shall be mixed together before counting begins so that the preponderance of votes in one area or in one congregation shall not be disclosed.

(3) When there has been a sole nomination, if the number voting For exceeds the number voting Against the nominee shall be declared appointed subject to the judgment of the courts of the Church. Otherwise it shall be declared that there has been a failure to elect.

(4) When there has been a leet a count shall be taken of the First Choice recorded on the voting-papers. If one of the nominees receives a majority of the whole votes cast he shall be declared appointed subject to the judgment of the courts of the Church. If not, then the voting-papers for those nominees the total number of whose votes taken together does not amount to the number of votes cast for the person standing next higher on the list shall be re-examined, and they shall be counted in respect of their Second Choice, such votes being added to the total already recorded in favour of the remaining nominees. If this still does not result in any nominee having a clear majority the process shall be repeated, counting the Second or Third Choice as the case may be – and so on until a nominee emerges with a clear majority, when it shall be declared that he has been appointed subject to the judgment of the courts of the Church.

(5) Should there be a tie between the remaining nominees, or should the votes "Against electing any of the above-named" exceed the votes cast for the remaining nominee it shall be declared that there has been failure to elect.

(6) After the counting has been completed the Interim Moderator shall sign a declaration in one of the forms of Schedule J hereto, and this shall be recorded in the minute of the Kirk Session or of the Kirk Sessions. An extract shall be affixed to the notice-board of the church, or of each of the churches, concerned. In presence of the Kirk Session the Interim Moderator shall then seal up the voting-papers along with the marked copy of the Electoral Register, and these shall be transmitted in due course along with the other documents specified in section 22 hereunder to the Presbytery Clerk.

WITHDRAWAL OF NOMINATION

19.(1) Should a nominee intimate withdrawal before the election-notice has been read the fact of his withdrawal shall be announced and the wording of the election-notice adjusted to suit the changed circumstances.

(2) Should intimation of withdrawal be received after the election-notice has been read a note intimating the withdrawal shall be prominently displayed in the voting-station and the name of the nominee shall be struck from each voting-paper before it is issued, the voting proceeding otherwise as in section 17 or 18 above.

(3) If the withdrawal is that of a sole nominee, or of the sole remaining member of a leet, declaration shall be made to the effect that there has been failure to elect (Schedule J).

(4) In the event of there having been failure to elect the Interim Moderator shall without delay inform the Convener of the Vacancy Committee of this fact, and the Convener shall summon a meeting of his Committee as soon as conveniently possible. At this meeting the Committee may decide to make a new nomination, or to take steps towards making a new nomination, and in this case the procedure laid down in section 15 above shall be followed. Alternatively the Committee may resolve to make no further nomination and to resign, in which case the procedure shall be as in section 21 hereunder.

THE CALL

20.(1) When the election has been by open vote the Interim Moderator may, after declaring the result of the election, invite those present to sign a Call prepared in terms of Schedule L hereunder. He shall also intimate further facilities that will be available for the call to be subscribed over a period of not fewer than eight days. When the election has been by ballot the Interim Moderator shall, along with the intimation regarding the result of the voting, intimate the arrangements made for members of the congregation over a period of not less than eight days to subscribe the call (Schedule L). Intimation shall be in the form of Schedule M hereto.

(2) The call may be subscribed on behalf of a member not present to sign in person, provided a mandate authorising such subscription is produced as in Schedule N. All such entries shall be initialled by the Interim Moderator or by the member of the Kirk Session appending them.

(3) A paper of concurrence in the call may be signed by regular worshippers in the congregation over 14 years of age and by adherents whose names have not been entered on the Electoral Register.

FAILURE TO NOMINATE: FAILURE TO ELECT

21.(1) If, six calendar months after their appointment, the Vacancy Committee have not intimated a nomination it shall be in order for ten qualified electors to submit in writing a requisition for the Interim Moderator to take steps with a view to a nomination being made. On receipt of such requisition the Interim Moderator shall intimate to the Clerk of the Vacancy Committee that unless a nomination is received by him within two calendar months of writing the Committee will be regarded as having failed to nominate. If a nomination is not received within the period stipulated the Interim Moderator shall cause intimation to be made on two Sundays in terms of Schedule O (i) that the congregation is to elect a new Vacancy Committee, and the normal procedure for such election shall thereafter be followed as in section 9 above.

(2) If there has been failure to elect as defined in sections 17 (3), 18 (3), 18 (5) and 19 (3) above and the Committee have resolved not to make a new nomination but to resign, then the same procedure shall be followed as in subsection (1) above, except that the intimation shall be in terms of Schedule O (ii).

(3) If, after having been elected, the nominee intimates in writing that he declines the appointment this fact shall at once be intimated to the Clerk of the Vacancy Committee who shall summon a meeting of that Committee. At such meeting the Committee may resolve to take steps towards making a new nomination or they may resolve to resign. In the latter case the

same procedure shall be followed as in subsection (1) above, the intimation being in terms of Schedule O (iii) hereto.

(4) If there has been failure to elect, or if the person elected has declined to accept the appointment the, notwithstanding the provisions of subsection (2) and (3) above, a requisition bearing the signature of not fewer that one-tenth of the number on the Electoral Register may be lodged with the Interim Moderator within one week after intimation of failure or declinature has been given, requiring him to call a meeting of the congregation for the purpose of determining whether the Committee shall be continued or whether a new Committee shall be appointed, and if so to appoint such a Committee. On receipt of such a requisition the Interim Moderator shall make arrangements for the holding of a congregational meeting and shall cause intimation of this to be made on two Sundays in terms of Schedule O (iv) hereto.

TRANSMISSION OF DOCUMENTS

22.(1) After an election has been made the Interim Moderator shall secure from the person appointed a letter of acceptance of the appointment, and this shall include an assurance that he has used no undue influence either by himself or by others to secure the call.

(2) The Interim Moderator shall then without delay transmit the relevant documents to the Clerk of the Presbytery. These are: the minute of nomination by the Vacancy Committee, all intimations made to the congregation thereafter, the declaration of the election and appointment, the voting-papers and marked copy of the Register in the case of a ballot, and the letter of acceptance. He shall also inform the Clerk of the steps taken in connection with the signing of the call, and shall arrange that, at the expiry of the period allowed for subscription, the call shall be transmitted by the Session Clerk to the Clerk of the Presbytery. All relevant Certificates required in the case of a probationer, or of a minister of another denomination, or of a minister who has not completed five years in his first charge, or of others requiring certification as set forth in section 14(2) above, shall have been lodged with the Presbytery Clerk at the time of that person's nomination.

(3) All of these documents shall be laid before the Presbytery at its first ordinary meeting or at an extraordinary meeting at which provision has been made for the matter to be dealt with. It shall be the duty of the Interim Moderator to cause intimation of this meeting and of the right of the congregation to attend for their interests to be made on one Sunday in terms of Schedule P hereto.

(4) After the person elected has been inducted to the charge the Presbytery Clerk shall destroy the intimations and voting-papers lodged with him in terms of subsection (2) above.

IUS DEVOLUTUM

23.(1) The exercise by a congregation of its right to call a minister shall be subject to a time-limit of six calendar months, and this period shall be calculated from the date of the Presbytery meeting referred to in section 3 above when intimation is given of the agreement to grant leave to call. If it appears that an appointment is not to be made within the allotted time the congregation may make application to the Presbytery for an extension, which will normally be for a further three months. In exceptional circumstances, and for clear cause shown, a further extension may be granted. If no election has been made and intimated to the Presbytery by the expiry of that time the permission to call shall be regarded as having lapsed. The Presbytery may thereupon look afresh at the whole question of readjustment. If the Presbytery is still satisfied that a minister should be appointed, it shall itself take steps to make such an appointment, proceeding as follows.

(2) The Presbytery shall strengthen the *ad hoc* Advisory Committee which had been involved in that case by the appointment of an additional minister and elder and shall remit to that Committee to bring forward to a subsequent meeting the name of a minister (or probationer) for appointment to the charge. It satisfied with the recommendation, and having assured itself that

the person is qualified for the appointment in terms of section 13 above, the Presbytery shall thereupon make the appointment and shall record accordingly in its minutes.

(3)   The Clerk of Presbytery shall thereupon intimate to the person concerned the fact of his appointment, shall request him to forward a letter of acceptance along with appropriate Certificates if these are required in terms of section 14 above, and shall arrange with him to conduct public worship in the vacant church or churches on an early Sunday.

(4)   The Clerk of Presbytery shall cause intimation to be made in terms of Schedule Q that the person appointed will conduct public worship on the day specified and that a call in the usual form will lie with the Session Clerk or other suitable person for not less than eight free days to receive the signatures of the congregation. The conditions governing the signing of the call shall be exactly as in section 20 above.

(5)   At the expiry of the time allowed, the call shall be transmitted by the Session Clerk to the Clerk of the Presbytery who shall lay it, along with the documents referred to in subsection (3) above, before the Presbytery at its first ordinary meeting or at an extraordinary meeting at which provision has been made for the matter to be dealt with.

(6)   The procedure thereafter shall be in accordance with sections 24 and 25 hereunder.

JUDGMENT OF PRESBYTERY

24.(1)   The call and other relevant documents having been laid on the table the Presbytery shall hear any person whom it considers to have an interest. In particular the Presbytery Advisory Committee shall be entitled to be heard if it so desires, or the Presbytery may ask for a report from it. The Presbytery shall then decide whether to sustain the appointment, and in doing so shall give consideration to the number of signatures on the call. It may delay reaching a decision and return the call to the Kirk Session to give further opportunity for it to be subscribed.

(2)   If the Presbytery sustain an appointment and call to a probationer, and there be no appeal tendered in due form against its judgment, it shall appoint the day and hour and place at which the ordination and induction will take place.

(3)   If the Presbytery sustain an appointment and call to a minister of the Church of Scotland not being a minister of a parish, or to a minister of another denomination, and there being no ecclesiastical impediment the Presbytery shall appoint the day and hour and place at which the induction shall take place.

(4)   If the documents lodged with the Presbytery Clerk in terms of section 22 above relate to a call addressed to a minister of a congregation within the bounds, the Clerk shall cause intimation to be made on one Sunday to that congregation in terms of Schedule R hereto, calling a meeting of the congregation to consider the situation in which they are placed and if so resolved to appoint commissioners to appear for their interests at the meeting of Presbytery at which the matter is to be considered. The Clerk shall also arrange for a ministerial member of Presbytery to preside at that meeting. If commissioners attend they shall be heard after those from the vacant congregation; if not, the congregation shall be held as concurring in the translation.

(5)   If a Presbytery sustain an appointment and call to a minister of a congregation within the bounds of another Presbytery is shall instruct its Clerk to forward to the Clerk of that other Presbytery and extract minute of Presbytery sustaining the call along with the call itself, and it may also, if it so desire, appoint commissioners to prosecute the call at the meeting of the other Presbytery. It may then go on to make provisional arrangements for the induction of the minister.

(6)   In receiving intimation in terms of subsection (5) above, a Presbytery Clerk shall intimate the call to the minister concerned and to his Session Clerk and shall cause intimation in terms of Schedule R to be made on one Sunday to the congregation concerned, calling a meeting of the congregation to consider the situation in which they are placed and if so resolved to appoint commissioners to appear for their interests at the meeting of Presbytery when the call is to be considered. The Clerk shall arrange for a ministerial member of Presbytery to preside at that meeting. If commissioners do not attend the congregation will be held as concurring in the translation.

(7) If the Presbytery decide to place the call in the hands of the minister to whom it is addressed, and if there be no appeal or complaint, and if the minister accept the call, the Presbytery shall give judgement that it agrees to the translation, shall declare that the minister remains minister of his present charge until the date of his admission to his new charge and shall instruct him to wait on the other Presbytery as to the time of the said admission. It shall also appoint an Interim Moderator in the prospective vacancy in terms of section 1 above.

(8) If the Presbytery resolve not to translate, the minister concerned shall have the right to appeal, as shall also the Presbytery prosecuting the call. The latter Presbytery, though it was not represented when the call was dealt with, shall have the right to intimate an appeal and to lodge reasons therefore with the Clerk of the Presbytery provided these are in his hands within ten days of judgment being given.

(9) If a minister wishes to accept a call from any congregation other than a congregation of the Church of Scotland he shall proceed by way of demission of his charge in terms of section 27 hereunder.

ADMISSION TO A CHARGE

25.(1) When the Presbytery has appointed a day for the ordination and induction of a probationer, or for the induction of a minister already ordained, the Clerk shall arrange for an edict in the form of Schedule S to be read to the congregation on the two Sundays preceding the day appointed, giving public intimation that the Presbytery intends to proceed to the ordination and induction, or the induction, of the person named unless objections to his life and doctrine be alleged and substantiated, and indicating the time and place of the Presbytery meeting to deal with objections of any; normally on the day of the induction at a slightly earlier hour and in the hall of the vacant church.

(2) At the time and place named in the edict, the Presbytery having been constituted, the Moderator shall call for the return of the edict attested as having been duly served. If the minister is being translated from another Presbytery the relevant minute agreeing to translation shall also be laid on the table. The Presbytery shall then arrange that further intimation be made by the Officer, or other person appointed for the purpose, that the Presbytery is now in session and is prepared to receive objections. Any objection to be valid at this stage, must be strictly directed to life or doctrine and must be substantiated immediately to the satisfaction of the Presbytery, in which case procedure shall be sisted and the Presbytery shall take appropriate steps to deal with the situation that has arisen. Otherwise the Presbytery shall proceed with the ordination and induction, or with the induction, as hereunder.

(3) The Presbytery shall proceed to the church where public worship shall be conducted by those appointed for the purpose. The Clerk shall read a brief narrative of the cause of the vacancy and of the steps taken for the settlement. The Moderator, having read the Preamble, shall, addressing him by name, put to the person to be inducted the questions prescribed (Schedule U (i)). Satisfactory answers having been given, the person to be inducted shall sign the Formula (Schedule U (ii)). If he has not already been ordained the person to be inducted shall then kneel, and the Moderator by prayer and the imposition of hands, in which all the ministers present join, shall ordain him to the office of the Holy Ministry. Prayer being ended, the Moderator shall say, "I now declare you to have been ordained to the office of the Holy Ministry, and in name of the Lord Jesus Christ, the King and Head of the Church, and by authority of this Presbytery, I induct you to this charge, and in token thereof we give you the right hand of fellowship". The Moderator with all other members of Presbytery present shall then give the right hand of fellowship. The Moderator shall then put the prescribed question to the members of the congregation (Schedule U (iii)). Suitable charges to the new minister and to the congregation shall then be given by the Moderator or by a minister appointed for the purpose.

(4) When an ordained minister is being inducted to a charge the act of ordination shall not be repeated and the relevant words shall be omitted from the declaration. In other respects the procedure shall be as in subsection (3) above.

(5)   When the appointment is for a limited period (Terminable Tenure) the service shall proceed as in subsections (3) and (4) above except that in the declaration the Moderator shall say "I induct you to this charge on a terminable basis in terms of minute of Presbytery of date .....".

(6)   After service the Presbytery shall resume its session when the name of the new minister shall be added to the Roll of Presbytery, the Clerk shall be instructed to send certified intimation of the induction to the Session Clerk to be engrossed in the minutes of the first meeting of Kirk Session thereafter, and, in the case of a translation from another Presbytery, to the Clerk of that Presbytery. The Clerk shall also furnish the new minister with an extract of the stipend arrangements (see section 5 above).

SERVICE OF INTRODUCTION

26.(1)   When a minister has been appointed to a linked charge the Presbytery shall determine in which of the churches of the linking the induction is to take place. This shall be a service of induction to the charge, in consequence of which the person inducted shall become minister of each of the congregations embraced in the linking. The edict regarding the induction, which shall be in terms of Schedule S, shall be read in all of the churches concerned. There shall be no other service of induction, but if the churches are far distant from one another, or for other good reason, the Presbytery may appoint a service of introduction to be held in the other church or churches. Intimation shall be given of such service, but not in edictal form. See subsection (6) hereunder.

(2)   When a Presbytery has resolved, with concurrence of the Assembly's Committee on Parish Reappraisal, that an Associate Ministry should be established in a parish it will in the said resolution have made provision regarding the method to be adopted in making the appointment. When an appointment to an Associateship has been made the matter shall be reported to the Presbytery, which, having satisfied itself as to the regularity of the procedure and as to the qualifications of the person appointed, shall duly ratify the appointment, and shall make arrangements for a service of introduction. If the person appointed is a probationer the Presbytery shall arrange a Service of Ordination to precede the introduction and shall cause edictal intimation of this to be made in terms of Schedule T.

(3)   When an appointment has been made to an extra-parochial office wholly or mainly under control of the Church (community ministry, full-time chaplaincy in hospital, industry, university, full-time clerkship, *etc*). the Presbytery may deem it appropriate to arrange a service of introduction to take place in a church or chapel suitable to the occasion. If ordination is involved, suitable arrangements shall be made and edictal intimation shall be given in some place or places deemed appropriate by the Presbytery, in terms of Schedule T.

(4)   In any case of deferred union or deferred linking the minister elected and appointed shall be inducted "to the vacant congregation of A in deferred union (or linking) with the congregation of B" and there shall be no need for any further act to establish his position as minister of the united congregation or of the linked congregation as the case may be. The Presbytery, however, shall in such a case arrange a service of introduction to the newly united congregation of AB or the newly linked congregation of B. Intimation shall be given of such service, but not in edictal form.

(5)   In any case of union or linking of congregations when one has a minister and it is a condition of the union or linking that he is to become minister of the united or linked charge, no induction shall take place, but the Presbytery shall arrange a service of declaration of union (or of linking) and of introduction to the united charge or to the linked charge as the case may be.

(6)   In all cases where a service of introduction is held it shall follow the lines of an induction except that instead of putting the normal questions to the minister the Moderator shall say to him, "Mr ...., on the occasion of your ordination you solemnly vowed that, believing in one God, Father, Son and Holy Spirit, and accepting His Word in Holy Scripture and the fundamental doctrines of the faith contained in the Confession of this Church, you would

seek the unity and peace of the Church, and that, inspired by zeal for the glory of God, by the love of Christ, and by a desire for the salvation of men, you would lead a godly and circumspect life and would cheerfully discharge the duties of your ministry – do you now reaffirm your adherence to this vow?" In the declaration the Moderator in place of "I induct you to ....", shall say "I welcome you as ....".

DEMISSION

27.(1) A minister wishing to demit his charge for any reason must seek and obtain the permission of Presbytery so to do. If a minister departs from his parish without such permission he shall be held to be in desertion and may be deposed. Any application for permission to demit must state the grounds upon which it is based.

(2) A minister may seek to demit his charge:
- (a) on grounds of age or infirmity;
- (b) to enable him to take up some other appointment under the jurisdiction of the Church of Scotland;
- (c) to accept a call to a charge in, or to take up an appointment under the jurisdiction of, a Church other than the Church of Scotland; or
- (d) to leave the service of the Church.

(3) When the Clerk of Presbytery receives an application for leave to demit he shall lay it on the table at the first ordinary meeting thereafter or at an earlier meeting *pro re nata* when the Presbytery shall appoint one or more of its number to meet with the minister concerned and to confer with him regarding his reasons. The Presbytery shall also agree to deal with the application at its next ordinary meeting or at an earlier meeting *in hunc effectum* and shall instruct the Clerk to cite the congregation to appear for their interests, intimation being made in terms of Schedule V hereto. The Clerk, shall also arrange for a ministerial member of Presbytery to preside at the congregational meeting.

(4) At the Presbytery meeting at which the matter is dealt with the Clerk shall lay on the table the letter of application to demit, those who met with the applicant shall report, and parties shall be heard. If it is agreed to allow demission then if the ground be age or infirmity the minister shall retain his seat in Presbytery, unless in terms of Act VIII 1980 he elects to resign it; in other cases, unless there be special grounds for withholding it, a Presbyterial Certificate shall be issued to the minister demitting. The Presbytery shall proceed to appoint an Interim Moderator in the prospective vacancy in terms of Section 1 above.

(5) In the case where it is a condition of some basis of readjustment that a minister shall demit his charge to facilitate union or linking, and the minister has agreed in writing in terms of the appropriate regulations governing unions and readjustments, formal application shall not be made to the Presbytery for permission to demit. The minister concerned shall be regarded as retiring in the interest of readjustment and he shall retain his seat in Presbytery unless in terms of Act VIII 1980 he elects to resign it.

(6) A minister who demits his charge without retaining his seat in Presbytery shall, if he retains his status as a minister, remain under the supervision of the Presbytery which accepted his demission unless and until he moves into the bounds of another Presbytery, in which case he shall without delay lodge a current Presbyterial Certificate with the Clerk of that Presbytery, and he shall then come under its supervision.

Share your bread with the hungry and shelter the homeless poor. Clothe the man you see to be naked and turn not from your own kin. Then will your light shine like the dawn... [Isaiah 58: 7-8]

Our priority is to end rough sleeping by Scots in London.

Please help us to continue our mission by sending any contribution you can to:

Stephen Convill, Borderline, Room B1, 48 Grosvenor Gardens, London SW1W 0EB. Telephone: 0171 881 9246

Client Freephone: 0800 174 047

BORDERLINE

SUPPORTING HOMELESS
SCOTS IN LONDON

SECTION 4

The
General Assembly
of 1999

(1) OFFICIALS OF THE GENERAL ASSEMBLY

The Lord High Commissioner:	The Right Hon. Lord Hogg of Cumbernauld
Moderator:	Right Rev. John B. Cairns LTh LLB
Chaplains to the Moderator:	Prof. Herbert A. Kerrigan QC
	Rev. Scott J. Brown
Principal Clerk:	Rev. Dr Finlay A.J. Macdonald
Depute Clerk:	Rev. Marjory A. MacLean
Procurator:	Mr R.A. Dunlop QC
Law Agent:	Mrs Janette S. Wilson
Convener of the Business Committee:	Mrs Ann I McCarter
Vice-Convener of the Business Committee:	Rev. David W. Lacy
Precentor:	Rev. Douglas Galbraith
Assembly Officer:	Mr George Stephenson
Assistant Assembly Officer	Mr David McColl

(2) THE MODERATOR
The Right Reverend John B. Cairns LTh LLB

THE Moderator of the General Assembly of the Church of Scotland for 1999 is the Rev. John Ballantyne Cairns, minister at Riverside Parish Church, Dumbarton.

John Cairns was born in London. Educated at Merton Court and Sutton Valence schools, both in Kent, Mr Cairns studied Law at Bristol University, played rugby for the University and captained the water polo team. He became a member of St Columba's (Pont Street) Church, London where his family worshipped. His brother, Sandy, is Associate Minister there.

While at Bristol University, he met his wife, Liz, who graduated in medicine from Bristol in 1966. They married in 1968 and today Mrs Cairns is a full-time GP in Dumbarton. They have three sons: William (29) who works with a company training unemployed people, Ben (27) a chartered accountant, and Dan (25) a gardener.

After graduating LLB (in 1964) Mr Cairns worked until 1968 in a London law firm, and for a time was in local government administration with East Lothian Council in Haddington. He did his theological training at New College, Edinburgh.

Licensed (1973) by the Presbytery of Haddington and Dunbar, he was assistant minister at St Giles' Church, Elgin, and was ordained there in 1974. He says that this is where he found that the real links between the academic and practical outworking of the theories in ministry came alive for him.

In Spring 1975 he was inducted as minister of Langholm, Ewes and Westerkirk parishes in

Dumfriesshire – set in a large rural area with the "Muckle Toon" at its centre and formed out of the union of two recent linkings, to which the parish of Canonbie was added in 1981. He was Clerk to the Presbytery of Annandale and Eskdale (1980-82).

After ten very happy years in the Borders, Mr Cairns was called to his present charge in Dumbarton, a busy congregation with a wide range of activities and many people involved in leading and organising. The church building was completely restored and refurbished in 1992.

In 1995-96 Mr Cairns acted as senior chaplain to the then Moderator of the General Assembly, the Very Rev. James Harkness. In 1997 he was appointed one of the nine Chaplains in Ordinary to the Queen in Scotland.

Mr Cairns has served on various committees of the General Assembly, his main interest in matters connected with ministry. From 1984-88, as Convener of the Maintenance of the Ministry Committee, he worked to introduce a scheme of pastoral care for, and personal development of, ministers. He was convener (1993-98) of the Committee on Chaplains to the Forces, and saw in the introduction of new, ecumenical management structures in the Royal Navy and Royal Air Force, and visited forces on active service in Northern Ireland and Bosnia. He has also served as Chairman of the Judicial Commission and is a General Trustee of the Church.

Mr Cairns has been an exchange minister to several congregations in the USA – particularly in California and the Carolinas, developing a number of links with bodies like the Alban Institute, a specialist group involved in the development of ministry and in dealing with conflict management at all levels in the Church.

He manages the Church of Scotland golf team which plays an annual match against colleagues in the Church of England, and lists Robert Burns, music, watching sport and gardening among his interests.

(Information supplied by the Press Office)

JOHN Cairns' proudest boast is that of being a Parish Minister, and congregations in Langholm and Dumbarton Riverside mirrored that pride in their response to his being appointed as Moderator. In tackling the Moderatorial duties John is drawing on a wealth of experience from the parish in listening to and learning of the communities, members and ministers where he has the privilege of sharing in their worship and living.

The wider church has known him over a number of years, not only through his able contributions from the floor of the General Assembly, but also for the sterling service given throughout the country as Convener of the Board of Ministry, the Judicial Commission and the Committee on Chaplains to the Forces. He also has more recent experience and the honour of being a Chaplain to Her Majesty the Queen. In all of this he has brought the acute and trained mind of the lawyer enhanced with a tremendously deep pastoral care of people and enlivened with an almost controlled sense of humour. His timely interventions have frequently brought the Kirk out of situations which could have become more difficult and more hurtful for the participants. Seemingly boundless energy has enabled him to cope with the demands of the various roles in parish, presbytery, and nation, and this continues in the enthusiasm shown in chairing the Assembly, in parish and Presbytery visits, in local and national events. The move to the Conference Centre for the 1999 Assembly enabled refreshing innovations in worship in addition to the usual staple fare. Typically the presence of the African Choir led to his visiting the deprived area of Africa where these orphan children came from.

His choice of Chaplains reflects not only personal friendships but also his width of vision of ministry in the active service of eldership and the Readership as well as the ordained ministry in its varied forms including Service Chaplaincy.

Each Moderator has made a unique and valuable contribution to the life of the Church and

Nation with his particular gifts and interests, and their diversity of backgrounds has richly enhanced the office. John Cairns has continued this tradition. He has tried to be sensitive to what people expect of the Moderator. The traditional Moderator's kit with what has been described as "vestigial" lace is worn as appropriate, but left at home when considered to be a hindrance rather than a help, but the tartan trews which he has sported for years have become part of the regular kit.

John has enjoyed the support of his sons and other members of his family and friends from home and abroad. As, over the years, his principal support has been from his wife, Liz. While continuing to serve her patients in a busy Dumbarton general practice, she has been with him at all weekends and has taken, and will take, time out to be with him throughout some of his Presbytery visits and on the work being undertaken by him abroad. They have made the Moderator's new flat a homely and welcoming place where they warmly entertain on behalf of the Kirk.

The Kirk asks of a Moderator in a year what many other churches would ask a leader to do over a much longer period. John Cairns is undertaking all these duties with understanding, care and humour – and still does more.

(Bert Kerrigan QC)

(3) THE GENERAL ASSEMBLY OF 1999

WHEN Commissioners agreed to hold the 1999 General Assembly in the Edinburgh International Conference Centre they could not possibly have forecast the background against which it would meet. Not only a war in Europe, but fearful refugees, desolate and exhausted, being met by Church folk in the West of Scotland, bearing gifts and baby buggies.

The first Parliament for more than 300 years was being sworn in in the Kirk's own Assembly Hall, and a son of the manse and a kirk elder was being elected as its first Presiding Officer while the Moderator watched. Another son of the manse, as Chancellor of the Exchequer, had addressed the commissioners. The sense of history being made was palpable, the emotion being felt undeniable. To be Scottish in those days was very heaven.

Yet there was a constant reminder throughout this unique Assembly of the Church's global commitment, of standing shoulder to shoulder with our sisters and brothers world-wide. Who will forget the poignant story of the Kosova refugees? Who was not moved by the description of the agony of Gaza? Who was not amazed at the good news coming out of Cuba? Whose heart was not stirred by the dignity of the Chinese delegate and her description of Christian life there?

Can there be greater evidence of the saving grace of the Almighty God than in the thrilling appearance of the African Children's Choir – orphans who have witnessed more atrocities in their homes in Sudan, Uganda and Rwanda than we could ever imagine, but who provided the most joyous moments of the Assembly?

In the future the 1999 Assembly will be seen as a landmark. It provided proof that changes in the Church's set-up are not only required but will be welcomed. The courageous examination of a ministry for the next millennium, of what forms of worship will be required, of the essentials of child care and protection, the demands for appropriate support in communities, the plans for new churches – all indicate this.

The concern for the poor, the marginalised, the jobless, and those with mental illness emerged as priority for Church and State who spoke with one voice on Third World Debt and the urgent need to eradicate it.

Controversial "internal" issues took up a great deal of Assembly time – too much some felt, and Commissions are coming to be seen as a way out as well as a way forward. This raises questions about the programming of Assembly business, and how it can best be accommodated. So, was the Conference Centre a better venue for the Kirk's annual meeting? People liked the extra room for mingling, and eating together, the new technology, the comfortable seats, the Centre staff, supporting our own faithful and committed volunteers. But the familiarity and atmosphere of the Assembly Hall were clearly missed. Debates lacked their "Mound" edge.

Though it will not be the same Hall the Assembly returns to on 20th May 2000 (many improvements have been made), there will be a strong sense of "returning home", but valuable lessons have been learned.

The Church which has kept the idea of devolution alive for over half a century in Scotland, far from being sidelined by the advent of Scotland's Parliament, can now take its proper place. Its first Assembly of the next millennium is bound to be a challenging and memorable one.

(Ann Davies, Senior Press Officer 1984 - 1999)

(4) DIGEST OF ASSEMBLY DECISIONS

The following, in the opinion of the Editor, are the decisions of the General Assembly of 1999 which are of most interest and concern. [The full volume of "Acts and Deliverances" may be obtained from the Principal Clerk. Committees are arranged in the order in which they appear in Section 1 of the Year Book.]

ACTS

II	Act anent the **Engagement by Ministers in Secular Employment** (1/24)
III	Declaratory Act anent **Moderators of Presbytery** regarding act of Ordaining (1/28)
IV	Act anent **Congregational Vows in Services of Induction** of a Minister (1/29)
V	Act **deleting Section 2 of Act IV, 1995** to enable ministers over 65 years of age to undertake terminable tenure appointments (1/29)
VI	Interim Act anent **Long-Term Illness of Ministers in charge** (31/2 as amended)
VII	Act amending Act V 1998 anent **Selection and Training for the Full-time Ministry and Eligibility for Ordination** (17/26)
VIII	Act amending Section 2(1) of Act III 1995 anent **Admission and Re-admission of Ministers** and Section 13(1) of Act V 1984 anent **Settlement of Ministers** (Daily Papers, p 34)
IX	Act amending Section 15 of Act IV 1984 anent **Unions and Readjustments redefining Terminable Tenure** (20/32)

REGULATIONS

1.	Revised Regulations anent **Nomination of the Moderator of the General Assembly** (1/25)
2.	Revised Regulations anent **Further Endowment** (17/17)
3.	Revised Regulations anent **New Charge Developments** (20/36)

INSTRUCTIONS

1.   **All Financial Boards to participate in the new Professional Indemnity Scheme** (1/11)
2.   Presbyteries and Kirk Sessions to contact **newly-elected MSPs and Councillors** with a view to partnership in caring for the people of Scotland (Daily Papers, p 126)
3.   Presbyteries and Congregations to notify Board of Parish Education of appointment of **Youth Workers** (28/4)

REMITS TO PRESBYTERIES

1.   Interim Act anent **Long-term Illness of Ministers in charge** (31/2 as amended)

RESOLUTIONS ("DELIVERANCES")
OF GENERAL INTEREST

BOARD OF PRACTICE AND PROCEDURE
- Fresh **examination of Parish Boundaries** to be undertaken.
- **Modems, Software and Internet Access** to be **supplied to Presbyteries.**
- Presbyteries to provide their own compatible computer hardware.
- Note Report of **Scottish Parliamentary Officer.**

GENERAL TRUSTEES
- Financial Boards encouraged to work **Glebes.**
- Financial Boards advised to insist that **contractors working with heat on buildings** comply with the recommendations of the Loss Prevention Council.

BOARD OF STEWARDSHIP AND FINANCE
- Congregations urged to practise **regular Christian Stewardship reviews.**
- **Members thanked for 5.1% increase in per capita offerings in 1998,** although total congregational offerings only rose by 2%.

THE GUILD
- Commended for its involvement in the **Consultation Process** in the setting up of the **Scottish Parliament.**
- **Action Group to address issues of membership** welcomed.

ASSEMBLY COUNCIL
- **Commended for steps taken to implement its revised remit.**
- **Rev. R.S. Blakey thanked for his services to the Council and the Church as Secretary.**
- **Special Commission appointed** to examine in depth the primary purposes of the Church and the shape of the Church of Scotland in the next millennium in consultation with other Scottish Churches, and to formulate proposals for continuing reform.

CHURCH AND NATION
- **Scottish Land Reform Convention** welcomed.
- **Farming communities thanked.**
- Church members asked to **support local and national food producers.**

- Scottish Office Ministers and the Scottish Executive asked to press for **equal trading conditions for Scottish farmers** in relation to other EU countries, and to encourage the greater distribution of farm products locally.
- Regret **inadequacy of HM Government's scheme for welfare reform.**
- Welcome H M Government's intention to ensure that there will be **"work for those who can and security for those who cannot".**
- H M Government urged to ensure that the **primary basis of its welfare reform** is to **minimise poverty** and not to reduce public expenditure.
- H M Government urged to ensure that **benefits system is accessible and understandable** to all, especially draft application forms.
- H M Government urged to **reconsider six months' time limit on Job Seeker's Allowance.**
- Scottish Executive asked to establish cross-party **Commission on Community Care** for those aged 16-28.
- Congregations urged to **develop partnerships with local Mental Health agencies** and Healthcare Trusts.
- Kirk Sessions and congregations urged to **welcome and support those suffering from mental illness and those with learning difficulties.**
- Scottish Executive urged to recognise the **contribution and needs of carers** by improved training and respite provision.
- H M Government and Scottish Executive encouraged to increase research into and resources available to **support mediation and restorative justice as alternatives to the Court system.**
- Scottish Parliament and Executive urged to **end sending fine defaulters to prison** and to use alternative sanctions.
- Scottish Executive urged to **improve through-care and after-care for those coming out of prison.**
- Scottish Executive urged to **ensure that the rights of victims are respected at every stage** and to encourage development of witness support groups.
- Scottish Parliament encouraged to make **respect for human rights** integral to its work.
- Declare that **violence against women** in all its forms is morally wrong and totally unacceptable.
- Recognise the existence of physical abuse and the existence of verbal, psychological and emotional **abuse of men by women.**
- Note with interest the **establishment of the Centre for non-violence** in Scotland at Scottish Churches House, Dunblane.
- H M Government urged to support the **appeal of Sandra Gregory** to the King of Thailand for review of her sentence.
- H M Government's intention to sign on to the **European Charter for Regional or Minority Languages** welcomed in respect of Gaelic in Scotland.
- Scottish Parliament urged to **give Gaelic its appropriate status** in the life of Scotland and its Parliament.
- **BBC Governors' decision to review news coverage in Scotland** in 2000 welcomed.
- Scottish Parliament urged to make **arts education for all** and **community participation in the arts** cornerstones of a cultural strategy.
- **H M Government called on to abandon its current nuclear defence strategy.**
- **Reaffirm abhorrence of ethnic, racial and religious intolerance.**
- H M Government urged to **ensure that NATO measures each decision** even in the short term conduct of war against its effect on the long term prospect for peace.
- H M Government and Church members urged to **respond most generously to refugees.**
- The Committee, in partnership with the Board of Practice and Procedure, to make **submissions to the Royal Commission on Proposed Reform of the House of Lords.**

PANEL ON DOCTRINE
- Wide range of interests represented in **discussions on Ordination** welcomed.

PANEL ON WORSHIP
- *Worship 2000* commended to Presbyteries, Kirk Sessions and Congregations for study and action.
- Panel instructed to **commission a video of creative worship practices** as soon as the necessary finance can be made available, to stimulate change and development in congregational worship.

CHURCH HYMNARY REVISION COMMITTEE
- **Presbyteries invited to advise the Committee on how best to be consulted.**

ARTISTIC MATTERS
- "New treasures" for the **enhancement of church buildings and the enrichment of worship** welcomed.
- Welcome advice being sought on the **furnishing of spaces for prayer and meditation** in public buildings for use by different faith communities.

BOARD OF MINISTRY.
- Development of **Interim Ministry** commended.
- **Obligatory training of ministers in Child Protection** reiterated.
- Caring, talented people to be challenged to consider **ministry as a vocation.**
- **Introduction of a rigorous medical check** noted as part of the application process for the ministry.
- **Budgetary implications** of increased conference provision, payment of students' fees, and a training allowance for placements noted.
- Intention to provide **financial support for candidates** in relation to their fees endorsed.
- Support provided by **FirstAssist telephone help-line** noted. Development of **Face-to-Face Counselling Service** welcomed.
- **Dr Thomas Manson, on retiring, thanked for establishing the Occupational Health Service.**
- **Minimum Stipend for 1999** and Service Supplement and other related allowances noted.
- **Travelling Expenses for 1999** noted.
- Ministers encourage to attend appropriate **Ministry Development Conferences.**
- Encouraging number of **applications for Study Leave** noted.

COMMITTEE ON CHAPLAINS TO HER MAJESTY'S FORCES
- H M Government urged to ensure that **resources for the Armed Forces** are adequate to meet commitments.
- Ministers encouraged to consider a **career in Service Chaplaincy**, especially in the Royal Navy and the RAF.
- Appreciation of the work of **Chaplains to the Cadet Forces** recorded. Ministers encouraged to serve in this way.
- Church's unwillingness noted to accept ordained service personnel, other than chaplains, to carry out a **ministry of Word and Sacrament within the Services.**

BOARD OF NATIONAL MISSION
- Establishing of **new charges in "brownfield sites"** welcomed, recognising the need to

develop new ways of being the Church.
- Challenge of **proposed establishment of numerous new communities** throughout Scotland welcomed.
- Congregations urged to pray for **"Workers for the Harvest"** in the urban underclass of society.
- **"The Well" recognised as a model of good practice in interfaith relations** by other churches throughout the UK.
- SRT Genetic Working Group thanked for producing *Engineering Genesis.*
- SRT Project congratulated on being awarded the **1999 Templeton UK Institutional Award.**
- SRT commended for engaging in the media and national and international debate on **human and animal cloning issues.** H M Government urged to exercise caution in cloning of animals.
- Survey on the **Alpha Course** noted Thanks given to God for its benefits for congregations.
- Working Group thanked for **Report on Infant Baptism and Mission and Evangelism** in the Church of Scotland. Report commended for study throughout the Church.
- SRT Project **Report on Genetically Modified Food** received. H M Government urged to continue to adopt a precautionary approach to its development.
- H M Government and the EU asked to require **mandatory labelling of all food genetically modified** or having identifiable traces of DNA or proteins.
- Concern expressed at **lack of public accountability in introduction of genetically modified soya and maize into the UK and EU.**
- H M Government asked, in its re-negotiation of the World Trade Organisation rules, to insist on its sovereign **right to forbid the importing of sensitive traded goods.**
- Appointment of Rev. Stuart Fulton as full-time Church of Scotland **Specialist Adviser in Prison Chaplaincy** welcomed.
- Plea for Joint Prison Chaplaincies Board to be involved in the appointment of **chaplains in private sector operated prisons.**
- NHS Trusts, Management and staff thanked for their support of **Healthcare Chaplaincy.**

IONA COMMUNITY
- **Community encouraged to seek new ways for its work, particularly on Iona.**
- **Community's continuing commitment to pursuing peace and justice** welcomed, particularly in combating racism, seeking the relief of poverty in Britain and overseas, and working for nuclear disarmament.

COMMITTEE ON THE PRIORITIES AREAS FUND
- **Napier University's evaluation of the Fund** noted with approval.
- The sum of **£220,000 to be available for allocation** noted with approval.
- Progress towards the **establishment of an inter-church fund** for community development warmly welcomed.

BOARD OF SOCIAL RESPONSIBILITY
- Board's comprehensive response to the **Royal Commission on the Funding of Long-Term Care of Elderly People** commended.
- **Production of a Strategic Development Plan** welcomed.
- Steps taken to improve the **Board's financial position** noted.
- Board congratulated on successful **Conference on human genetics** in co-operation with the University of Aberdeen.
- Establishment of a **Liaison Group** between the Board and the SRT Project with specific reference to **human genetics and cloning welcomed.**

- Church's position on abortion as expressed in 1988 reaffirmed.
- Report on prostitution welcomed and commended to the Church for study.

BOARD OF WORLD MISSION

- Acknowledgement that the **pain of poverty is most sharply felt by women**; admission that the Church's silence has colluded in the subjection of women to deprivation, violence and indignity; and pledge to remain in solidarity with women in their struggles for life and wholeness.
- Congregations encouraged to **promote the campaign** to liberate communities oppressed by the burden of unpayable debt.
- Increasing incidence of **violent attacks on Christian communities**, especially in India, noted with deep concern.
- Increase in **ecumenical appointments to the Church in Bangladesh** welcomed.
- Congregations and individuals visiting the land of Christ's birth encouraged to meet the "living stones".
- Delegate or **representative from the body of Jews who now believe in Christ** as their Saviour and Lord **invited to attend the General Assembly in 2000.**
- Sharp **economic decline being suffered by already impoverished African countries** noted with deep concern.
- **Renewal of links with the Presbyterian Church of Nigeria welcomed.**
- **Initial contacts with the Presbyterian Church in Cuba welcomed.**
- Guild thanked for its support of the Project to **help the Reformed Church in Croatia rebuild churches destroyed during the war.**
- Development and expansion of **Faithshare programme commended.**
- Continuing expansion and development of **Scottish Churches World Exchange welcomed**.
- Establishment of **St Colm's International House welcomed**.
- Project for the **development of the Sea of Galilee Centre at Tiberias approved** subject to precise funding arrangements.
- **Commission appointed to investigate matters affecting the Board.**

COMMITTEE ON ECUMENICAL RELATIONS

- Commitment of the Church of Scotland to **raise gender awareness** affirmed.
- **Return of the Dutch Reformed Church in South Africa** to the World Alliance of Reformed Churches welcomed.
- **Local ecumenical initiatives** encouraged as a help to the work of ACTS.
- **Statistics of ministers and office-bearers** to be recorded by gender.
- **All gender discrimination**, including positive discrimination, **to be resisted** by the Church.

DEPARTMENT OF EDUCATION

- Importance of **values in school education** and need to provide **a rounded education** for children welcomed.
- Department instructed to consider urgently the question of **disruption in the classroom** with a view to teachers being given adequate sanctions.
- Committee to seek to ensure that **Religious and Moral Education** is given its rightful place in the school curriculum, with, in part, the appointment of Principal Teachers.
- Committee's conclusions and recommendations on **denominational schools** approved. Committee encouraged to hold to the ideal of integrated schooling and to continue conversations with the Catholic Education Commission and interfaith groups, and to hold talks with local authorities and the Scottish Parliament.

- Scottish Parliament's policy and guidelines on **school closures in rural communities** to be taken up the Minister for Education in Scotland.
- Local authorities to be urged to **continue to make schools generally and easily available as a community resource.**

BOARD OF PARISH EDUCATION

- **Dr David Goodburn thanked** for outstanding service over fourteen years.
- **Youth Assembly to meet in April 2000.**
- Continuing success of the **General Assembly Youth Night** welcomed.
- **Special educational needs** of those with learning difficulties, learning and sensory impairments and other disabilities recognised.
- Ongoing success of the **Scottish Churches' Open College** welcomed.
- The broadening work of **Eldership Training** welcomed.
- Successful completion of the **sale of Carberry Tower** by the Board to the Carberry Trust welcomed.

JOINT REPORT ON PROTECTION OF CHILDREN AND YOUNG PEOPLE

- **Establishment of a network of volunteer trainers** welcomed.
- Work of the **Child Protection Unit** to be reviewed.

BOARD OF COMMUNICATION

- **End of the dispute over proposed changes to the Board's structure** and operating methods welcomed.
- **Ann Davies thanked** for sixteen years' distinguished service **as Senior Press Officer.**
- **Patricia Holdgate welcomed as head of Media Relations.**
- **Pathway Production personnel thanked for the audio visual presentations** throughout the General Assembly.

SECTION 5

Presbytery Lists

SECTION 5 – PRESBYTERY LISTS

In each Presbytery list the congregations are listed in alphabetical order. Under the name of the congregation will be found the name of the minister and, where applicable, that of an Associate Minister, Auxiliary Minister, and member of the Diaconate. In a linked charge the names appear under the first named congregation. The years indicated after a minister's name in the congregational section of each Presbytery list are the Year of Ordination (Col 1) and the Year of current Appointment (Col 2). Where only one date is given, it is both the year of Ordination and the year of Appointment.

In the second part of each Presbytery list those listed are listed alphabetically. The first date is the Year of Ordination and the following date is the Year of Appointment or Retirement. If the person concerned is retired, then the appointment last held will be shown in brackets.

KEY TO ABBREVIATIONS

(E)	Indicates a Church Extension charge.
(GD)	Indicates a charge where it is desirable that the minister should have a knowledge of Gaelic.
(GE)	Indicates a charge where public worship must be regularly conducted in Gaelic.
(H)	Indicates that a Hearing Aid Loop system has been installed. In Linked charges the (H) is placed beside the appropriate building as far as possible.
(L)	Indicates that a Chair Lift has been installed.
(T)	Indicates that the minister has been appointed on the basis of Terminable Tenure.

PRESBYTERY NUMBERS

1	Edinburgh	18	Dumbarton
2	West Lothian	19	South Argyll
3	Lothian	20	Dunoon
4	Melrose and Peebles	21	Lorn and Mull
5	Duns	22	Falkirk
6	Jedburgh	23	Stirling
7	Annandale and Eskdale	24	Dunfermline
8	Dumfries and Kirkcudbright	25	Kirkcaldy
9	Wigtown and Stranraer	26	St Andrews
10	Ayr	27	Dunkeld and Meigle
11	Irvine and Kilmarnock	28	Perth
12	Ardrossan	29	Dundee
13	Lanark	30	Angus
14	Paisley	31	Aberdeen
15	Greenock	32	Kincardine and Deeside
16	Glasgow	33	Gordon
17	Hamilton	34	Buchan

35	Moray
36	Abernethy
37	Inverness
38	Lochaber
39	Ross
40	Sutherland
41	Caithness
42	Lochcarron – Skye
43	Uist
44	Lewis
45	Orkney
46	Shetland
47	England
48	Europe
49	Jerusalem

(1) EDINBURGH

Meets at Palmerston Place Church, Edinburgh, on the first Tuesday of October, November, December, February, April and May and on the second Tuesday in September and on the last Tuesday of June. When the first Tuesday of April falls in Holy Week the meeting is on the second Tuesday

Clerk: REV. W. PETER GRAHAM MA BD   10 Palmerston Place, Edinburgh EH12 5AA   0131 225 9137

1   Abercorn linked with Dalmeny (T)
James Brown BA BD DipHSW DipPsychol 1973   1995   Dalmeny, South Queensferry EH30 9TT   0131 331 1869

2   Edinburgh: Albany Deaf Church of Edinburgh (H) (0131 556 3128)
Vacant

3   Edinburgh: Balerno (H)
Martin J. McKean BD DipMin   1984   1993   3 Johnsburn Road, Balerno, Midlothian EH14 7DN   0131 449 3830
Charles Barrington MA BD (Assoc)   1997   3 Newmills Road, Balerno, Midlothian EH14 5AG   0131 449 4249

4   Edinburgh: Barclay (0131 229 6810)
D. Graham Leitch MA BD   1974   1980   38 Cluny Gardens EH10 6BN   0131 447 8702

5   Edinburgh: Blackhall St Columba (0131 332 4431)
Alexander B. Douglas BD   1979   1991   5 Blinkbonny Crescent EH4 3NB   0131 343 3708

6   Edinburgh: Bristo Memorial Craigmillar
Angus L. Bayne LTh BEd MTh   1969   1994   72 Blackchapel Close, Bramley Park EH15 3SL   0131 657 4151
Agnes M. Rennie (Miss) DCS   3/1 Craigmillar Court EH16 4AD   0131 661 8475

7   Edinburgh: Broughton St Mary's (H) (0131 556 4786)
I. Alasdair Elders MA BD   1964   1973   103 East Claremont Street EH7 4JA   0131 556 7313 (Tel)
[e-mail: alelders@msn.com]   0131 558 7313 (Fax)

8   Edinburgh: Canongate (H)
Charles Robertson MA   1965   1978   Manse of Canongate EH8 8BN   0131 556 3515

9   Edinburgh: Carrick Knowe (H) (0131 334 1505)
William W. Clinkenbeard BSc BD STM   1966   1971   107 The Moorings, St David's Harbour, Dalgety Bay KY11 5GP   01383 824011
[e-mail: bkclinks@compuserve.com]

10   Edinburgh: Cluny (H) (0131 447 6745)
George A.M. Munro   1968   1973   20 Braidburn Crescent EH10 6EN   0131 447 1617

11   Edinburgh: Colinton (H) (0131 441 2232)
George J. Whyte BSc BD   1981   1992   The Manse, Colinton EH13 0JR   0131 441 2315

#	Charge / Minister	Dates	Address	Phone
12	**Edinburgh: Colinton Mains (H)**			
	Ian A. McQuarrie BD	1993	17 Swanston Green EH10 7EW	0131 445 3451
13	**Edinburgh: Corstorphine Craigsbank (H) (0131 334 6365)**			
	George D.W. Grubb BA BD BPhil DMin	1962 1971	22 Belgrave Road EH12 6NF	0131 334 3557
	Ann Inglis (Mrs) LLB BD (Assoc)	1986	4 Sycamore Gardens EH12 7JJ	0131 334 8882
14	**Edinburgh: Corstorphine Old (H) (0131 334 7864)**			
	Ian D. Brady BSc ARCST BD	1967 1976	23 Manse Road EH12 7SW	0131 334 5425
15	**Edinburgh: Corstorphine St Anne's (0131 316 4740)**			
	J. William Hill BA BD	1967 1976	23 Belgrave Road EH12 6NG	0131 334 3188
16	**Edinburgh: Corstorphine St Ninian's (H)**			
	Alexander T. Stewart BD	1975 1995	17 Templeland Road EH12 8RZ	0131 334 2978
17	**Edinburgh: Craigentinny St Christopher's**			
	Lilly C. Easton (Mrs)	1999	61 Milton Crescent EH15 3PQ	0131 669 2429
18	**Edinburgh: Craiglockhart (H)**			
	Andrew Ritchie BD DipMin	1984 1991	202 Colinton Road EH14 1BP	0131 443 2020
19	**Edinburgh: Craigmillar Park (T) (H) (0131 667 5862)**			
	Sarah E.C. Nicol (Mrs) BSc BD	1985 1994	14 Hallhead Road EH16 5QJ	0131 667 1623
20	**Edinburgh: Cramond (H)**			
	G. Russell Barr BA BD	1979 1993	Manse of Cramond EH4 6NS [e-mail: rev.r.barr@dial.pipex.com]	0131 336 2036
	I. Maxwell Homewood MSc BD (Assoc)	1997	5 Essex Brae EH4 6LN	0131 339 3554
21	**Currie (H) (0131 451 5141)**			
	Willis A. Jones BA MDiv DMin	1964 1992	43 Lanark Road West, Currie EH14 5JX	0131 449 4719
	Margaret Gordon (Mrs) DCS		92 Lanark Road West, Currie, Midlothian EH14	0131 449 2554
22	**Dalmeny** see Abercorn			
23	**Edinburgh: Davidson's Mains (H) (0131 312 6282)**			
	J.R.H. Middleton LLB BD	1981 1988	1 Hillpark Terrace EH4 7SX	0131 336 3078
24	**Edinburgh: Dean**			
	Mark M. Foster BSc BD	1998	1 Ravelston Terrace EH4 3EF	0131 332 5736

25	**Edinburgh: Drylaw (0131 343 6643)**			
	Adrian J.T. Rennie BA BD	1987	15 House o' Hill Gardens EH4 2AR	0131 332 3785
			[e-mail: adrian@drylawmanse.freeserve.co.uk]	
26	**Edinburgh: Duddingston**			
	David Donaldson MA BD	1969	Manse of Duddingston EH15 3PX	0131 661 4240
27	**Edinburgh: Fairmilehead (H) (0131 445 2374)**			
	John R. Munro BD	1976	40 Frogston Road West EH10 7AJ	0131 445 1789
28	**Edinburgh: Gilmerton (H)**			
	D.M. Skinner MBE JP FIES	1962	43 Ravenscroft Street EH17 8QJ	0131 664 2147
29	**Edinburgh: Gorgie (H) (0131 337 7936)**			
	Peter I. Barber MA BD	1984	90 Myreside Road EH10 5BZ	0131 337 2284
30	**Edinburgh: Granton (H) (0131 552 3033)**			
	Lynne MacMurchie (Miss) LLB BD	1998	8 Wardie Crescent EH5 1AG	0131 551 2159
31	**Edinburgh: Greenbank (H) (0131 447 9969)**			
	Ian G. Scott BSc BD STM	1965	112 Greenbank Crescent EH10 5SZ	0131 447 4032
			[e-mail: iangscott@greenbankmanse.u-net.com]	
32	**Edinburgh: Greenside (H) (0131 556 5588)**			
	Andrew F. Anderson MA BD	1981	80 Pilrig Street EH6 5AS	0131 554 3277 (Tel/Fax)
			[e-mail: afanderson@compuserve.com]	
33	**Edinburgh: Greyfriars Tolbooth and Highland Kirk (G)(H) (0131 225 1900)**			
	David M. Beckett BA BD	1964	12 Tantallon Place EH9 1NZ	0131 667 8671
34	**Edinburgh: High (St Giles') (0131 225 4363)**			
	Gilleasbuig I. Macmillan			
	CVO MA BD Drhc	1969	St Giles' Cathedral EH1 1RE	0131 225 4363
	Karen K. Watson (Mrs) BD (Assist)	1997	64 Inchview Terrace EH7 6TH	0131 657 3145
35	**Edinburgh: Holyrood Abbey (H) (0131 661 4883)**			
	Philip R. Hair BD	1980	100 Willowbrae Avenue EH8 7HU	0131 652 0640
36	**Edinburgh: Holy Trinity (H) (0131 442 3304)**			
	Stanley A. Brook BD	1977	16 Thorburn Road EH13 0BQ	0131 441 7167
	Michael S. Dawson BTech BD (Assoc)	1979	12 Sighthill Crescent EH11 4QE	0131 453 6279
	Joyce Mitchell (Mrs) DCS		16/4 Murrayburn Place EH14 2RR	0131 453 6548

No.	Charge / Minister	Years	Address	Phone
37	**Edinburgh: Inverleith (H)** D. Hugh Davidson MA	1965 1975	43 Inverleith Gardens EH3 5PR	0131 552 3874
38	**Edinburgh: Juniper Green (H)** Bernard P. Lodge BD	1967 1998	476 Lanark Road, Juniper Green EH14 5BQ	0131 453 3494
39	**Edinburgh: Kaimes Lockhart Memorial** Iain D. Penman BD	1977 1995	76 Lasswade Road EH16 6SF	0131 664 2287
40	**Edinburgh: Kirkliston** Glenda Keating (Mrs) MTh	1996	14 Kirklands Park Crescent, Kirkliston EH29 9EP	0131 333 3298
41	**Edinburgh: Kirk o' Field (T)(H)** Ian D. Maxwell MA BD PhD	1977 1996	31 Hatton Place EH9 1UA	0131 667 7954
42	**Edinburgh: Leith North (H) (0131 553 7378)** Alistair G.C. McGregor QC BD	1987	22 Primrose Bank Road EH5 3JG	0131 551 2802
43	**Edinburgh: Leith St Andrew's (H)** John Cook MA BD	1967 1984	13 Claremont Park EH6 7PJ	0131 554 7695
44	**Edinburgh: Leith St Serf's (T)(H)** Sara R. Embleton (Mrs) BA BD	1977 1999	20 Wilton Road EH16 5NX	0131 478 1624
45	**Edinburgh: Leith St Thomas' Junction Road (T)** Shirley Blair (Miss) BD DipMin	1990 1991	28 Summerside Street EH6 4NU	0131 554 5039
46	**Edinburgh: Leith South (H) (0131 554 2578)** Ian Y. Gilmour BD	1985 1995	37 Claremont Road EH6 7NN [e-mail: ianyg@ad.com]	0131 554 3062
	Jennifer Booth (Mrs) BD (Assoc)	1996	39 Lilyhill Terrace EH8 7DR	0131 661 3813
47	**Edinburgh: Leith Wardie (H) (0131 551 3847)** Brian C. Hilsley LLB BD	1990	35 Lomond Road EH5 3JN	0131 552 3328
48	**Edinburgh: Liberton (H)** John N. Young MA BD PhD	1996	7 Kirk Park EH16 6HZ	0131 664 3067
49	**Edinburgh: Liberton Northfield (H) (0131 551 3847)** Vacant		9 Claverhouse Drive EH16 6BR	0131 658 1754
50	**Edinburgh: London Road (H) (0131 661 1149)** William L. Armitage BSc BD	1976 1991	26 Inchview Terrace EH7 6TQ [e-mail: billarm@cableinet.co.uk]	0131 669 5311

51 Edinburgh: Marchmont St Giles' (H) (0131 447 4359)
Donald M. Stephen TD MA BD ThM   1962   19 Hope Terrace EH9 2AP   0131 447 2834
Elspeth G. Dougall (Mrs) MA BD   1989 1991   60B Craigmillar Park EH16 5PU   0131 668 1342

52 Edinburgh: Mayfield Salisbury (0131 667 1522)
Alexander W. Young BD DipMin   1988 1993   26 Seton Place EH9 2JT   0131 667 1286

53 Edinburgh: Morningside Braid (0131 447 9430)
John R. Wells BD DipMin   1991   5 Cluny Avenue EH10 4RN   0131 447 4647

54 Edinburgh: Morningside United (H) (0131 447 3152)
John R. Smith MA BD   1973 1998   1 Midmar Avenue EH10 6BS   0131 447 8724
[e-mail: jsmith4772@aol.com]

55 Edinburgh: Muirhouse St Andrew's [E]
Frederick D.F. Shewan MA BD   1970   1980   35 Silverknowes Road EH4 5LL   0131 336 4546

56 Edinburgh: Murrayfield (H) (0131 337 1091)
Clarence W. Musgrave BA BD ThM   1966   1980   45 Murrayfield Gardens EH12 6DH   0131 337 5431

57 Edinburgh: Newhaven (H)
Grant MacLaughlan BA BD   1998   11 Laverockbank Terrace EH5 3BL   0131 552 8906

58 Edinburgh: New Restalrig (H) (0131 661 5676)
Vacant   19 Abercorn Road EH8 7DP   0131 661 4045

59 Edinburgh: Old Kirk (H)
Thomas Preston BD   1978   1992   24 Pennywell Road EH4 4HD   0131 332 4354
Ronald M. MacKinnon DCS   30 West Pilton Gardens EH4 6AF   0131 332 0413

60 Edinburgh: Palmerston Place (H) (0131 220 1690)
Colin A.M. Sinclair BA BD   1981   1996   30B Cluny Gardens EH10 6BJ   0131 447 9598
0131 225 3312 (Fax)

61 Edinburgh: Pilrig St Paul's (0131 553 1876)
John M. Tait BSc BD   1985   1999   78 Pilrig Street EH6 5AS   0131 554 1842
[e-mail: john.m.tait@btinternet.com]

62 Edinburgh: Polwarth (H) (0131 346 2711)
John K.S. McMahon MA BD   1998   9 Merchiston Bank Gardens EH10 5EB   0131 447 2741
[e-mail: jksmcmahon@hotmail.com]

No.	Congregation / Minister	Ordained / Inducted	Address	Telephone
63	**Edinburgh: Portobello Old (H)** Neil Buchanan BD	1991	6 Hamilton Terrace EH15 1NB	0131 669 5312
64	**Edinburgh: Portobello St James' (H)** Malcolm M. McDougall BD	1981	34 Brighton Place EH15 1LT	0131 669 1767
65	**Edinburgh: Portobello St Philip's Joppa (H) (0131 669 3641)** John Weir Cook MA BD Alison M. Jack (Mrs) MA BD PhD (Ass)	1962 1988 1998	6 St Mary's Place EH15 2QF 7/2 Marchhall Crescent EH16 7HL	0131 669 2410 0131 662 0433
66	**Edinburgh: Priestfield (H) (0131 667 5644)** Thomas N. Johnston LTh	1972 1990	13 Lady Road EH16 5PA	0131 668 1620
67	**Edinburgh: Queensferry (H)** John G. Carrie BSc BD	1971	1 Station Road, South Queensferry EH30 9HY [e-mail: john.carrie@virgin.net]	0131 331 1100
68	**Edinburgh: Ratho** Ian J. Wells BD	1999	Ratho, Newbridge EH28 8NP	0131 333 1346
69	**Edinburgh: Reid Memorial (H) (0131 662 1203)** Brian M. Embleton BD	1976 1985	20 Wilton Road EH16 5NX	0131 667 3981
70	**Edinburgh: Richmond Craigmillar (H) (0131 661 6561)** Elizabeth M. Henderson (Miss) MA BD	1985 1997	13 Wisp Green EH15 3QX	0131 669 1133
71	**Edinburgh: St Andrew's and St George's (H) (0131 225 3847)** Andrew R.C. McLellan MA BD STM	1970 1986	25 Comely Bank EH4 1AJ	0131 332 5324
72	**Edinburgh: St Andrew's Clermiston** Alistair H. Keil BD DipMin	1989	87 Drum Brae South EH12 8TD	0131 339 4149
73	**Edinburgh: St Catherine's Argyle (H) (0131 667 7220)** Victor W.N. Laidlaw BD	1975	5 Palmerston Road EH9 1TL	0131 667 6855
74	**Edinburgh: St Colm's (T)(H)** Stewart M. McPherson BD CertMin Mary Gargrave (Mrs) DCS	1991	1 Merchiston Gardens EH10 5DD 229/2 Calder Road EH11 4RG	0131 337 1107 0131 476 3493
75	**Edinburgh: St Cuthbert's (H) (0131 229 1142)** Tom C. Cuthell MA BD Peter Neilson MA BD (Assoc)	1965 1975	22 Learmonth Terrace EH4 1PG 12 Strathalmond Court EH4 8AE	0131 332 6138 0131 339 4536

76 Edinburgh: St David's Broomhouse (H) (0131 443 9851)
Neil J. Dougall BD 1991 33 Traquair Park West EH12 7AN [e-mail: neild3344@aol.com] 0131 334 1730

77 Edinburgh: St George's West (H) (0131 225 7001)
Peter J. MacDonald BD DipMin 1986 1998 6 Wardie Avenue EH5 2AB [e-mail: pjmacdon@aol.com] 0131 552 4333

78 Edinburgh: St John's Oxgangs
Yvonne E.S. Atkins (Mrs) BD 1997 2 Caiystane Terrace EH10 6SR 0131 445 1688

79 Edinburgh: St Margaret's (H) (0131 554 7400)
Ewan R. Aitken BA BD 1992 1995 43 Moira Terrace EH7 6TD 0131 669 7329
Liz Crocker (Mrs) DCS 77C Craigcrook Road EH4 3PH 0131 332 0227
Marion Buchanan (Mrs) DCS 6 Hamilton Terrace EH15 1NB 0131 669 5312

80 Edinburgh: St Martin's
Elizabeth B. Ross (Ms) BD 1996 1999 5 Duddingston Crescent EH15 3AS 0131 657 9894

81 Edinburgh: St Michael's (H)
Margaret R. Forrester (Mrs) MA BD 1974 1980 25 Kingsburgh Road EH12 6DZ 0131 337 5646

82 Edinburgh: St Nicholas' Sighthill
Kenneth J. Mackay MA BD 1971 1976 122 Sighthill Loan EH11 4NT 0131 453 6921

83 Edinburgh: St Stephen's Comely Bank (0131 315 4616)
Graham T. Dickson MA BD 1985 1996 8 Blinkbonny Crescent EH4 3NB [e-mail: grahamdickson@compuserve.com] 0131 332 3364 (Tel/Fax)

84 Edinburgh: Slateford Longstone
Gordon R. Palmer MA BD STM 1986 1994 50 Kingsknowe Road South EH14 2JW [e-mail: gordonrp@aol.com] 0131 443 2960

85 Edinburgh: Stenhouse St Aidan's
Mary B. Morrison (Mrs) MA BD DipEd 1978 1994 65 Balgreen Road EH12 5UA 0131 337 7711
Mary Gargrave (Mrs) DCS 229/3 Calder Road EH11 4RG 0131 476 3493

86 Edinburgh: Stockbridge (H) (0131 332 0122)
Anne T. Logan (Mrs) MA BD 1981 1993 19 Eildon Street EH3 5JU 0131 557 6052

87 Edinburgh: Tron Kirk Moredun
Stephen Manners MA BD 1989 467 Gilmerton Road EH17 7JG 0131 666 2584

88 Edinburgh: Viewforth (T)(H) (0131 229 1917)
Anthony P. Thornthwaite MTh 1995 91 Morningside Drive EH10 5NN 0131 447 6684

Name	Charge / Position			Address	Tel
Aitken, Alexander R. MA	(Newhaven)	1965	1997	36 King's Meadow EH16 5JW	0131 667 1404
Alexander, Ian W. BA BD STM	(Board of World Mission)	1990	1995	c/o 121 George Street EH2 4YN	0131 225 5722
Anderson, David J.B. MA BD	General Secretary: Evangelical Alliance (Scot)	1974	1994	46 Elliot Road EH14 1DZ	0131 441 7399
Anderson, Hugh MA BD PhD DD	(University of Edinburgh)	1951	1985	23/13 Maxwell Street EH10 5HT	0131 447 1401
Auld, A. Graeme MA BD PhD	University of Edinburgh	1973	1973	Nether Swanshiel, Hobkirk, Bonchester Bridge, Hawick TD9 8JU	
Baigrie, R.A. MA	(Kirkurd with Newlands)	1945	1985	32 Inchcolm Terrace, South Queensferry EH30 9NA	0131 331 4311
Baxter, Richard F. OBE MA BD	(Assistant at St Andrew's and St George's)	1954	1990	138 Braid Road, Edinburgh EH10 6JB	0131 447 7735
Brown, William D. MA	(Wishaw Thornlie)	1963	1989	121 Dalkeith Road EH16 5AJ	0131 667 1124
Burnside, William MA	(West Kilbride Overton)	1942	1982	14 Larchfield Neuk, Balerno EH14 7NL	0131 449 5182
Cameron, G. Gordon MA BD STM	(Juniper Green)	1957	1997	4 Ladywell Grove, Clackmannan FK10 4JQ	01259 723769
Cameron, John W.M. MA BD	(Liberton)	1957	1996	10 Plewlands Gardens EH10 5JP	0131 447 1277
Carmichael, William BSc FIS	(Restalrig)	1972	1987	60 Kirk Brae EH16 6HU	0131 664 2779
Cattanach, William D. DD	(Geneva)	1951	1990	145 Craigleith Road EH4 2ED	0131 332 4503
Chalmers, John P. BD	Department of Ministry	1979	1995	10 Liggars Place, Dunfermline KY12 7XZ	01383 739130
Chalmers, Murray MA	Hospital Chaplain	1965	1991	25 Greenbank Road EH10 5RX	0131 447 3387
Cheyne, Alexander C. MA BD BLitt DLitt	(University of Edinburgh)	1958	1986	12 Crossland Crescent, Peebles EH45 8LF	01721 722288
Cowie, James M. BD	Community Minister at Craigmillar	1976	1996	c/o Thistle Foundation, Niddrie Mains Road EH16 4AE [e-mail: jim@iimcowie.demon.co.uk]	0131 661 3366
Cross, Brian F. MA	(Coalburn)	1961	1998	23 Broomlee Court, Broomlee Crescent, West Linton EH46 7EY	01968 660705
Davidson, Ian M.P. MA BD	(Stirling: Allan Park South with Church of the Holy Rude)	1957	1994	13/8 Craigend Park EH16 5XX	0131 664 0074
Doyle, Ian B. MA BD PhD	(Department of National Mission)	1946	1991	21 Lygon Road EH16 5QD	0131 667 2697
Drummond, R. Hugh	(Balmaclellan with Kells)	1953	1991	19 Winton Park EH10 7EX	0131 445 3634
Drummond, Rhoda (Miss) DCS	(Deaconess)			Flat K, 23 Grange Loan EH9 2ER	0131 668 3631
Dunn, W. Iain C. DA LTh	(Pilrig and Dalmeny Street)	1983	1998	10 Fox Covert Avenue EH12 6UQ	0131 334 1665
Elliot, George MA BD STM	(Board of Stewardship and Finance)	1958	1989	28 Pentland Gardens EH10 6NW	0131 447 4017
Finlayson, J. Clarence MA	(Grange)	1930	1972	52 Falcon Avenue EH10 4AW	0131 447 6550
Forrester, Duncan B. MA BD DPhil DD	University of Edinburgh	1962	1978	25 Kingsburgh Road EH12 6DZ	0131 337 5646
Galbraith, Douglas MA BD BMus MPhil ARSCM	Office for Worship, Doctrine and Artistic Matters	1965	1995	c/o 121 George Street EH2 4YN	0131 240 2233
Gibson, John C.L. MA BD DPhil	(University of Edinburgh)	1959	1994	Cairnbank, Morton Street South EH15 2NB	0131 669 3635
Gillon, J. Blair MA	(Borthwick with Heriot)	1935	1980	15D Cramond Green, Cramond Road North EH4 6NH	0131 336 2551
Glass, Irene (Miss) DCS	(Deaconess)			3E Falcon Road West EH10 4AA	0131 447 6554
Gordon, Tom MA BD	Chaplain: Fairmile Marie Curie Centre	1974	1994	7 Buckstone Row EH10 6TW	0131 445 3566
Graham, W. Peter MA BD	Presbytery Clerk	1967	1993	23/6 East Comiston EH10 6RZ	0131 445 5763
Hardy, Basil G. MA BD	(Dundee Meadowside St Paul's)	1946	1984	14 Elliot Place EH14 1DR	0131 441 3449
Harkness, James CB OBE QHC MA LB	(Chaplain General: Army)	1961	1995	13 Saxe Coburg Place EH3 5BR	0131 343 1297
Haslett, Howard J. BA BD	Chaplain: The Edinburgh Academy	1972	1974	The Edinburgh Academy EH3 5BL	0131 343 1569
Henderson, Charlotte (Mrs)	(Hospital Chaplain)	1986	1994	89 West Savile Terrace EH9 3DP	0131 667 7123

Name	Years	Position	Address	Tel.
Hepburn, James L. MA BD	1950 1991	(Ardoch with Blackford)	16 Marchmont Road. EH9 1HZ	0131 229 6170
Houston, Graham R. BSc BD MTh PhD	1978 1990	National Bible Society of Scotland	3 Ramsay Place, Penicuick EH26 9JS [e-mail: ghouston@aol.com]	01968 672752
Hutchison, Maureen (Mrs) DCS	1954 1994	(Deaconess)	23 Drylaw Crescent EH4 2AU	0131 332 8020
Jeffrey, Eric W.S. JP MA	1954 1994	(Edinburgh Bristo Memorial)	18 Gillespie Crescent, Edinburgh EH10 4HT	0131 229 7815
Johnston, William B. MA BD DD DLitt				
Johnstone, Helen G. (Mrs) MA BD HDipRE	1945 1991	(Colinton)	15 Elliot Road EH14 1DU	0131 441 3387
Kant, Everard FVCM MTh	1982 1995	(Zambia)	Flat 56, The Bond, John's Place EH6 7EN	0131 553 1316
Kelly, Ewan MB ChB BD	1953 1988	(Kinghorn)	38 Redford Loan EH13 0AX	0131 441 3853
Kesting, Sheilagh M. (Miss) BA BD	1994 1998	Chaplain: Edinburgh Royal Infirmary	29 Buckstone Crescent EH10 6RJ	0131 451 5932
Kingston, David V.F. BD	1980 1993	Ecumenical Relations	43 Currievale Drive, Currie, Midlothian EH14 5RN	01875 822026
Kirk, John F. MA BD PhD	1993 1993	Army Chaplain	1 Rawlinson Road, Catterick Garrison, North Yorks DL9 3AR	0131 667 6111
Lamont, A. Donald BSc BD	1955 1990	(Morningside)	36 Esslemont Road EH16 5PY	0131 447 4665
Lawson, Kenneth C. MA BD	1941 1975	(Nakuru)	36 St Clair Terrace EH10 5PS	0131 539 3311
Lyall, David BSc BD STM PhD	1963 1984	Adviser in Adult Education	56 Easter Drylaw View EH4 2QP	0131 443 7640
Lyon, D.H.S. MA BD STM	1965 1990	University of Edinburgh	1 North Megetland EH14 1XG	0131 449 5031
Macdonald, Donald M. MA BD	1952 1986	(Board of World Mission and Unity)	30 Mansfield Road, Balerno EH14 7JZ	0131 552 4046
Macdonald, Finlay A.J. MA BD PhD	1940 1985	(Kippen)	1 Cargil Court, Cargil Terrace EH5 3NE	0131 225 5722
Macdonald, James I.H. MA BD MTh PhD	1971 1996	Principal Clerk	c/o 121 George Street EH2 4YN	
McDonald, William J.G. DD	1958 1980	University of Edinburgh	23 Ravelston House Road EH4 3LP	0131 332 2172
McGillivray, A. Gordon MA BD STM	1953 1992	(Mayfield)	7 Blacket Place EH9 1RN	0131 667 2100
MacGregor, Margaret S. (Miss) MA BD DipEd	1951 1993	(Presbytery Clerk)	7 Greenfield Crescent, Balerno, Midlothian EH14 7HD	0131 449 4747
McGregor, T. Stewart MBE MA BD	1985 1994	(Calcutta)	16 Learmonth Court EH4 1PB	0131 332 1089
McIntosh, Hamish MC MA BD	1957 1998	(Chaplain: Edinburgh Royal Infirmary)	19 Lonsdale Terrace EH3 9HL [e-mail: cetsm@dir.con.uk]	0131 229 5332
McIntyre, John CVO DLitt DD Drhc FRSE	1943 1983	(Auchterarder St Andrew's and West)	19 Falcon Gardens EH10 4AP	0131 447 3516
McKean, David MA STM	1941 1986	(University of Edinburgh)	22/4 Minto Street EH9 1RQ	0131 667 1203
Maclean, Ailsa G. (Mrs) BD DipCE	1942 1982	(Paris)	79 Baberton Mains Drive EH14 3DA	0131 442 2128
McLean, Campbell M. MA	1979 1988	Chaplain: George Heriot's School	28 Swan Spring Avenue EH10 6NJ	0131 445 1320
MacLean, Marjory (Miss) LLB BD	1949 1992	Board of Practice and Procedure	16 West Terrace, South Queensferry EH30 9LL	0131 319 1320
McLeod, Roderick MA BD	1991 1998	(Cramond)	121 George Street, Edinburgh EH2 4YN	0131 225 5722
Macmillan, W.B.R. LLD DD	1951 1990	(Lochwinnoch)	2 East Savile Road EH16 5ND	0131 667 1475
McPheat, Elspeth DCS	1954 1993	(Dundee: St Mary's)	Flat 5, 3 Craigend Park EH16 5XY	0131 672 1832
McPhee, Duncan C. MA BD	1953 1993	Deaconess: Social Responsibility	11/5 New Orchardfield, Leith EH6 5ET	0131 554 4143
Macpherson, Allan S. MA	1967 1993	Department of National Mission	94 Balgreen Road EH12 5UB	0131 337 5230
Macpherson, Colin C.R. MA BD	1958 1996	Chaplain: Merchiston Castle School	The Fairway, Merchiston Castle School EH13 0PU	0131 667 1456
Macpherson, Fergus MA PhD	1946 1988	(Dunfermline St Margaret's)	7 Eva Place EH9 3ET	0131 672 1253
Mactaggart, Ian. MA BD	1941 1983	(British Council of Churches)	19 Cameron Toll Gardens EH16 4TF	0131 667 3091
Mackie, Steven G. MA BD	1956 1994	(Craigmillar Park)	15 West Mains Road EH9 3BG	0131 667 9532
		(University of St Andrews)	38 Grange Loan EH9 2NR	

Name			Appointment	Address	Tel.
Mathieson, Angus R MA BD	1988	1998	Department of Ministry	2nd Floor, 7 Novar Drive, Glasgow G12 9PX [e-mail: angus.mathieson@which.net]	0141 334 4665
Mechie, William M.	1946	1984	(Kirknewton and East Calder)	Flat 62, 77 Barnton Park View EH4 6EL	0131 339 1644
Mickelson, May B. (Miss) DCS			(Deaconess)	31 Milton Road East EH15 2NL	0131 669 0482
Miller, I David OBE MA	1992	1999	Prison Chaplain (PT)	146 Craigleith Road EH4 2EQ	0131 332 6378
Miller, J. Stewart MA BD STM	1954	1997	(Morningside United)	54 Mayfield, East Craigs EH12 8UH	0131 339 0537
Morrice, William G. MA BD STM PhD	1957	1991	(St John's College Durham)	Flat 37, The Cedars, 2 Manse Road, Corstorphine EH12 7SN [e-mail: w.g.morrice@btinternet.com]	0131 316 4845
Morton, Andrew R. MA BD DD	1956	1994	(Board of World Mission and Unity)	11 Oxford Terrace EH4 1PX	0131 332 6592
Morton, R. Colin BA BD	1960	1998	(Jerusalem)	313 Lanark Road West, Currie EH14 5RS	0131 449 7359
Moyes, Sheila A. (Miss) DCS			(Deaconess)	158 Pilton Avenue EH5 2JZ	0131 551 1731
Mulligan, Anne (Miss) DCS			Deaconess: Hospital Chaplain's Assistant	1/6 Coxfield, Gorgie EH11 2SY	0131 346 7092
Murison, William G.	1951	1990	(Department of World Mission and Unity)	21 Hailes Gardens EH13 0JL	0131 441 2460
Murrie, John BD	1953	1996	(Kirkliston)	31 Nicol Road, The Whins, Broxburn EH52 6JJ	01506 852 464
Nicol, Douglas A.O. MA BD	1974	1991	National Mission Secretary	24 Corbiehill Avenue EH4 5DR	0131 336 1965
O'Neill, John C. BA BD PhD	1960	1996	(University of Edinburgh)	9 Lonsdale Terrace EH3 9HN	0131 229 6070
Orr, John F. MA	1949	1987	(St John's Oxgangs)	2/34 Pentland Drive EH10 6PX	0131 445 2876
Page, Ruth MA BD DPhil	1976	1979	University of Edinburgh	7 Seton Place EH9 2JT	0131 662 4564
Paterson, Ian M. MA	1947	1985	(Eccles with Greenlaw)	45/15 Maidencraig Crescent EH4 2UU	0131 332 9735
Paterson, J.M.K. MA ACII BD DD	1964	1987	(Milngavie St Paul's)	58 Orchard Drive EH4 2DZ	0131 332 5876
Patterson, John M.	1976	1987	(Blackbraes and Shieldhill)	9 Saughtonhall Circus EH12 5RG	0131 337 0095
Philip, James MA	1948	1997	(Holyrood Abbey)	3 Ferguson Gardens, Musselburgh EH21 6XF	0131 653 2310
Philp, Connie (Miss) BD	1980	1995	(Arbuthnott with Bervie)	22/5 South Elixa Place, Baronscourt View EH8 7PG	0131 661 3124
Porteous, Norman W. DD	1929	1968	(University of Edinburgh)	3 Hermitage Gardens EH10 6DL	0131 447 4632
Potts, Jean (Miss) DCS			(Deaconess)	28B East Claremont Street EH7 4JP	0131 557 2144
Reid, J.K.S. CBE TD MA DD	1939	1976	(University of Aberdeen)	8 Abbotsford Court, 18 Colinton Road EH10 5EH	0131 447 6855
Reid, W. Scott BD MA DipPS PhD	1950	1990	(London Road)	14/37 Ethel Terrace EH10 5NA	0131 447 7642
Renton, Ian P.	1958	1990	(St Colm's)	37 Newbattle Terrace EH10 4SF	0131 447 8112
Ronald, Norma A. (Miss) MBE DCS			(Deaconess)	43/26 Gillespie Crescent EH10 4HY	0131 228 1008
Ross, Andrew C. MA BD STM PhD	1958	1966	University of Edinburgh	27 Colinton Road EH10 5DR	0131 447 5987
Ross, Kenneth R. BD	1982	1999	General Secretary, Board of World Mission	121 George Street EH2 4YN	0131 225 5722
Sandilands, Ian S.	1986	1999	(Black Mount)	51 Little Road, Edinburgh EH16 6SH	0131 664 6924
Schofield, Melville F. MA	1960	1988	Chaplain: Western General Hospitals	25 Rowantree Grove, Currie EH14 5AT	0131 449 4745
Searle, David C. MA DipTh	1965	1993	Warden: Rutherford House	38 Rosslyn Crescent, Edinburgh EH6 5AX	0131 554 5713
Shepherd, Henry A. MA BD	1962	1998	(Christ Church, Warwick, Bermuda)	7 Winton Grove EH10 7AS	0131 445 1276
Sim, John G. MA	1946	1987	(Kirkcaldy Old)	7 Grosvenor Crescent EH12 5EP	0131 226 3190
Sloan, Elma C. (Miss) DCS			(Deaconess)	7 Dunedin Street, Edinburgh EH7 4JB	0131 556 3496
Steel, David MA BD DD LLD	1936	1976	(Linlithgow St Michael's)	39 Newbattle Terrace EH10 4SF	0131 447 2180
Stevenson, Douglas F. BD DipMin	1991	1998	Chaplain: Edinburgh Royal Infirmary	128 Church Street, Tranent EH33 1BL	0131 445 3960
Stevenson, John MA BD	1963	1993	Department of Education	12 Swanston Gardens, Edinburgh EH10 7DL	0131 225 8177
Stiven, Iain K. MA BD	1960	1997	(Strachur and Strathlachlan)	3 Gloucester Place EH3 6EE	
Taylor, Howard G. BSc BD MTh	1971	1998	Chaplain: Heriot Watt University	The Chaplaincy, Heriot Watt University EH14 4AS	0131 449 5111 (ext 4508)
Teague, Yvonne (Mrs) DCS			Deaconess: Secretary, The Diaconate	46 Craigcrook Avenue EH4	

Name	(Charge / Status)			Address	Tel.
Thom, Helen (Miss) DCS	(Deaconess)	1951	1981	84 Great King Street EH3 6QU	0131 556 5687
Thomson, J.G.S.S. MA BD BA PhD	(Wigtown)	1954	1990	4 Drum Brae South EH12 8SJ	0131 334 6035
Thomson, Thomas MA	(Leith Wardie)	1964	1999	8/7 Craigend Park EH16 5XX	0131 672 3585
Thomson, William H	(Liberton Northfield)	1954	1989	3 Baird's Way, The Grange, Bonnyrigg EH19 3NS	0131 654 9799
Torrance, James B. MA BD	(University of Aberdeen)	1940	1979	3 Greenbank Crescent, Edinburgh EH10 5TE	0131 447 3230
Torrance, Thomas F. MBE DLitt DD DSc DrTheol DrTeol FBA FRSE	(University of Edinburgh)			37 Braid Farm Road EH10 6LE	
Walker, Grahame R. FCH	(Torphins)	1959	1987	40/2 West Craigs Crescent EH12 8NA	0131 339 7372
Walker, R.W. MB ChB	(Lesmahagow Abbeygreen)	1941	1981	16 Cumin Place EH9 2JX	0131 667 0578
Webster, W. Thoms MA	(Dean)	1944	1986	3 Columba Road EH4 3QU	0131 343 2071
Whitton, John P.	Assistant Chaplain General	1977	1999	HQ Army Scotland, Craigiehall, South Queensferry EH30 9TN	
Whyte, Iain A. BA BD STM	Chaplain: University of Edinburgh	1968	1994	34 Shandon Crescent EH11 1QF	0131 337 3559
Wigglesworth, J. Christopher MBE BSc PhD BD	St Andrew's College, Selly Oak	1967	1998	12 Leven Terrace EH3 9LW	0131 228 6335
Wilkie, James L. MA BD	(Board of World Mission)	1959	1998	7 Comely Bank Avenue EH4 1EW [e-mail:jl.wilkie@btinternet.com]	0131 343 1552
Wilkinson, John BD MD FRCP DTM&H	(Kikuyu)	1946	1975	70 Craigleith Hill Gardens EH4 2JH	0131 332 2994
Williams, Jenny (Miss) BSc CQSW BD	Christian Fellowship of Healing	1996	1997	3 Milton Mill, Milton Bridge, Penicuik EH26 0NS	

EDINBURGH ADDRESSES

Albany	Albany Street
Balerno	Johnsburn Road, Balerno
Barclay	Barclay Place
Blackhall St Columba	Queensferry Road
Bristo Memorial	Peffermill Road, Craigmillar
Broughton St Mary's	Bellevue Crescent
Canongate	Canongate
Carrick Knowe	North Saughton Road
Cluny	Cluny Gardens
Colinton	Dell Road
Colinton Mains	Oxgangs Road North
Corstorphine	
Craigsbank	Craig's Crescent
Old	Kirk Loan
St Anne's	Kaimes Road
St Ninian's	St John's Road
Craigentinny	
St Christopher's	Craigentinny Road
Craiglockhart	Craiglockhart Avenue
Craigmillar Park	Craigmillar Park
Cramond	Cramond Glebe Road
Currie	Kirkgate, Currie
Davidson's Mains	Quality Street
Dean	Dean Path
Drylaw	Groathill Road North
Duddingston	Old Church Lane, Duddingston
Fairmilehead	Frogston Road West, Fairmilehead
Gilmerton	Ravenscroft Street
Gorgie	Gorgie Road
Granton	Boswall Parkway
Greenbank	Braidburn Terrace
Greenside	Royal Terrace
Greyfriars Tolbooth Highland Kirk	Greyfriars Place
High (St Giles')	High Street
Holyrood Abbey	Dalziel Place x London Road
Holy Trinity	Hailesland Place, Wester Hailes
Inverleith	Inverleith Gardens
Juniper Green	Lanark Road, Juniper Green
Kaimes Lockhart M'l	Gracemount Drive
Kirkliston	The Square, Kirkliston
Kirk o' Field	Pleasance
Leith	
North	Madeira Street off Ferry Road
St Andrew's	Easter Road
St Serf's	Ferry Road
St Thomas' Junction Road	Great Junction Street
South	Kirkgate
Wardie	Primrosebank Road
Liberton	Liberton
Northfield	Gilmerton Road, Liberton
London Road	London Road
Marchmont St Giles'	Kilgraston Road
Mayfield/Salisbury	Mayfield Road x W. Mayfield
Morningside Braid	Nile Grove
Morningside United	Bruntsfield Place x Chamberlain Road
Muirhouse St Andrew's	Pennywell Gardens
Murrayfield	Abinger Gardens
Newhaven	Craighall Road
New Restalrig	Willowbrae Road
Old Kirk	Pennywell Road
Palmerston Place	Palmerston Place
Pilrig St Paul's	Pilrig Street
Polwarth	Polwarth Terrace x Harrison Road
Portobello Old	Belfield Street

EDINBURGH ADDRESSES (cont'd)

Portobello (cont'd)		Richmond Craigmillar	Niddrie Mains Road	St Margaret's	Restalrig Road South
St James'	Rosefield Place	St Andrew's and St George's	George Street	St Martin's	Magdalene Drive
St Philip's, Joppa	Abercorn Terrace	St Andrew's Clermiston	Clermiston View	St Michael's	Slateford Road
Priestfield	Dalkeith Road x Marchall Place	St Catherine's-Argyle	Grange Road x Chalmers Crescent	St Nicholas' Sighthill	Calder Road
Queensferry	The Loan, South Queensferry	St Colm's	Dalry Road x Cathcart Place	St Stephen's Comely Bank	Comely Bank
Ratho	Baird Road, Ratho	St Cuthbert's	Lothian Road	Slateford-Longstone	Kingsknowe Road North
Reid Memorial	West Savile Terrace	St David's Broomhouse	Broomhouse Crescent	Stenhouse St Aidan's	Chesser Avenue
		St George's West	Shandwick Place	Stockbridge	Saxe Coburg Street
		St John's Oxgangs	Oxgangs Road	Tron Moredun	Fernieside Drive
				Viewforth	Gilmore Place

(2) WEST LOTHIAN

Meets in St John's Church Hall, Bathgate on the first Tuesday of every month except December when the meeting is on the second Tuesday and January, July and August when there is no meeting.

Clerk: REV. DUNCAN SHAW BD MTh   St John's Manse, Mid Street, Bathgate EH48 1QD   01506 653146

Addiewell linked with Longridge and Breich linked with Stoneyburn
Douglas M. Main BD   1986   Stoneyburn, Bathgate EH47 8AU   01501 762018
Mark Evans DCS   1999   c/o Church Office, Main Street, Longridge, Bathgate EH47 8AU   01501 772020

Armadale (H)
Geoffrey H. Smart LTh   1994   70 Mount Pleasant, Armadale EH48 3HB   01501 730358

Avonbridge linked with Torphichen
Vacant   Torphichen, Bathgate EH48 4LT   01506 652794

Bathgate: Boghall (H)
John McLean MA BD   1967   1970   1 Manse Place, Ash Grove, Bathgate EH48 1NJ   01506 652940

Bathgate: High (H)
Ronald G. Greig MA BD   1987   1998   19 Hunter Grove, Bathgate EH48 1NN   01506 652654

Bathgate: St David's
Elliot G.S. Wardlaw BA BD DipMin   1984   Marjoribanks Street, Bathgate EH48 1AH   01506 653177

Bathgate: St John's (H)
Duncan Shaw BD MTh   1975   1978   Mid Street, Bathgate EH48 1QD   01506 653146

Blackburn
Robert A. Anderson MA BD DPhil — 1980 — Blackburn, Bathgate EH47 4QR — 01506 652825

Blackridge linked with Harthill St Andrew's
H. Warner Hardie BD — 1979 — Harthill, Shotts ML7 5QW — 01501 751239

Broxburn (H)
Richard T. Corbett BSc MSc PhD BD — 1992 — 2 Church Street, Broxburn EH52 5EL — 01506 852825

Fauldhouse: St Andrew's
Alan T. McKean BD — 1982 — 48 Main Street, Fauldhouse EH47 9BQ — 01501 771190

Harthill St Andrew's See Blackridge

Kirknewton and East Calder
Ann M. Ballentine (Miss) MA BD — 1981 — 8 Manse Court, East Calder EH53 0HF — 01506 880802

Kirk of Calder (H)
John M. Povey MA BD — 1981 — 19 Maryfield Park, Mid Calder EH53 0SB — 01506 882495

Linlithgow: St Michael's (H)
John L. Paterson MA BD STM — 1964 — Linlithgow EH49 7AL — 01506 842195
Thomas S. Riddell BSc (Aux) — 1994 — 4 The Maltings, Linlithgow EH49 6DS — 01506 843251

Linlithgow: St Ninian's Craigmailen (H)
Iain C. Morrison BA BD — 1990 — 29 Philip Avenue, Linlithgow EH49 7BH [e-mail: cmo2@dial.pipex.com] — 01506 845535

Livingston Ecumenical Parish
Incorporating the Worship Centres at:
Carmondean and Craigshill (St Columba's)
Vacant — 53 Garry Walk, Craigshill, Livingston EH54 5AS — 01506 434536

Knightsridge and Ladywell (St Paul's)
Colin R. Douglas MA BD STM — 1969 — 27 Heatherbank, Ladywell, Livingston EH54 6EE — 01506 432326

Dedridge (The Lanthorn)
Marion Keston MB ChB MTh — 1987 — 12B Carrick Gardens, Murieston, Livingston EH54 9ET — 01506 410668
(Scottish Episcopal Church)

Livingston: Old (H)
Graham W. Smith BA BD FSAScot — 1995 — Manse of Livingston, Charlesfield Lane, Livingston EH54 7AJ — 01506 420227

Longridge and Breich See Addiewell

Pardovan, Kingscavil and Winchburgh
A. Scott Marshall DipComm BD — 1984 1998 — The Manse, Winchburgh EH52 6TT — 01506 890919

Polbeth Harwood
William McLaren MA BD — 1990 1994 — 150 Chapelton Drive, Polbeth EH55 8SG — 01506 871247

Stoneyburn See Addiewell

Strathbrock
David W. Black BSc BD — 1968 1984 — Manse Park, Uphall, Broxburn EH52 6JR — 01506 852550

Torphichen See Avonbridge

Uphall South (T)(H)
Vacant — 8 Fernlea, Uphall, Broxburn EH52 6DF — 01506 852788

West Kirk of Calder
Mary D. Dilbey BD — 1997 — 27 Learmonth Crescent, West Calder EH55 8AF — 01506 871589

Whitburn: Brucefield (H)
Robin Brough BA — 1968 1977 — Whitburn, Bathgate EH47 8NU — 01501 740263

Whitburn: South (H)
Gordon A. McCracken BD — 1988 — 5 Mansewood Crescent, Whitburn EH47 8HA — 01501 740333

Name			Description	Address	Phone
Cameron, Ian MA BD	1953	1981	(Kilbrandon and Kilchattan)	37 Burghmuir Court, Linlithgow EH49 7LJ	01506 847987
Crichton, Thomas JP ChSJ MA	1965	1989	Hospital Chaplain	18 Carlton Terrace, Edinburgh EH7 5DD	0131 557 0009
Dickson, A. Stuart	1963	1995	(Glasgow: Govan Old – Assoc)	74 Netherwood Park, Deans, Livingston EH54 8RW	01506 420167
Dundas, Thomas B.S. LTh	1969	1996	(West Kirk of Calder)	35 Coolkill, Sandyford, Dublin 18	00353 12953061
Fletcher, J. Arnold BA	1951	1997	(Blackburn)	7 Merrick Gardens, Ibrox, Glasgow G51 2LF	0141 427 6461
McDonald, Alexander BA CMIWSC	1968	1988	Department of Ministry	95 Glasgow Road, Bathgate EH48 2AN	01506 635129
Manson, Robert L. MA DPS	1956	1991	(Chaplain: Royal Edinburgh Hospital)	4 Murieston Drive, Livingston EH54 9AU	01506 434746
Moore, J.W. MA	1950	1983	(Daviot with Rayne)	31 Lennox Gardens, Linlithgow EH49 7PZ	01506 842534
Morrice, Charles S. MA BD PhD	1959	1997	(Kenya)	104 Baron's Hill Avenue, Linlithgow EH49 7JG	01506 847167
Moyes, Andrew	1959	1992	(Broxburn)	5 Grange Road, Broxburn EH52 5HL	01506 858203
Murray, Ronald N.G. MA	1946	1986	(Pardovan and Kingscavil with Winchburgh)		
Napier, James K. MA	1939	1978	(Balmaghie)	42 Lennox Gardens, Linlithgow EH49 7QA	01506 845680
Nelson, Georgina (Mrs) MA BD PhD DipEd	1990	1995	Hospital Chaplain	2 Crusader Court, Livingston EH54 6QH	01506 414284
Robertson, Emmanuel ThM ThD	1953	1993	(Armadale)	6 Pentland Park, Craigshill, Livingston EH54 5NR	01506 434874
				39 Drumcross Road, Bathgate EH48 4HF	01506 654766

Russell, Archibald MA	1949	1991	(Duror with Glencoe)	4 Bonnytoun Avenue, Linlithgow EH49 7JS 01506 842530
Smith, W. Ewing BSc	1962	1994	(Livingston: Old)	8 Hardy Gardens, Bathgate EH48 1NH 01506 652028
Stirling, A. Douglas BSc	1956	1994	(Rhu and Shandon)	162 Avontoun Park, Linlithgow EH49 6QH 01506 845021
Trimble, Robert DCS			(Deacon)	5 Temple Rise, Dedridge, Livingston EH54 6PJ 01506 412504
Walker, Ian BD MEd DipMS	1943	1984	Parish Education	92 Carse Knowe, Linlithgow EH49 7LG 01506 844412
Wotherspoon, Robert LTh	1976	1998	(Corsock and Kirkpatrick Durham with Crossmichael and Parton)	49 Keith Gardens, Broxburn EH52 6XS 01506 858954

(3) LOTHIAN

Meets at Musselburgh: St Andrew's High Parish Church on the last Thursday of January and June and the first Thursday of other months except February, July and August when there is no meeting.

Clerk: MR JOHN D. McCULLOCH CA DL   Auchindinny House, Penicuik EH26 8PE   01968 676300 (Tel/Fax)
[e-mail: lothianpresbytery@dial.pipex.com]

Aberlady (H) linked with Gullane (H)
Norman L. Faulds MA BD FSAScot   1968   1986   Hummel Road, Gullane EH31 2BG   01620 843192 (Tel/Fax)

Athelstaneford linked with Whitekirk and Tyninghame
Kenneth D.F. Walker MA BD   1976   Athelstaneford, North Berwick EH39 5BE   01620 880378

Belhaven (H) linked with Spott
Laurence H. Twaddle MA BD MTh   1977   1978   Belhaven Road, Dunbar EH42 1NH   01368 863098

Bolton and Saltoun linked with Humbie linked with Yester (H)
Donald Pirie LTh   1975   1999   Tweeddale Avenue, Gifford, Haddington EH41 4QN   01620 810515

Bonnyrigg (H)
John Mitchell LTh CMin   1991   9 Viewbank View, Bonnyrigg EH19 2HU   0131 663 8287

Borthwick (H) linked with Newtongrange (H)
John L. McPake BA BD PhD   1987   7 Maesterton Place, Newtongrange, Dalkeith EH22 4UF   01875 822772

Cockenzie and Port Seton: Chalmers Memorial (H)
Robert L. Glover BMus BD ARCO   1971   1997   Braemar Villa, 2 Links Road, Port Seton, Prestonpans EH32 0HA   01875 812481

Cockenzie and Port Seton: Old (H)
Ronald J. Maxwell Stitt   1979 1993   1 Links Road, Port Seton, Prestonpans EH32 0HA   01875 812310
BA ThM BREd DMin FSAScot

Cockpen and Carrington (H) linked with Lasswade (H) linked with Rosewell (H)
Wendy F. Drake (Mrs) BD   1978 1992   11 Pendreich Terrace, Bonnyrigg EH19 2DT   0131 663 6884

Cranstoun, Crichton and Ford (H) linked with Fala and Soutra (H)
Peter M. Gardner MA BD   1988 1989   Cranstoun Cottage, Ford, Pathhead EH37 5RE   01875 320314

Dalkeith: St John's and King's Park (H)
Alistair K. Ridland MA BD   1982 1988   13 Weir Crescent, Dalkeith EH22 3JN   0131 663 3114

Dalkeith: St Nicholas' Buccleuch (H)
J. Edward Andrews MA BD DipCG   1985 1991   116 Bonnyrigg Road, Dalkeith EH22 3HZ   0131 663 3036
[e-mail: edward.andrews@btinternet.com]

Dirleton (H) linked with North Berwick: Abbey (H) (01620 890110)
David J. Graham BSc BD PhD   1982 1998   20 Westgate, North Berwick EH39 4AF   01620 892410

Dunbar (H)
Alexander B. Noble MA BD ThM   1982 1993   Bayswell Road, Dunbar EH42 1AB   01368 863749

Dunglass
Anne R. Lithgow (Mrs) MA BD   1992 1994   The Manse, Cockburnspath, TD13 5XZ   01368 830713

Fala and Soutra See Cranstoun, Crichton and Ford

Garvald and Morham linked with Haddington: West (H)
Cameron Mackenzie BD   1997   15 West Road, Haddington EH41 3RD   01620 822213

Gladsmuir linked with Longniddry (H)
A. Graham Black MA   1964 1973   The Manse, Elcho Road, Longniddry EH32 0LB   01875 853195
Florence A. Underwood (Mrs) BD (Assist)   1992   The Sheiling, Main Street, Stenton, Dunbar EH42 1TE   01368 850629

Glencorse (H) linked with Roslin (H)
James A. Manson LTh   1981   38 Penicuik Road, Roslin EH25 9LH   0131 440 2012

Gorebridge (H)
Vacant   100 Hunterfield Road, Gorebridge EH23 4TT   01875 820387

Gullane See Aberlady

Charge / Minister	Year	Address	Tel.
Haddington: St Mary's (H) Clifford E. Hughes MA BD	1993	21 Sidegate, Haddington EH41 4BZ	01620 823109
Haddington: West See Garvald and Morham			
Howgate (H) linked with Penicuik: South (H) Frank Ribbons MA BD DipEd	1985	18 Broomhill Avenue, Penicuik EH26 9EG	01968 674692
Humbie See Bolton and Saltoun			
Lasswade See Cockpen and Carrington			
Loanhead Andrew F. Swan BD	1983	120 The Loan, Loanhead EH20 9AS	0131 440 0182
Longniddry See Gladsmuir			
Musselburgh: Northesk (H) Alison P. Matheson (Mrs) MA BD	1991	16 New Street, Musselburgh EH21 6JP	0131 665 2128
Musselburgh: St Andrew's High (H) (0131 665 7239) Violet C.C. McKay (Mrs) BD	1988 1998	8 Ferguson Drive, Musselburgh EH21 6XA	0131 665 5583
Musselburgh: St Clement's and St Ninian's Moira McDonald (Ms) MA BD	1997	Wallyford Loan Road, Wallyford, Musselburgh EH21 8BU	0131 653 6588
Musselburgh: St Michael's Inveresk Andrew B. Dick MA BD DipMin	1986	8 Hope Place, Musselburgh EH21 7QE	0131 665 0545
Newbattle (H) Jared W. Hay BA MTh DipMin	1987	70 Newbattle Abbey Crescent, Dalkeith EH22 3LW [e-mail: jared.hay@virgin.net]	0131 663 3245 (Tel/Fax) 07050 216433 (Mbl)
Newton James Robertson LTh	1970 1976	Newton, Dalkeith EH22 1SR	0131 663 3845
Newtongrange See Borthwick			
North Berwick: Abbey See Dirleton			
North Berwick: St Andrew Blackadder (H) Edward C. McKenna BD DPS	1989	7 Marine Parade, North Berwick EH39 4LD [e-mail: eddiemckenna@compuserve.com]	01620 892132 (Tel/Fax)
Ormiston linked with Pencaitland Mark Malcolm MA BD	1999	Pencaitland, Tranent EH34 5DL	01875 340208

Pencaitland See Ormiston

Penicuik: North (H)
John W. Fraser MA BD   1974   1982   93 John Street, Penicuik EH26 8AG   01968 672213

Penicuik: St Mungo's (H)
William D. Irving LTh   1985   31a Kirkhill Road, Penicuik EH26 8JB   01968 672916

Penicuik: South See Howgate
Prestonkirk See Traprain

Prestonpans: Prestongrange
Robert R. Simpson BA BD   1994   East Loan, Prestonpans EH32 9ED   01875 810308

Rosewell See Cockpen and Carrington
Roslin See Glencorse
Spott See Belhaven
Stenton See Traprain

Tranent
Thomas M. Hogg BD   1986   244 Church Street, Tranent EH33 1BW   01875 610210

Traprain
Vacant   Preston Road, East Linton EH40 3DS   01620 860227

Whitekirk and Tyninghame See Athelstaneford
Whittingehame See Traprain
Yester See Bolton and Saltoun

Name			(Congregation)	Address	Phone
Adamson, T. Sidney S. MA BD	1937	1985	(Musselburgh: St Michael's Inveresk)	48 Hailes Gardens, Edinburgh EH13 0JH	0131 441 2471
Brown, Ronald H.	1974	1998	(Musselburgh: Northesk)	6 Monktonhall Farm Cottages, Musselburgh EH21 6RZ	0131 653 2531
Brown, William BD	1972	1997	(Edinburgh: Polwarth)	13 Thornyhall, Dalkeith EH22 2ND	0131 654 0929
Chalmers, William R. MA BD STM	1953	1992	(Dunbar)	c/o 62 Mayne Road, Elgin IV30 1PD	01343 547620
Day, Colin T. MA	1947	1984	(Warden, Carberry Tower)	20 Hadfast Road, Cousland, Dalkeith EH22 2NU	0131 660 5777
Donaldson, Colin V.	1981	1998	(Ormiston with Pencaitland)	3A Playfair Terrace, St Andrews KY16 9HX	01334 472889
Fraser, John W. BEM MA BD PhD	1950	1983	(Farnell)	12 Quarryfoot Green, Bonnyrigg EH19 2EJ	0131 663 8037
Gilfillan, James LTh	1967	1997	(East Kilbride: Old)	15 Long Cram, Haddington EH41 4NS	01620 824843
Hill, Arthur T.	1940	1981	(Ormiston with Prestonpans: Grange)	8A Hamilton Road, North Berwick EH39 4NA	01620 893961
Hutchison, Alan E.W.			(Deacon)	132 Lochbridge Road, North Berwick EH39 4DR	01620 894077
Lennie, Robert C. MA BD	1942	1985	(Aberlady)	9 Abbeyfield, Paterson Place, Haddington EH41 3DU	01620 822582
Macdonell, Alasdair W. MA BD	1955	1992	(Haddington: St Mary's)	St Andrews Cottage, Duns Road, Gifford, Haddington EH41 4QW	01620 810341

MacLeod, Roderick N.   1986 1992   Chaplain, Army   Army Training Regiment, Glencorse Barracks, Penicuik EH26 0NP

Macrae, Norman C. MA DipEd   1942 1985   (Loanhead)   6 Lonsdale Terrace, Edinburgh EH3 9HN   0131 228 6283

Maule-Brown, Robert MA   1949 1985   (Strathy and Halladale)   5 Acredales Walk, Haddington EH41 4RR   01620 824959

Ritchie, James McL. MA BD   1950 1985   (Coalsnaughton)   46 St James's Gardens, Penicuik EH26 9DU   01968 676123

Sanderson, W. Roy DD   1933 1973   (Stenton with Whittinghame)   1A York Road, North Berwick EH39 4LS   01620 892780

Sawers, E.A.H. VRD   1950 1989   (Cranstoun Crichton and Ford with Fala and Soutra)

Stein, Jock MA BD   1973 1986   (Joint Warden, Carberry)   18 Lydgait Gardens, Haddington EH41 3DB   01620 825830
Carberry, Musselburgh EH21 8PY   0131 665 3135
[e-mail: carberry@dial.pipex.com]

Stein, Margaret E. DA BD DipRE   1984 1986   (Joint Warden, Carberry)   Carberry, Musselburgh EH21 8PY   0131 665 3135
[e-mail: carberry@dial.pipex.com]

Torrance, David W. MA BD   1955 1991   (Earlston)   38 Forth Street, North Berwick EH39 4JQ   01620 895109

Turner, Duncan M. MBE MA   1940 1977   (Innerwick with Spott)   1 Main Street, Spott, Dunbar EH42 1RJ   01368 862668

Underwood, Geoffrey H. BD DipTh FPhS   1964 1992   (Cockenzie and Port Seton: Chalmers Memorial)   The Sheiling, Main Street, Stenton, Dunbar EH42 1TE   01368 850629

Whiteford, David H. CBE MA BD PhD   1943 1985   (Gullane)   3 Old Dean Road, Longniddry EH32 0QY   01875 852980

(4) MELROSE AND PEEBLES

Meets at Innerleithen, on the first Tuesday of February, March, May, October, November, December, and on the fourth Tuesday of June. and in places to be appointed on the first Tuesday of September.

Clerk: REV. JACK M. BROWN BSc BD   High Road, Galashiels TD1 2BD   01896 752420 (Tel/Fax)

Ashkirk linked with Selkirk (H)
James W. Campbell BD   1995   1 Loanside, Selkirk TD7 4DJ   01750 22833
George McD. McCann BSc ATI (Aux)   1994   Rosbeg, Parsonage Road, Galashiels TD1 3HS   01896 752055

Bowden (H) linked with Newtown
Alasdair J. Morton MA BD DipEd FEIS   1960 1994   Newtown St Boswells TD6 0PL   01835 822106

Broughton, Glenholm and Kilbucho linked with Skirling linked with Stobo and Drumelzier linked with Tweedsmuir
Rachel J.W. Dobie (Mrs) LTh   1991 1996   Broughton, Biggar ML12 6HQ   01899 830331
[e-mail: racheldobie@compuserve.com]

Caddonfoot (H) linked with Galashiels St Ninian's (H)
Vacant   Mossilee Road, Galashiels TD1 1NF   01896 752058

Carlops linked with Kirkurd and Newlands (H) linked with West Linton St Andrew's (H)			
Thomas W. Burt BD	1985	West Linton, Peeblesshire EH46 7EN	01968 660221
Channelkirk linked with Lauder Old			
John M. Shields MBE LTh	1972 1997	Lauder, Berwickshire TD2 6QD	01578 722320
Earlston			
Michael D. Scouler MBE BSc BD	1988 1992	Earlston, Berwickshire TD4 6DE	01896 849236
Eddleston (H) linked with Peebles Old (H)			
James B. MacLean MTheol DipPTheol	1986 1997	Innerleithen Road, Peebles EH45 8BD	01721 720568
Ettrick linked with Yarrow			
Bruce B. Lawrie BD	1974 1986	Yarrow, Selkirk TD7 5LA	01750 82219
Galashiels: Old and St Paul's (H)			
Leslie M. Steele MA BD	1973 1988	Barr Road, Galashiels TD1 3HX [e-mail: lms@gala.prestel.co.uk]	01896 752320
Galashiels: St Aidan's (H)			
Jack M. Brown BSc BD	1977 1981	High Road, Galashiels TD1 2BD	01896 752420 (Tel/Fax)
Galashiels: St John's (H)			
Stephen F. Clipston MA BD	1982	Hawthorn Road, Galashiels TD1 2JZ	01896 752573 (Tel) 01896 758561 (Fax)
Galashiels: St Ninian's See Caddonfoot			
Innerleithen (H) linked with Traquair linked with Walkerburn			
John Wilson BD	1985	Innerleithen, Peeblesshire EH44 6HL	01896 830309
Kirkurd and Newlands See Carlops			
Lauder: Old See Channelkirk			
Lyne and Manor			
Nancy M. Norman (Miss) BA MDiv MTh	1988 1998	25 March Street, Peebles EH45 8EP	01721 721699
Maxton and Mertoun linked with St Boswells			
Bruce F. Neill MA BD	1966 1996	St Boswells, Roxburghshire TD6 0BB	01835 822255
Melrose (H)			
Alistair G. Bennett BSc BD	1978 1984	Melrose, Roxburghshire TD6 9ST	01896 822217

Newtown See Bowden
Peebles: Old See Eddleston

Peebles: St Andrew's Leckie (H)
James H. Wallace MA BD 1973 1983 Mansefield, Innerleithen Road, Peebles EH45 8BE 01721 721749 (Tel/Fax)

St Boswells See Maxton and Mertoun
Selkirk See Ashkirk
Skirling See Broughton, Glenholm and Kilbucho
Stobo and Drumelzier See Broughton, Glenholm and Kilbucho

Stow: St Mary of Wedale and Heriot
Stanley Kennon BA BD 1992 Stow, Galashiels TD1 2RE 01578 730237

Traquair See Innerleithen
Tweedsmuir See Broughton, Glenholm and Kilbucho
Walkerburn See Innerleithen
West Linton St Andrew's See Carlops
Yarrow See Ettrick

Auld, Ian A. MA	1935	1972	(Banchory Devenick)	Whitestoneknowe, Hydro Avenue, Peebles EH45 8LU	01721 720709
Brown, Robert BSc	1962	1997	(Kilbrandon and Kilchattan)	11 Thornfield Terrace, Selkirk TD7 4DU	01750 20311
Cashman, P. Hamilton BSc	1985	1998	(Dirleton with North Berwick: Abbey)	38 Abbotsford Road, Galashiels TD1 3HR	01896 752711
Dick, J. Ronald BD	1973	1996	Hospital Chaplain	5 Georgefield Farm Cottages, Earlston TD4 6BH	01896 848956
Donald, Thomas W. LTh CA	1977	1987	(Bowden with Lilliesleaf)	The Quest, Huntly Road, Melrose TD6 9SB	01896 822345
Duncan, Charles A MA	1956	1992	(Heriot with Stow St Mary of Wedale)	10 Elm Grove, Galashiels TD1 3JA	01896 753261
Duncan, John H. MA BD	1933	1976	(Earlston)	20 Elliot Park, Edinburgh EH14 1DX	0131 441 2911
Jamieson, H.M. MA BD	1938	1976	(Ashkirk with Lilliesleaf)	Birchfield, High Cross Avenue, Melrose TD6 9SQ	01896 822173
Kellet, John M. MA	1962	1995	(Leith: South)	4 High Cottages, Walkerburn, Peebles-shire EH43 6QW	01896 870351
Laing, William F. DSC VRD MA	1952	1986	(Selkirk: St Mary's West)	10 The Glebe, Selkirk TD7 5AB	01750 21210
Lyall, J. Farquhar	1950	1989	(Armsheen Barrhill with Colmonell)	32 Shawpark Crescent, Selkirk TD7 4EX	01750 22900
MacFarlane, David C MA	1957	1997	(Eddleston with Peebles Old)	61 Viewlands Road, Perth PH1 1ND	01738 624996
Moore, W. Haisley BA	1966	1996	(Secretary: The Boys' Brigade)	17 Shawpark Crescent, Selkirk TD7 4EX	01750 22566
Morton, Gillian M. (Mrs) MA BD PGCE	1983	1996	(Hospital Chaplain)	The Manse, Newtown St Boswells TD6 0SG	01835 822106
Rae, Andrew W.	1951	1987	(Annan: St Andrew's Greenknowe Erskine)	Roseneuk, Tweedside Road, Newtown St Boswells TD6 0PQ	01835 823783
Rogerson, A.E. MA	1937	1980	(Galashiels: Ladhope St Cuthbert's)	24 Cotgreen Road, Tweedbank, Galashiels TD1 3SG	01896 754817
Slack, J.W.	1968	1985	(Ashkirk with Selkirk Lawson Memorial)	17 Grenville Avenue, St Anne's-on-Sea, Fylde FY8 2RR	01253 728863
Taverner, Glyn R. MA BD	1957	1995	(Maxton and Mertoun with St Boswells)	Woodcot Cottage, Waverley Road, Innerleithen EH44 6QW	01896 830156
Thomson, G.F.M. MA	1956	1988	(Dollar Associate)	49 High Cross Avenue, Melrose TD6 9SX	01896 823312

(5) DUNS

Meets at Duns, in the Old Parish Church Hall, on the first Tuesday of February, March, April, May, October, November, December on the last Tuesday in June; and in places to be appointed on the first Tuesday of September.

Clerk:　　REV. JAMES S.H CUTLER, BD CEng MIStructE　　The Manse, Duns Road, Coldstream TD12 4DP　　01890 882537

Ayton (H) linked with Burnmouth linked with Grantshouse and Houndwood linked with Reston
David J. Hebenton MA BD　1958　1983　Grey Gables, Beanburn, Ayton, Eyemouth TD14 5QY　018907 81333

Berwick-on-Tweed: St Andrew's Wallace Green (H) and Lowick
Alison A. Meikle (Mrs) BD　1999　3 Meadow Grange, Berwick-on-Tweed TD15 1NW　01289 303304

Bonkyl and Preston linked with Chirnside (H) linked with Edrom Allanton (H)
William Paterson BD　1977　1993　Chirnside, Duns TD11 3XL　01890 818269

Burnmouth See Ayton
Chirnside See Bonkyl and Preston

Coldingham linked with Eyemouth linked with St Abb's
Daniel G. Lindsay BD　1978　1979　Victoria Road, Eyemouth TD14 5JD　018907 50327

Coldstream (H) linked with Eccles
James S.H. Cutler BD CEng MIStructE　1986　1995　Duns Road, Coldstream TD12 4DP　01890 882537

Duns (H)
Andrew Morrice MA BD　1999　The Manse, Duns, Berwickshire TD11 3DP　01361 883755

Eccles See Coldstream
Edrom Allanton See Bonkyl and Preston
Eyemouth See Coldingham

Fogo and Swinton linked with Ladykirk linked with Leitholm linked with Whitsome (H)
Alan C.D. Cartwright BSc BD　1976　1986　Swinton, Duns TD11 3JJ　01890 860228

Foulden and Mordington linked with Hutton and Fishwick and Paxton
Geraldine H. Hope (Mrs) MA BD　1986　Hutton, Berwick on Tweed TD15 1TS　01289 386396

Gordon: St Michael's linked with Greenlaw (H) linked with Legerwood linked with Westruther
Thomas S. Nicholson BD DPS　1982　1995　The Manse, Todholes, Greenlaw, Berwickshire TD10 6XD　01361 810316

Grantshouse and Houndwood See Ayton
Greenlaw See Gordon St Michael's
Hutton and Fishwick and Paxton See Foulden and Mordington

Kirk of Lammermuir linked with Langton and Polwarth

Alexander Slorach CA BD	1970 1983		Cranshaws, Duns TD11 3SJ	01361 890289

Ladykirk See Fogo and Swinton
Langton and Polwarth See Kirk of Lammermuir
Legerwood See Gordon St Michael's
Leitholm See Fogo and Swinton
Lowick See Berwick-on-Tweed St Andrew's Wallace Green
Reston See Ayton
St Abb's See Coldingham
Westruther See Gordon St Michael's
Whitsome See Fogo and Swinton

Dunnett, W. Gavin MBE	1968 1985	(Foulden and Mordington with Hutton and Fishwick and Paxton)	Old Smithy Cottage, Hutton, Berwick-on-Tweed TD15 1TS	01289 86225
Gaddes, Donald R.	1961 1994	(Kelso North and Ednam)	35 Winterfield Gardens, Duns TD11 3EZ	01361 883172
Gale, Ronald A.A. LTh	1982 1995	(Dunoon Old and St Cuthbert's)	55 Lennel Mount, Coldstream TD12 4NS	01890 883699
Hay, Bruce J.L.	1957 1997	(Makerstoun and Smailholm with Stichill, Hume and Nenthorn)	Tweed House, Tweed Street, Berwick-upon-Tweed TD15 1NG	01289 303171
Jackson, John MA	1958 1990	(Bonnybridge)	2 Milne Graden West, Coldstream TD12 4HE	01890 883435
Macleod, Allan M. MA	1945 1985	(Gordon St Michael's with Legerwood with Westruther)	Silverlea, Machrihanish, Argyll	
Prentice, Donald K. BSc BD	1989 1992	Chaplain: Army	RDMC, Fort Blockhouse, Gosport PO12 2AB	01705 765272

(6) JEDBURGH

Meets at Jedburgh on the first Wednesday of February, March, May, October, November and December and on the last Wednesday of June. Meets in the Moderator's church on the first Wednesday of September

Clerk	REV. ALAN D. REID MA BD	23 Langholm Street, Newcastleton TD9 0QX	013873 75242
		[e-mail: ad@reid63.freeserve.co.uk]	

Ancrum linked with Crailing and Eckford with Lilliesleaf (T)

W. Frank Campbell BA BD	1989 1991	22 The Glebe, Ancrum, Jedburgh TD8 6UX	01835 830318

Charge / Name	Year(s)	Address	Telephone
Bedrule linked with Denholm (H) linked with Minto			
William Longmuir LTh	1984	Denholm, Hawick TD9 8NB	01450 870268
Cavers and Kirkton linked with Hawick St Mary's and Old			
Rev. William R. Taylor MA BD	1983 1998	Braid Road, Hawick TD9 9LZ	01450 377865
Crailing and Eckford linked with Oxnam linked with Roxburgh			
Vacant		Oxnam, Jedburgh TD8 6RD	01835 862492
Denholm See Bedrule			
Ednam See Kelso: Tweedside			
Hawick: Burnfoot			
Charles J. Finnie LTh DPS	1991 1997	29 Wilton Hill, Hawick TD9 8BA [e-mail: charles@finnierev.freeserve.co.uk]	01450 373181
Ann Merrilees (Miss) DCS		60 Hillend Drive, Hawick TD9 8DU [e-mail: annmerri@aol.com]	01450 370181
Hawick: Teviot (H) and Roberton			
Neil R. Combe BSc MSc BD	1984	Buccleuch Road, Hawick TD9 0EL [e-mail: neil.combe@btinternet.com]	01450 372150
Hawick: St Mary's and Old H) See Cavers and Kirkton			
Hawick: Trinity (H)			
E.P. Lindsay Thomson MA	1964 1972	Fenwick Park, Hawick TD9 9PA	01450 372705
Hawick: Wilton linked with Teviothead			
John Shedden BD	1971 1998	4 Wilton Hill Terrace, Hawick TD9 8BE	01450 370744
Hobkirk and Southdean			
Continued Vacancy			
Jedburgh: Old and Edgerston			
Bruce McNicol JP BL BD	1967 1992	Honeyfield Drive, Jedburgh TD8 6LQ	01835 863417
Jedburgh: Trinity			
John A. Riddell MA BD	1967	42 High Street, Jedburgh TD8 6DQ	01835 863223
Kelso: Old (H) and Sprouston			
Marion E. Dodd (Miss) MA BD LRAM	1988 1989	Glebe Lane, Kelso, Roxburghshire TD5 7JE [e-mail: mariondodd@scotborders.co.uk]	01573 226254
Kelso: Tweedside (H) (01573 224154)			
Tom McDonald	1994	20 Forrestfield, Kelso TD5 7BX	01573 224677

Liddesdale (H)
Alan D. Reid MA BD   1989   23 Langholm Street, Newcastleton TD9 0QX   013873 75242
[e-mail: ad@reid63.freeserve.co.uk]

Lilliesleaf See Ancrum

Linton linked with Morebattle and Hownam linked with Yetholm (H)
Robin D. McHaffie BD   1979   1991   Kirk Yetholm, Kelso TD5 8RD   01573 420308

Makerstoun and Smailholm See Kelso: Tweedside
Minto See Bedrule
Morebattle and Hownam See Linton

Oxnam
Continued Vacancy

Roxburgh See Kelso: Tweedside
Stichill, Hume and Nenthorn See Kelso: Tweedside
Teviothead See Hawick: Wilton
Yetholm See Linton

Bowie, Adam McC.	1976 1996	(Cavers and Kirkton with Hobkirk and Southdean)	Glenbield, Redpath, nr Earlston TD4 6AD	01896 848173
Brown, Joseph MA	1954 1991	(Linton with Hownam and Morebattle with Yetholm)	Rowanbank, Southdean, Hawick TD9 8TH	01450 860223
Fox, G. Dudley A.	1972 1988	(Kelso Old)	Pinnacle Hill Farm, Kelso TD5 8HD	01573 223335
Hamilton, Robert MA BD	1938 1979	(Kelso Old)	1 Churston Close, Galmpton, Brixham, Devon	
Leadbeater, Dennis TD	1946 1999	(The Glens)	Flat 30, Douglas Haig Court, Linden Crescent, Hawick	
McConnell, Robert	1959 1983	(Hawick St Margaret's and Wilton South with Roberton)		
Ritchie, Garden W.M.	1961 1995	(Ardersier with Petty)	Flat 9, Queensfort Court, Carryduff, Belfast BT8 8NF	01573 224419
Thompson, W.M.D. MA	1950 1997	(Crailing and Eckford with Oxnam with Roxburgh)	23 Croft Road, Kelso TD5 7EP	
			The Old Manse, Oxnam, Jedburgh TD8 6RD	01835 862492

HAWICK ADDRESSES

Burnfoot	Fraser Avenue	Teviot	off Buccleuch Road
St Mary's and Old	Kirk Wynd	Trinity	Central Square
		Wilton	Princes Street

(7) ANNANDALE AND ESKDALE

Meets on the first Tuesday of February, May, September and December and the third Tuesday of March, June and October in a venue to be determined by Presbytery.

Clerk: REV. C. BRYAN HASTON LTh   The Manse, Gretna Green DG16 5DU   01461 338313 (Tel)
[e-mail: cbhaston@cofs.demon.co.uk]   0870 1640 119 (Fax)

Annan: Old (H)
Duncan J. Macpherson BSc BD   1993   1997   12 Plumdon Park Avenue, Annan DG12 6EY   01461 201405 (Tel)
[e-mail: duncan.macpherson@ukonline.co.uk]   01461 201408 (Fax)

Annan: St Andrew's Greenknowe Erskine (H)
George K. Lind BD MCIBS   1998   1 Annerley Road, Annan DG12 6HE   01461 202626
[e-mail: glind98293@aol.com]

Applegarth and Sibbaldbie (H) linked with Lochmaben (H)
John J.C. Owen LTh   1967   1980   Lochmaben, Lockerbie DG11 1QF   01387 810590 (Tel/Fax)

Brydekirk linked with Hoddam
S. Edwin P. Beveridge BA   1959   1993   Ecclefechan, Lockerbie DG11 3BU   01576 300357

Canonbie (H)
Linda J. Williams (Mrs) BD   1993   1999   Kirtlebridge, Lockerbie DG11 3LY   01461 500378

Carlisle: Chapel Street linked with Longtown: St Andrew's
William D. Brown BD CQSW   1987   197 Brampton Road, Carlisle CA3 9AX   01228 401655

Dalton linked with Hightae linked with St Mungo
W. Logan Kirk MA BD MTh   1988   Hightae, Lockerbie DG11 1JL   01387 811499

Dornock
Ronald S. Seaman MA   1967   Dornock, Annan DG12 6NR   01461 40268

Eskdalemuir linked with Hutton and Corrie linked with Tundergarth
Vacant   Hutton Manse, Boreland, Lockerbie DG11 2PB   01576 610213

Gretna: Old (H), Gretna: St Andrew's and Half Morton and Kirkpatrick Fleming
C. Bryan Haston LTh   1975   Gretna Green DG16 5DU   01461 338313 (Tel)
[e-mail: cbhaston@cofs.demon.co.uk]   0870 1640119 (Fax)

Hightae See Dalton
Hoddam See Brydekirk
Hutton and Corrie See Eskdalemuir

Johnstone linked with Kirkpatrick Juxta (H)
John M. Stewart MA BD   1964 1986   Beattock, Moffat DG10 9RF   01683 300349

Kirkpatrick Juxta See Johnstone

Kirtle-Eaglesfield linked with Middlebie linked with Waterbeck
Trevor C. Williams LTh   1990 1999   Kirtlebridge, Lockerbie DG11 3LY   01461 500378

Langholm, Ewes and Westerkirk
Vacant   Langholm DG13 0BL   01387 380252

Lochmaben See Applegarth and Sibbaldbie

Lockerbie: Dryfesdale
David M. Almord BD   1996   The Manse, 5 Carlisle Road, Lockerbie DG11 2DW   01576 202361

Longtown St Andrew's See Carlisle Chapel Street
Middlebie See Kirtle-Eaglesfield

Moffat St Andrew's (H) linked with Wamphray
Gerald C. Moule BA BD   1974 1975   Moffat DG10 9EJ   01683 220128 (Tel)
                                                            01683 220758 (Fax)

St Mungo See Dalton
Tundergarth See Eskdalemuir
Wamphray See Moffat St Andrew's
Waterbeck See Kirtle-Eaglesfield

Annand, James M. MA BD   1955 1995   (Lockerbie Dryfesdale)   48 Main Street, Newstead, Melrose TD6 9DX
Baillie, David R.   1979 1990   (Crawford with Lowther)   1 Preston Court, Annan DG12 5HS   01461 201486
        [e-mail: annan@baillie.abcl.co.uk]
Byers, Alan J   1959 1992   (Gamrie with King Edward)   Meadowbank, Plumdon Road, Annan DG12 6SJ   01461 206512
Byers, Mairi (Mrs) BTh CPS   1992 1998   (Jura)   Meadowbank, Plumdon Road, Annan DG12 6SJ   01461 206512
Fisher, D. Noel MA BD   1939 1979   (Glasgow Sherbrooke St Gilbert's)   Leetside, 14 Woodlands Road, Coldstream TD12 4LL   01890 2228
McLean, Margaret G. BD   1978 1991   (Community Minister: Annandale and Eskdale)   84 Union Road, Gretna DG16 5JT   01461 338491
MacMillan, William M. LTh   1980 1998   (Kilmory with Lamlash)   61 Queen Street, Lochmaben DG11 1PP   01387 811528

| Rennie, James D. MA | 1962 | 1996 | (Broughton, Glenholm and Kilbucho with Skirling with Stobo and Drumelzier with Tweedsmuir) | Dundoran, Ballplay Road, Moffat DG10 9JX [e-mail: dundoran@aol.com] | 01683 220223 |
| Ross, Alan C. CA BD | 1988 | 1997 | (Annan: St Andrew's Greenknowe Erskine) | Yarra, Ettrickbridge, Selkirk TD7 5JN [e-mail: alkaross@aol.com] | 01750 52324 |

(8) DUMFRIES AND KIRKCUDBRIGHT

Meets at Dumfries, on the first Wednesday of February, March, April, May, September, October, November, December, and the last Wednesday of June.

Clerk: REV. GORDON M.A. SAVAGE MA BD | 11 Laurieknowe, Dumfries DG2 7AH | 01387 252929

Anwoth and Girthon linked with Borgue
| Austin U. Erskine | 1986 | 1990 | Gatehouse of Fleet, Castle Douglas DG7 2EQ | 01557 814233 |

Auchencairn and Rerrick linked with Buittle and Kelton
| James H. Sinclair MA BD | 1966 | 1992 | Auchencairn, Castle Douglas DG7 1QS | 01556 640288 |

Balmaclellan and Kells (H) linked with Carsphairn linked with Dalry (H)
| David S. Bartholomew BSc MSc PhD BD | 1994 | | Dalry, Castle Douglas DG7 3PJ | 01644 430380 |

Balmaghie linked with Tarff and Twynholm (H)
| Christopher Wallace BD | 1988 | | Twynholm, Kirkcudbright DG6 4NY | 01557 860381 |

Borgue See Anwoth and Girthon
Buittle and Kelton See Auchencairn and Rerrick

Caerlaverock
Continued Vacancy

Carsphairn See Balmaclellan and Kells

Castle Douglas (H)
| John H. Fraser LTh | 1973 | 1990 | 1 Castle View, Castle Douglas DG7 1BG | 01556 502171 |

Closeburn linked with Durisdeer
| James W. Scott MA CDA | 1952 | 1953 | Durisdeer, Thornhill, Dumfriesshire DG3 5BJ | 01848 500231 |

Colvend, Southwick and Kirkbean
Barry Knight BD | 1991 | 1996 | Colvend, Dalbeattie DG5 4QN [e-mail: barryknight@hotmail.com] | 01556 630255

Corsock and Kirkpatrick Durham linked with Crossmichael and Parton
Vacant | | | Knockdrocket, Clarebrand, Castle Douglas DG7 3AH | 01556 503645

Crossmichael and Parton See Corsock and Kirkpatrick Durham

Cummertrees linked with Mouswald linked with Ruthwell (H)
James Williamson BA BD | 1986 | 1991 | Ruthwell, Dumfries DG1 4NP | 01387 870217

Dalbeattie (H) linked with Urr (H)
Norman M. Hutcheson MA BD | 1973 | 1988 | 36 Mill Street, Dalbeattie DG5 4HE | 01556 610029

Dalry See Balmaclellan

Dumfries: Greyfriars (T) (H)
W.C. Campbell-Jack BD MTh PhD | 1979 | 1999 | 4 Georgetown Crescent, Dumfries DG1 4EQ·· | 01387 257045

Dumfries: Lincluden linked with Holywood (T)
John Spencer MA BD | 1962 | 1995 | 96 Glasgow Road, Dumfries DG2 9DE | 01387 264298

Dumfries: Lochside
Thomas M. Bryson BD | 1997 | | 27 St Anne's Road, Dumfries DG2 9HZ | 01387 252912

Dumfries: Maxwelltown West (H)
Gordon M.A. Savage MA BD | 1977 | 1984 | 11 Laurieknowe, Dumfries DG2 7AH | 01387 252929

Dumfries: St George's (H)
Donald Campbell BD | 1997 | | 9 Nunholm Park, Dumfries DG1 1JP | 01387 252965

Dumfries: St Mary's (H)
Graham D.S. Deans MA BD | 1978 | 1987 | 47 Moffat Road, Dumfries DG1 1NN | 01387 254873

Dumfries: St Michael's and South
Maurice S. Bond MTh BA DipEd PhD | 1983 | 1999 | 39 Cardoness Street, Dumfries DG1 3AL | 01387 253849

Dumfries: Troqueer (H)
William W. Kelly BSc BD | 1994 | | Troqueer Road, Dumfries DG2 7DF [e-mail: 100410.3003@compuserve.com] | 01387 253043

Dunscore linked with Glencairn and Moniaive
Christine Sime BSc BD | 1994 | | Wallaceton, Auldgirth, Dumfries DG2 0TJ | 01387 820245

Durisdeer See Closeburn
Glencairn and Moniaive See Dunscore
Holywood See Dumfries: Lincluden

Kirkconnel (H)			
David Deas Melville BD	1989	Kingsway, Kirkconnel, Sanquhar DG4 6PN	01659 67241
Kirkcudbright (H)			
Douglas R. Irving LLB BD WS	1984 1998	6 Bourtree Avenue, Kirkcudbright DG6 4AU	01557 330489
Kirkgunzeon			
Continued Vacancy			
Kirkmahoe			
Dennis S. Rose LTh	1996	Kirkmahoe, Dumfries DG1 1ST	01387 710572
Kirkmichael linked with Tinwald linked with Torthorwald			
Vacant		Tinwald, Dumfries DG1 3PL	01387 710246
Elizabeth A. Mack (Miss) DipPEd (Aux)	1994 1999	24 Roberts Crescent, Dumfries DG2 7RS	01387 264847
Kirkpatrick Irongray linked with Lochrutton linked with Terregles			
David K.P. Bennett BA	1974 1987	Irongray Manse, Dumfries DG2 9TR	01387 720227
Lochend linked with New Abbey			
William Holland MA	1967 1971	New Abbey, Dumfries DG2 8BY	01387 850232

Lochrutton See Kirkpatrick Irongray
Mouswald See Cummertrees
New Abbey See Lochend

Penpont, Keir and Tynron (T)			
Robert Gehrke BSc BD CEng MIEE	1994	Penpont, Thornhill DG3 4BH	01848 330430

Rerrick See Auchencairn
Ruthwell (H) See Cummertrees

Sanquhar: St Bride's (H)			
Vacant		Glasgow Road, Sanquhar DG4 6BS	01659 50247

Tarff and Twynholm See Balmaghie
Terregles See Kirkpatrick Irongray

Thornhill (T)(H)			
John E. Gisbey MA BD MSc	1964 1997	Thornhill, Dumfriesshire DG3 5ER	01848 331191

Tinwald See Kirkmichael
Torthorwald See Kirkmichael
Urr See Dalbeattie

Name			Description	Address	Phone
Calderwood, Walter M. MA BD	1934	1974	(Leven Forman)	1 Rossway Road, Kirkcudbright DG6 4BS	01557 330128
Craig, N. Douglas MA BD	1947	1987	(Dalbeattie Craignair with Urr)	33 Albert Road, Dumfries DG2 9DN	01387 252187
Elder, Albert B. MA	1960	1998	(Dumfries: St Michael's & South)	87 Glasgow Street, Dumfries DG2 9AG	01387 249811
Geddes, Alexander J. MA BD	1960	1998	(Stewarton: St Columba's)	166 Georgetown Road, Dumfries DG1 4DT	01387 252287
Gillespie, Ann M. (Miss) DCS			(Deaconess)	Barlochan House, Palnackie, Castle Douglas DG7 1PF	01556 600378
Grant, G.V.R. MA	1948	1982	(Urray and Kilchrist)	Drum Cottage, Kirkbean, Dumfries DG2 8DL	01387 880209
Grant, James BA	1961	1987	(Penpont Keir and Tynron)	147A Drumlanrig Street, Thornhill DG3 5LJ	01848 330829
Greer, A. David C. LLB DMin DipAdultEd	1956	1996	(Barra)	10 Watling Street, Dumfries DG1 1HF	01387 256113
Hamill, Robert BA	1956	1989	(Castle Douglas St Ringan's)	11 St Andrew Drive, Castle Douglas DG7 1EW	01556 502962
Hutchison, Mary L. (Mrs) BD	1982	1995	(Dumfries Lincluden with Holywood)	Monzie, 25 Twiname Way, Heathhall, Dumfries DG1 3ST	01387 250610
Johnston, John MA BD	1963	1999	(Hospital Chaplain)	Near Bye, Amisfield, Dumfries DG1 3LN	01387 710254
Leishman, James S LTh BD MA(Div)	1969	1999	(Kirkmichael with Tinwald with Torthorwald)	11 Hunter Avenue, Heathhall, Dumfries DG1 3UX	01387 249241
Mackay, Donald MBE FCP FSAScot	1951	1986	(Ardrossan: St John's)	8 Urquhart Crescent, Dumfries DG1 8XF	01387 259132
McKenzie, William M. DA	1958	1993	(Dumfries: Troqueer)	41 Kingholm Road, Dumfries DG1 4SR	01387 253688
Miller, John R. MA BD	1958	1991	(Carsphairn with Dalry)	7 Fairgreen Court, Rhonehouse, Castle Douglas DG7 1SA	01556 680428
Robertson, Ian W. MA BD	1956	1995	(Colvend, Southwick and Kirkbean)	10 Marjoriebanks, Lochmaben, Lockerbie DG11 1QH	01387 810541
Robertson, Thomas R. MA BD	1934	1976	(Broughton, Glenholm and Kilbucho with Skirling)	1 Church Row, Kirkcudbright DG6 4AP	01557 330795
Smith, Richmond OBE MA BD	1952	1983	(World Alliance of Reformed Churches)	Aignish,Merse Way, Kippford, Dalbeattie DG5 4LH	01556 620624
Strachan, Alexander E MA BD	1974	1999	(Dumfries Health Care Chaplain)	Netherwood Lodge, Glencaple Road, Dumfries DG1 4TY	01387 267585
Vincent, C. Raymond MA FSAScot	1952	1992	(Stonehouse)	Rosebank, Newton Stewart Road, New Galloway, Castle Douglas DG7 3RT	01644 420451
Wilkie, James R. MA MTh	1957	1993	(Penpont, Keir and Tynron)	31 West Morton Street, Thornhill, Dumfriesshire DG3 5NF	01848 331028
Young, John MTh DipMin	1963	1999	(Airdrie: Broomknoll)	Craigview, North Street, Moniaive, Thornhill DG3 4HR	01848 200318

DUMFRIES ADDRESSES

Greyfriars	Church Crescent	Maxwelltown West	Laurieknowe
Lincluden	Stewartry Road	St George's	George Street
Lochside	Lochside Road	St Mary's	St Mary's Street
		St Michael's and South	St Michael's Street
		Troqueer	Troqueer Road

(9) WIGTOWN AND STRANRAER

Meets at Glenluce, in Old Luce Parish Church on the first Tuesday of each month except, January, April, July and August, when there is no meeting; June, when it meets on the fourth Tuesday and October, when it meets in the Moderator's Church.

Clerk: REV. D.W. DUTTON BA   High Kirk Manse, Leswalt High Road, Stranraer DG9 0AA   01776 703268

Bargrennan (H) linked with Newton Stewart: Penninghame St John's (H)
Neil G. Campbell BA BD   1988 1989   Newton Stewart DG8 6HH   01671 402259

Ervie Kirkcolm linked with Leswalt
Michael J. Sheppard BD   1997   Ervie Manse, Stranraer DG9 0QZ   01776 854225
[e-mail: michael@erviecos.freeserve.co.uk]

Glasserton and Isle of Whithorn linked with Whithorn: St Ninian's Priory
Alexander I. Currie BD CPS   1990   Whithorn, Newton Stewart DG8 8PY   01988 500267

Inch linked with Stranraer: St Andrew's (H)
John H. Burns BSc BD   1985 1988   Bay View Road, Stranraer DG9 8BE   01776 702383

Kirkcowan (H) linked with Wigtown (H)
Martin Thomson BSc DipEd BD   1988   Harbour Road, Wigtown, Newton Stewart DG8 9AL   01988 402242
[e-mail: martin thomson@compuserve.com]

Kirkinner linked with Sorbie (H)
Jeffrey M. Mead BD   1978 1986   Kirkinner, Newton Stewart DG8 9AL   01988 840643

Kirkmabreck linked with Monigaff (H)
Hugh D. Steele LTh DipMin   1994   Cree Bridge, Newton Stewart DG8 6NR   01671 403361

Kirkmaiden (H) linked with Stoneykirk
Ian McIlroy BSS BD   1996   Church Street, Sandhead, Stranraer DG9 9JJ   01776 830337
Mary Munro (Mrs) BA (Aux)   1993   High Barbeth, Leswalt DG9 0QS   01776 870250

Leswalt See Ervie Kirkcolm

Mochrum (H)
Roger A.F. Dean LTh   1983 1995   Port William, Newton Stewart DG8 9QP   01988 700257

Monigaff (H) See Kirkmabreck

New Luce (H) linked with Old Luce (H)
Thomas M. McWhirer MA MSc BD   1992 1997   Glenluce, Newton Stewart DG8 0PU   01581 300319

Newton Stewart: Penninghame St John's See Bargrennan
Old Luce See New Luce

Portpatrick linked with Stranraer: St Ninian's (H)
Vacant   London Road, Stranraer DG9 9AB   01776 702443

Sorbie See Kirkinner
Stoneykirk See Kirkmaiden

Stranraer: High Kirk (H)
David W. Dutton BA   1973 1986   Leswalt High Road, Stranraer DG9 0AA   01776 703268

Stranraer: Old (H)
Samuel McC. Harris BA BD   1974 1990   Linden, Leswalt High Road, Stranraer DG9 0AA   01776 706387

Stranraer St Andrew's See Inch
Stranraer St Ninian's See Portpatrick
Whithorn: St Ninian's Priory See Glasserton and Isle of Whithorn
Wigtown See Kirkcowan

Andrews, John I. MA BD	1943	1983	(Kirkmaiden)	Old Schoolhouse, Sandhead, Stranraer DG9 9JG	01776 830350
Cairns, Alexander B. MA	1957	1997	(Ervie Kirkcolm with Leswalt)	Beechwood. Main Street, Sandhead, Stranraer DG9	01776 830389
Cordiner, John	1950	1986	(Portpatrick)	Tara, Fellview Road, Stranraer DG9 8BK	01776 704720
Harkes, George	1962	1988	(Cumbermauld Old)	11 Main Street, Sorbie, Newton Stewart DG8 8EG	01988 850255
Jesson, W.J.M.	1971	1984	(Mochrum)	4 Mote Brae, Mochrum, Newton Stewart DG8 9LZ	01988 700257
McCreadie, David W.	1961	1995	(Kirkmabreck)	77 St John Street, Creetown, Newton Stewart DG8	01671 820390
McGill, Thomas W.	1972	1990	(Portpatrick with Stranraer St Ninian's)	Ravenstone Moor, Dramrae, Whithorn, Newton Stewart DG8	01988 00449
Ogilvy, Oliver M.	1959	1985	(Leswalt)	8 Dale Crescent, Stranraer DG9 OHG	01776 706285

(10) AYR

Meets in Ayr, in Alloway Church Hall, on the first Tuesday of every month from September to May, excluding January; and on the fourth Tuesday of June.

Clerk: REV. JAMES CRICHTON MA BD MTh   30 Garden Street, Dalrymple KA6 6DG   01292 560263 (Tel) / 01292 560574 (Fax)

Alloway (H) Neil A. McNaught BD MA	1987	1999	7 Doonholm Road, Alloway, Ayr KA7 4QQ	01292 441252
Annbank (H) Kenneth L. Johnston BA LTh	1969	1989	57 Annbank Road, Annbank, Ayr KA6 5AG	01292 520257
Arnsheen Barrhill linked with Colmonell John S. Lochrie BSc BD PhD	1967	1999	Colmonell, Girvan KA26 0SA	01465 881224
Auchinleck (H) Daniel M. Robertson MA	1960	1967	28 Mauchline Road, Auchinleck KA18 2BN	01290 421108
Ayr: Auld Kirk of Ayr (St John the Baptist) (H) David R. Gemmell MA BD	1991	1999	58 Monument Road, Ayr KA7 2UB	01292 262580 (Tel/Fax)
Ayr: Castlehill (H) Ian R. Stirling BSc BD	1990	1994	3 Hillfoot Road, Ayr KA7 3LF	01292 267332
Ayr: Newton on Ayr (H) G. Stewart Birse CA BD BSc	1980	1989	5 Montgomerie Terrace, Ayr KA7 1JL	01292 264251
Ayr: St Andrew's (H) Vacant			31 Bellevue Crescent, Ayr KA7 2DP	01292 262621
Ayr: St Columba (H) Fraser R. Aitken MA BD	1978	1991	2 Hazelwood Road, Ayr KA7 2PY	01292 283125
Ayr: St James' Gillian Weighton (Mrs) BD STM	1992		1 Prestwick Road, Ayr KA8 8LD	01292 262420
Ayr: St Leonard's (H) Robert Lynn MA BD	1984	1989	24 Longbank Drive, Ayr KA7 4SD	01292 442109

Charge / Minister	Year 1	Year 2	Address	Telephone
Ayr: St Quivox (H) David T. Ness LTh	1972	1988	11 Springfield Avenue, Prestwick KA9 2HA	01292 478306
Ayr: Wallacetown (H) A.M. McPhail BA	1968		87 Forehill Road, Ayr KA7 3JR	01292 269161
Ballantrae (H) Robert P. Bell BSc	1968	1998	Ballantrae, Girvan KA26 0NH	01465 831252
Barr linked with Dailly George C. Helon BA BD	1984		Dailly, Girvan KA26 9SD	01465 811238
Catrine linked with Sorn George A. Chalmers MA BD MLitt	1962	1994	Catrine, Mauchline KA5 6NA	01290 553057
Colmonell See Arnsheen Barrhill				
Coylton linked with Drongan: The Schaw Kirk Paul R. Russell MA BD	1984	1991	4 Hamilton Place, Coylton, Ayr KA6 6JQ	01292 570272
Craigie linked with Symington Margaret A. Whyte (Mrs) BA BD	1988		16 Kerrix Road, Symington, Kilmarnock KA1 5QD	01563 830205
Crosshill linked with Dalrymple James Crichton MA BD MTh	1969		30 Garden Street, Dalrymple KA6 6DG	01292 560263 (Tel) 01292 560574 (Fax)
Dailly See Barr				
Dalmellington Kenneth B. Yorke BD DipEd	1982	1999	4 Carsphairn Road, Dalmellington, Ayr KA6 7RE	01292 550353
Dalrymple See Crosshill **Drongan: The Schaw Kirk** See Coylton				
Dundonald (H) Robert Mayes BD	1982	1988	Dundonald, Kilmarnock KA2 9HG	01563 850243
Fisherton (H) linked with Maybole: West Thomas C. Bogle BD	1983	1996	Maybole, Ayrshire KA19 7EB	01655 883102
Girvan: North (Old and St Andrew's) (H) Douglas G. McNab BA BD	1999		38 The Avenue, Girvan KA26 9DS	01465 713203

Girvan: South Ian K. McLauchlan MA BD	1999	30 Henrietta Street, Girvan KA26 9AL	01465 713370
Kirkmichael linked with Straiton: St Cuthbert's W. Gerald Jones MA BD MTh	1984 1985	Kirkmichael, Maybole KA19 7PJ	01655 750286
Kirkoswald (H) James A. Guthrie	1969 1974	Kirkoswald, Maybole KA19 8JA	01655 760210
Lugar linked with Old Cumnock: Old (H) John W. Paterson BSc BD DipEd	1994	33 Barrhill Road, Cumnock KA18 1PJ	01290 420769
Mauchline (H) Alan B. Telfer BA BD	1983 1991	4 Westside Gardens, Mauchline KA5 5DJ	01290 550386
Maybole: Old David Whiteman BD	1998	64 Culzean Road, Maybole KA19 8AH	01655 889456
Maybole: West See Fisherton			
Monkton and Prestwick: North (H) Vacant		40 Monkton Road, Prestwick KA9 1AR	01292 477499
Muirkirk (H) William Hannah BD MCAM MIPR	1987	2 Smallburn Road, Muirkirk, Cumnock KA18 3QD	01290 661157 (Tel/Fax)
New Cumnock (H) Gordon Kennedy BSc BD	1993	New Cumnock, Cumnock KA18 4AG	01290 338296
Ochiltree linked with Stair Carolyn M. Baker (Mrs) BD	1997	10 Mauchline Road, Ochiltree, Cumnock KA18 2PZ	01290 700365
Old Cumnock: Crichton West linked with St Ninian's Vacant		46 Ayr Road KA18 1DW	01290 420119
Old Cumnock: Old See Lugar **Old Cumnock: St Ninian's** See Old Cumnock Crichton West			
Patna Waterside Vacant			

Prestwick: Kingcase (H)

T. David Watson BSc BD		1988 1997	15 Bellrock Avenue, Prestwick KA9 1SQ	01292 479571

Prestwick: St Nicholas' (H)

George R. Fiddes BD		1979 1985	3 Bellevue Road KA9 1NW	01292 477613

Prestwick: South (H)

Kenneth C. Elliott BD CertMin		1989	68 St Quivox Road KA9 1JF	01292 478788

Sorn See Catrine
Stair See Ochiltree
Straiton St Cuthbert's See Kirkmichael
Symington See Craigie

Tarbolton

Mary C. Shaw (Mrs) LTh		1997 1999	1 Kirkport, Tarbolton, Mauchline KA5 5QJ	01292 541236

Troon: Old (H)

Alastair H. Symington MA BD		1972 1998	85 Bentinck Drive, Troon KA10 6HZ	01292 313644

Troon: Portland (H)

Ronald M.H. Bcyd BD DipMin		1995 1999	89 South Beach, Troon KA10 6EQ	01292 313285

Troon: St Meddan's (H)

David L. Harper BSc BD		1972 1979	27 Bentinck Drive, Troon KA10 6HX	01292 311784

Name	Years	Position	Address	Phone
Andrew, R.J.M. MA	1955 1994	(Uddingston Old)	6A Ronaldshaw Park, Ayr KA7 2TS	01292 263430
Banks, John BD	1968 1988	Hospital Chaplain, Ailsa	16 Victoria Drive, Troon KA10 6JF	01292 317758
Bird, John W.	1965 1997	(Bathgate High)	14 Springfield Avenue, Prestwick KA9 2HA	01292 476037
Black, William BD AMIMechE	1968 1989	(Durness with Kinlochbervie)	27 Neilshill Park, Mossblown, Ayr KA6 5AU [e-mail: hitam@selamat27.freeserve.co.uk]	01292 521036
Blyth, James G.S. BSc BD	1963 1986	(Glenmuick)	40 Robsland Avenue, Ayr KA7 2RW	01292 261276
Campbell, Effie C. (Mrs) BD	1981 1991	(Old Cumnock Crichton West with St Ninian's)		
Dickie, Michael M. BSc	1955 1994	(Ayr Castlehill)	7 Landsowne Road, Ayr KA8 8LS	01292 264282
Garrity, T. Alan W. BSc BD MTh	1969 1999	Christ Church, Warwick, Bermuda	8 Noltmire Road, Ayr KA8 9ES	
Glencross, William M. LTh	1968 1999	(Bellshill: Macdonald Memorial)	PO Box PG88, Paget PG BX, Bermuda	
Grant, J. Gordon MA BD	1957 1997	(Edinburgh: Dean)	1 Lochry Place, Troon KA10 7HH	01292 317097
Hollins, Roger M. BSc DipEd FEIS	1957 1988	(Lecturer in Religious Education)	72 Arrol Drive, Ayr KA7 4AN	01292 262223
Kent, Arthur F.S.	1966 1999	(Monkton and Prestwick: North)	Smithy Cottage, Dunure, Ayr KA7 4LH	01386 500273
Macdonald, Ian U.	1960 1997	(Tarbolton)	17 St David's Drive, Evesham, Worcs WR11 6AS	01386 421562
			18 Belmont Road, Ayr KA7 2PF	01292 283085

McGinty, J. Walter BA PhD	1964 1998	(Alloway)	49 Finlas Avenue, Ayr KA7 4SN	01292 442837
McNidder, Roderick H. BD	1987 1997	Chaplain, South Ayrshire Hospitals Trust	10 Hollow Park, Alloway KA7 4SR	01292 442554
Morton, John MA	1950 1983	(Dalmellington Kirk of the Covenant)	17 Bunting Place, Kilmarnock KA1 3LE	01563 542732
Phillips, John S. MA	1939 1978	(Ayr Lochside)		
Saunders, Campbell M. MA BD	1952 1989	(Ayr St Leonard's)	42 Marle Park, Ayr KA7 4RN	01292 441673
Sutherland, Alexander S.	1952 1987	(Symington with Craigie)	Fintry Bay House, Millport KA28 0HA	01475 530403
Whitelaw, William D.	1984 1998	(Bothkennar and Carronshore)	10 Leslie Crescent, Ayr KA7 3BW	01292 267067
Wightman, J.P.E. BA	1938 1973	(Girvan St Andrew's)	25 Roodlands Road, Girvan KA26 9DE	01465 712104

AYR ADDRESSES

Ayr

Auld Kirk	Kirkport (116 High Street)
Castlehill	Castlehill Road x Hillfoot Road
Lochside	Lochside Road x Murray Street
Newton-on-Ayr	Main Street
St Columba	Park Circus
St James'	Midton Road x Carrick Park
	Prestwick Road x
	Falkland Park Road
St Leonard's	St Leonard's Road x
	Monument Road
Wallacetown	John Street x Church Street

Girvan

North	Montgomerie Street
South	Stair Park

Maybole

Old	Centre of Cassillis Road
West	Foot of Coral Glen

Prestwick

Kingcase	Waterloo Road
Monkton and	Monkton Road
Prestwick North	

St Nicholas	Main Street	01563 525311
South	Main Street	

Troon

Old	Ayr Street	
Portland	St Meddan's Street	01560 320484
St Meddan's	St Meddan's Street	01563 523552

(11) IRVINE AND KILMARNOCK

The Presbytery meets ordinarily at 6.30pm in the Hall of Howard St Andrew's Church, Kilmarnock, on the first Tuesday of each month from September to May; (except January when it meets on the second Tuesday for the celebration of Holy Communion and in conference or socially) and on the fourth Tuesday in June.

Clerk:	REV. COLIN G.F. BROCKIE BSc(Eng) BD	51 Portland Road Kilmarnock KA1 2EQ [e-mail: revcol@revcol.demon.co.uk]	01563 525311
Depute Clerk:	REV. ROBERT TRAVERS BA BD	46 West Main Street, Darvel KA17 4AQ	01560 320484
Treasurer:	JAMES McINTOSH BA CA	15 Dundonald Rd, Kilmarnock	01563 523552

Crosshouse

Rona M. Young (Mrs) BD DipEd	1991	27 Kilmarnock Road, Crosshouse KA2 0EZ	01563 521035

Darvel

Robert Travers BA BD	1993	46 West Main Street, Darvel KA17 4AQ [e-mail: robert@travers46.freeserve.co.uk]	01560 320484

Dreghorn and Springside
Gary E. Horsburgh BA   1976   96A Townfoot, Dreghorn KA11 4EZ   01294 217770

Dunlop
Maureen M. Duncan (Mrs) BD   1996   4 Dampark, Dunlop KA3 4BZ   01560 484083

Fenwick (H)
David R. Gemmell MA BD   1991   2 Kirkton Place, Fenwick KA3 6DW   01560 600217
                                                                                  [e-mail: drgemmell@aol.com]

Galston (H)
T.J. Loudon Blair MA BD   1965   Galston Ayrshire KA4 8DX   01563 820246
                                                                                  [e-mail: louden.blair@virgin.net]

John H.B. Taylor MA BD DipEd (Assoc)   1952   62 Woodlands Grove, Kilmarnock KA3 1TZ   01563 526698

Hurlford
James D. McCulloch BD MIOP   1996   12 Main Road, Crookedholm KA3 6JT   01563 535673

Irvine: Fullarton
Neil Urquhart BD DipMin   1989   48 Waterside, Irvine KA12 8QJ   01294 279909
                                                                                  neil.urquhart@btinternet.com]

Irvine: Girdle Toll
Vacant   2 Littlestane Rise, Irvine KA11 2BJ   01294 213565

Irvine: Mure (H)
Hugh M. Adamson BD   1976   West Road, Irvine KA12 8RE   01294 279916

Irvine: Old (H) (01294 273503)
Vacant   23 Kirk Vennel, Irvine, Ayrshire KA12 0DQ   01294 279265

Irvine: Relief Bourtreehill (H)
Robert A. Hamilton BA BD   1995   4 Kames Court, Irvine KA11 1RT   01294 216939
                                                                                  [e-mail: rabbie@thegirdle.freeserve.co.uk]

Irvine: St Andrew's (H) (01294 276051)
Vacant   206 Bank Street, Irvine KA12 0YB   01294 211403

Kilmarnock: Grange (H) (01563 534490)
Colin G.F. Brockie BSc(Eng) BD   1967   51 Portland Road, Kilmarnock KA1 2EQ   01563 525311
                                                                                  [e-mail: revcol@revcol.demon.co.uk]

Congregation / Minister			Address	Telephone
Kilmarnock: Henderson (H) (01563 541302) David W. Lacy BA BD	1976		52 London Road, Kilmarnock KA3 7AJ	01563 523113
Kilmarnock: Howard St Andrew's (H) Malcolm MacLeod BA BD	1979	1989	1 Evelyn Villas, Holehouse Road, Kilmarnock KA3 7AX [e-mail: calmacleod@aol.com]	01563 522278
Kilmarnock: Laigh (H) Vacant			1 Holmes Farm Road, Kilmarnock KA1 1TP	01563 525416
Kilmarnock: Old High Kirk (H) William M. Hall BD	1972	1979	107 Dundonald Road, Kilmarnock KA1 1UP	01563 525608
Kilmarnock: Riccarton Thomas W. Jarvie BD	1953	1968	2 Jasmine Road, Kilmarnock KA1 2HD	01563 525694
Kilmarnock: St Andrew's Glencairn R.A.K. Martin MA	1957	1970	19 Holehouse Rd. Kilmarnock KA3 7AU	01563 525023
Kilmarnock: St John's Onthank Susan M. Anderson (Mrs) Catherine A.M. Shaw MA (Aux)	1997 1998		84 Wardneuk Drive, Kilmarnock KA3 2EX 40 Merrygreen Place, Stewarton KA3 5EP	01563 521815 01560 483352
Kilmarnock: St Kentigern's S. Grant Barclay LLB BD	1995		89 Mure Avenue, Kilmarnock KA3 1TT [e-mail: grant.barclay@bigfoot.com]	01563 571280
Kilmarnock: St Marnock's (H) (01563 541337) James McNaughtan BD DipMin	1983	1989	35 South Gargieston Drive, Kilmarnock KA1 1TB [e-mail: jmcnaughton@mcmail.com]	01563 521665
Kilmarnock: St Ninian's Bellfield (T) (01563 524705) Vacant			186 Whatriggs Road, Kilmarnock KA1 3TJ	01563 525480
Kilmarnock: Shortlees (T) Rolf H. Billes BD	1996		14 McLelland Drive, Kilmarnock KA1 1SE [e-mail: rbilles@aol.com]	01563 529920
Kilmarnock: West High Robert S. Christie MA BD ThM	1964	1973	69 Dundonald Road, Kilmarnock KA1 1TJ	01563 525302
Kilmaurs: St Maur's Glencairn John A. Urquhart	1993		9 Standalane, Kilmaurs KA3 2NB	01563 538289

Newmilns: Loudoun (H)
Vacant   Newmilns, Ayrshire KA16 9HH   01560 320174

Stewarton: John Knox
Samuel Hosain BD MTh   1979   1993   27 Avenue St Stewarton KA3 5AP   01560 482418

Stewarton: St Columba's (H)
Elizabeth A. Waddell   1999   1 Kirk Glebe, Stewarton KA3 5BJ   01560 482453

Ayrshire Mission to the Deaf
S. Grant Barclay LLB BD (Chaplain)   1991   1998   89 Mure Avenue, Kilmarnock KA3 1TT   01563 571280
[e-mail: grant.barclay@bigfoot.com]

Name			Charge	Address	Phone
Boath, Gibson K. BA	1951	1989	(Kilmarnock Howard St Andrew's)	6 Woodlands Place, Kilmarnock KA3 1UA	01563 571170
Campbell, George H.	1957	1992	(Stewarton: John Knox)	20 Woodlands Grove, Kilmarnock KA3 1TZ	01563 536365
Crawford, Robert MA	1933	1972	(Annan Erskine)	11 Glencraig Terrace, Fenwick KA3 6DE	01560 600458
Downie, Andrew A. BD	1994	1999	(Prison Chaplain)	HMP Bowhouse, Mauchline Road, Kilmarnock	
Goudie, Stuart M. MA BD	1951	1988	(Perceton and Dreghorn)	6 Charles Drive, Troon KA10 7AG	01292 311610
Greig, James	1966	1999	(Irvine: Old)	127A Ayr Road, Prestwick KA9 1TW	
Hare, Malcolm M.W. BA BD	1956	1994	(Kilmarnock St Kintigern's)	21 Raith Road, Fenwick KA3 6DB	01560 600388
Hay, W.J.R. MA BD	1959	1995	(Buchanan with Drymen)	18 Jamieson Place, Stewarton KA3 3AY	01560 482799
Huggett, Judith A. (Miss) BA BD	1990	1998	Hospital Chaplain	4 Westmoor Crescent, Kilmarnock KA1 1TX	
Jamieson, Robert C. MA	1943	1980	(Galston Old)	20 Brewland Street, Galston KA4 8DR	01563 820304
Lane, Christina M. BD	1983	1999	(Irvine: Girdle Toll)	5 Carters Place, Irvine KA12 0BU	
MacDonald, James M.	1964	1987	(Kilmarnock St John's Onthank)	29 Carmel Place, Kilmaurs, Kilmarnock KA3 2QU	01563 525254
McGarva, Sarah (Miss) DCS			(Deaconess)	87 Hunter Drive, Irvine KA12 9BS	01294 271257
Patience, Donald MA	1954	1993	(Kilmaurs)	Kirkhill, 42 Fenwick Road, Kilmaurs	01563 544447
Roy, James BA	1967	1982	(Irvine Girdle Toll)	10A Graham Terrace, Stewarton KA3 5BB	01560 484602
				[e-mail: jroy@dougyr.globalnet.co.uk]	
Scott, Thomas T.	1968	1989	(Kilmarnock St Marnock's)	6 North Hamilton Place, Kilmarnock KA1 2QN	01563 531415
				[e-mail: 101725.216@compuserve.com]	
Urquhart, Barbara (Mrs) DCS			Deaconess, Part-time Hospital Chaplain and Presbytery S.S. Adviser	9 Standalane, Kilmaurs, Kilmarnock KA3 2NB	01563 538289

IRVINE and KILMARNOCK ADDRESSES

Irvine

Dreghorn and Springside	Townfoot x Station Brae
Fullarton	Marress Road x Church Street
Girdle Toll	Bryce Knox Court
Mure	West Road
Old Parish	Kirkgate
Relief	Crofthead, Bourtreehill
St Andrew's	Caldon Road x Oaklands Ave

Kilmarnock

Ayrshire Mission to the Deaf	
Grange	10 Clark Street
Henderson	Woodstock Street
Howard	London Road
Laigh	5 Portland Road
Old High	John Dickie Street
Riccarton	Church Street x Soulis Street
	Old Street
St Andrew's	St Andrew's Street
Glencairn	84 Wardneuk Street
St John's Onthank	St Marnock's Street
St Marnock's	Whatriggs Road
St Ninian's Bellfield	Central Avenue
Shortlees	Portland Street
West High	

(12) ARDROSSAN

Meets at Saltcoats: New Trinity, on the first Tuesday of February, March, April, May, September, October, November and December, and on the second Tuesday of January and June

Clerk: REV. DAVID BROSTER   BA DipTh CPS   Manse of St Columba's, Kilbirnie KA25 7JU   01505 683342 (Tel)
[e-mail: pres@davbros.demon.co.uk]   01505 684024 (Fax)
0836 380383 (Mbl)
07669 .036762 (24hr pager)

Ardrossan: Barony St John's (H) (01294 465009)
Colin Alexander Sutherland LTh   1995   1999   10 Seafield Drive, Ardrossan KA22 8NU   01294 463868

Ardrossan: Park (01294 463711)
William Johnston BD   1998   35 Ardneil Court, Ardrossan KA22 7NQ   01294 471808
Marion L.K. Howie (Mrs) MA ACRS (Aux)   1992   51 High Road, Stevenston KA20 3DY   01294 466571
[e-mail: marion.howie@ndirect.co.uk]

Beith: High (H) (01505 502686) linked with Beith: Trinity (H)
Andrew R. Black   1987 1998   2 Glebe Court, Beith KA15 1ET   01505 503858
Fiona C. Ross BD DipMin (Assoc)   1996   16 Spiers Avenue, Beith KA15 1JD   01505 502131

Beith: Trinity (H) See Beith: High

Brodick linked with Corrie
Ian MacLeod LTh BA MTh PhD   1969   1974   4 Manse Crescent, Brodick, Isle of Arran KA27 8AS   01770 302334

Corrie See Brodick

Cumbrae
Marjory H. Mackay BD DipEd CCE — 1998 — Millport, Isle of Cumbrae KA28 0ED — 01475 530416

Dalry: St Margaret's
A. Douglas Lamb MA — 1964 1973 — Dalry, Ayrshire KA24 4DA — 01294 832234

Dalry: Trinity (H)
David I.M. Grant MA BD — 1969 — Dalry, Ayrshire KA24 5DX — 01294 832363

Fairlie (H)
Robert J. Thorburn BD — 1978 1980 — 14 Fairlieburne Gardens, Fairlie, Largs KA29 0ER
[e-mail: rjthorburn@aol.com] — 01475 568342

Fergushill linked with Kilwinning Erskine
T. Malcolm F. Duff MA BD — 1985 1987 — 14 McLuckie Drive, Kilwinning KA13 6DL
[e-mail: malcduff@aol.com] — 01294 551565

Kilbirnie: Auld Kirk (H)
Ian W. Benzie BD — 1999 — 49 Holmhead, Kilbirnie KA25 6BS — 01505 682348

Kilbirnie: St Columba's (H) (01505 685239)
David Broster BA DipTh CPS — 1969 1983 — Kilbirnie, Ayrshire KA25 7JU
[e-mail: pres@davbros. demon.co.uk]
01505 683342 (Tel)
01505 684024 (Fax)
0836 380383 (Mbl)
07669 036762 (24 hr pager)

Kilmory linked with Lamlash
William B. Ross LTh CPS — 1988 1998 — Lamlash, Brodick, Isle of Arran KA27 8LE — 01770 600318

Kilwinning: Abbey (H)
William Buchan DipTheol BD — 1987 — 54 Dalry Road, Kilwinning KA13 7HE — 01294 552606

Kilwinning: Erskine (01294 552188) See Fergushill

Kilwinning: Mansfield Trinity (01294 550746)
Douglas S. Paterson — 1976 — 27 Treesbank, Kilwinning KA13 6LY — 01294 552453

Lamlash See Kilmory

Largs: Clark Memorial (H) (01475 675186)
Stephen J. Smith BSc BD — 1993 1998 — 31 Douglas Street, Largs KA30 8PT — 01475 672370

Charge / Minister	Dates	Address	Tel.
Largs: St Columba's (01475 686212) David M. McKay MA BD	1979	17 Beachway, Largs KA30 8QH	01475 673107
Largs: St John's (H) (01475 674468) Andrew F. McGurk BD	1983 1992	1 Newhaven Grove, Largs KA30 8NS	01475 676123
Lochranza and Pirnmill linked with Shiskine (H) Andrew Barrie BSc BD	1984	Shiskine, Brodick, Isle of Arran KA27 8EP [e-mail: asbarrie@compuserve.com]	01770 860380
Saltcoats: New Trinity (H) (01294 472001) Alexander D. McCallum BD	1987 1994	1 Montgomerie Crescent, Saltcoats KA21 5BR	01294 461143
Saltcoats: North (01294 464679) Calum D. Macdonald BD	1993	25 Longfield Avenue, Saltcoats KA21 6DR	01294 604923
Saltcoats: St Cuthbert's (H) Brian H. Oxburgh BSc BD	1980 1988	10 Kennedy Road, Saltcoats KA21 5SF	01294 602674
Shiskine See Lochranza and Pirnmill			
Stevenston: Ardeer G. Gray Fletcher BSc BD	1989	40 Shore Road, Stevenston KA20 3LA	01294 463814
Stevenston: High (H) Ann C. McCool (Mrs) BD DSD IPA ALCM	1989	Stevenston, Ayrshire KA20 3DL	01294 463356
Stevenston: Livingstone (H) John M.M. Lafferty	1999	32 High Road, Stevenston KA20 3DR	01294 464180
West Kilbride: Overton (H) Norman Cruickshank BA BD	1983	Goldenberry Avenue, West Kilbride KA23 9LJ	01294 823186
West Kilbride: St Andrew's (H) (01294 829902) D. Ross Mitchell BA BD	1972 1980	7 Overton Drive, West Kilbride KA23 9LQ	01294 823142
Whiting Bay and Kildonan Elizabeth R.L. Watson (Miss) BA BD	1981 1982	Whiting Bay, Isle of Arran KA27 8RE	01770 700289
Dailly, J.R. BD DipPS	1979 1979	St Andrew's, Queens Avenue, Aldershot GU11 2BY Staff Chaplain: Army	
Downie, Alexander S.	1975 1997	14 Korsankel Wynd, Saltcoats KA21 (Ardrossan: Park)	01294 464097

Ewing, James MA BD	1948 1987	(Ardrossan Barony)	8 Semple Crescent, Fairlie, Largs KA29 0EN	01475 568115
Fisher, Kenneth H.	1969 1994	(Stronsay with Eday)	33 Halfway Street, West Kilbride KA23 9EQ	01294 829973
Harbison, David J.H.	1958 1998	(Beith: High with Beith: Trinity)	42 Mill Park, Dalry KA24 1BB	01294 834092
Kirkwood, Hugh BA BD	1942 1981	(Saltcoats Erskine)	2 Alton Way, West Kilbride KA23 9JJ	01294 823932
McIlroy, Alexander M. LTh	1972 1987	(Darvel Irvinebank and Easton Memorial)	25 Hillcrest Drive, Stevenston KA20 3AP	01294 601609
McKay, Johnston R. MA BA	1969 1987	Religious Broadcasting (BBC)	41 Stakehill, Largs KA30 9PH	01475 672960
MacKenzie, Andrew H.	1963 1969	(Acharacle with Ardnamurchan)	Avonpark Nursing Home, Strathaven ML10 6BZ	
MacKinnon, John M. MA	1930 1973	(Dollar West)	142 Glencairn Street, Stevenston KA20 3BU	01294 461455
Maclagan, David W. MA ThD	1965 1991	(Largs: St John's)	Flat C, 1 Greenock Road, Largs KA30 8PQ	01475 673258
Reid, Agnes A. (Miss)	1985 1994	(Auchindoir and Kildrummy)	91 New Street, Dalry KA24 5BY	01294 835362
Roy, Iain M. MA BD	1960 1997	(Stevenston: Livingstone)	2 The Fieldings, Dunlop, Kilmarnock KA3 4AU	01560 483072
Taylor, Andrew S. BTh FPhS	1959 1992	(Greenock Union)	9 Raillies Avenue, Largs KA30 8QY	01475 674709
Thomson, Margaret (Mrs)	1988 1993	(Saltcoats: Erskine)	72 Knockrivoch Place, Ardrossan KA22 7PZ	01294 468685
Walker, David S. MA	1939 1978	(Markerstoun with Smailholm with Stichill, Hume and Nenthorn)	6 Stairlie Crescent, West Kilbride KA23 9BT	01294 823061
Weir, D. Gordon	1949 1992	(Saltcoats Landsborough and Trinity)	Flat 4, Lauriston Court, 2 South Beach Road, Ardrossan KA22 8AU	01294 462969

(13) LANARK

Meets at Lanark on the first Tuesday of February, March, April, May, September, October, November and December; and on the third Tuesday of June

Clerk: REV. IAIN D. CUNNINGHAM MA BD — 9 Station Road, Carluke ML8 5AA — 01555 771262 (Tel/Fax)
[e-mail: IainDC@aol.com]
[http://www.biggar.net.co.uk/lanark]

Biggar (H)
Gavin J. Elliot MA BD — 1976 1995 — 61 High Street, Biggar ML12 6DA — 01899 220227 (Tel/Fax)
[e-mail: 100541.1325@compuserve.co]

Black Mount
Vacant — The Manse, Dunsyre, Carnwath ML11 8NQ — 01899 810321

Cairngryffe linked with Symington
John Brown MA BD — 1995 — 16 Abington Road, Symington, Biggar ML12 6JX — 01899 308838 (Tel/Fax)

Carluke: Kirkton (H)
Iain D. Cunningham MA BD — 1979 1987 — 9 Station Road, Carluke ML8 5AA — 01555 771262 (Tel/Fax)
[e-mail: IainDC@aol.com]

Carluke: St Andrew's (H)			
Helen E. Jamieson (Mrs) BD DipED	1989	120 Clyde Street, Carluke ML8 5BG	01555 771218
Carluke: St John's (H)			
Michael W. Frew BSc BD	1978	1991	18 Old Bridgend, Carluke ML8 4HN	01555 772259
		[e-mail: mwfrew@aol.com]	
Carnwath (H)			
Beverly G.D.D. Gauld MA BD	1972	1978	The Manse, Carnwath, Lanark ML11 8JY	01555 840259
(Auchengray Tarbrax and Woolfords)			
Carstairs linked with Carstairs Junction			
J. Melvyn Coogan LTh	1992	1996	80 Lanark Road, Carstairs ML11 8QH	01555 870250
Carstairs Junction See Carstairs			
Coalburn linked with Lesmahagow: Old			
Sheila M. Mitchell (Miss) BD MTh	1995	Calsay Cottage, 103 New Trows Road, Lesmahagow ML11 0ER	01555 892425
Crossford linked with Kirkfieldbank			
Steven Reid BAcc CA BD	1989	1997	The Manse, Crossford,Carluke ML8 5RE	01555 860415
Culter linked with Libberton and Quothquan			
Stephen A. Pacitti MA	1963	1997	6 Cardon Drive, Biggar ML12 6EZ	01899 220625
Douglas: St Bride's linked with Douglas Water and Rigside			
Lawrie I. Lennox MA BD	1991	1991	The Manse, Douglas, Lanark ML11 0RB	01555 851213
Forth: St Paul's (H)			
James Bain BD DipMin	1996	22 Lea-Rig, Forth, Lanark ML11 8EA	01555 811748
Glencaple linked with Lowther			
Andrew Munro MA BD PhD	1972	1995	66 Carlisle Road, Crawford, Biggar ML12 6TW	01864 502625
Kirkfieldbank See Crossford			
Kirkmuirhill (H)			
David A. Young	1972	1974	2 Lanark Road, Kirkmuirhill, Lanark ML11 9RB	01555 892409 (Tel/Fax)
		[e-mail: DavidKCS @ aol.com]	
Lanark: Greyfriars			
Catherine E.E. Collins (Mrs) MA BD	1993	2 Friarsdene, Lanark ML11 9EJ	01555 663363
David A. Collins BSc BD	1993	[e-mail: greyfriars@mcmail.com]	

Lanark: St Nicholas'
John M.A. Thomson BD ThM   1978 1988   32 Braxfield Road, Lanark ML11 9BS   01555 662600

Law
William A.F. Izett   1968   53 Lawhill Road, Law, Carluke ML8 5EZ   01698 373180

Lesmahagow: Abbeygreen
David S. Carmichael   1982   Abbeygreen Manse, Lesmahagow, Lanark ML11 0DB   01555 893384

Lesmahagow: Old (H) See Coalburn
Libberton and Quothquan See Culter
Lowther See Glencaple
Symington See Cairngryffe

Name				Charge	Address	Tel
Craig, William BA LTh	1974	1997		(Cambusbarron: The Bruce Memorial)	31 Heathfield Drive, Blackwood, Lanark ML11 9SR	01555 893710
Jones, Philip H.	1968	1987		(Bishopbriggs Kenmure)	81 Vere Road, Kirkmuirhill, Lanark ML11 9RP	01555 894326
Kennedy, David A LTCL	1959	1983		(Lanark Cairns)	63 Hall Road, Nemphlar, Lanark ML11	01555 664484
Lambie, Andrew E. BD	1957	1991		(Carmichael, Covington, Thankerton, Pettinain)	1 Mercat Loan, Biggar ML12 6DG	01899 221352
McCormick, W. Cadzow MA BD	1943	1983		(Glasgow Maryhill Old)	82 Main Street, Symington, Biggar ML12 6LJ	01899 308221
McLauchlan, Laurence S. MA	1940	1974		(Haywood, Wilsontown and Braehead)	57 Sandend Road, Glasgow G53 7DH	0141 882 4046
McMahon, Robert J. BD	1959	1997		(Crossford with Kirkfieldbank)	7 Ridgepark Drive, Lanark ML11 9PG	01555 663844
Seath, Thomas J.G.	1980	1992		(Motherwell: Manse Road)	1 Allan Avenue, Carluke ML8 5UA	01555 771644
Thomson, John S. MA	1934	1972		(Covington and Thankerton with Libberton and Quothquan)	20 Whitehouse Loan, Edinburgh EH9 2EZ	0131 447 9455

(14) PAISLEY

Meets at Paisley, in St James' Church Hall, on the second Tuesday of each month, except January, July and August.

Clerk: REV. DAVID KAY BA BD MTh   6 Southfield Avenue, Paisley PA2 8BY   0141 884 3600 (Tel/Fax)

Barrhead: Arthurlie (H) (0141 881 8442)
James S.A. Cowan BD   1986 1998   10 Arthurlie Avenue, Barrhead G78 2BU   0141 881 3457
Senga Nicol (Miss) DCS   Flat 2/1, 160 Tollcross Road, Glasgow G31 4UX   0141 554 3028

Barrhead: Bourock (H) (0141 881 9813)
Maureen Leitch (Mrs) BA BD — 1995 — 14 Maxton Avenue, Barrhead G78 1DY — 0141 881 1462

Barrhead: South and Levern (H) (0141 881 7825)
R.M. Hetherington MA BD — 1966 — 3 Colinbar Circle, Barrhead G78 2BE — 0141 571 4059
Senga Nicol (Miss) DCS — 1977 — Flat 2/1, 160 Tollcross Road, Glasgow G31 4UX — 0141 554 3028

Bishopton (H)
Vacant — Newton Road, Bishopton PA7 5JP — 01505 862161

Bridge of Weir: Freeland (H) (01505 612610)
Kenneth N. Gray BA BD — 1988 — 15 Lawmarnock Crescent, Bridge of Weir PA11 3LJ — 01505 690919

Bridge of Weir: St Machar's Ranfurly (01505 614364)
Suzanne Dunleavy (Miss) BD DipEd — 1990 1992 — 9 Glen Brae PA11 3BH — 01505 612975

Caldwell
Vacant — Uplawmoor, Glasgow G78 4AL — 01505 850215

Elderslie Kirk (H) (01505 323348)
David N. McLachlan BD — 1985 — 282 Main Road, Elderslie PA5 9EF — 01505 321767

Houston and Killellan (H)
Georgina M. Baxendale (Mrs) BD — 1981 — Houston PA6 7EL — 01505 612569

Howwood
Benjamin J.A. Abelado BTh DipTh PTh — 1991 — The Manse, Beith Road, Howwood PA9 1AS — 01505 703678

Inchinnan (H) (0141 812 1263)
Marilyn MacLaine (Mrs) LTh — 1995 — Inchinnan PA4 9PH — 0141 812 1688

Johnstone: High (H) (01505 336303)
Randolph Scott MA BD — 1991 — 76 North Road, Johnstone PA5 8NF — 01505 320006

Johnstone: St Andrew's Trinity
J.C. MacColl BSc BD — 1966 — The Grange, Park Road, Johnstone PA5 8LS — 01505 320142

Johnstone: St Paul's (H) (01505 321632)
James A.S. Boag BD — 1992 — 61 Auchenlodement Road, Elderslie PA5 9PA — 01505 343947
Linda Black (Miss) BSc DCS — 127B Spateston Road, Johnstone PA5 0SY — 01505 345735

Kilbarchan: East
Alister W. Bull BD DipMin — 1994 — Church Street, Kilbarchan PA10 2JQ — 01505 702621

Kilbarchan: West
Arthur Sherratt BD — 1994 — Kilbarchan PA10 2JR — 01505 702669

Linwood (H) (01505 328802)
T. Edward Marshall BD — 1987 — Linwood PA3 3DL — 01505 325131
Margaret McBain (Miss) DCS — 33 Quarry Road, Paisley PA2 7RD — 0141 884 2920

Lochwinnoch (T)
Robin N. Allison BD DipMin — 1994 — 1999 — Riverside, Burnfoot Road, Lochwinnoch PA12 4AN — 01505 843484

Neilston (0141 881 9445)
Alexander Macdonald MA BD — 1966 1984 — Neilston, Glasgow G78 3NP — 014 881 1958

New Erskine (0141 812 4620)
Ian W. Bell LTh — 1990 — 7 Leven Place, Linburn, Erskine PA8 6AS — 0141 812 2439
Morag Erskine (Miss) DCS — 1998 — 111 Main Drive, Erskine PA8 7JJ — 0141 812 6096

Paisley: Abbey (H) (Tel: 0141 889 7645   Fax: 0141 887 3929)
Alan D. Birss MA BD — 1979 1988 — 15 Main Road, Paisley PA2 6AJ — 0141 889 3587

Paisley: Castlehead (T)
Esther J. Ninian MA BD — 1993 1998 — 28 Fulbar Crescent, Paisley PA2 9AS — 01505 812304

Paisley: Glenburn (0141 884 2602)
George C. MacKay BD CertMin — 1994 — 10 Hawick Avenue, Paisley PA2 9LD — 0141 884 4903
Greta Gray (Miss) DCS — 11 Skye Crescent, Paisley PA2 8EN — 0141 884 6178

Paisley: Laigh Kirk (H) (0141 889 7700)
Thomas M. Cart MA BD — 1964 1972 — 18 Oldhall Road, Paisley PA1 3HL — 0141 882 2277

Paisley: Lylesland (H) (0141 561 7139)
Andrew W. Bradley BD — 1975 1998 — 36 Potterhill Avenue, Paisley PA2 8BA — 0141 884 2882

Paisley: Martyrs (0141 889 6603)
Alison Davidge (Mrs) MA BD — 1991 1997 — 12 Low Road, Paisley PA2 6AG — 0141 889 2182

Paisley: Oakshaw Trinity (H) (Tel: 0141 887 4647   Fax: 0141 848 5139   e-mail: iancurrie@hawkhead.freeserve.co.uk)
Ian S. Currie MBE BD — 1975 1980 — 9 Hawkhead Road, Paisley PA1 3ND — 0141 887 0884
Christopher L. Levison MA BD — 1972 1983 — 178 Glasgow Road, Paisley PA1 3LT — 0141 889 3316

Paisley: St Columba Foxbar (01505 812377)
Anthony J.R. Fowler BSc BD — 1982 1985 — 13 Corsebar Drive, Paisley PA2 9QD — 0141 889 9988
Mary Johnston (Miss) DCS — 19 Lounsdale Drive, Paisley PA2 9ED — 0141 849 1615

Paisley: St James' (0141 889 2422)

| Eleanor J. McMahon (Miss) BEd BD | 1994 | 38 Woodland Avenue, Paisley PA2 8BH [e-mail: eleanormcmahon@classic.msa.com] | 0141 884 3246 |

Paisley: St Luke's (H)

| D. Ritchie M. Gillon BD DipMin | 1994 | 31 Southfield Avenue, Paisley PA2 8BX [e-mail: ritchie@aol.com] | 0141 884 6215 |

Paisley: St Mark's Oldhall (H) (0141 882 2755)

| Alistair H. Morrison BTh DipYCS | 1985 1989 | 36 Newtyle Road, Paisley PA1 3JX | 0141 889 4279 |

Paisley: St Ninian's Ferguslie (E) (0141 887 9436)

| Archibald Speirs BD | 1995 | 10 Stanely Drive, Paisley PA2 6HE [e-mail: 100412.124@compuserve.com] | 0141 884 3875 |

Paisley: Sandyford (Thread Street) (0141 889 5078)

| David Kay BA BD MTh | 1974 | 6 Southfield Avenue, Paisley PA2 8BY | 0141 884 3600 |

Paisley: Sherwood Greenlaw (H (0141 889 7060))

| Alasdair F. Cameron BD CA | 1986 | 5 Greenlaw Drive, Paisley PA1 3RX | 0141 889 3057 |
| May Bell (Mrs) (Assistant) | 1998 | 7 Leven Place, Linburn, ERskine PA8 6AS | 0141 818 6096 |

Paisley: Wallneuk North (Tel: 0141 889 9265   Fax: 0141 887 6670))

| Thomas Macintyre MA BD | 1972 1988 | 27 Mansionhouse Road, Paisley PA1 3RG | 0141 581 1505 |
| John Cathcart DCS | 1989 1996 | Flat 2/1, 39 Broomlands Street, Paisley PA1 2NQ | 0141 848 5163 |

Renfrew: North (0141 885 2154)

| E. Lorna Hood (Mrs) MA BD | 1979 | 1 Alexandra Drive, Renfrew PA4 8UB | 0141 886 2074 |

Renfrew: Old (Tel/Fax: 0141 886 6913)

| Alexander C. Wark MA BD STM | 1982 | 31 Gibson Road, Renfrew PA4 0RH | 0141 886 2005 |

Renfrew: Trinity (H) (0141 885 2129)

| Stuart C. Steell BD | 1992 | 25 Paisley Road, Renfrew PA4 8JH | 0141 886 2131 |

Alexander, Douglas N. MA BD	1961 1999	(Bishopton)	West Morningside, Main Road, Langbank PA4 6XP	0141 840 2479
Cameron, Margaret (Miss) DCS	1961 1999	(Deaconess)	2 Rowans Gate, Paisley PA2 6RD	01334 474708
Cubie, John P. MA BD	1948 1991	(Caldwell)	36 Winram PLace, St Andrews KY16 8XH	01578 740263
Kerr, Andrew MA BLitt		(Kilbarchan West)	Meikle Harelaw, Westruther, Berwickshire TD10 6XT	0141 889 7497
Low, Nan (Mrs) DCS		(Chaplain's Assistant: RAF)	46 Benmore Drive, Paisley PA2 7NH	
Lowe, Edwin MA BD	1950 1988	(Caldwell)	45 Duncarnock Crescent, Neilston, Glasgow G78 3HH	0141 580 5726

McLachlan, Duncan MA BD ThM	1955 1992	(Paisley: Sherwood)	27 Penilee Road, Paisley PA1 3EU	0141 882 6353
Marr, E.R. MA	1933 1977	(Buittle)	Firwood, Uplawmoor, Glasgow G78	01505 850294
Mathers, J. Allan C.	1950 1989	(Inchinnan)	19 Braemar Road, Inchinnan	0141 812 3210
Moffet, James R. BA	1942 1979	(Paisley: St Matthew's)	21 Paton's Lane, Montrose DD10 8JA	01674 677289
O'Leary, Thomas BD	1983 1998	(Lochwinnoch)	1 Carters Place, Irvine KA12 0BU	
Palmer, S.W. BD	1980 1991	(Kilbarchan: East)	4 Bream Place, Houston PA6 7ZJ	01505 615280
Prentice, George BA BTh	1964 1997	(Paisley: Martyrs)	46 Victoria Gardens, Corsebar Road, Paisley PA2 9AQ	0141 842 1585
Rule, James A.	1952 1991	(Renfrew: Moorpark)	6 St Andrew's Road, Renfrew PA4 0SN	0141 886 2896
Steele, Jean (Miss) DCS		(Deaconess)	93 George Street, Paisley PA1 2JX	0141 889 9512

PAISLEY ADDRESSES

Abbey	Town Centre	Oakshaw: Trinity	Churchill
Castlehead	Canal Street	St Columba Foxbar	Amochrie Road, Foxbar
Glenburn	Nethercraigs Drive off Glenburn Road	St James'	Underwood Road
Laigh	Causeyside Street	St Luke's	Neilston Road
Lylesland	Rowan Street off Neilston Road	St Mark's Oldhall	Glasgow Road, Ralston
Martyrs'	Broomlands	St Ninian's Ferguslie	Blackstoun Road
		Sandyford (Thread St)	Gallowhill
		Sherwood Greenlaw	Glasgow Road
		Wallneuk North	off Renfrew Rd

(15) GREENOCK

Meets at Greenock, in Ardgowan Parish Church Hall, on the second Tuesday of December, February and May, on the fourth Tuesday of October and March, on the third Tuesday of June, and in the Moderator's Church on the second Tuesday of September.

Clerk: REV. DAVID MILL KSJ MA BD   105 Newark Street, Greenock PA16 7TW   01475 639602
[e-mail: Greenock.Presbytery@dial.pipex.com]

Gourock: Old Gourock and Ashton (H)
Frank J. Gardner MA   1966   1979   90 Albert Road, Gourock PA19 1NN   01475 631516

Gourock: St John's (H)
Vacant   6 Barrhill Road, Gourock PA19 1JX   01475 632143

Greenock: Ardgowan
Vacant   72 Forsyth Street, Greenock PA16 8SX   01475 790849

Greenock: Cartsdyke
Peter Webster BD   1977   1981   84 Forsyth Street, Greenock PA16 8QY   01475 721439

Congregation / Minister			Address	Telephone
Greenock: Finnart St Paul's (H) David Mill KSJ MA BD	1978	1979	105 Newark Street, Greenock PA16 7TW	01475 639602
Greenock: Mount Kirk James H. Simpson BD LLB	1964	1965	76 Finnart Street, Greenock PA16 8HJ	01475 722338
Greenock: Old West Kirk C. Ian W. Johnson MA BD Eileen Manson (Mrs) DipCE (Aux)	1997 1994		39 Fox Street, Greenock PA16 8PD 1 Cambridge Avenue, Gourock PA19 1XT	01475 888277 01475 632401
Greenock: St George's North W. Douglas Hamilton BD	1975	1986	67 Forsyth Street, Greenock PA16 8SX	01475 724003
Greenock: St Luke's (H) William C. Hewitt BD DipPS	1977	1994	50 Ardgowan Street, Greenock PA16 8EP	01475 721048
Greenock: St Margaret's (01475 781953) Isobel J.M. Kelly (Miss) MA BD DipEdt	1974	1998	105 Finnart Street, Greenock PA16 8HN	01475 786590
Greenock: St Ninian's Allan G. McIntyre BD Joyce Nicol (Mrs) DCS	1985		5 Auchmead Road, Greenock PA16 OPY 93 Brisbane Street, Greenock PA16 8NY	01475 631878 01475 723235
Greenock: Wellpark Mid Kirk Vacant			101 Brisbane Street, Greenock PA16 8PA	01475 721741
Inverkip (H) Janet E. Gillies (Mrs) BD	1998		Inverkip, Greenock PA16 OAT	01475 521207
Kilmacolm: Old (H) Gordon D. Irving BD	1994	1998	Glencairn Road, Kilmacolm, Renfrewshire PA13 4NJ	0150587 3174
Kilmacolm: St Columba (H) R. Douglas Cranston MA BD	1986	1992	6 Churchill Road, Kilmacolm PA13 4LH	0150587 3271
Langbank (T) Anna S. Rodwell (Mrs) BD DipMin	1998		Langbank, Port Glasgow PA14 6XB	01475 540252
Port Glasgow: Hamilton Bardrainney David J McAdam BSc BD	1990		80 Bardrainney Avenue, Port Glasgow PA14 6HD	01475 706551
Port Glasgow: St Andrew's (H) Andrew T. MacLean BA BD	1980	1993	Barr's Brae, Port Glasgow PA14 5QA	01475 741486

Port Glasgow: St Martin's
John G. Miller BEd BD LTh   1983   1998   Clunebraehead, Clune Brae, Port Glasgow PA14 5SL   01475 704115

Skelmorlie and Wemyss Bay
William R. Armstrong BD   1979   8 Eglinton Gardens, Skelmorlie PA17 5AR   01475 520703

Bruce, A. William MA	1942	1981	(Fortingall and Glenlyon)	75 Union Street, Greenock PA16 8BG	01475 787534
Chestnut, Alexander MBE BA	1948	1987	(Greenock St Mark's Greenbank)	5 Douglas Street, Largs KA30 8PS	01475 674168
Copland, Agnes M. (Mrs) MBE DCS			(Deaconess)	3 Craigmuschat Road, Gourock PA19 1SE	01475 631870
Crumlish, Elizabeth A. (Mrs) BD	1995	1996	Hospital Chaplain	110 Eldon Street, Greenock PA16 7RL	01475 727750
McCully, M. Isabel (Miss) DCS			(Deacon)	10 Broadstone Avenue, Port Glasgow PA14 5BB	01475 742240
MacQuien, Duncan DCS			(Deacon)	2 Manor Crescent, Gourock PA19 1UY	01475 633407
Marshall, Fred J. BA	1946	1992	(Bermuda)	Flat 4, Varrich House, 7 Church Hill, Edinburgh EH10 4BG	0131 446 0205
Montgomery, Robert A. MA	1955	1992	(Quarrier's Village: Mount Zion)	11 Myreton Avenue, Kilmacolm PA13 4LJ	01505 872028
Porteous, Alexander MA BD	1965	1987	(Greenock Mid Kirk)	Strathmore, Golf Road, Millport KA28 0HB	01475 530460
Pyper, J. Stewart BA	1951	1986	(Greenock St George's North)	39 Brisbane Street, Greenock PA16 8NR	01475 785959
Scott, Ernest M. MA	1959	1992	(Port Glasgow St Andrew's)	17 Brueacre Road, Wemyss Bay PA18 6ER	01475 522267
Stevenson, Alex	1951	1976	(Greenock St Andrew's)	34E St John's Road, Gourock PA19 1PQ	01475 631834
Stone, W. Vernon MA BD	1949	1985	(Langbank)	Santis, Finlaystone Road, Kilmacolm PA13 4RE	01505 872644
Swan, Andrew MA	1941	1983	(Greenock: St Margaret's)	11 The Terrace, Ardbeg, Rothesay, Isle of Bute PA20 0NE	01700 502138
Whyte, John H. MA	1946	1986	(Gourock: Ashton)	6 Castle Levan Manor, Cloch Road, Gourock PA19 1AY	01475 636788

GREENOCK ADDRESSES

Gourock
Old Gourock and Ashton   41 Royal Street
St John's   Bath Street x St John's Road

Greenock
Ardgowan   31 Union Street
Cartsdyke   14 Crescent Street
Finnart St Paul's   Newark Street x Bentinck Street
Mount Kirk   Dempster Street at Murdieston Park

Old West Kirk   Esplanade x Campbell Street
St George's North   George Square
St Margaret's   Finch Road x Kestrel Crescent
St Ninian's   Warwick Road, Larkfield
St Luke's   9 Nelson Street
Wellpark Mid Kirk   Cathcart Square

Port Glasgow
Hamilton-Bardrainney   Bardrainney Avenue x Auchenbothie Road
St Andrew's   Princes Street
St Martin's   Mansion Avenue

158   Presbytery of GLASGOW (16)

(16) GLASGOW

Meets at New Govan Church, Govan Cross, Glasgow, on the second Tuesday of each month, except June when the meeting takes place on the fourth Tuesday, and January, July and August when there is no meeting

Clerk: REV. ALEXANDER CUNNINGHAM MA BD
Hon. Treasurer: T.G. FIELDING Esq
260 Bath Street, Glasgow G2 4JP
[e-mail: cofs.glasgow.presbytery@dial.pipex.com]
0141 332 6606 (Tel/Fax)

No	Charge	Year	Year	Address	Phone
1	**Banton linked with Twechar** Jean R.M. Blackley (Mrs) BD	1989		Manse of Banton, Kilsyth G65 0QL	01236 826129
2	**Bishopbriggs: Kenmure** Iain A. Laing MA BD	1971	1992	5 Marchfield, Bishopbriggs, Glasgow G64 3PP	0141 772 1468
3	**Bishopbriggs: Springfield** William Ewart BSc BD	1972	1978	39 Springfield Road, Bishopbriggs Glasgow G64 1PL	0141 772 1540
4	**Blairbeth Rodger Memorial (T)** Brian S. Sheret MA BD DPhil	1982	1990	4 Milrig Road, Rutherglen, Glasgow G73 2NH	0141 647 6762
5	**Broom (0141 639 3528)** James Whyte BD	1981	1987	3 Laigh Road, Newton Mearns G77 5EX	0141 639 2916 / 0141 639 3528 (Fax)
6	**Burnside (0141 634 4130)** David J.C. Easton MA BD	1965	1977	59 Blairbeth Road, Burnside, Glasgow G73 4JD	0141 634 1233 (Tel) / 0141 634 7383 (Fax)
7	**Busby (0141 644 2073)** Jeremy Eve BSc BD	1998		17A Carmunnock Road, Busby G76 8SZ	0141 644 3670
8	**Cadder (0141 772 7436)** Vacant			6 Balmuildy Road, Bishopbriggs Glasgow G64 3BS	0141 772 1363
9	**Cambuslang; Flemington Hallside** R. David Currie BSc BD	1984		103 Overton Road, Cambuslang, Glasgow G72 7XA	0141 641 2097
10	**Cambuslang; Old** Alan H. Ward MA BD	1978	1985	74 Stewarton Drive, Cambuslang, Glasgow G72 8DG	0141 641 3261

11 Cambuslang: St Andrew's
John Stevenson LTh
1998
37 Brownside Road, Cambuslang, Glasgow G72 8NH
0141 641 3847 (Tel)
0141 641 0773 (Fax)

12 Cambuslang: Trinity St Paul's
David Stewart MA DipEd BD MTh
1977
1989
4 Glasgow Road, Cambuslang, Glasgow G72 7BW
[e-mail: revdavid@compuserve.com]
0141 641 3414 (Tel)
0141 646 1260 (Fax)

13 Campsie (01360 310939)
David J. Torrance BD DipMin
1993
19 Redhills View, Lennoxtown Glasgow G65 7BL
01360 312527

14 Chryston (H)
Martin A.W. Allen MA BD ThM
John Urquhart (Assoc)
1977
1998
Main Street, Chryston Glasgow G69 9LA
27 Laverock Terrace, Chryston, Glasgow G69 0AZ
0141 779 1436
01236 872943

15 Eaglesham Old and Carswell (01355 302047)
W. Douglas Lindsay BD CPS
1978
East Kilbride Road, Eaglesham Glasgow G76 ONS
01355 303495

16 Fernhill and Cathkin
Douglas W. Wallace MA BD
1981
1990
82 Blairbeth Road, Rutherglen, Glasgow G73 4JA
0141 634 1508

17 Gartcosh (H) (01236 873770) linked with Glenboig (01236 875625)
Alexander M. Fraser BD DipMin
1985
66 Coatbridge Road, Glenboig ML5 2PU
01236 872274

18 Giffnock: Orchardhill (0141 638 3604)
John M. Spiers LTh MTh
1972
1977
23 Huntly Avenue, Giffnock G46 6LW
0141 571 7675 (Tel/Fax)

19 Giffnock: South (0141 638 2599)
Edward V. Simpson BSc BD
1972
1983
5 Langtree Avenue, Whitecraigs, Glasgow G46 7LN
0141 638 8767 (Tel)
0141 620 0605 (Fax)

20 Giffnock: The Park
Michael Gibson BD STM
1974
41 Rouken Glen Road, Thornliebank Glasgow G46 7JD
0141 638 3023

21 Glenboig See Gartcosh

22 Greenbank (H)
Alistair N. Shaw MA BD

Fiona Gardner BD (Assist)
1982
1999

1997
Greenbank Manse, Clarkston, Glasgow G76 7DJ
[e-mail: alistairn@shaw98.freeserve.co.uk]
120 Craighlaw Avenue, Waterfoot, Glasgow G76 0HA
0141 644 1395 (Tel)
0141 644 4804 (Fax)
0141 644 5939

23 Kilsyth: Anderson
Charles M. MacKinnon BD
1989
1999
Anderson Manse, Kilsyth, Glasgow G65 0HR
01236 822345

No.	Charge / Minister	Ord.	Ind.	Address	Telephone
24	**Kilsyth: Burns and Old** T.A. McLachlan BSc	1972	1983	The Grange, Glasgow Road, Kilsyth G65 9AE	01236 823116
25	**Kirkintilloch: Hillhead** George A.R. Forbes BD	1971	1977	81 Hillhead Road, Kirkintilloch G66 2HY	0141 776 1198
26	**Kirkintilloch: St Columba's (H)** David M. White BA BD	1988	1992	14 Crossdykes, Kirkintilloch G66 3EU	0141 578 4357
27	**Kirkintilloch: St David's Memorial Park (H)** John Hay Paterson BD	1977	1989	2 Roman Road, Kirkintilloch G66 1EA	0141 776 1434
28	**Kirkintilloch: St Mary's** Frank Haughton MA BD	1942	1947	The Manse, Union Road, Kirkintilloch G66 1DH	0141 776 1252
29	**Lenzie: Old (H)** Vacant			41 Kirkintilloch Road, Lenzie, Glasgow G66 4LB	0141 776 2184
30	**Lenzie: Union (H)** James B. Ferguson LTh	1972	1984	1 Larch Avenue, Lenzie, Glasgow G66 4HX	0141 776 3831
31	**Maxwell Mearns Castle** David C. Cameron BD CertMin	1993		122 Broomfield Avenue, Newton Mearns G77 5JR	0141 616 0642
32	**Mearns (H) (90141 639 6555)** Joseph A. Kavanagh BD DipPTh	1992	1998	Manse of Mearns, Newton Mearns G77 5BU	0141 616 2410
33	**Milton of Campsie (H)** Diane E. Stewart BD	1988		33 Birdstone Road, Milton of Campsie G65 8BX	01360 310548 (Tel/Fax)
34	**Netherlee (H)** Ian R. Boyd MA BD PhD	1989	1997	532 Clarkston Road, Glasgow G44 3RT	0141 637 2884 (Tel/Fax)
35	**Newton Mearns (H) (0141 639 7373)** Angus Kerr BD CertMin ThM Margaret McLellan (Mrs) DCS	1983	1994	28 Waterside Avenue, Newton Mearns G77 6TJ 5 Kinloch Road, Newton Mearns G77 6LY	0141 616 2079 0141 639 6853
36	**Rutherglen: Old** Alexander Thomson BSc BD MPhil PhD	1973	1985	31 Highburgh Drive, Rutherglen, Glasgow G73 3RR	0141 647 6178
37	**Rutherglen: Stonelaw (0141 647 5713)** Alastair M. Morrice MA BD	1968	1987	80 Blairbeth Road, Rutherglen, Glasgow G73 4JA	0141 634 4366 (Tel/Fax)

38	**Rutherglen: Wardlawhill** George Cranston BD	1976	26 Parkhill Drive, Rutherglen, Glasgow G73 2PW	0141 563 9590
39	**Rutherglen: West** John W. Drummond MA BD	1971	12 Albert Drive, Rutherglen, Glasgow G73 3RT	0141 569 8547
40	**Stamperland (0141 637 4999) (H)** Alastair J. Cherry BA BD	1982	109 Ormonde Avenue, Glasgow G44 3SN [e-mail: a.j.cherry@btintemet.com]	0141 637 4976 (Tel/Fax)
41	**Stepps (H)** Kenneth S. Baird MSc PhD BD CEng MIMarE	1998	2 Lenzie Road, Stepps, Glasgow G33 6DX	0141 779 9556
42	**Thornliebank (H)** Robert M. Silver BD	1995	19 Arthurlie Drive, Giffnock G46 6UR	0141 620 2133
43	**Torrance (T)** Nigel L. Barge BSc BD	1991	27 Campbell Place, Torrance G64 4HR	01360 622379
44	**Twechar See Banton**			
45	**Williamwood** G. Hutton B. Steel MA BD	1982	125 Greenwood Road, Clarkston, Glasgow G76 7LL	0141 571 7949
46	**Glasgow: Anderston Kelvingrove (0141 221 9408)** Gordon Kirkwood BSc BD	1987	16 Royal Terrace G3 7NY	0141 332 3136
47	**Glasgow: Baillieston Mure Memorial (0141 773 1216)** Allan S. Vint BSc BD	1989 1996	28 Beech Avenue, Baillieston, Glasgow G69 6LF	0141 771 1217
48	**Glasgow: Baillieston St Andrew's (0141 771 6629)** Thomas C. Houston BA	1975	12 Oakhill Avenue, Baillieston, Glasgow G69 7ES	0141 771 1791
49	**Glasgow: Balshagray Victoria Park** David L. Court BSc BD	1989	20 St Kilda Drive G14 9JN	0141 954 9780
50	**Glasgow: Barlanark Greyfriars** James S.A. Cunningham MA BD BLitt PhD	1992	4 Rhindmuir Grove, Glasgow G69 6NE	0141 771 1240
51	**Glasgow: Battlefield East (H) (0141 632 4206)** Alan C. Raeburn MA BD	1971	110 Mount Annan Drive G44 4RZ	0141 632 1514

No.	Name		Date	Address	Telephone
52	**Glasgow: Blawarthill**				
	Ian M.S. McInnes BD DipMin		1995	46 Earlbank Avenue G14 9HL	0141 579 6521
53	**Glasgow: Bridgeton St Francis in the East (H)**				
	Howard R. Hudson MA BD		1982 1984	10 Albany Drive, Rutherglen, Glasgow G73 3QN	0141 647 9973
	Alex Mair DCS			53 Gardenside Grove, Fernlee Meadows, Carmyle G32 8DS	0141 646 2165
	Margaret S. Beaton (Miss) DCS			64 Gardenside Grove, Fernlee Meadows, Carmyle G32 8DS	0141 646 2297
54	**Glasgow: Broomhill (0141 334 2540)**				
	William B. Ferguson BA BD		1971	27 St Kilda Drive G14 9LN	0141 959 3204
55	**Glasgow: Calton Parkhead (0141 554 3866)**				
	Ronald Anderson BD DipTh		1992	98 Drumover Drive G31 5RP	0141 556 2520
	Karen Hamilton (Mrs) DCS			61D Lenzie Place G21 3TZ	0141 558 3195
56	**Glasgow: Cardonald (0141 882 1051)**				
	Eric McLachlan BD		1978	133 Newtyle Road, Paisley PA1 3LB	0141 561 1891
57	**Glasgow: Carmunnock**				
	Robert J.M. Anderson BD		1993	The Manse, 161 Waterside Road, Carmunnock G76 9AJ	0141 644 1578 (Tel/Fax)
58	**Glasgow: Carmyle linked with Kenmuir Mount Vernon**				
	Vacant			3 Meryon Road, Glasgow G32 9NW	0141 778 2625
59	**Glasgow: Carntyne Old linked with Eastbank**				
	Ronald A.S. Craig BACC BD		1983	211 Sandyhills Road G32 9NB	0141 778 1286
60	**Glasgow: Carnwadric (E)**				
	Graeme K. Bell BA BD		1983	62 Loganswell Road G46 8AX	0141 638 5884
	Christine M. McVean (Miss) DCS			38 Cruachan St Glasgow G46 8LY	0141 638 9035
61	**Glasgow: Castlemilk: East (H) (0141 634 2444)**				
	John D. Miller BA BD		1971	15 Castlemilk Drive G45 9TL	0141 631 1244
	Ann Lyall (Miss) DCS			117 Barlia Drive, Glasgow G45 0AY	0141 631 3643
62	**Glasgow: Castlemilk: West (H) (0141 634 1480)**				
	Charles Cameron		1998	156 Old Castle Road G44 5TW	0141 637 5451
63	**Glasgow: Cathcart Old**				
	Neil W. Galbraith BD CertMin		1996	21 Courthill Avenue, Cathcart G44 5AA	0141 633 5248 (Tel/Fax)
64	**Glasgow: Cathcart South (H) (0141 637 6658)**				
	Andrew M. Smillie LTh		1990	82 Merrylee Road G43 2QZ	0141 633 3744

65	**Glasgow: Cathedral (High or St Mungo's)**			
	William Morris DD PhD LLD JP	1951	1 Whitehill Grove, Newton Mearns G77 5DH	0141 639 6327
66	**Glasgow: Colston Milton (0141 772 1922)**			
	Christopher D. Park BSc BD	1977	118 Birsay Road G22 7QP	0141 772 1958
67	**Glasgow: Colston Wellpark (H)**			
	Christine M. Goldie (Miss) LLB BD	1984	16 Bishop's Gate Gardens, Colston G21 1XS	0141 402 4002
68	**Glasgow: Cranhill (H) (0141 774 5593)**			
	James A. Trevorrow LTh	1971	31 Lethamhill Crescent G33 2SH	0141 770 6873
	J.B. MacPherson DCS		13 Leslie Street, Glasgow G41 2LQ	0141 423 6868
69	**Glasgow: Crofttfoot (H) (0141 637 3913)**			
	John M. Lloyd BD CertMin	1984	20 Victoria Road, Burnside, Rutherglen G73 3QG	0141 647 5524
70	**Glasgow: Crosshill Queen's Park**			
	Vacant		32 Queen's Drive G42 8DD	0141 423 2533
71	**Glasgow: Dennistoun Blackfriars (H)**			
	Vacant		41 Broompark Drive G31 2JB	0141 554 8667
72	**Glasgow: Dennistoun Central**			
	Ada Younger (Mrs) BD	1978	45 Broompark Drive G31 2JB	0141 550 4487
73	**Glasgow: Drumchapel Drumry St Mary's (0141 944 1998)**			
	Hilda C. Smith (Miss) MA BD	1992	8 Fruin Road G15 6SQ	0141 944 4493
74	**Glasgow: Drumchapel St Andrew's (0141 944 3758)**			
	John S. Purves LLB BD	1983	6 Firdon Crescent G15 6QQ	0141 944 4566
	Elizabeth Gregson (Mrs) BD (Assist)	1996	17 Westfields, Bishopbriggs G64 3PL	0141 563 1918
75	**Glasgow: Drumchapel St Mark's**			
	Elizabeth Smith (Mrs) BD	1996	146 Garscadden Road G15 6PR	0141 944 5440
76	**Glasgow: Eastbank** See Carntyne Old			
77	**Glasgow: Easterhouse St George's and St Peter's (E) (0141 781 0800)**			
	Malcolm Cuthbertson BA BD	1984	3 Barony Gardens, Baillieston G69 6TS	0141 573 8200 (Tel)
				0141 773 4878 (Fax)
78	**Glasgow: Eastwood**			
	Vacant		54 Mansewood Road G43 1TL	0141 632 0724

79 Glasgow: Gairbraid (H)
Ian C. MacKenzie MA BD — 1970 — 1515 Maryhill Road G20 7XL — 0141 946 1568

80 Glasgow: Gardner Street (GE)
Roderick Morrison MA BD — 1974 — 148 Beechwood Drive G11 7DX — 0141 563 2638

81 Glasgow: Garthamlock and Craigend East (E)
Valerie J. Duff (Miss) DMin — 1993 — 175 Tillycairn Drive, Garthamlock G33 5HS — 0141 774 6364
James Hamilton DCS — 61 Lenzie Place G21 3TZ — 0141 558 3195

82 Glasgow: Gorbals
Ian F. Galloway BA BD — 1976 — 44 Riverside Road G43 2EF — 0141 649 5250
William G. McKaig BD (Assoc) — 1976 — 19 Thistle Terrace G5 0SJ — 0141 485 1185

83 Glasgow: Govan Old (0141 445 1941)
T.A. Davidson Kelly MA BD FSAScot — 1975 — 4 Dalziel Quadrant, Pollokshields G41 4NR — 0141 427 0321
Michael S. Edwards BD (Assoc) — 1982 — Flat 1G, Ascot Court, Dorchester Avenue G12 0BE — 0141 334 0143

84 Glasgow: Govanhill Trinity
Sigrid Marten (Mrs) BD — 1997 — 143 Albert Road G42 8UE — 0141 422 1293
[e-mail: smarten@gn.apc.org]

85 Glasgow: High Carntyne (0141 778 4186)
Peter W. Nimmo BD ThM — 1996 — 165 Smithycroft Road G33 2RD — 0141 770 6464

86 Glasgow: Hillington Park (H)
Ian Morrison BD — 1991 — 61 Ralston Avenue G52 3NB — 0141 882 7000

87 Glasgow: Househillwood St Christopher's
Alan K. Sorensen — 1983 — 29 Torridon Avenue G41 5AT — 0141 427 2596
BD MTh DipMin FSAScot

88 Glasgow: Hyndland (H) (0141 339 1804)
John C. Christie BSc BD — 1990 — 24 Hughenden Gardens G12 9YH — 0141 334 1002

89 Glasgow: Ibrox (H) (0141 427 0896)
C. Blair Gillon BD — 1975 — 3 Dargarvel Avenue G41 5LD — 0141 427 1282

90 Glasgow John Ross Memorial Church for Deaf People
(Voice Text: 0141 420 1759 Text Only: 0141 429 6682 Fax: 0141 429 6860 ISDN Video Phone: 0141 418 0579)
Richard C. Durno DSW CQSW — 1989 — 1998 — 31 Springfield Road, Bishopbriggs G64 1DQ — 0141 772 1052
[www.deafconnections.co.uk]

No.	Charge / Minister		Address	Telephone
91	**Glasgow: Jordanhill (0141 959 2496)**			
	Colin C. Renwick BMus BD	1989 1996	96 Southbrae Drive G13 1TZ	0141 959 1310 (Tel)
				0141 959 2496 (Fax)
92	**Glasgow: Kelvin Stevenson Memorial (0141 339 1750)**			
	William McAreavey BA	1950 1956	94 Hyndland Road G12 9PZ	0141 334 5352
93	**Glasgow: Kelvinside Hillhead (T)**			
	Valerie G.C. Watson (Miss) MA BD STM	1987	39 Athole Gardens G12 9BQ	0141 339 2865
94	**Glasgow: Kenmuir Mount Vernon** See Carmyle			
95	**Glasgow: King's Park (H) (0141 632 1131)**			
	G. Stewart Smith MA BD STM	1966 1979	1101 Aikenhead Road G44 5SL	0141 637 2803 (Tel/Fax)
96	**Glasgow: Kinning Park (0141 427 3063)**			
	Vacant		Flat 9, 10 Mavisbank Gardens G51 1HF	0141 427 2191
97	**Glasgow: Knightswood St Margaret's (H)**			
	Andrew P. Lees BD	1984 1989	26 Airthrey Avenue G14 9LJ	0141 959 1094
98	**Glasgow: Langside (0141 632 7520)**			
	John Owain Jones MA BD FSAScot	1981 1998	36 Madison Avenue G44 5AQ	0141 637 0797
99	**Glasgow: Lansdowne**			
	Roy J.M. Henderson MA BD DipMin	1987 1992	18 Woodlands Drive G4 9EH	0141 339 2794
	Helen M. Hughes (Miss) DCS		Flat 2/2, 43 Burnbank Terrace G20 6UQ	0141 333 9459
100	**Glasgow: Linthouse St Kenneth's**			
	James Macfarlane PhD	1991	51 Morriston Crescent, Deanpark, Renfrew PA4 0XU	0141 885 2597
101	**Glasgow: Lochwood**			
	Stuart M. Duff BA	1997	42 Rhindmuir Road, Swinton G69 6AZ	0141 773 2756
102	**Glasgow: Martyrs', The**			
	Ewen MacLean BA BD	1995	30 Louden Hill Road, Robroyston, Glasgow G33 1GA	0141 558 7451
103	**Glasgow: Maryhill (H) (0141 946 3512)**			
	Anthony J.D. Craig BD	1987	111 Maxwell Avenue G61 1HT	0141 570 0642
			[e-mail: craig.glasgow@net.ntl.com]	
	Margaret H. Johnston (Miss) BD (Assoc)	1988	111 Rannoch Drive, Bearsden G61 2BQ	0141 943 0292
104	**Glasgow: Merrylea (0141 637 2009)**			
	Sidney H. Coleman BA BD MTh	1961 1982	37 Burnhead Road, Newlands G43 2SU	0141 5712410

No. Charge / Minister		Address	Telephone
105 Glasgow: Mosspark (H) (0141 882 2240)			
D. Muir McLaren MA BD MTh PhD	1971 1984	396 Kilmarnock Road G43 2DJ [e-mail: cellmuir@dial.pipex.com]	0141 632 1247 0378 480 514 (Mbl)
106 Glasgow: Mount Florida (H)			
Hugh M. Wallace MA BD	1981 1987	90 Mount Annan Drive G44 4RZ	0141 632 8868
107 Glasgow: New Cathcart (H)			
Vacant		69 Parklands Road G44 3RA	0141 637 1687
108 Glasgow: New Govan (H)			
John Patrick Wright BD	1977 1989	19 Dumbreck Road G41 5LJ	0141 427 3197
109 Glasgow: Newlands South (H) (0141 632 3055)			
John D. Whiteford MA BD	1989 1997	24 Monreith Road G43 2NY	0141 632 2588
110 Glasgow: North Kelvinside			
William G. Alston	1961 1971	41 Mitre Road G14 9LE	0141 954 8250
111 Glasgow: Partick South			
Alan L. Dunnett BD LLB	1994 1997	17 Munro Road G13 1SQ	0141 959 3732
112 Glasgow Partick Trinity (H)			
Stuart J. Smith BEng BD	1994 1994	8 Beaumont Gate G12 9EE	0141 339 2651
113 Glasgow: Penilee St Andrew (H) (0141 882 2691)			
Esther M.M. Leitch (Miss) BD	1984	80 Tweedsmuir Road G52 2RX	0141 882 3432
114 Glasgow: Pollokshaws			
Vacant			
Anne M. MacFadyen (Mrs) BSc BD (Aux)	1995	33 Mannering Road G41 3SW 295 Mearns Road, Newton Mearns G77 5LT	0141 649 4981 0141 639 3605
115 Glasgow: Pollokshields (H)			
David R. Black MA BD	1986 1997	36 Glencairn Drive G41 4PW	0141 423 4000
Anne MacDonald (Miss) BA DCS		81 Arbroath Avenue G52 3HJ	0141 883 5618
116 Glasgow: Possilpark			
Martin R. Forrest BA MA BD	1988	11E 231 Westercommon Road G22 5ND	0141 336 3127
117 Glasgow: Priesthill and Nitshill			
Douglas M. Nicol BD CA	1987 1996	36 Springkell Drive G41 4EZ	0141 427 7877

118 Glasgow: Renfield St Stephen's (Tel: 0141 332 4293   Fax: 0141 332 8482)
David W. Lunan MA BD   1970   1987   101 Hill Street G3 6TY   0141 353 3395

119 Glasgow: Robroyston
Keith McKillop MB ChB BD   1999   7 Beckfield drive, Robroyston G33 1SR   0141 558 8414

120 Glasgow: Ruchazie (0141 774 2759)
William F. Hunter MA BD   1986   1999   18 Borthwick Street G33 3UU
[e-mail: bhunter@tesco.net]   0141 774 6860
Janet Anderson (Miss) DCS   322 Gartcraig Road G33 2TB   0141 774 5329

121 Glasgow: Ruchill (0141 946 0466)
John C. Matthews MA BD   1992   9 Kirklee Road G12 ORQ   0141 357 3249

122 Glasgow: St Andrew's East (0141 554 1485)
Janette G. Re:d (Miss) BD   1991   43 Broompark Drive G31 2JB   0141 554 3620

123 Glasgow: St Columba (GE) (0141 221 3305)
Vacant   "Sunnyside", 70 Neilston Rd, Uplawmoor G78 4AF   01505 850540

124 Glasgow: St David's Knightswood (0141 959 1024)
Graham M. Thain LLB BD   1988   1999   60 Southbrae Drive G13 1QD   0141 959 2904

125 Glasgow: St Enoch's Hogganfield (H) (0141 770 5694)
Andrew J. Philip BSc BD   1996   43 Smithycroft Road G33 2RH   0141 770 7593

126 Glasgow: St George's Tron (0141 221 2141)
Sinclair B. Ferguson MA BD PhD   1972   1998   29 Vancouver Drive G14 9HR   0141 959 2535
Murdo Mac:ean (Assoc)   1997   9 Micklehouse Oval, Baillieston, Glasgow G69 6TJ   0141 781 4440

127 Glasgow: St James' (Pollok) (0141 882 4984)
Helen Ham:lton (Miss) BD   1991   30 Ralston Avenue G52 3NA   0141 883 7405

128 Glasgow: St John's Renfield (0141 339 7021)
Dugald J.R. Cameron BD DipMin MTh   1990   26 Leicester Avenue G12 OLU   0141 339 4637

129 Glasgow: St Luke's and St Andrew's
Ian C. Fraser BA BD   1982   10 Chalmers Street G40 2HHA   0141 556 3883

130 Glasgow: St Margaret's Tollcross Park
George M. Murray LTh   1995   31 Kenmuir Avenue, Sandyhills G32 9LE   0141 778 5060

131 Glasgow: St Nicholas' Cardonald
Roderick I.T. MacDonald BD   1992   104 Lamington Road G52 2SE   0141 882 2065

132 Glasgow: St Paul's Provanmill (0141 770 8559)
R. Russell McLarty BD   1985   38 Lochview Drive G33 1QF   0141 770 9611

133 Glasgow: St Rollox
E. Gwynfai Jones BA   1964   1967   42 Melville Gardens, Bishopbriggs, Glasgow G64 3DE   0141 772 2848

134 Glasgow: St Thomas' Gallowgate
Irene A. Bristow (Mrs) BD   1989   1997   8 Helenvale Court G31 4LH   0141 554 0997

135 Glasgow: Sandyford Henderson Memorial
C. Peter White BVMS BD MRCVS   1974   66 Woodend Drive G13 1TG   0141 954 9013

136 Glasgow: Sandyhills
John P.F. Martindale BD   1994   60 Wester Road G32 9JJ   0141 778 2174

137 Glasgow: Scotstoun (T)
Vacant   15 Northland Drive G14 9BE   0141 959 4637

138 Glasgow: Shawlands (0141 649 2012)
Alastair M. Sanderson BA LTh   1971   1976   29 St Ronan's Drive G41 3SQ   0141 632 9046
Alastair D. McLay BSc BD (Assoc)   1989   1990   47 Dinmont Road G41 3UJ   0141 632 5817
                                                         [e-mail: alastair@mclay79.freeserve.co.uk]

139 Glasgow: Sherbrooke St Gilbert's (H) (0141 427 1968)
Donald Macleod BD LRAM DRSAM   1987   9 Springkell Gate G41 4BY   0141 423 3912

140 Glasgow: Shettleston Old (T) (0141 778 2484)
David K. Speed LTh   1969   1999   57 Mansionhouse Road, North Mount Vernon G32 0RP   0141 778 8904

141 Glasgow: South Carntyne (H) (0141 778 1343)
Gary Wilson BD   1996   47 Broompark Drive G31 2JB   0141 554 5930

142 Glasgow: South Shawlands (T) (0141 649 4656)
Vacant   391 Kilmarnock Road G43 2NU   0141 632 0013

143 Glasgow: Springburn (H) (0141 557 2345)
Vacant   3 Tofthill Avenue, Bishopbriggs, Glasgow G64 3PA   0141 762 1844

144 Glasgow: Strathbungo Queen's Park (0141 423 3654)
Norma D. Stewart MA MEd BD   1977   1979   5 Newark Drive G41 4QJ   0141 423 4818

145 Glasgow: Temple Anniesland (0141 959 1814)
Vacant   76 Victoria Park Drive North G14 9PJ   0141 959 5835

No.	Charge / Minister		Address	Telephone
146	**Glasgow: Toryglen (H)** Keith W. Ross MA BD	1984 1991	28 Snuffmill Road, Cathcart G44 5TR	0141 569 6892
147	**Glasgow: Townhead Blochairn** William P. Finlay MA BD	1969 1988	9/3, 39 Rosemount Street G21 2JT	0141 552 2740
148	**Glasgow: Trinity Possil and Henry Drummond** Richard G. Buckley BD MTh	1990 1995	50 Highfield Drive G12 0HL	0141 339 2870
149	**Glasgow: Tron St Mary's** William Wilson BSc BD	1999	3 Hurly Hawkin', Bishopbriggs G64 1YL	0141 772 8555
150	**Glasgow: Victoria Tollcross** Richard Coley LTh	1971	228 Hamilton Road G32 9QU	0141 778 2413
151	**Glasgow: Wallacewell** John McGregor BD	1999	54 Etive Crescent, Bishopbriggs G64 1ES	0141 772 1453
152	**Glasgow: Wellington (H) (0141 339 0454)** M. Leith Fisher MA BD	1967 1990	27 Kingsborough Gardens G12 9NH	0141 339 3627
153	**Glasgow: Whiteinch** Alan McWilliam BD	1993 1999	24 Dunglass Avenue G14 9ED	0141 950 2352
154	**Glasgow: Yoker Old linked with Yoker St Matthew's (T)** Neil A. Simpson BA BD PhD	1992	15 Coldingham Avenue G14 0PX	0141 952 3620
155	**Glasgow: Yoker St Matthew's** See Yoker Old			

Name	Dates	(Charge)	Address	Telephone
Aitken, Andrew J. BD APhS MTh PhD	1951 1981	(Tollcross Central with Park)	18 Dorchester Avenue G12 0EE	0141 357 1617
Alexander, Eric J MA BD	1958 1997	(St George's Tron)	PO Box 14725, St Andrews KY16 8WB	
Allan, A.G.	1959 1989	(Candlish Polmadie)	30 Dalrymple Drive, East Mains, East Kilbride G74 4LF	01355 226190
Barr, Alexander C. MA BD	1950 1992	(St Nicholas' Cardonald)	25 Fisher Drive, Phoenix Park, Paisley PA1 2TP	0141 848 5941
Barr, David MA BD	1938 1984	(Chaplain: Royal Infirmary)	17 Victoria Park Gardens South G11 7BX	0141 339 5364
Beattie, John A.	1951 1984	(Dalmuir Overtoun)	0/1, 15 Kelvindale Gardens, Kelvindale Road G20 8DW	0141 946 5978
Beautyman, Paul H. MA BD	1993 1998	(Mission Co-ordinator)	59 Elmbank Street G2 4PQ	0141 352 6946
Bell, John L. MA BD FRSCM	1978 1988	(Iona Community)	Flat 2/1, 31 Lansdowne Crescent G20 6NH	0141 334 0688
Black, Sandra (Mrs) BSc BD	1988 1997	(Hospital Chaplain)	36 Glencairn Drive G41 4PW	0141 423 4000
Brain, Ernest J.	1955 1985	(Liverpool St Andrew's)	14 Chesterfield Court, 1240 Great Western Road G12 0BJ	0141 357 2249
Brain, Isobel J. (Mrs) MA	1987 1997	(Ballantrae)	14 Chesterfield Court, 1240 Great Western Road G12 0BJ	0141 357 2249
Brice, Dennis G. BSc BD	1981	(Taiwan)	18 Hermitage Avenue, West Hadleigh, Essex ES7 1TQ	

Name	Position / Charge			Address	Telephone
Bryden, William A. BD	(Yoker Old with St Matthew's)	1977	1984	145 Bearsden Road G13 1BS	0141 959 5213
Campbell, A. Iain MA DipEd	(Busby)	1961	1997	430 Clarkston Road G44 3QF	0141 637 7460
Campbell, Colin MA BD	(Williamwood)	1940	1989	4 Golf Road, Clarkston G76 7LZ	0141 638 1215
Campbell, John MA BA	Adviser in Mission and Evangelism	1973	1986	3 Herries Road G41 4DE [e-mail: campbellglasgow@compuserve.com]	0141 423 3760
Carmont, Robert	(Sandyhills)	1958	1994	11 Mossgeil Gardens, Uddingston G71 6EP	01698 329109
Cartidge, G.R.G. MA BD STM	Religious Education RE Teacher,	1977	1993	5 Briar Grove, Newlands G43 2TD	0141 637 3228
Chester, Stephen	International Christian College General Director, Scripture Union	1999		Flat 1/2, 7 Craighouse Street, Ruchazie, Glasgow G33 3RU	(Tel) 0141 634 4256 (Fax) 0141 332 5925
Clark, David M. MA BD	(Fowlis Wester with Monzie)	1989	1996	39 Blairbeth Road G73 4JF	0141 638 4749
Cooke, John M. MA BD PhD	(Kilmarnock: St John's Onthank)	1950	1982	2 Wellfield Court, Giffnock G46 7QJ	0141 637 8244
Cullen, William T. BA LTh	Presbytery Clerk	1984	1996	71 Fenwick Road, Giffnock G46 6AX	
Cunningham, Alexander MA BD	(Community Minister)	1961	1980	The Glen, 103 Glenmavis Road, Airdrie ML6 OPQ	01236 763012
Currie, Robert MA	Frontier Youth Trust, Scottish Network Development Officer	1955	1990	Flat 3/2, 13 Redlands Road G12 0SJ	0141 334 5111
Dunnett, Linda (Mrs) DCS				795B Argyle Street, Glasgow G3 8DS	0141 204 4800
Fairweather, Ian C.M. MA BD	(Jordanhill College of Education)	1945	1985	86 Whitinghame Court, Glasgow G12 0BH	0141 334 7577
Fenton, Robert J. MA	(St Kiaran's Dean Park)	1940	1976	Eastwoodhill, 238 Fenwick Road, Glasgow G46 6UU	0141 638 5127
Forrest, Gavin W. MA BD	(Whitburn South)	1984	1987	12 Vancouver Road G14 9HJ	0141 954 9110
Galloway, Allan D. MA BD STM MTh PhD FRSE	(University of Glasgow)	1948	1982	5 Straid Bheag, Barremman, Clynder, Helensburgh G84 OQX	01436 83432
Gibson, H. Marshall MA BD	(St Thomas' Gallowgate)	1957	1996	39 Buralbroom Drive G69 7XG	0141 771 0749
Gilchrist, George R. MA BD DD	(Dalrymple)	1940	1980	53 Alexander Avenue, Eaglesham G76 ODP	01355 32272
Graham, David J. BSc BD PhD	Glasgow Bible College	1982	1983	9 Crofthill Avenue, Uddingston, Glasgow G71 7AF	01698 813487
Grimstone, A. Frank MA	(Calton Parkhead)	1949	1986	144C Howth Drive, Parkview Estate, Anniesland G13 1RL	0141 954 1009
Haley, Derek BD DPS	(Chaplain, Gartnavel Royal)	1960	1977	9 Kinnaird Crescent, Bearsden, Glasgow G61 2BN	0141 942 9281
Harper, Anne J.M. (Miss) BD STM MTh CertSocPsych	Hospital Chaplain	1979	1990	122 Greenock Road, Bishopton PA7 5AS	01505 862466
Harvey, W. John BA BD	Adult Christian Education "The Craighead Institute"	1965	1988	501 Shields Road G41 2RF	0141 429 3774
Herron, Andrew DD LLD	(Presbytery Clerk)	1934	1981	44 McLaren Court, Glasgow G46	0141 638 0791
Hislop, David T. MA	(Maryhill High)	1940	1983	92 Balcarres Avenue G12 OQN	0141 357 2866
Hope, Evelyn P. (Miss) BA BD	(Wishaw: Thornlie)	1990	1998	0/1, 48 Moss-side Road, Glasgow G41 3UA	0141 649 1522
Hunter, Alastair G. MSc BD	University of Glasgow	1976	1980	487 Shields Road G41 2RG	0141 429 1687
Hunter, George	(Scotstoun West)	1950	1987	Flat 1C, 256 Great Western Road G4 9EJ	0141 332 7228
Hutcheson, J. Murray MA	(Possilpark)	1943	1987	88 Ainslie Road, Kildrum, Cumbernauld G67 2ED	01236 729378
Hutchison, Henry MA BEd BD MLitt PhD LLCM	(Carmunnock)	1948	1993	4A Briar Grove, Newlands, Glasgow G43 2TG	0141 637 2766
Irvine, Euphemia H.C. (Mrs) BD	(Milton of Campsie)	1972	1988	32 Baird Drive, Bargarran, Erskine PA8 6BB	0141 812 2777
Johnstone, Robert W.M. MA BD STM	(Temple Anniesland)	1964	1999	13 Kilmardinny Crescent, Bearsden, Glasgow G61 3ND	0141 931 5862
Johnstone, David MC MA BD	(Belhaven Westbourne)	1951	1987	140 Hyndland Road G12 9PN	0141 339 5896
Jolly, John BA	(Old Partick)	1950	1990	10 Kensington Court, 20 Kensington Road G12 9NX	0141 339 8815

Name			Charge / Position	Address	Tel.
Jones, John D. BA	1935	1972	(Kirkconnel St Mark's)	50 Melville Gardens, Bishopbriggs G64 3DD	0141 772 4776
Lewis, E.M.H. MA	1962	1994	(Drumchapel St Andrew's)	7 Cleveden Place, Glasgow G12 0HG	0141 334 5411
Liddell, Matthew MA BD	1943	1982	(St Paul's (Outer High) and (St David's (Ramshorn))	17 Traquair Drive G52 2TB	0141 810 3776
Lindsay, James A. MC MA	1936	1976	(Burnside)	113 Rosslyn Avenue, Rutherglen, Glasgow G73 3EZ	0141 647 5053
Macarthur, J.M.M.	1966	1996	(St Columba)	5 Polquhap Gardens, Thorncroft Park, Crookston G53 7FW	0141 891 5385
Macaskill, Donald MA BD PhD	1994	1994	Board of Parish Education	44 Forfar Avenue, Cardonald, Glasgow G52 3JQ	0141 883 5956
Macaskill, Marjory (Mrs) LLB BD	1990	1998	Chaplain: University of Strathclyde	44 Forfar Avenue, Cardonald, Glasgow G52 3JQ	0141 883 5956
MacBain, Iain W.	1971	1993	(Coatbridge: Coatdyke)	24 Thornyburn Drive, Baillieston G69 7ER	0141 771 7030
Macdonald, Murdo Ewen DD	1939	1984	(University of Glasgow)	68 Lauderdale Gardens G12 9QW	0141 334 2087
McDonald, Ross J. EA BD ThM	1998		Director/Chaplain, Lodging House Mission	35 East Campbell Street, Glasgow G1 5DT	0141 552 0285
Macfarlane, Thomas G. BSc PhD BD	1956	1992	(South Shawlands)	0/2, 19 Corrour Road G43 2DY	0141 632 7966
McKinnon, Lily F. (Mrs) MA BD	1993	1999	(South Shawlands)	14B Herries Road, Pollokshields, Glasgow G41 4DF	
McLean, John MA	1948	1977	(St Andrew's Plantation)	18 Pelham Road, Droitwich, Worcester WR9 8NT	
MacLeod, Charles Angus BD	1996		Chaplain Army	1 KOSB, Dreghorn Barracks, Edinburgh EH13 9QM	
MacLeod, William J. DipTh	1963	1988	(Kirkintilloch St David's Memorial)	42 Hawthorn Drive, Banknock, Bonnybridge FK4 1LF	01324 840667
MacMahon, Janet P.H. (Mrs) MSc BD	1992	1992	Chaplain: Southern General Hospital	6 Jubilee Gardens, Bearsden G61 2RT	0141 942 3671
McMurtrie, D.W. MA ATCL ARPS	1939	1965	(Summertown)	9 Iain Drive, Bearsden, Glasgow G61 4PD	0141 942 0293
Macnaughton, J.A. MA BD	1949	1989	(Hyndland)	62 Lauderdale Gardens G12 9QW	0141 339 1294
Mathieson, Fiona C. (Mrs) BEd BD	1988	1995	Chaplain: University of Glasgow	11 The Square G12 8QQ	0141 339 8855
Millar, David A.R. MA	1956	1989	(Glasgow University)	310A Albert Drive G41 5RS	0141 429 2249
Millar, James	1949	1989	(Shawlands Old)	9 Glenbank Court G46 7EJ	0141 638 6250
Mitchell, David BD DipPTheol	1988	1998	Chaplain: Marie Curie Hospice, Glasgow	48 Leglin Wood Drive, Wallacewell Park, Glasgow G21	0141 402 2869
Moir, Ian A. MA BD	1962	1991	Adviser for Urban Priority Areas	47 Millersneuk Drive, Lenzie G66 5JE	0141 776 1479
Morton, Thomas MA BD LGSM	1945	1986	(Rutherglen Stonelaw)	54 Greystone Avenue, Burnside, Rutherglen G73 3SW	0141 647 2682
Muir, Fred C. MA BD ThM ARCM	1961	1997	(Stepps)	20 Alexandra Avenue, Stepps G33 6BP	0141 779 2504
Murray, Douglas M. MA BD PhD	1976	1989	University of Glasgow	28 Sherbrooke Drive G41 5PA	
Myers, Frank BA	1952	1978	(Springburn)	18 Birmingham Close, Grantham NG31 8SD	01476 594430
Neil, Herbert K.	1951	1978	(Portmoak)	111 Hyndland Road G12 9JB	0141 339 7753
Newlands, George M. MA BD PhD	1970	1986	University of Glasgow	29 Clermiston Road, Edinburgh EH12 6XD	0131 476 9377
Norwood David W. BA	1948	1980	(Lisbon)	15 Brooklands, Hockley Road, Rayleigh, Essex SS8 6BE	01268 774095
Peterkin, W. Neilson MA	1945	1986	(Broom)	7 Craigie Drive, Newton Mearns G77 5DA	0141 639 2329
Philip, George M. MA	1953	1996	(Sandyford Henderson Memorial)	44 Beech Avenue, Bearsden G61 3EX	0141 942 1327
Philip, Robert A. BA BD	1937	1981	(Stepps St Andrew's)	2 Hockley Court, Weston Park West, Bath BA1 4AR	0122 3 33041
Porter, Richard MA	1953	1988	(Govanhill)	58 Hillend Road G76 8XT	0141 639 4169
Rae, D.L.	1955	1990	(Kolhapur)	29 Falcon Avenue, Edinburgh EH10 4AL	0131 447 3158
Ramsay, W.G.	1967	1999	(Springburn)	53 Kelvinvale, Kirkintilloch G66 1RD	0141 776 2915
Robertson, Archibald MA BD	1957	1999	(Eastwood)	19 Canberra Court, Briadpark Drive, Glasgow G46 6NS	0141 637 7572
Robertson, Blair MA BD ThM	1990	1998	Chaplain: Southern General Hospital	c/o Chaplain's Office, Southern General Hospital, Glasgow	0141 201 2156
Ross, Donald M. MA	1953	1994	(Industrial Mission Organiser)	14 Cartsbridge Road, Busby G76 8DH	0141 644 2220
Ross, James MA BD	1968	1998	(Kilsyth: Anderson)	53 Turnberry Gardens, Westerwood, Cumbernauld G68 0AY	01236 730501
Rushton, John BVMS BD	1983	1996	Overseas Missionary Fellowship	25 Abbey Drive, Glasgow G14	

Scrimgeour, Alice M. (Miss) DCS	1960	1996	(Deaconess)	265 Golfhill Drive G31 2PB	0141 564 9602
Shackleton, William	1983	1988	(Greenock: Wellpark West)	3 Tynwald Avenue, Burnside, Glasgow G73 4RN	0141 569 9407
Shanks, Norman J. MA BD	1971	1997	(Iona Community)	1 Marchmont Terrace G12 9LT	0141 339 4421
Smith, A McLaren	1945	1982	(Cumbrae)	27 Fenwick Road, Glasgow G46 6AU	0141 776 0870
Smith, J. Rankine MA BD	1956	1991	(Barmulloch)	44 Middlemuir Road, Lenzie G66 4ND	0141 883 9666
Smith, James S.A.	1962	1999	(Drongan, The Schaw Kirk)	146 Aros Drive, Glasgow G52 1TJ	01360 850117
Stewart, Angus T. MA BD PhD JP	1984	1996	(Greenbank)	"Mansfield", Buchlyvie, Stirling FK8 3NE	
Storran, William F.	1963	1995	University of Glasgow	35 Strathalmond Park, Edinburgh EH4 8AH	
Sutherland, Denis I.	1972	1996	(Hutchesontown)	19 Boyd Orr Crescent, Kilmaurs KA3 2QB	01563 520641
Sutherland, Elizabeth W. (Miss) BD	1967	1995	(Balornock North with Barmulloch)	20 Kirkland Avenue, Blanefield, Glasgow G63 9BZ	01360 770154
Tait, A.	1976	1991	(St Enoch's Hogganfield)	26 Nicolson Court, Stepps G33 6HY	0141 779 3370
Thomson, Andrew BA	1937	1971	(Renfrew: Trinity)	21 Upper Bourtree Drive, Burnside, Glasgow G73 4EJ	0141 634 4046
Thomson, H.C. MA BD PhD	1976	1990	(Anniesland Cross)	Balmanno House, 3 Cleveden Road G12 0NT	
Turner, Angus BD	1957	1995	Industrial Chaplain	46 Keir Street, Pollokshields, Glasgow G41 2LA	0141 424 0493
Tuton, Robert M. MA	1955	1988	(Shettleston: Old)	6 Holmwood Gardens, Uddingston G71 7BH	01698 321108
Walker, A.L.	1964	1998	(Trinity Possil and Henry Drummond)	11 Dundas Avenue, Torrance G64 4BD	01360 622281
Webster, John G. BSc			(St John's Renfield)	Plane Tree, King's Cross, Isle of Arran KA27	
White, Elizabeth (Miss) DCS			(Deaconess)	17 Clincarthill Road, Rutherglen G73 2LF	0141 647 2683

GLASGOW ADDRESSES

Congregation	Address
Banton	Kelvinhead Road, Banton
Bishopbriggs	
Kenmure	Viewfield Road, Bishopbriggs
Springfield	Springfield Road
Blairbeth Rodger Memorial	Kirkcriggs Gardens
Broom	Mearns Road, Newton Mearns
Burnside	Church Avenue, Burnside
Busby	Church Road, Busby
Cadder	Cadder Road, Glasgow
Cambuslang	
Flemington Hallside	265 Hamilton Road
Old	Cairns Road
St Andrew's	Main Street x Clydeford Road
Trinity St Paul's	Main Street
Campsie	Main Street, Lennoxtown
Chryston	Main Street, Chryston
Eaglesham Old and Carswell	Montgomery Street, Eaglesham
Fernhill and Cathkin	Neilvaig Drive
Gartcosh	113 Lochend Road, Gartcosh
Glenboig	138 Main Street, Glenboig
Giffnock	
Orchardhill	Church Road
South	Eastwood Toll
The Park	Ravenscliffe Drive
Greenbank	Eaglesham Road, Clarkston
Kilsyth	
Anderson	Kingston Road
Burns and Old	Church Street
Kirkintilloch	
Hillhead	Newdyke Road
St Columba's	Waterside Road nr Old Aisle Road
St Columba's Mem Pk	Alexander Street
St Mary's	High Street
Lenzie Old	Kikintilloch Road x Garngaber Avenue
Union	Moncrieff Ave x Kirkintilloch Road
Maxwell	Waterfoot Road
Mearns Castle	Mearns Road Newton Mearns
Mearns	
Milton of Campsie	Antermony Road, Milton of Campsie
Netherlee	Ormonde Drive x Ormonde Avenue
Newton Mearns	Ayr Road, Newton Mearns
Rutherglen	
Old	Main Street at Queen Street
Stonelaw	Stonelaw Road x Dryburgh Avenue
Wardlawhill	Hamilton Road
West	Glasgow Road nr Main Street
Stamperland	Stamperland Gardens, Clarkston
Stepps	Whitehill Avenue
Thornliebank	Woodlands Road
Torrance	School Road, Torrance
Twechar	Main Street, Twechar

Congregation	Address
Williamwood	Vardar Avenue x Seres Ave, Clarkston
Glasgow	
Anderston Kelvingrove	Argyle Street x Elderslie Street
Baillieston	
Mure Memorial	Beech Avenue, Garrowhill
St Andrew's	Church Street
Balshagray Victoria Pk	Broomhill Cross
Barlanark Greyfriars	Edinburgh Road x Hallhill Road
Battlefield East	1216 Cathcart Road
Blawarthill	Millbrix Avenue
Bridgeton St Francis in the East	Queen Mary Street x Bernard Street
Broomhill	Randolph Rd x Marlborough Ave
Calton Parkhead	122 Helenvale Street
Cardonald	2141 Paisley Road West
Carmunnock	Kirk Road, Carmunnock
Carmyle	South Carmyle Avenue
Carmyle Old	862 Shettleston Road
Carnwadric	556 Boydstone Road, Thornliebank
Castlemilk	
East	Barlia Terrace
West	Carmunnock Road
Cathcart Old	119 Carmunnock Road
South	92 Clarkston Road
Cathedral	Cathedral Square
Colston Milton	Egilsay Crescent
Colston Wellpark	1378 Springburn Road
Cranhill	Bellrock Crescent x Bellrock Street
Croftfoot	Croftpark Ave x Crofthill Road
Crosshill Queen's Park	40 Queen's Drive, Dennistoun
Dennistoun Blackfriars	Whitehill Street
Central	Armadale Street
Drumchapel Drumry St Mary's	Drumry Road East
St Andrew's	Garscadden Road
St Mark's	Kinfauns Drive
Eastbank	679 Old Shettleston Road
Easterhouse St George's and St Peter's	Boyndie Street
Eastwood	Mansewood Road
Gairbraid	1517 Maryhill Road
Gardner Street	Gardner Street x Muirpark Street
Garthamlock and Craigend East	Porchester Street x Balveny Street
Gorbals	Eglinton Street x Cumberland Street
Govan Old	866 Govan Road
Govanhill Trinity	Daisy Street nr Allison Street
High Carntyne	358 Carntynehall Road
Hillington Park	24 Berryknowes Road
Householhwood	
St Christopher's	Meikle Road
Hyndland	Hyndland Road, opp Novar Drive
Ibrox	Carillon Road x Clifford Street
John Ross Memorial	100 Norfolk Street G5 9EJ
Jordanhill	Woodend Street x Munro Road
Kelvin Stevenson Mem	Belmont Street at Belmont Bridge
Kelvinside Hillhead	Huntly Gardens
Kenmuir Mount Vernon	London Road, Mount Vernon
King's Park	242 Castlemilk Road
Kinning Park	Eaglesham Place
Knightswood St Margaret's	Knightswood Cross
Langside	Ledard Road x Lochleven Road
Lansdowne	Gt Western Road at Kelvin Bridge
Linthouse St Kenneth's	9 Skipness Drive
Lochwood	Lochend Road x Lift Place
Martyrs', The	St Mungo Avenue
Maryhill	1990 Maryhill Road
Merrylea	78 Merrylee Road
Mosspark	149 Ashkirk Drive
Mount Florida	1123 Cathcart Road
New Cathcart	Newlands Road nr Clarkston Road
New Govan	Govan Cross
Newlands South	Riverside Road x Langside Drive
North Kelvinside	153 Queen Margaret Drive
Partick South	Dumbarton Road
Trinity	20 Lawrence Street
Penilee St Andrew	Bowfield Cres x Bowfield Avenue
Pollokshaws	223 Shawbridge Street
Pollokshields	Albert Drive x Shields Road
Possilpark	124 Saracen Street
Priesthill and Nitshill	Freeland Drive x Muirshiel Cres
Renfield St Stephen's	260 Bath Street
Robroyston	
Ruchazie	Elibank Street x Milncroft Road
Ruchill	Shakespeare Street nr Maryhill
Road	
St Andrew's East	681 Alexandra Parade
St Columba	300 St Vincent Street
St David's	
Knightswood	Boreland Drive nr Lincoln Avenue
St Enoch's Hogganfield	860 Cumbernauld Road
St George's Tron	163 Buchanan Street
St James' (Pollok)	Lyoncross Rd x Byrebush Road
St John's Renfield	22 Beaconsfield Road
St Luke's and St Andrew's	Well Street at Bain Square
St Margaret's Tollcross Pk	179 Braidfauld Street
St Nicholas' Cardonald	Hartlaw Crescent nr Gladsmuir Road
St Paul's Provanmill	Langdale Street x Greenrig Street
St Rollox	Fountainwell Road
St Thomas Gallowgate	Gallowgate opp Bluevale Street
Sandyford-Henderson Memorial	Kelvinhaugh Street at Argyle Street
Sandyhills	28 Baillieston Rd nr Sandyhills Rd
Scotstoun & Whiteinch	Earlbank Avenue x Ormiston Avenue
Shawlands	Shawlands Cross
Sherbrooke St Gilbert's	Nithsdale Rd x Sherbrooke Avenue
Shettleston Old	111 Killin Street
South Carntyne	538 Carntyne Road
South Shawlands	Regwood Street x Deanston Drive
Springburn	Springburn Road x Atlas Street
Strathbungo Queen's Park	170 Queen's Drive
Temple Anniesland	869 Crow Road
Torglen	Glenmore Ave nr Prospecthill Road
Townhead Blochairn	178 Roystonhill
Trinity Possil and Henry Drummond	
Tron St Mary's	Crowhill Street x Broadholm Street
	128 Red Road
Victoria Tollcross	1134 Tollcross Road
Wallacewell	57 Northgate Road
	Ryehill Road x Quarrywood Road
Wellington	University Ave x Southpark Avenue
Yoker Old	Dumbarton Road
St Matthew's	Hawick Street

(17) HAMILTON

Meets at Motherwell: Dalziel St Andrew's Parish Church Halls, on the first Tuesday of February, March, May, September, October, November, December and on the third Tuesday of June

Presbytery Office:		18 Haddow Street, Hamilton ML3 7HX	01698 286837 (Tel)
			01698 457258 (Fax)
Clerk:	REV. JAMES H. WILSON LTH	21 Austine Drive, Hamilton ML3 7YE	01698 457042
Treasurer:	MR DAVID FORRESTER CA	Belmont, Lefroy Street, Coatbridge ML5 1PN	01236 421892

1 Airdrie Broomknoll (H) (01236 762101) linked with Calderbank
Vacant — 51 Cromarty Road, Airdrie ML6 9RL — 01236 751555

2 Airdrie Clarkston
Thomas L. Pollock
JP BA BD MTh FSAScot — 1982 1992 — Forrest Street, Airdrie ML6 7BE — 01236 769676

3 Airdrie: Flowerhill (H)
Andrew Gardner BSc BD PhD — 1997 — 31 Victoria Place, Airdrie ML6 9BX — 01236 763025

4 Airdrie: High
W. Richard Houston BSc BD — 1998 — 17 Etive Drive, Airdrie ML6 9QL — 01236 762010

5 Airdrie: Jackson (01236 733508)
Sharon E.F. Colvin (Mrs)
BD LRAM LTCL — 1985 1998 — 48 Dunrobin Road, Airdrie ML6 8LR — 01236 763154

6 Airdrie: New Monkland (H) linked with Greengairs
Alan A. Ford BD AIBScot — 1977 — Glenmavis, Airdrie ML6 0NW [e-mail: ALANxFORD@MSN.COM] — 01236 763286 (Tel/Fax)

7 Airdrie: St Columba's
Margaret F. Currie BEd BD — 1980 1987 — 52 Kennedy Drive, Airdrie ML6 9AW — 01236 763173

8 Airdrie: The New Wellwynd (H)
R. Fraser Penny BA BD — 1984 1995 — 20 Arthur Avenue, Airdrie ML6 9EZ [e-mail: fraserpenn@aol.com] — 01236 763022

9 Bargeddie (H)
Henry B. Mealyea BArch BD — 1984 1993 — Bargeddie, Baillieston, Glasgow G69 6UB — 0141 771 1322

10 Bellshill: Macdonald Memorial
Vacant

32 Adamson Street, Bellshill ML4 1DT   01698 843176

11 Bellshill: Orbiston linked with Bellshill: St Andrew's
H. Martin J. Johnstone MA BD   1989

65 Crossgates, Bellshill ML4 2EE   01698 841912

12 Bellshill: St Andrew's See Bellshill: Orbiston

13 Bellshill: West (H) (01698 747581)
Quintin A. Blane BSc BD   1979 1994

16 Croftpark Street, Bellshill ML4 1EY
[e-mail: qablane@surfaid.org]   01698 842877

14 Blantyre: Livingstone Memorial
Vacant

286 Glasgow Road, Blantyre G72 9DB   01698 823794

15 Blantyre: Old (H)
Rosemary A. Smith (Ms) BD   1997

High Blantyre G72 9UA   01698 823130

16 Blantyre: St Andrew's
Ian Meredith BA MTh   1980 1993

332 Glasgow Road, Blantyre, Glasgow G72 9LQ   01698 827982

17 Bothwell (H)
James M. Gibson LTh LRAM   1978 1989

Manse Avenue, Bothwell, Glasgow G71 8PQ
[e-mail: james gibson1@compuserve.com]   01698 853189 (Tel)
                                          01698 853229 (Fax)

18 Caldercruix Longriggend and Meadowfield (H)
Ian M. Watson LLB DipLP BD   1998

Main Street, Caldercruix, Airdrie ML6 7RF
[e-mail: ikwatson@aol.com]   01236 842279

19 Carfin linked with Newarthill
George S. Noble DipTh   1972

Church Street, Newarthill ML1 5HS   01698 860316

20 Chapelhall (H)
James R. Nelson BD DipTheol   1986

Chapelhall, Airdrie ML6 8SG   01236 763439

21 Chapelton linked with Strathaven: Rankin (H)
Shaw J. Paterson BSc BD   1991

15 Lethame Road, Strathaven ML10 6AD   01357 520019 (Tel)
                                         01357 529316 (Fax)

22 Cleland (H)
John A. Jackson BD   1997

Bellside Road, Cleland ML1 5NP   01698 860260

23 Coatbridge: Blairhill Dundyvan (H)
John M. Black MA BD   1963 1991

18 Blairhill Street, Coatbridge ML5 1PG   01236 432304

24	**Coatbridge: Calder (H)** Vacant		26 Bute Street, Coatbridge ML5 4HF	01236 421516
25	**Coatbridge: Clifton (H)** Leslie W. Thorne BA LTh	1987	132 Muiryhall Street, Coatbridge ML5 3NH	01236 421181
26	**Coatbridge: Middle** James Grier BD	1991	47 Blair Road, Coatbridge ML5 1JQ	01236 432427
27	**Coatbridge: Old Monkland** James G. Munton BA	1969	Old Monkland Manse, Coatbridge ML5 5QT	01236 423788
28	**Coatbridge: St Andrew's** Ian G. Wotherspoon BA LTh	1967	77 Eglinton Street, Coatbridge ML5 3JF	01236 437271
29	**Coatbridge: Townhead (H)** David Hood BD Cert Min	1997	Crinan Crescent, Coatbridge ML5 2LH	01236 423150
30	**Dalserf** D. Cameron McPherson BSc BD	1982	Dalserf, Larkhall ML9 3BN	01698 882195
31	**East Kilbride: Claremont (H) (01335 238088)** John K. Collard MA BD	1986	17 Deveron Road, East Kilbride G74 2HR	01355 248526
32	**East Kilbride: Greenhills (E) (01355 221746)** John Brewster MA BD DipEd	1988	21 Turnberry Place, East Kilbride G75 8TB	01355 242564
33	**East Kilbride: Moncreiff (H) (01355 223328)** Alastair S. Lusk BD	1974	16 Almond Drive, East Kilbride G74 2HX	01355 238639
34	**East Kilbride: Mossneuk (E) (01355 260954)** Vacant		30 Eden Grove, Mossneuk, East Kilbride G75 8XU	01355 234196
35	**East Kilbride: Old (H)** Douglas W. Clark LTh	1993	40 Maxwell Drive, East Kilbride G74 4NG	01355 220732
36	**East Kilbride: South (H)** John C. Sharp BSc BD PhD	1980	7 Clamps Wood, East Kilbride G74 2HB	01355 247993
37	**East Kilbride: West (H)** David E.P. Currie BSc BD	1983	1 Barr Terrace, East Kilbride G74 1AP	01355 220753

No.	Congregation / Minister	Year	Address	Telephone
38	**East Kilbride: Westwood (H) (01355 245657)** Kevin Mackenzie BD DPS	1989	16 Inglewood Crescent, East Kilbride G75 8QD	01355 223992
39	**Glasford linked with Strathaven East** William T. Stewart BD	1980	68 Townhead Street, Strathaven ML10 6BA	01357 521138
40	**Greengairs** See Airdrie New Monkland			
41	**Hamilton: Burnbank linked with Hamilton North (H)** Raymond D. McKenzie BD	1978 1987	9 South Park Road, Hamilton ML3 6PJ	01698 424609
42	**Hamilton: Cadzow (H) (01698 428695)** Arthur P. Barrie LTh	1973 1979	3 Carlisle Road, Hamilton ML3 7BZ	01698 421664 (Tel) 01698 891126 (Fax)
43	**Hamilton: Gilmour and Whitehill (H)** Vacant		86 Burnbank Centre, Burnbank ML3 ONA	01698 284201
44	**Hamilton: Hillhouse** David W.G. Burt BD DipMin William Wishart DCS	1989 1998	66 Wellhall Road, Hamilton ML3 9BY 17 Swift Bank, Earrock, Hamilton ML3 8PX [e-mail: bill@wwishart.freeserve.co.uk]	01698 422300 01698 429371
45	**Hamilton: North** See Hamilton Burnbank			
46	**Hamilton: Old (H) (01698 281905)** Hugh R. Wyllie MA FCIBS DD	1962	62 Union Street, Hamilton ML3 6NA	01698 420002
47	**Hamilton: St Andrew's (T)** Norma Moore MA BD	1995	15 Bent Road, Hamilton ML3 6QB [e-mail: normamoore@cableinet.co.uk]	01698 891361
48	**Hamilton: St John's (H) (01698 283492)** Robert M. Kent MA BD	1973	12 Castlehill Crescent, Hamilton ML3 7DG	01698 425002
49	**Hamilton: South (H) (01698 281014) linked with Quarter** Fraser K. Turner LTh	1994	Quarter, Hamilton ML3 7XA	01698 424511
50	**Hamilton: Trinity (01698 284254)** Karen E. Harbison (Mrs) MA BD	1991	69 Buchan Street, Hamilton ML3 8JY	01698 425326
51	**Hamilton: West (H) (01698 284670)** J. Stanley Cook BD DipPSS	1974	43 Bothwell Road, Hamilton ML3 OBB [e-mail: stan.cook@virgin.net]	01698 458770

No.	Congregation / Minister	Year	Year	Address	Telephone
52	**Holytown** James S. Salmond BA BD MTh ThD	1979		Holytown, Motherwell ML1 5RU	01698 832622
53	**Kirk o' Shotts (H)** Sheila M. Spence (Mrs) MA BD	1979		Salsburgh, Shotts ML7 4NS	01698 870208
54	**Larkhall: Chalmers (H)** James S.G. Hastie CA BD	1990		Quarry Road, Larkhall ML9 1HH	01698 882238
55	**Larkhall: St Machan's (H)** Iain M. Greenshields BD DipRS ACMA MTh	1985	1993	2 Orchard Gate, Larkhall ML9 1HG [e-mail: machan@cablenet.co.uk]	01698 882457
56	**Larkhall: Trinity** Lindsay Schluter (Miss) ThE CertMin	1995		13 Machan Avenue, Larkhall ML9 2HE	01698 881401
57	**Motherwell: Crosshill (H)** W. Stuart Dunn LTh	1970	1982	15 Orchard Street, Motherwell ML1 3JE	01698 263410
58	**Motherwell: Dalziel St Andrew's (H) (01698 264097)** Derek W. Hughes BSc BD DipEd	1990	1996	4 Pollock Street, Motherwell ML1 1LP [e-mail: derek@hughes04.freeserve.co.uk]	01698 263414 (Tel/Fax)
	Colin M. Brough BSc BD (Assoc)	1998		5 Bredin Way, Motherwell ML1 3PD [e-mail: colin.brough@btinternet.com]	01698 252527
59	**Motherwell: Manse Road** Vacant			10 Hamilton Drive, Motherwell ML1 2QA	01698 267345
60	**Motherwell: North (H)** Derek H.N. Pope BD	1987	1995	Kirkland Street, Motherwell ML1	01698 266716
61	**Motherwell: St Margaret's** Andrew M. Campbell BD	1984		70 Baron's Road, Motherwell ML1 2NB	01698 263803
62	**Motherwell: St Mary's (H)** David W. Doyle MA BD	1977	1987	19 Orchard Street, Motherwell ML1 3JE	01698 263472
63	**Motherwell: South Dalziel (H)** Phyllis M. Wilson (Mrs) DipCom DipRE	1985	1994	62 Manse Road, Motherwell ML1 2PT	01698 263054
64	**Newarthill** See Carfin				

65 Newmains: Bonkle (H) linked with Newmains: Coltness Memorial (H)
Graham L. Duffin BSc BD DipEd | 1989 | 5 Kirkgate, Newmains, Wishaw ML2 9BT | 01698 383858

66 Newmains: Coltness Memorial See Newmains: Bonkle

67 New Stevenston: Wrangholm Kirk
Paul Amed LTh DPS | 1992 | 222 Clydesdale Street, New Stevenston ML1 4JQ | 01698 832533

68 Overtown
J. Mary Henderson (Miss) MA BD DipEd PhD | 1990 | Overtown, Wishaw ML2 0QP | 01698 372330

69 Quarter See Hamilton South

70 Shotts: Calderhead Erskine
William D. Beattie BD DPS | 1985 | The Manse, Kirk Road, Shotts ML1 5ET | 01501 820042
James Zamborini LJA Dip (Aux) | 1997 | 100 Old Manse Road, Netherton, Wishaw ML2 0EP | 01698 350889

71 Stonehouse: St Ninian's (H)
Thomas Nelson BSc BD | 1992 | 4 Hamilton Way, Stonehouse ML9 3PU | 01698 792364

72 Strathaven: Avendale Old and Drumclog (H) (01357 529748)
R. Forbes Walker BSc BD ThM | 1987 1988 | Strathaven, Lanarkshire ML10 6BA | 01357 520077

73 Strathaven: East See Glasford
74 Strathaven: Rankin See Chapelton

75 Strathaven: West
Stuart D. Rogerson BSc BD | 1980 | 6 Avenel Crescent, Strathaven ML10 6JF [e-mail: s.rogerson@cnetwork.co.uk] | 01357 529086 (Tel/Fax)

76 Uddingston: Burnhead (H)
Robert A. Mackenzie LLB BD | 1993 | 90 Laburnum Road, Uddingston G71 5DB | 01698 813716
Raymond Deans DCS | | 22 Garrowhill Drive, Garrowhill, Glasgow G69 6HL | 0141 771 6847

77 Uddingston: Old (H) (01698 814015)
Norman B. McKee BD | 1987 1994 | 1 Belmont Avenue, Uddingston G71 7AX [e-mail: normanb.mckee@uddingston89.freeserve.co.uk] | 01698 814757

78 Uddingston: Park (T)(H)
W. Bruce McDowall BA BD | 1989 1999 | 25 Douglas Gardens, Uddingston G71 7HB | 01698 817256

79 Uddingston: Viewpark (H)
Scott McKenna BA BD | 1994 | 14 Holmbrae Road, Uddingston G71 6AP | 01698 813113

80	**Wishaw: Cambusnethan North (H)**			
	Mhorag Macdonald (Ms) MA BD	1989	350 Kirk Road, Wishaw ML2 8LH [e-mail: mhorag@mhorag force9.co.uk]	01698 381305
81	**Wishaw: Cambusnethan Old and Morningside**			
	Iain C. Murdoch MA LLB DipEd BD	1995	22 Coronation Street, Wishaw ML2 8LF	01698 384235
82	**Wishaw: Chalmers (H) (01698 375306)**			
	Ian O. Coltart CA BD	1988	161 Kirk Road, Wishaw ML2 7BZ	01698 372464
83	**Wishaw: Craigneuk and Belhaven (H)**			
	Scott Raby LTh	1991	100 Glen Road, Wishaw ML2 7NP [e-mail: revscott@rabyfamily28.freeserve.co.uk]	01698 372495
84	**Wishaw: Old (H)**			
	James Davidson BD Dip AFH	1989	130 Glen Road, Wishaw ML2 7NP [e-mail:revjames@davidson130.freeserve.co.uk]	01698 375134 (Tel/Fax) 07788 747808 (Mbl)
85	**Wishaw: St Mark's**			
	Henry J.W. Findlay MA BD	1965 1967	Coltness Road, Wishaw ML2 7EX	01698 384596 (Tel) 01698 386025 (Fax)
86	**Wishaw: Thornlie (H)**			
	Klaus O.F. Buwert LLB BD	1984 1999	West Thornlie Street, Wishaw ML2 7AR	01698 372356

Name	Dates		Position	Address	Phone
Allan, James B. BA	1965	1993	(Motherwell: South Dalziel)	42 Catherine Street, Motherwell ML1 2RN	01698 264756
Anderson, Catherine B. (Mrs) DCS			(Deaconess)	13 Mosshill Road, Bellshill ML4 1NQ	01698 745907
Baird, George W. MA	1944	1984	(Crimond with St Fergus)	42 Neilsland Drive, Motherwell ML1 3EB	01698 262088
Beattie, William G. BD BSc	1951	1986	(Hamilton St Andrew's)	33 Dungavel Gardens, Hamilton ML3 7PE	01698 423804
Campbell, John	1974	1985	(Coatbridge Middle)	18 Bellsdyke Road, Airdrie ML6 9BU	01236 753607
Cowper, Macknight C. MA BD STM	1947	1983	(East Kilbride West)	17 Manor Place, Edinburgh EH3 7DH	0131 225 6214
Douglas, Andrew M. MA	1937	1978	(Hamilton Cadzow)	21 Allanshaw Street, Hamilton ML3 6NZ	01698 429176
Dunn, James F.	1959	1993	(Coatbridge: Dunbeth)	167 Silvertonhill Avenue, Hamilton ML3 7PP	01698 426043
Fraser, James P.	1951	1988	(Strathaven Avendale Old and Drumclog)	26 Hamilton Road, Strathaven ML10 6JA	01357 522758
Handley, John	1954	1993	(Motherwell: Clason Memorial)	12 Airbles Crescent, Motherwell ML1 3AR	01698 262733
Heron, John	1951	1979	(Ochiltree)	Springvale Hotel, 18 Lethame Road, Strathaven ML10 6AD	
Hunter, James E. LTh	1974	1997	(Blantyre: Livingstone Memorial)	57 Dalwhinnie Avenue, Blantyre G72 9NQ	01698 826177
King, Crawford S. MA	1958	1984	(Glenboig)	77 Faskine Avenue, Airdrie ML6 9EA	01236 761753
Learmonth, Adam J.	1966	1993	(Airdrie: Wellwynd)	13 Drumbathie Terrace, Airdrie ML6 7EU	01236 763248
McCabe, George	1963	1996	(Airdrie: High)	Flat 8, Park Court, 2 Craighouse Park, Edinburgh EH10 5LD	0131 447 9522
McCance, Andrew BSc	1986	1995	(Coatbridge: Middle)	6a Manse Road, Bearsden, Glasgow G61 3PT	0141 942 2373
Martin, James MA BD DD	1946	1987	(Glasgow: High Carntyne)	9 Magnolia Street, Wishaw ML2 7EQ	01698 385825

Melrose, J.H. Loudon MA BD MEd	1955 1996	(Gourock: Old Gourock & Ashton [Assoc])	24 Avonbridge Drive, Hamilton ML3 7EJ	01698 891033
Niven, William LTCL	1955 1994	(Lesmahagow: Old)	92 Linden Lea, Hamilton ML3 9AG	01698 420653
Price, Peter O. CBE QHC BA FPhS	1960 199	(Blantyre Old)	20A Old Bothwell Road, Bothwell G71 8AW	01698 854032
Wilson, James H.	1970 1996	(Cleland)	21 Austine Drive, Hamilton ML3 7YE	01698 457042

HAMILTON ADDRESSES

Airdrie

Broomknoll	Broomknoll Street
Clarkston	Forrest Street
Flowerhill	89 Graham Street
High	North Bridge Street
Jackson	Glen Road
New Monkland	Glenmavis
St Columba's	Thrashbush Road
The New Wellwynd	Wellwynd

Coatbridge

Blairhill Dundyvan	Blairhill Street
Calder	Calder Street
Clifton	Muiryhall Street x Jackson Street
Middle	Bank Street
Old Monkland	Woodside Street
St Andrew's	Church Street
Townhead	Crinan Crescent

East Kilbride

Claremont	High Common Road, St Leonard's
Greenhills	Greenhills Centre
Moncreiff	Calderwood Road
Mossneuk	Eden Drive

East Kilbride (cont'd)

Old	Montomery Street
South	Baird Hill, Murray
West	Kittoch Street
Westwood	Belmont Drive, Westwood

Hamilton

Burnbank	High Blantyre Road
Cadzow	Woodside Walk
Gilmour and	Glasgow Road, Burnbank
Whitehill	Abbotsford Road, Whitehill
Hillhouse	Clerkwell Road
North	Windmill Road
Old	Leechlee Road
St Andrew's	Avon Street
St John's	Duke Street
South	Strathaven Road
Trinity	Neilsland Square off North Road
West	Burnbank Road

Motherwell

Crosshill	Windmillhill Street x Airbles Street
Dalziel St Andrew's	Merry Street and Muir Street

Motherwell (cont'd)

Manse Road	Gavin Street
North	Chesters Crescent
St Margaret's	Shields Road
St Mary's	Avon Street
South Dalziel	504 Windmillhill Street

Uddingston

Burnhead	Laburnum Road
Old	Old Glasgow Road.
Park	Main Street
Viewpark	Old Edinburgh Road

Wishaw

Cambusnethan	
North	Kirk Road
Old	Kirk Road
Chalmers	East Academy Street
Craigneuk and Belhaven	
Old	Craigneuk Street
St Mark's	Main Street
Thornlie	Coltness Road
	West Thornlie Street

(18) DUMBARTON

Meets at Dumbarton in Riverside Church Halls, on the first Tuesday of February, March, April, May, October, November, December, and on the second Tuesday of June and September (and April when the first Tuesday falls in Holy Week).

Clerk: REV. DAVID P. MUNRO MA BD STM   14 Birch Road, Killearn, Glasgow G63 9SQ   01360 550098 (Tel) / 01360 551198 (Fax) / 0410 866982 (Mbl)

Alexandria
Elizabeth W. Houston (Miss) MA BD DipEd   1985   1995   32 Ledrish Avenue, Balloch G83 8JB   01389 751933
Archibald M. Ferguson MSc PhD CEng FRINA (Aux)   1989   1997   The Whins, Barrowfield, Cardross G82 5NL   01389 841517

Arrochar linked with Luss
H. Dane Sherrard BD   1971   1998   Luss, Alexandria G83 8NZ   01436 860240

Baldernock (H)
Harold A.M. Steven LTh   1970   1994   Bardowie, Milngavie G62 6ES   01360 620471

Bearsden: Killermont (H)
G. Fraser H. Macnaughton MA BD   1982   1997   8 Clathic Avenue, Bearsden, Glasgow G61 2HF   0141 942 0021

Bearsden: New Kilpatrick (H) (0141 942 8827)
David D. Scott BSc BD   1981   1999   51 Manse Road, Bearsden, Glasgow G61 3PN   0141 942 0035

Bearsden: North (H) (0141 942 2818)
Keith T. Blackwood BD Dip Min   1997   5 Fintry Gardens, Bearsden, Glasgow G61 4RJ
[e-mail: ktb@clara.co.uk]   0141 942 0366

Bearsden: South (H)
John W.F. Harris MA   1967   1987   61 Drymen Road, Bearsden, Glasgow G61 2SU   0141 942 0507

Bearsden: Westerton Fairlie Memorial (H) (0141 942 6960)
Eric V. Hudson LTh   1971   1990   3 Canniesburn Road, Bearsden G61 1PW
[e-mail: evhudson@surfaid.org]   0141 942 2672
Alistair E. Ramage BA ADB CertEd (Aux)   1996   16 Claremont Gardens, Milngavie G62 6PG
[e-mail: A.Ramage@gcal.ac.uk]   0141 956 2897

Bonhill (H) (01389 756516)
Ian H. Miller BD   1975   1 Glebe Gardens, Bonhill, Alexandria G83 9NZ   01389 753039

Charge / Minister		Address	Phone
Cardross (H) (01389 841322) Andrew J. Scobie MA BD	1963 1965	Cardross, Dumbarton G82 5LB	01389 841289
Clydebank: Abbotsford Roderick G. Hamilton MA BD	1992 1996	35 Montrose Street, Clydebank G81 2PA [e-mail: rhamilton@zetnet.co.uk]	0141 952 5151
Clydebank: Faifley Gregor McIntyre BSc BD	1991	Kirklea, Cochno Road, Hardgate Clydebank G81 6PT	01389 876836
Agnes Tait (Mrs) DCS		2 Lennox Drive, Faifley, Clydebank G81 5JU	01389 873196
Clydebank: Kilbowie St Andrew's Roderick P. Grahame BD CPS	1991	5 Melfort Avenue, Clydebank G81 2HX	0141 951 2455
Clydebank: Radnor Park Margaret J.B.Yule (Mrs) BD	1992	Spencer Street, Clydebank G81 3AS	0141 951 1007
Clydebank: St Cuthbert's (T) Ian A. Manson BA BD	1989 1992	1 Peterson Drive, Glasgow G13 4JY [e-mail: imanson@zetnet.co.uk]	0141 941 3469
Roy Wilson DA ARIBA ARIAS	1986 1997	20 William Ure Place, Bishopbriggs G64 3BH	0141 563 1829
Craigrownie linked with Rosneath St Modan's (H) Malcolm Wright LTh	1970 1984	Edenkiln, Argyll Road, Kilcreggan G84 OJW [e-mail: malcolmwright@compuserve.com]	01436 842274
Dalmuir Barclay (0141 941 3988) James F. Gatherer BD	1984	Parkhall Road, Dalmuir, Clydebank G81 3RJ	0141 941 3317
Dumbarton: Riverside (H) (01389 742551) John B. Cairns LTh LLB	1974 1985	5 Kirkton Road, Dumbarton G82 4AS	01389 762512
Dumbarton: St Andrew's (H) Leslie G. Donaghy BD DipMin PGCE FSAScot	1990 1998	17 Mansewood Drive, Dumbarton G82 3EU [e-mail:standrews@ledi.globalnet.co.uk]	01389 604259
Dumbarton: West Kirk (H) Vacant		3 Havoc Road, Dumbarton G82 4JW	01389 767529
Duntocher (H) Vacant		Roman Road, Duntocher, Clydebank G81 6BT	01389 878846
Garelochhead (01436 810589) Alastair S. Duncan MA BD	1989	Old School Road, Garelochhead Helensburgh G84 OAT	01436 810022

Charge / Minister	Year(s)	Address	Tel
Helensburgh: Park (H) (01436 671714) James H. Brown BD	1977	35 East Argyle Street, Helensburgh G84 7EL [e-mail: jh@jhbrown.freeserve.co.uk]	01436 672209
Helensburgh: St Columba (H) Frederick M. Booth LTh	1982	46 Suffolk Street, Helensburgh G84 9QZ	01436 672054
Helensburgh: The West Kirk (H) (01436 676880) David W. Clark MA BD	1975 1986	37 Campbell Street, Helensburgh G84 9NH	01436 674063
Jamestown (H) Kenneth G. Russell BD CCE	1991	Appin House, Drymen Road, Balloch, Alexandria G83 8HT	01389 752734
Kilmaronock Gartocharn Andrew S. Mitchell BA BD HDipREd AdvDipEd(Open)	1965 1992	Kilmaronock Manse, Alexandria G83 8SB	01360 660295
Luss See Arrochar			
Milngavie: Cairns (H) (0141 956 4868) Andrew Frater BA BD	1987 1994	4 Cairns Drive, Milngavie, Glasgow G62 8AJ	0141 956 1717
Milngavie: St Luke's (0141 956 4226) Ramsay B. Shields BA BD	1990 1997	70 Hunter Road, Milngavie, Glasgow G62 7BY [e-mail: ramsayb@shields70.freeserve.co.uk]	0141 956 4740 (Tel) 0141 956 5361 (Fax)
Milngavie: St Paul's (H) (0141 956 4405) Fergus C. Buchanan MA BD	1982 1988	8 Buchanan Street, Milngavie, Glasgow G62 8DD	0141 956 1043
Old Kilpatrick Bowling Alistair J. MacKichan MA BD	1984	Old Kilpatrick, Glasgow G60 5JQ	01389 873130
Renton Trinity (H) Vacant		38 Main Street, Renton, Dumbarton G82 4PU	01389 752017
Rhu and Shandon (H) Alison Paul (Miss) MA BD DipTheol	1986 1994	Ardenconnel Way, Rhu, Helensburgh G84 8LX	01436 820213
Rosneath St Modan's See Craigrownie			

Name			Appointment	Address	Tel.
Brown, Scott J. BD	1993		Chaplain: Royal Navy	HMS Neptune, HMNB Clyde, Faslane, Helensburgh G84 8HL	01436 674321
Buchanan, George OBE MA DD	1931	1977	(Christ Church, Bermuda)	Site 46, Compartment 28, Galiano Island, Vancouver 1 PO, BC, Canada	
Crombie, W.M.D. MA BD	1947	1987	(Calton New with St Andrew's)	32 Westbourne Drive, Bearsden G61 4BH	0141 943 0235
Davidson, Professor Robert MA BD DD FRSE	1956	1991	(University of Glasgow)	30 Dumgoyne Drive, Bearsden G61 3AP	0141 942 1810
Easton, I.A.G. MA FIPM	1945	1988	Lecturer	6 Edgehill Road, Bearsden G61 3AD	0141 942 4214
Gray, Ian A.	1949	1981	(Buchanan with Drymen)	6 Station Road, Helensburgh G84 7BQ	01436 673283
Hamilton, David S.M. MA BD STM	1958	1996	(University of Glasgow)	2 Roselea Drive, Milngavie, Glasgow G62 8HQ	0141 956 1839
Houston, Peter M. FFhS	1952	1997	(Renfrew Old)	25 Honeysuckle Lane, Jamestown, Alexandria G83 8PL	01389 721165
Hunter, G. Lindsay BD PhD APhS	1949	1990	(Teacher: Religious Education)	16 Restway Wall, Chepstow, Mon NP6 5EF	01291 629445
Jack, Robert MA BD	1950	1996	(Bearsden: Killermont)	142 Turnhill Drive, Erskine PA8 7AH	0141 812 8370
Keddie, David A. MA BD	1966	1983	Teacher: Religious Education	21 Ilay Road, Bearsden G61 1QG	0141 942 1408
Lawson, Alexander H. ThM ThD FPhS	1950	1988	(Clydebank Kilbowie)	1 Glebe Park, Mansewood, Dumbarton G82 3HE	01389 742030
McFadzean, Iain MA BD	1989	1999	Chaplain: Royal Navy	HMS Neptune, Faslane, Helensburgh G84 8HL	01436 674321
Macfarlane, William J.E. MA BD	1953	1987	(Alexandria St Andrew's)	3 Inchfad Road, Balloch G83 8SY	01389 758185
McIntyre, J. Ainslie MA BD	1963	1984	(University of Glasgow)	60 Bonnaughton Road, Bearsden G61 4DB	0141 942 5143
Mackenzie, Ian M. MA	1967	1989	(BBC)	1 Glennan Gardens, Helensburgh G84 8XT	01436 673429
Morton, Andrew Q. MA BSc BD FRSE	1949	1987	(Culross and Torryburn)	4 Upper Adelaide Street, Helensburgh G84 7HT	01436 675152
Munro, David P. MA BD STM	1953	1996	(Bearsden North)	14 Birch Road, Killearn, Glasgow G63 9SQ	01360 550098
Rae, Scott M. MBE BD CPS	1976	1981	Chaplain: Royal Navy	12 Primrose Place, Kilmarnock KA1 2RR	01563 541609
Spence, C.K.O. MC TD MA BD	1949	1983	(Craigrownie)	8B Cairndhu Gardens, Helensburgh G84 8PG	01436 678838

DUMBARTON ADDRESSES

Clydebank
Abbotsford	Town Centre
Faifley	Faifley Road
Kilbowie St Andrew's	Kilbowie Road
Radnor Park	Radnor Street
St Cuthbert's	Linnvale

Dumbarton
Riverside	High Street
St Andrew's	Off Bonhill Road
West Kirk	West Bridgend

Helensburgh
Park	Charlotte Street
St Columba	Sinclair Street
The West Kirk	Colquhoun Square

(19) SOUTH ARGYLL

Meets at Tarbert on the first Wednesday of February, March, November, December and the first Tuesday of May, June and September

Clerk: MR MICHAEL A.J. GOSSIP OBE JP BL   Tigh-na-Coille, Ardrishaig, Argyll PA30 8EP   01546 603454 (Tel/Fax)

Ardrishaig (H) linked with South Knapdale
David Carruthers BD   1998   Ardrishaig, Argyll PA30 8HD   01546 603269

Campbeltown: Highland (H)
Michael J. Lind LLB BD   1984 1997   Kirk Street, Campbeltown, Argyll PA28 6BN   01586 551146

Campbeltown: Lorne and Lowland (H)
John Oswald BSc PhD BD   1997   Castlehill, Campbeltown, Argyll PA28 6AN   01586 552468

Craignish linked with Kilninver and Kilmelford
Michael J. Erskine MA BD   1985 1992   Kilmelford, by Oban, Argyll PA34 4XA   01582 200373

Cumlodden, Lochfyneside and Lochgair
Roderick MacLeod
 MA BD PhD(Edin) PhD(Open)   1966 1985   Furnace, Inveraray, Argyll PA32 8XU   01499 500288

Gigha and Cara (H)(GD)
Continuing Vacancy   Gigha, Argyll PA41 7AA   01583 505245

Glassary and Kilmartin and Ford
Alison J. Ross (Mrs) BD   1995 1999   Kilmichael Glassary, Lochgilphead, Argyll PA31 8QA   01546 606926

Glenaray and Inveraray
W. Brian Wilkinson MA BD   1968 1993   Inveraray, Argyll PA32 8XT   01499 302060

Jura (GD)
[Dwin Capstick]   1999   Craighouse, Isle of Jura PA60 7XG   01496 820384

Kilarrow (H) linked with Kilmeny
Anne McIvor (Miss) SRD BD   1996   Bowmore, Isle of Islay PA43 7LH   01496 810271

Kilberry linked with Tarbert (H)
Jane C. Taylor (Miss) BD DipMin   1990 1995   Tarbert, Argyll PA29 6TY   01880 820288

Kilcalmonell linked with Skipness
Charles R. Wood LTh DipYL FRGS   1993   Whitehouse, Tarbert, Argyll PA29 6XS   01880 730224

Kilchoman (GD) linked with Portnahaven (GD)
Vacant   Port Charlotte, Isle of Islay PA48 7TX   01496 850241

Kildalton and Oa (GD)(H)
Norman MacLeod   1999   Port Ellen, Isle of Islay PA42 7DB   01496 302447

Killean and Kilchenzie (H)
John H. Paton JP BSc BD   1983 1984   Muasdale, by Tarbert, Argyll PA29 6XD   01583 421249

Kilmeny See Kilarrow
Kilninver and Kilmelford See Craignish

Lochgilphead
Alastair H. Gray MA BD   1996   Manse Brae, Lochgilphead, Argyll PA31 8QZ   01546 602238

North Knapdale
Robert J. Malloch BD   1987 1997   Tayvallich, by Lochgilphead, Argyll PA31 8PG   01546 870611

Portnahaven See Kilchoman

Saddell and Carradale (H)
Alistair J. Dunlop MA FSAScot   1965 1979   Carradale, by Campbeltown, Argyll PA28 6QG   01583 431253

Skipness See Kilcalmonell

Southend (H)
Callum T. O'Donnell MA BD   1984 1997   Southend, Campbeltown, Argyll PA28 6RQ   01586 830274

South Knapdale See Ardrishaig
Tarbert See Kilberry

Bristow W.H.G.
  BEd HDipRE DipSpecEd   Part time Hospital Chaplain: Campbeltown   The Manse, Isle of Gigha PA41 7AA   01583 505245
Callen, John R. MA BD   1951 1970   (Lochgilphead)   Argyll and Bute Hospital, Lochgilphead PA31 8JF
Campbell, Margaret M. (Miss) DCS   1962 1995   (Deaconess)   Tigh-an-Rudha, Pier Road, Port Ellen, Islay PA42 7DJ   01496 302006
Cormack, Robert C.M. MA   1948 1991   (Craignish with Kilninver and Kilmelford)   13 The Glebe, Kilmelford, Argyll PA34 4AF   01852 200346
Cormack, John R.H. MA BD   1941 1981   (Campbeltown Lowland)   21 Dell Road, Campbeltown PA28   01586 554265
Davidson David W (Aux)   1987 1998   Moderator's Chaplain   Grianail, Glenegedale, Port Ellen, Isle of Islay PA42 7AS   01496 302194

Gibson, Frank S. BL BD STM DSWA DD	1963	1995	(Kilarrow with Kilmeny)	163 Gilbertstoun, Edinburgh EH15 2RG	0131 657 5208
Gordon, David C.	1953	1988	(Gigha and Cara)	16 Braeside Avenue, Largs KA30 8HD	
Gunneberg, Herbert F.	1962	1998	(Gigha and Cara)	Flat 3/2, 6 Turnberry Road, Glasgow G11 5AE	0141 339 8659
Henderson, Charles M.	1952	1989	(Campbeltown Highland)	Springbank House, Askomill Walk, Campbeltown PA28 6EP	01586 552759
Hosie, James MA BD MTh	1959	1998	(Ardrishaig with South Knapdale)	Hilbre, Strachur, Cairndow, by Dunoon, Argyll PA27 8BY	01369 860634
Montgomery, David	1961	1996	(North Knapdale)	Dyalla, Tayvallich, Lochgilphead PA31 8PR	01546 870603
Morrison, Angus W MA BD	1959	1999	(Kildalton and Oa)	1 Livingstone Way, Port Ellen, Isle of Islay PA42	01496 300043
Ritchie, Malcolm A.	1955	1990	(Kilbrandon and Kilchattan)	Roadside Cottage, Tayvallich, Argyll PA31 8PN	01546 870616
Somerville, A.G. MA	1942	1982	(Glenaray and Inveraray)	2 Orchard Park, Ardrishaig, Argyll PA30 8EZ	01546 602831
Stewart, Jean E. (Mrs)	1983	1989	(Kildalton and Oa)	Tigh-na-Truain, Port Ellen, Isle of Islay PA42 7AH	01496 302068

SOUTH ARGYLL
Communion Sundays

Ardrishaig	4 Ap., 1 Nv.	Kilarrow	1 Mr., Je., Sp., Dc.	North Knapdale	3 Oc., 2 My.
Campbeltown – Highland	1 My., Nv.	Kilberry with Tarbert	1 My., Oc.	Inverlussa and Bellanoch	2 My., Nv.
Lorne and Lowland	4 Ap., 1 Nv.	Kilcalmonell	1 Jl., 3 Nv.	Tayvallich	2 My., Nv.
Craignish	1 Je., Nv.	Kilchoman	1 Jl., 2 Dec., E.	Portnahaven	3 Jl.
Cumlodden, Lochfyneside and and Lochgair	1 My., 3 Nv.	Kildalton	Lst Ja., Je., Oc. E.	Saddell and Carradale	2 My., 1 Nv.
Gigha and Cara	1 My., Nv.	Killean and Kilchenzie	1 Mr., Jl., Oc.	Skipness	2 My., Nv.
Glassary, Kilmartin and Ford	1 Ap., Sp.	Kilmeny	2 My., 3 Nv.	Southend	1 Je., Dc.
Glenaray and Inveraray	1 Ap., Jl., Oc., Dc.	Kilninver and Kilmelford	2 Je., Oc.	South Knapdale	4 Ap., 1 Nv.
Jura	Passion Sun. 2 Jl. 3 Nv.	Lochgair	2 Oct (Gaelic)		
		Lochgilphead	1 Ap., Nv.		

(20) DUNOON

Meets at Dunoon St John's, on the first Tuesday of February, April, June and November; at Rothesay Trinity on the first Tuesday of March, October and December, and at the Moderator's Church on the first Tuesday of September.

Clerk:	REV. RONALD SAMUEL TD BSc BD STM	12 Crichton Road, Rothesay, Isle of Bute PA20 9JR	01700 502797 (Tel/Fax)

Ascog linked with Rothesay Craigmore St Brendan's

Vacant		Craigmore, Rothesay, Isle of Bute PA20 9LD	01700 502506

Dunoon: Old and St Cuthbert's (H)
I. Pat Lang (Miss) BSc   1996   1 Royal Crescent, Dunoon PA23 7AH   01369 701291

Dunoon: St John's linked with Sandbank (H)
Joseph Stewart LTh   1979 1989   23 Bullwood Road, Dunoon, Argyll PA23 7QJ   01369 702128

Innellan (H) linked with Inverchaolain and Toward (H)
Hugh Conkey BSc BD   1987   7A Matheson Lane, Innellan, Argyll PA23 7SH [e-mail: conkey@tesco.net]   01369 830276

Inverchaolain and Toward (H) See Innellan

Kilfinan linked with Kyles (H)
David J. Kellas BD   1966 1998   Tighnabruaich, Argyll PA21 2DX   01700 811887 (Tel/Fax)

Kilmodan and Colintraive
Robert M. Donald BA   1969 1998   Glendaruel, Colintraive, Argyll PA22 3AA [e-mail: robdon@colglen.freeserve.co.uk]   01369 820232 (Tel/Fax)

Kilmun (St Munn's) (H) linked with Strone (H) and Ardentinny
Evelyn M. Young (Mrs) BSc BD   1984 1997   Blairmore, Dunoon PA23 8TE   01369 840313

Kingarth and Kilchattan Bay linked with Rothesay The High Kirk
Vacant   10 Bishop Terrace, Rothesay PA20 9HF   01700 502407

Kirn (H)
May M. Allison (Mrs) BD   1988   Stewart Street, Kirn, Dunoon PA23 8DS [e-mail: revmay@kirnpc.freeserve.co.uk]   01369 702220

Kyles See Kilfinan

Lochgoilhead (H) and Kilmorich
R.H.M. McAlpine BA FSAScot   1968 1990   Lochgoilhead, Argyll PA24 8AA   01301 703369

North Bute
Vacant

Rothesay: Craigmore St Brendan's See Ascog
Rothesay: The High Kirk See Kingarth and Kilchattan Bay

Rothesay: Trinity (H)
Ronald Samuel TD BSc BD STM   1960 1970   12 Crichton Road, Rothesay PA20 9JR   01700 502797 (Tel/Fax)

Sandbank See Dunoon St John's

Strachur and Strathlachlan
Robert K. Mackenzie MA BD PhD   1976   1998   Strachur, Argyll PA27 8DG   01369 860246

Strone and Ardentinny See Kilmun

Cumming, David P.L. MA	1957 1997	(Kilmodan and Colintraive)	Shillong, Tarbat Ness Road, Portmahomack, Ross-shire IV20 1YA	01862 871794
Fenemore, John H.C.	1980 1993	(Edinburgh Colinton Mains)	Seaford Cottage, 74e Shore Rd, Innellan PA23 7TR	01369 830678
Forrest, Alan B. MA	1956 1993	(Uphall: South)	126 Shore Road, Innellan, Dunoon PA23 7SX	01369 830424
Gray, John A.	1950 1986	(Glasgow Baillieston Mure Memorial)	Holyns, Ardentinny, Dunoon PA23 8TR	01369 810243
Hamilton, Patrick J.R. MA	1948 1979	(East Kilbride South)	La Madrugada, Tighnabruaich PA21 2BE	01700 811586
McKenzie, Mary O. (Miss)	1976 1996	(Edinburgh Richmond Craigmillar)	4 Dunellan Avenue, Moodiesburn, Glasgow G69 0GB	01236 870180
Marshall, James S. BA BD FFA MDiv	1986 1989	(Lochgoilhead and Kilmorich)	7 Manse Gardens, Strachur, Cairndow PA27 8DS	01369 860311
Miller, Harry Galbraith MA BD	1941 1985	(Iona and Ross of Mull)	An Cala Ciatach, Bannatyne Mains Road, Port Bannatyne, Rothesay PA20 OPH	01700 502920
Stewart, Donald MA	1944 1984	(Fenwick)	Seafield, Toward, Dunoon PA23 7UG	01369 870206
Watson, James LTh	1968 1994	(Bowden with Lilliesleaf)	7 Lochan Avenue, Kirn, Dunoon PA23 8HT	01369 702851
Watt, J.H. Innes MA BD	1960 1994	(Mochrum)	30 Crichton Road, Rothesay PA20 9JR	01700 505300

DUNOON
Communion Sundays

Ascog	2 My., 1 Nv.
Craigmore	2 My., 1 Nv.
Dunoon	
Old and St Cuthbert's	1 Fb., Je., Oc.
St John's	1 Mr., Je., Nv.
Innellan	1 Mr., Je., Sp.,Dc.
Inverchaolain and Toward	Lst Fb, My. Au. Nv
Kilfinan	Lst Ap. Oc.
Kilmodan	
and Colintraive	1 Ap., Sp.
Kilmun	Lst Je., Nv.
Kingarth and Kilchattan Bay	Lst Fb., Je., Oc.
Kirn	1 My., Nv.
Kyles	1 My., Nv.
Lochgoilhead and	
Kilmorich	Lst Ap., Oc.
	2 Mr., Je., Sp. Nv.
	1 Au., E.
North Bute	1 My., Nv.
Rothesay	
The High Kirk	1 Fb., My., Nv.
Trinity	1 Fb., My., Nv.
Sandbank	1 Ja., My., Nv.
Strachur and Strathlachlan	1 Mr., Je., Nv.
Strone and Ardentinny	Lst Fb., Je., Oc.

(21) LORN AND MULL

Meets at Oban, in the Church of Scotland Centre, Glencruitten Rd., on the first Tuesday of May, June, September and October and on the first Wednesday of February, April, November and December and at Tobermory on the first Tuesday of March.

Clerk: REV. WILLIAM T. HOGG MA BD	The Manse, Tynedrum, Crianlarich FK20 8RY	01838 400240
Treasurer: DONALD J.F. MACDONALD	4 William Street, Oban	01631 564191

Appin linked with Lismore
Douglas R. Robertson BSc BD   1991   1995   Appin, Argyll PA38 4DD   01631 730206
[e-mail: douglas@appinmanse.freeserve.co.uk]

Ardchattan (H)
Jeffrey A. McCormick BD   1984   Ardchattan, Connel, Argyll PA37 1QZ   01631 710364

Coll
Continuing Vacancy   Arinagour, Isle of Coll PA78 6SY   01879 230366

Colonsay and Oronsay linked with Kilbrandon and Kilchattan
Freda Marshall (Mrs) BD FCII   1993   1997   The Manse, Winterton Road, Balvicar, Argyll PA34   01852 300240
[e-mail: f.marshall@ukonline.co.uk]

Connel
Ronald Gall BSc BD   1985   1991   St Oran's Manse, Connel, Argyll PA37 1PJ   01631 710242
[e-mail: ronniegall@aol.com]

Glenorchy and Innishael linked with Strathfillan
William T. Hogg MA BD   1979   1981   The Manse, Tynedrum, Crianlarich FK20 8RY   01838 400240
[e-mail:wthogg@easynet.co.uk]

Iona linked with Kilfinichen and Kilvickeon and the Ross of Mull
David J. Taylor MA BD   1982   1993   Bunessan, Isle of Mull PA67 6DW   01681 700227

Kilbrandon and Kilchattan See Colonsay and Oronsay

Kilchrenan and Dalavich linked with Muckairn
Margaret R.M. Millar (Miss) BTh   1977   1996   Taynuilt, Argyll PA35 1HW   01866 822204
[e-mail: macoje@aol.com]

Kilfinichen and Kilvickeon and the Ross of Mull　See Iona

Kilmore (GD) and Oban
Andrew B. Campbell　BD DPS　　1979　　Strathearn, Breadalbane Street, Oban　PA34 5PA　　01631　562322
[e-mail: revabc@obancofs.freeserve.co.uk]

Mull, Isle of, Kilninian and Kilmore linked with Salen (H) and Ulva
linked with Tobermory (GD) (H) linked with Torosay (H) and Kinlochspelvie
Alan T. Taylor　BD　　1980　　Tobermory, Isle of Mull　PA75 6PS　　01688　302226
01688　302037　(Fax)
01680　300359

William Pollock　MA BD PhD (Assoc)　　1987　　Salen, Aros, Isle of Mull　PA72 6JF

Lismore　See Appin
Muckairn　See Kilchrenan
Salen and Ulva　See Mull
Strathfillan　See Glenorchy

Tiree (GD)
Robert D. Higham　BD　　1985　1996　　Isle of Tiree　PA77 6TN　　01879　220377

Tobermory　See Mull
Torosay and Kinlochspelvie　See Mull

Galbraith, David O.　MA BD	1940 1980	(Muckairn)	Achnameadhonach, Balindeor, Taynuilt, Argyll　PA35 1JS	
Lamont, Archibald	1952 1994	(Kilcalmonell with Skipness)	8 Achlonan, Taynuilt, Argyll PA35	01866 822385
MacKechnie, J.M.　MBE MA	1938 1978	(Kilchrenan and Dalavich)	Eastwing, Manton Grounds, Windermere, Cumbria	
Troup, Harold J.G.　MA	1951 1980	(Garelochhead)	Tighshee, Isle of Iona　PA76	01681 700309

(22) FALKIRK

Meets at St Andrew's West, Falkirk on the first Tuesday of September, October, November, December and March, and on the fourth Tuesday of January and June; and in one of the Cumbernauld churches by rotation on the first Tuesday in May.

Clerk:　REV. IAN W. BLACK　MA BD　　Zetland Manse, Ronaldshay Crescent, Grangemouth　FK3 9JH　　01324 472868
[Internet: http://www.falkirkp.dabsol.co.uk]
Assoc Clerk:　REV. D.E. McCLEMENTS　MA BD MTh　　30 Russel Street, Falkirk　FK2 7BS　　01324 624461
Treasurer:　MR. I. MACDONALD　　1 Jones Avenue, Larbert　FK5 3ER　　01324 553603

Airth (H)
John Fairful BD — 1994 — Airth, Falkirk FK2 8JQ — 01324 831474

Blackbraes and Shieldhill
James H. Drysdale LTh — 1987 1997 — Shieldhill, Falkirk FK1 2EG [e-mail: 106412.2152@compuserve.com] — 01324 621938

Bo'ness: Old
William McPherson BD DipEd — 1994 — 10 Dundas Street, Bo'ness EH51 ODG — 01506 822206

Bo'ness: St Andrew's
Albert O. Bogle BD MTh — 1981 — Bo'ness EH51 9DT [e-mail:a.bogle@cableinet.co.uk] [Internet: wwwstandrewsparishchurch.organisation.uk] — 01506 822195

Bonnybridge St Helen's (H) (01324 815756)
Donald G.B. McCorkindale BD DipMin — 1992 — 133 Falkirk Road, Bonnybridge FK4 1BA [e-mail: dgbmcc@bigfoot.com] [Internet: www.bigfoot.com/~dgbmcc] — 01324 812621 (Tel/Fax)

David Wandrum (Aux) — 1993 — 42C Clouden Road, Kildrum, Cumbernauld G67 2EW — 01236 723288

Bothkennar and Carronshore
Patricia A. Carruth (Mrs) BD — 1998 — 11 Hunter's Place, Greenmount Park, Carronshore FK2 8QS — 01324 570525

Brightons (H)
Scott R. McL. Kirkland BD MAR — 1996 — The Manse, Maddiston Road, Brightons, Falkirk FK2 OJP [e-mail: scott@kirkland46.freeserve.co.uk] — 01324 712062

Carriden
R. Gordon Reid BSc BD AMIEE — 1993 — Carriden, Bo'ness EH51 9LW — 01506 822141
John Jenkinson LTCL ALCM DipEd (Aux) — 1991 — 8 Rosehall Terrace, Falkirk FK1 1PY — 01324 625498

Cumbernauld: Abronhill (H)
Neil W. Barclay BSc BEd BD — 1986 — 26 Ash Road, Cumbernauld G67 3ED — 01236 723833
Marilyn Douglas (Miss) DCS — 201 Almond Road, Cumbernauld G67 3LS — 01236 732136

Cumbernauld: Condorrat (H)
H. Taylor Brown BD CertMin — 1997 — 11 Rosehill Drive, Cumbernauld G67 4FD — 01236 721464
Janette McNaughton (Miss) DCS — 6 Dunellan Avenue, Moodiesburn, Glasgow G69 0GB — 01236 890180

Cumbernauld: Kildrum (H)
James Cochrane LTh — 1994 — Clouden Road, Cumbernauld G67 2JQ — 01236 723204
David Nicholson DCS — 2D Doon Side, Kildrum, Cumbernauld G67 2HX — 01236 732260

Congregation / Minister		Address	Tel
Cumbernauld: Old (H)			
Catriona Ogilvie (Mrs) BD	1999	Baronhill, Cumbernauld, Glasgow G67 2SD	01236 721912
Colin Ogilvie DCS		6 Ranfurly Drive, Cumbernauld G68 0DS	01236 728301
Cumbernauld: St Mungo's			
Vacant		The Manse, Fergusson Road, Cumbernauld G67 1LS	01236 721513
Elsie M. Miller (Miss) DCS		30 Swinton Avenue, Rowanbank, Baillieston, Glasgow G69 6JR	0141 771 0857
Denny: Dunipace (H)			
Jean W. Gallacher (Miss) BD	1989	Dunipace Manse, Denny, Stirlingshire FK6 6QJ	01324 824540
Denny: Old			
Richard Smith BD	1976 1983	31 Duke Street, Denny FK6 6NR	01324 824508
Denny: Westpark (H)			
Vacant		13 Baxter Crescent, Denny FK6 5EZ	01324 823782
Falkirk: Bainsford			
Brian R. Hendrie BD	1992 1997	1 Valleyview Place, Newcarron Village, Falkirk FK2 7JB	01324 621087
Falkirk: Camelon Irving (H)			
Sally Foster Fulton (Mrs) BA BD	1999	Dorrator Road, Camelon, Falkirk FK1 4BN	01324 623035
Falkirk: Camelon St John's			
James K. Wallace MA BD STM	1988	24 Rennie Street, Falkirk FK1 5QW	01324 623631
Margaret Corrie (Miss) DCS		44 Sunnyside Street, Falkirk FK1 4BH	01324 670656
Falkirk: Erskine (H)			
Glen D. Macauley BD	1999	Burnbrae Road, Falkirk FK1 5SD	01324 623701
Falkirk: Grahamston United (H)			
Duncan E. McClements MA BD MTh	1967 1976	30 Russel Street, Falkirk FK2 7HS	01324 624461
Falkirk: Laurieston linked with Redding and Westquarter			
Ronald J. McDowall BD	1980	11 Polmont Road, Laurieston FK2 9QQ	01324 621196
Falkirk: Old and St Modan's (H)			
A. Sheila Blount (Mrs) BD BA	1978 1998	9 Major's Loan, Falkirk FK1 5QF [e-mail: gkblount@aol.com]	01324 623063 (Tel/Fax)
Ronald W. Smith BA BEd BD (Assoc)	1978	19 Neilson Street, Falkirk FK1 5AQ	01324 621058
Falkirk: St Andrew's West (H)			
Alastair M. Horne BSc BD	1989 1997	1 Maggiewood's Loan, Falkirk FK1 5SJ	01324 623308

Charge / Minister			Address	Telephone
Falkirk: St James' Eric McKimmon BA BD MTh	1983	1992	13 Wallace Place, Falkirk FK2 7EN	01324 622757
Grangemouth: Charing Cross and West (H) Daniel L. Mathers BD	1982		36 Thistle Avenue, Grangemouth FK3 8YQ	01324 474511
Grangemouth: Dundas Douglas B. Blair LTh	1969		5 Abbotsgrange Road, Grangemouth FK3 9JD	01324 482467
Grangemouth: Kerse Andrew C. Donald BD DPS	1992		8 Naismith Court, Grangemouth FK3 9BQ	01324 482109
Grangemouth: Kirk of the Holy Rood J.G. Finlay (Mrs) DipMusEd BD	1996		Bowhouse Road, Grangemouth FK3 0EX	01324 471595
Grangemouth: Zetland (H) Ian W. Black MA BD Colin Mailer (Aux)	1976 1996	1991 1999	Ronaldshay Crescent, Grangemouth FK3 9JH Innis Chonian, Back Row, Polmont FK2 0RD	01324 472868 01324 712401
Haggs (H) Helen Christie (Mrs) BD	1998		5 Watson Place, Dennyloanhead FK4 2BG	01324 813786
Larbert: East Melville D. Crosthwaite BD DipEd DipMin	1984	1995	1 Cortachy Avenue, Carron, Falkirk FK2 8DH	01324 562402
Larbert: Old (H) Clifford A.J. Rennie MA BD	1973	1985	38 South Broomage Avenue, Larbert FK2 3ED	01324 562868
Larbert: West (H) Gavin Boswell BTheol	1993	1999	11 Carronvale Road, Larbert FK5 3LZ	01324 562878
Muiravonside Joan Ross (Miss) BSc BD PhD	1999		Maddiston, Falkirk FK2 0LX	01324 712876
Polmont Old Vacant			Polmont, Falkirk FK2 0QY	01324 715166
Redding and Westquarter See Falkirk Laurieston				
Slamannan Raymond Thomson BD DipMin	1992		Slamannan, Falkirk FK1 3EN	01324 851307
Stenhouse and Carron (H) Robert K. Hardie MA BD	1968	1969	Stenhousemuir, Larbert FK5 4BU	01324 562393

Name			Position	Address	Telephone
Acklam, Cliff BD	1997		Chaplain: Army	Hyderabad Barracks, Colchester, Essex CO2 7TB	
Allan, Robert S.T. LLB DipLP BD	1997	1999	Education and Development Officer, Department of Ministry	1 Lime Grove, Larbert FK5 3LY	01324 562500
Blount, Graham K. LLB BD PhD	1976	1998	Parliamentary Officer	(Office) 14 Johnston Terrace, Edinburgh EH1 2PW [e-mail: gkblount@dial.pipex.com] (Home) 9 Majors Loan, Kalkirk FK1 5QF	0131 622 2278
Ferguson, Gordon	1972	1996	(Grangemouth Kirk of the Holy Rood)	16 Primrose Avenue, Grangemouth	01324 623063
Fulton, R. Stuart M. MA BD	1991	1998	Specialist Adviser in Chaplaincy to HM Prison Services	(Office) c/o Scottish Prison Service HQ, Calton House, 5 Redheugh Rig, Edinburgh (Home) Irving Manse, Dorrator Road, Falkirk FK1 4BN	01324 484935 0131 244 8459 01324 683035
Gillon, George MA CF JP	1940	1980	(Airth)	43 Strathmore Avenue, Dunblane FK15 9HX	01786 823495
Goodman, Richard A.	1976	1986	(Isle of Mull Associate)	13/2 Glenbrae Court, Falkirk FK1 1YT	01324 21315
Hendrie, Yvonne (Mrs) MA BD	1995	1997	Part-time Hospital Chaplain	1 Valleyview Place, Newcarron Village, Falkirk FK2 7JB	01324 621087
Heriot, Charles R. JP BA	1962	1996	(Brightons)	20 Eastcroft Drive, Polmont FK2 0SU	01324 711352
Hill, Stanley LTh	1967	1996	(Muiravonside)	28 Creteil Court, Falkirk FK1 1UL	01324 634483
Holland, John C.	1976	1985	(Strone and Ardentinny)	2 Breadalbane Place, Polmont, Falkirk FK2 ORF	01324 712716
Kellock, Chris BD	1998		Scripture Union Evangelist	10 Hillcrest, Bo'ness EH51 9HT	01506 511279
McCallum, John	1962	1998	(Falkirk: Irving Camelon)	11 Burnbrae Gardens, Falkirk FK1 5SB	
McDonald, William G. MA BD	1959	1975	(Falkirk Grahamstown United)	19 Union Street, Bridge of Allan FK9 4NS	01786 834535
Maclaren, William B. MA JP	1944	1983	(Bothkennar and Carronshore)	7 Malcolm Drive, Stenhousemuir FK5 4JP	01324 551274
McMullin, Andrew MA	1960	1996	(Blackbraes and Shieldhill)	33 Eastcroft Drive, Polmont FK2	01324 624938
Martin, Neil DCS			(Deacon)	1 Strathmiglo Place, Stenhousemuir FK5 4UQ	01324 551362
Munroe, Henry BA LTh LTI	1971	1988	(Denny Dunipace North with Old)	Viewforth, High Road, Maddiston, Falkirk FK2 OBL	01324 712446
Murray, Eric J.	1958	1995	(Larbert: East)	21 Redpath Drive, Greenmount Park, Stenhousemuir, Larbert	01324 563764
Paul, Iain BSc PhD BD PhD	1976	1991	(Wishaw Craigneuk and Belhaven)	116 Tryst Road, Larbert FK5 4QJ	01324 562641
Robertson, Iain M. MA	1967	1992	(Carriden)	17 Inchewan, Birnam, Dunkeld PH8 0DL	01350 727455
Robson, James MA BD	1951	1987	(Falkirk, Camelon St John's)	59 Anson Avenue, Falkirk FK1 5JB	01324 626913
Talman, Hugh MA	1943	1987	(Polmont Old)	Niagara, 70 Lawers Crescent, Polmont FK2 ORQ	01324 711240

FALKIRK ADDRESSES

Falkirk

Bainsford	Hendry Street, Bainsford
Camelon	Dorrator Road, Camelon
Irving	Glasgow Road x Stirling Road
St John's	Cockburn Street x Hodge Street
Erskine	
Grahamston	Bute Street
Laurieston	Main Falkirk Road
Old and St Modan's	Kirk Wynd
St Andrew's West	Newmarket Street
St James'	Thornhill Road x Firs Street

Grangemouth

Charing Cross and West	Charing Cross
Dundas	Bo'ness Road
Kerse	Abbot's Road
Kirk of the Holy Rood	Bowhouse Road
Zetland	Ronaldshay Crescent

(23) STIRLING

Meets at Dunblane, in the Cathedral Hall, on the second Thursday of September, and at Bridge of Allan Chalmers, on the second Thursday of every other month except January, July and August when there is no meeting.

Presbytery Office: St Columba's Church, Park Terrace, Stirling FK8 2NA
[e-mail: barrydunsmore@compuserve.com]
01786 449522 (Tel)
01786 473930 (Fax)
(Mon-Fri: 9.30 am - 12 noon)

Clerk: REV. BARRY W. DUNSMORE MA BD St Columba's Manse, 5 Clifford Road, Stirling FK8 2AQ   01786 475802

Aberfoyle (H) linked with Port of Menteith (H)
Vacant — The Manse, Loch Ard Road, Aberfoyle, Stirling FK8 3SZ — 01877 382391

Alloa: North (H)
David S.F. Couper MA BD 1988 — 30 Claremont, Alloa FK10 2DF — 01259 216845

Alloa: St Mungo's (H)
Alan F.M. Downie MA BD 1977 1996 — 37a Claremont, Alloa FK10 2DG — 01259 213872

Alloa: West
Allan McKenzie BSc BD 1988 — 29 Claremont, Alloa FK10 2DF — 01259 214204

Alva
James N.R. McNeil BSc BD 1990 1997 — The Manse, 34 Ochil Road, Alva FK12 5JT — 01259 760262

Balfron linked with Fintry (H)
John Turnbull 1994 — Balfron, Glasgow G63 OSX — 01360 440285

Balquhidder linked with Killin and Ardeonaig (H)
John Lincoln MPhil BD 1986 1997 — The Manse, Killin FK21 8TN
[e-mail: gmojol@zetnet.co.uk] — 01567 820247

Bannockburn: Allan(H)
Jim Landels BD CertMin 1990 — Bogend Road, Bannockburn FK7 8NP
[e-mail: jimlandels@virgin.net] — 01786 814692

Bannockburn: Ladywell (H)
Elizabeth M.D. Robertson (Miss) BD CertMin 1997 — 57 The Firs, Bannockburn FK7 OEG — 01786 812467

Bridge of Allan: Chalmers (H)
Alexander G. Horsburgh MA BD — 1996
34 Kenilworth Road, Bridge of Allan, Stirling FK9 4EH
[e-mail: alexanderhorsburgh@compuserve.com]
01786 832118 (Tel)
01786 831176 (Fax)

Bridge of Allan: Holy Trinity (H) (01786 834155)
John C. Nicol MA BD — 1965 1985
29 Keir Street, Bridge of Allan, Stirling FK9 4QJ
[e-mail: johncnicol@aol.com]
01786 832093

Buchanan linked with Drymen
Alexander J. MacPherson BD — 1986 1997
Buchanan Manse, Drymen, Glasgow G63 0AQ
01360 870212

Buchlyvie (H) linked with Gartmore (H)
Moira G. MacCormick BA LTh — 1986
8 Culbowie Crescent, Buchlyvie, Stirling FK8 3NH
01360 850249

Callander (H) (Tel/Fax 01877 331409]
Iain M. Goring BSc BD — 1976 1985
3 Aveland Park Road, Callander FK17 8FD
[e-mail: gorings@globalnet.co.uk]
01877 330097

June Cloggie (Mrs) (Aux) — 1997 1998
8 Trossachs Road, Aberfoyle FK8 3SW
01877 382382

Cambusbarron: The Bruce Memorial (H)
Brian Webster BSc BD — 1998
14 Woodside Court, Cambusbarron FK7 9PH
[e-mail: revwebdial@pipex.com]
01786 450579

Clackmannan (H)
J. Gordon Matthew MA BD — 1973 1999
The Manse, Clackmannan FK10 4JH
01259 214238 (Tel)
01259 211255 (Fax)

Cowie (H) linked with Plean
Vacant
The Manse, Plean, Stirling FK7 8BX
01786 813287

Dollar (H) linked with Glendevon linked with Muckhart
John P.S. Purves BSc BD — 1978 1990
2 Manse Road, Dollar FK14 7AJ
[e-mail: dollar.parish@btinternet.com]
01259 743432

Margaret McArthur BD DipMin (Assoc) — 1995
The Manse, Muckhart FK14 7JIN
01259 781464

Jean S. Watson (Miss) MA (Aux) — 1993 1998
29 Strachan Crescent, Dollar FK14 7HL
01259 742872

Drymen See Buchanan

Dunblane: Cathedral (H)
Colin G. McIntosh BSc BD — 1976 1988
Cathedral Manse, Dunblane FK15 0AQ
01786 822205

Dunblane: St Blane's (H)
George G. Cringles BD — 1981 1988
49 Roman Way, Dunblane FK15 9DJ
01786 822268

Fallin
Eleanor D. Muir (Miss) MTheol DipPTheol | 1986 | 4 King Street, Fallin, Stirling FK7 7JY | 01786 812243

Fintry See Balfron

Gargunnock linked with Kincardine in Menteith
Catherine A. Hepburn (Miss) BA BD | 1982 1994 | The Manse, Gargunnock, Stirling FK8 3BQ | 01786 860678

Gartmore See Buchlyvie
Glendevon See Dollar

Killearn (H)
Philip R.M. Malloch LLB BD | 1970 1993 | 2 The Oaks, Killearn, Glasgow G63 9SF | 01360 550045

Killin and Ardeonaig (H) See Balquhidder

Kilmadock
Vacant | Doune, Perthshire FK16 6EL | 01786 841437

Kincardine in Menteith See Gargunnock.

Kippen (H) linked with Norrieston
Gordon MacRae BA BD | 1985 1998 | The Manse, Kippen, Stirling FK8 3DN | 01786 870229

Lecropt (H)
William M. Gilmour MA BD | 1969 1983 | 5 Henderson Street, Bridge of Allan, Stirling FK9 4NA | 01786 832382

Logie (H)
Vacant | 128 Causewayhead Road, Stirling FK9 5HJ | 01786 463060

Menstrie (H)
George T. Sherry LTh | 1977 | The Manse, Menstrie FK11 7EA | 01259 761461

Muckhart See Dollar
Norrieston See Kippin
Plean See Cowie
Port of Menteith See Aberfoyle

Sauchie and Coalsnaughton
Agnes A. Moore (Miss) BD | 1987 1995 | Parish Church Manse, Main Street, Sauchie FK10 3JX | 01259 212037

Stirling: Allan Park South (H) linked with Church of the Holy Rude (H)
Morris C. Coull BD | 1974 1996 | 22 Laurelhill Place, Stirling FK8 2JH | 01786 473999

Stirling: Church of the Holy Rude (H) See Allan Park South (H)

Stirling: North (H)				
Paul M.N. Sewell MA BD	1970	1978	18 Shirra's Brae Road, Stirling FK7 0BA	01786 475378
Stirling: St Columba's (H) (01786 449516)				
Barry W. Dunsmore MA BD	1982	1988	5 Clifford Road, Stirling FK8 2AQ [e-mail: barrydunsmore@compuserve.com]	01786 475802 (Tel) / 01786 473930 (Fax)
Stirling: St Mark's				
Rodney P.T. Robb	1995		176 Drip Road, Stirling FK8 1RR	01786 473716
Stirling: St Ninian's Old (H)				
Gary J. McIntyre BD DipMin	1993	1998	7 Randolph Road, Stirling FK8 2AJ	01786 474421
Stirling: Viewfield (T)(H)				
Ian Taylor BD ThM	1995		7 Windsor Place, Stirling FK8 2HY	01786 474534
Strathblane (H)				
Alex H. Green MA BD	1986	1995	Strathblane, Glasgow G63 9AQ	01360 770226
Tillicoultry (H)				
John Russell MA	1959	1978	The Manse, Dollar Road, Tillicoultry FK13 6PD	01259 750340 / 01259 752951 (Fax)
Tullibody St Serf's (H)				
Vacant			Tullibody, Alloa FK10 2RG	01259 213236

Aitken, E. Douglas MA	1961	1998	(Clackmannan)	1 Dolan Grove, Saline KY12 9UP	01383 852730
Anderson, Robert S.	1988	1987	Director: SCWE	St John's, Muir Crescent, Doune FK16 6DA	01786 841386
Benson, James W. BA BD DipEd	1975	1996	(Balquhidder)	1 Sunnyside, Dunblane FK15 9HA	01786 822624
Burnett, John B.	1964	1985	(Dollar: Associate)	30 Manor House Road, Dollar FK14	01259 742892
Campbell, Patrick D.G. MA	1949	1984	(Geneva)	30 Harviestoun Road, Dollar FK14 7HG	01259 742172
Cruikshank, Alistair A.B. MA	1991		Auxiliary	2A Chapel Place, Dollar FK14	01259 742549
Doherty, Arthur James DipTh	1957	1993	(Fintry)	1 Murdiston Avenue, Callander FK17 8AY	
Edie, Charles B. MA	1946	1984	(Stirling, Church of the Holy Rude)	6 Calton, Shirras Brae Road, Stirling FK7 0AX	01786 474271
Fleming, Alexander F.	1966	1995	(Strathblane)	4 Horsburgh Avenue, Kilsyth G65 9BZ	01236 821461
Gallan, Alex MA	1955	1989	(Wishaw Cambusnethan North)	16 Dundas Road, Stirling	01786 470796
Irvine, R.W.W.	1965	1993	(Kincardine-in-Menteith with Norrieston)	9 Fraser Place, Causewayhead, Stirling FK9 5RE	01786 448802
Jamieson, G.T. BA	1936	1969	(Stirling Viewfield)	10 Grendon Court, Snowdon Place, Stirling	01786 461646
Jamieson, John LTh	1967	1993	(Balfron)	Ardnablane, Dunblane FK15	01786 828361

Names, charges and years

Name	(Charge / Appointment)		
Laing, John M. MA	(Buchlyvie with Gartmore)	1948	1985
McCallum, Iain D. MA	(Stirling Allan Park South)	1943	1984
McCutcheon, George A. MA	(Clackmannan)	1948	1984
Macdonald, R.M. OBE MA DD	(Calabar)	1929	1968
McIntosh, Hamish N.M. MA	(Fintry)	1949	1987
Macrae, Elaine H.(Mrs) BD	Prison Chaplain	1985	1998
McRae, Malcolm H. MA PhD	(Coalsnaughton)	1986	1994
McWilliam, Stuart W. MA STM	(Killearn)	1941	1981
Maxton, Ronald M. MA	(Dollar: Associate)	1955	1995
Orrock, Archibald. A. MA BD	(Teacher: Religious Instruction)	1938	1982
Ovens, Samuel B. BD	(Slamannan)	1982	1993
Poustie, G.T.		1966	1993
Pryce, Stuart F.A.	(Dumfries: St George's)	1963	1997
Reid, Alan A.S. MA BD STM	(Bridge of Allan Chalmers)	1962	1995
Reid, David T. BA BD	(Cleish linked with Fossoway St Serf's and Devonside)	1954	1993
Rennie, Alistair M. MA BD	(Kincardine Croick and Edderton)	1939	1986
Robertson, Alex	(Baldernock)	1974	1993
Sangster, Ernest G. BD ThM	(Alva)	1958	1997
Scott, James F.	(Dyce)	1957	1997
Scoular, J. Marshall	(Kippen)	1954	1996
Silcox, John R. BD	School Chaplain	1976	1984
Stirling, J BSc BD	(Stirling: St Ninian's Old)	1962	1998
Swinburne, Norman B.A	(Sauchie)	1960	1993
Symington, Robert C BA	(Community Minister: Lorn and Mull)	1954	1997
Todd, A. Stewart MA BD DD	(Aberdeen: St Machar's Cathedral)	1952	1993
Turner, William MA BD	(Gargunnock)	1934	1970
Watt, Robert MA BD	(Aberdeen Woodside South)	1943	1982

58 Carseview, Bannockburn, Stirling FK7 8LH
Mount View House, Bracklinn Road, Callander FK18
13 Harviestoun Road, Dollar FK14 7HG
Pinewood Nursing Home, Leny Road, Callander FK17 8EG
1 Forth Crescent, Stirling
The Manse, Kippen FK8 3DN
10B Victoria Place, Stirling FK7
Terreran, Main Street, Gartmore, Stirling FK8 3RN
5 Rulley View, Denny FK6 6QQ
3 Kilbryde Court, Dunblane FK15 9AX
Ruellen, 28 Norwood Avanue, Alloa FK10 2BY
40 Wallace Road, Dunblane
36 Forth Park, Bridge of Allan, Stirling FK9 5NT
Wayside Cottage, Bridgend, Ceres, Fife KY15 5LS
14 Argyle Park, Dunblane FK15 9DZ
13 Tullich Terrace, Tillicoultry FK13 6RD
4 Moray Park, Doune
6 Law Hill Road, Dollar FK14 7BG
5 Gullipen View, Callander FK17
2H Buccleuch Court, Dunblane FK15 0AH
Queen Victoria School, Dunblane FK15 OJA
42 Fairies Road, Perth PH1 1LZ
Damerosehay, Birch Hill Lane, Kirkbride, Carlisle CA5 5HZ
3 Belmont, The Crescent, Dunblane FK15 0DW
Culearn, Balquhidder, Lochearnhead, Perthshire FK19 8PB
Tulmore, Gargunnock, Stirling FK8 3BQ
1 Coldstream Avenue, Dunblane FK15 9JN

Telephone numbers (printed order)

01786 815448
01877 330760
01259 742609
01786 470453
01786 870229
01877 382640
01324 825441
01786 822821
01259 216172
01786 824110
01786 831026
01786 824863
01259 751563
01786 841894
01786 825976
01786 824944
01738 442953
01697 351497
01786 823902
01877 384662
01786 860206
01786 823632

STIRLING ADDRESSES

Allan Park South	Dumbarton Road
Holy Rude	St John Street
North	Springfield Road
St Ninians Old	Kirk Wynd
St Ninians; Viewfield	Barnton Street
St Columba's	Park Terrace
St Mark's	Drip Road

(24) DUNFERMLINE

Meets at Dunfermline, in the Abbey Church Hall, Abbey Park Place on the first Thursday of each month except January, July and August when there is no meeting and June when it meets on the last Thursday.

Clerk: REV. WILLIAM E. FARQUHAR BA BD   Townhill Manse, Dunfermline KY12 OEZ   01383 723835 (Tel/Fax)

Charge / Minister	Year	Year	Address	Tel/Fax
Aberdour St Fillan's (H) Peter B. Park BD MCIBS	1997		36 Bellhouse Road, Aberdour, Fife KY3 OTL	01383 860349
Ballingry Vacant			Ballingry, Lochgelly KY5 8PA	01592 861663
Beath (H) and Cowdenbeath North Peter C. Rae BSc BD	1968	1969	North Manse, Stuart Place, Cowdenbeath KY4 9BN	01383 511033
Cairneyhill (H) linked with Limekilns (H) Norman M. Grant BD	1990		Limekilns, Dunfermline KY11 3HT	01383 872341
Carnock and Oakley (H) Elizabeth S.S. Kenny (Miss) BD RGN SCM	1989		Carnock, Dunfermline KY12 9IG	01383 850327
Cowdenbeath: Trinity (H) David G Adams BD	1991	1999	66 Barclay Street, Cowdenbeath KY4 9LD	01383 515089
Culross and Torryburn (H) Vacant			Culross, Dunfermline KY12 8JD	01383 880231
Dalgety (H) Peter K. Elston Ian Cunningham DCS	1963	1971	9 St Colme Drive, Dalgety Bay, Dunfermline KY11 5LQ 5 Forth Court, Dalgety Bay, Dunfermline KY11 5SF	01383 822316
Dunfermline: Abbey (H) Alistair L. Jessamine MA BD	1979	1991	12 Garvock Hill, Dunfermline KY12 7UU	01383 721022
Dunfermline: Gillespie Memorial (H) (01383 621253) A. Gordon Reid BSc BD	1982	1988	4 Killin Court, Dunfermline KY12 7XF	01383 723329
Dunfermline: North Gordon F.C. Jenkins MA BD PhD	1968	1998	13 Barbour Grove, Dunfermline KY12	01383 721061

Dunfermline: St Andrew's Erskine
Moira Herkes (Mrs) BD — 1985 — 1998 — 71A Townhead Road, Dunfermline KY12 0BN — 01383 734657

Dunfermline: St Leonard's (01383 620106)
Alexander B. Mitchell BD — 1981 — 12 Torvean Place, Dunfermline KY11 4YY — 01383 721054
Andrew E. Paterson (Aux) — 1994 — 61 Elmwood Terrace, Kelty KY4 — 01383 830998

Dunfermline: St Margaret's
Fiona Richard (Mrs) — 1996 — 38 Garvock Hill, Dunfermline KY12 7UU — 01383 723955

Dunfermline: St Ninian's
Elizabeth A. Fisk (Mrs) BD — 1996 — 51 St John's Drive, Dunfermline KY12 7TL — 01383 722256
Joanna White (Ms) BSc DCS — 1B Allan Crescent, Abbeyview, Dunfermline KY12 4HE — 01383 626563

Dunfermline: St Paul's
Frank T. Smith MA — 1957 — 1964 — 6 Park Avenue, Dunfermline KY12 7HX — 01383 721124

Dunfermline: Townhill (H)
William E. Farquhar BA BD — 1987 — 161 Main Street, Townhill, Dunfermline KY12 0EZ — 01383 723835

Inverkeithing St John's linked with North Queensferry (T)
Sheila Munro (Miss) BD — 1995 — 34 Hill Street, Inverkeithing KY11 1AB — 01383 412422

Inverkeithing: St Peter's (01383 412626)
George G. Nicol BD DPhil — 1982 — 1988 — 20 Struan Drive, Inverkeithing KY11 1AR — 01383 410032

Kelty
Vacant — 15 Arlick Road, Kelty KY4 0BH — 01383 830291

Limekilns See Cairneyhill

Lochcraig
James F. Todd BD CPS — 1984 — 4 Manse Road, Glencraig, Lochgelly KY5 8AQ — 01592 860315

Lochgelly: Macainsh
Mary Ann Rennie (Mrs) BD MTh — 1998 — 82 Main Street, Lochgelly KY5 9AA — 01592 780435

Lochgelly: St Andrew's (T)(H)
Robert F. Durcan MTheol — 1986 — 1990 — Station Road, Lochgelly KY5 9QX — 01592 780319

Mossgreen and Crossgates See Cowdenbeath Trinity
North Queensferry See Inverkeithing St John's

Rosyth

Name	Years	Address	Phone
Stanley Scoular	1963 1971	42 Woodside Avenue, Rosyth KY11 2LA	01383 412776
Morag Crawford (Miss) DCS		118 Wester Drylaw Place, Edinburgh EH4 2TG	0131 332 2253

Saline and Blairingone

Name	Years	Address	Phone
Richard J. Hammond BA BD	1993	Main Street, Saline, Dunfermline KY12 9PL	01383 852240

Tulliallan and Kincardine

Name	Years	Address	Phone
James G. Redpath BD DipPTh	1988	62 Toll Road, Kincardine, by Alloa FK10 4QZ	01259 730538

Name	Years	Charge/Role	Address	Phone
Archibald, D.Y. BA BD MPhil	1949 1983	(Cairneyhill with Torryburn and Newmills)	Flat 31, Runnymeade Court, Park Hill Rise, Croydon CR0 5JF	0181 681 8398
Baird, William G.G.	1977 1993	(Inverkeithing: St Johns with North Queensferry)	51 Charles Street, Pittenweem, Fife KY10 2RA	01333 311397
Bardgett, Frank D. MA BD PhD	1987 1997	Department of National Mission	6 Inchcolme Drive, North Queensferry KY11 1LD	01383 416863
Brown, Peter MA BD FRAScot	1953 1987	(Holm)	24 Inchmickery Drive, Dalgety Bay KY11 5NF	01383 822456
Campbell, John MA	1943 1978	(Urquhart)	15 Foulden Place, Dunfermline KY12 7TQ	01383 738055
Goring, John M. MA	1955 1988	(Dunfermline Gillespie Memorial)	57 Rose Street, Dunfermline KY12 0QT	01383 723971
Hall, Robert K. LTh	1968 1988	(Carnock)	31 Hawkcraig Road, Aberdour KY3 OXB	01383 860441
Mackenzie, R.P. MA BD	1936 1980	(Dunfermline St Leonard's)	23 Foulis Crescent, Juniper Green, Edinburgh EH14 5BN	0131 453 3599
Macpherson, Stewart M. MA	1953 1990	(Dunfermline Abbey)	176 Halbeath Road, Dunfermline KY11 4LB	01383 722851
Norman, Alison E.P. (Miss) MA BD	1986	Chaplain RN	HMS Raleigh, Torpoint, Cornwall PL11 2PD	
Orr, J M'Michael MA BD PhD	1949 1986	(Aberfoyle with Port of Menteith)	9 Overhaven, Limekilns, Fife KY11 3JH	01383 872245
Pogue, Victor C. BA BD	1945 1980	(Baird Research Fellow)	120 Buckstone Terrace, Edinburgh EH10 6QR	0131 445 1628
Reid, David MSc LTh FSAScot	1961 1992	(St Monans with Largoward)	North Lethans, Saline, Dunfermline KY12 9TE	01383 733144
Ross, Evan J LTh	1986 1998	(Cowdenbeath: West with Mossgreen and Crossgates)	43 Auld Mart Road, Milnathort, Kinross KY13 7FR	01577 861484
Scott, John LTh	1969 1996	(Aberdour St Fillan's)	32 White's Quay, St David's Harbour, Dalgety Bay KY11 5HT	01383 820896
Smith, T. Forrest	1959 1986	(Arbuthnott with Kinneff)	Room 15, Hanover Court, 175 Stenhouse Road, Cowdenbeath KY4	
Stuart, Anne (Miss) DCS		(Deaconess)	19 St Colme Crescent, Aberdour, Fife KY3 0ST	01383 860049
Whyte, Isabel H. (Mrs) BD	1993	Chaplain: Queen Margaret Hospital, Dunfermline	34 Shandon Crescent, Edinburgh EH11 1QF	0131 337 0866

(25) KIRKCALDY

Meets at Kirkcaldy, in St Brycedale Hall, on the first Tuesday of February, March, April, May, November and December, on the second Tuesday of September, and on the fourth Tuesday of June.

Clerk:	REV. BRYAN L. TOMLINSON TD	83 Milton Road, Kirkcaldy KY1 1TP [e-mail: ha49@dial pipex.com]	01592 204319 (Office) 01592 260315 (Tel/Fax)
Depute Clerk:	REV. JOHN C. DUNCAN BD MPhil	21 Ramsay Crescent, Burntisland KY3 9JL [e-mail: john.duncanc@btinternet.com]	01592 874303 (Tel/Fax)

Auchterderran linked with Cardenden St Fothad's linked with Kinglassie
J. Ewen R. Campbell MA BD   1967   1977   7 Woodend Road, Cardenden KY5 0NE   01592 720213

Auchtertool linked with Kirkcaldy Linktown (H) (01592 641080)
Vacant   16 Raith Crescent, Kirkcaldy KY2 5NN   01592 265536

Buckhaven (01592 715577)
Bryce Calder MA BD   1995   181 Wellesley Road, Buckhaven KY8 1JA   01592 712870

Burntisland (H)
John C. Duncan BD MPhil   1987   21 Ramsay Crescent, Burntisland KY3 9JL [e-mail: john.duncanc@btinternet.com]   01592 874303 (Tel/Fax)

Cardenden St Fothad's See Auchterderran

Denbeath linked with Methilhill
Elizabeth F. Cranfield (Miss) MA BD   1988   9 Chemiss Road, Methilhill KY8 2BS   01592 713142

Dysart (H)
Tilly Wilson (Miss) MTh   1990   1998   1 School Brae, Dysart KY1 2XB   01592 655887

Glenrothes: Christ's Kirk
James MacMillan BD   1997   12 The Limekilns, Glenrothes KY6 3QJ   01592 620536

Glenrothes: St Columba's (01592 752539)
Alistair G. McLeod   1988   40 Liberton Drive, Glenrothes KY6 3PB   01592 744558
Muriel Wilson (Miss) DCS   22 Well Gardens, Woodside, Glenrothes KY7 5HW   01592 753885

Glenrothes: St Margaret's (H) (01592 610310)
John P. McLean   1994   8 Alburne Park, Glenrothes KY7 5RB   01592 752241

Glenrothes: St Ninian's
Vacant
Carol Dickson (Miss) DCS   1 Cawdor Drive, Glenrothes KY6 2HN   01592 611963
South Lodge, Walkerton Drive, Leslie KY5 3EY   01592 743272

Innerleven East (H)
James L. Templeton BSc BD   1975   77 McDonald Street, Methil KY8 3AJ   01333 426310

Kennoway and Windygates and Balgonie : St Kenneth's (01333 351372) [e-mail: administration@st-kenneth's.freeserve.co.uk]
Richard Baxter MA BD   1997   2 Fernhill Gardens, Windygates, Leven KY8 5DZ   01333 352329
[e-mail: richard.baxter@msn.com]

Kinghorn
James Reid BD   1985   1997   17 Myre Crescent, Kinghorn, Fife KY3 9UB   01592 890269
[e-mail: jim17reid@aol.com]

Kinglassie   See Auchterderran

Kirkcaldy: Abbotshall (H)
Bryan L. Tomlinson TD   1969   1980   83 Milton Road, Kirkcaldy KY1 1TP   01592 260315   (Tel/Fax)
[e-mail: ha49@dial.pipex.com]

Kirkcaldy: Linktown (01592 641080)   See Auchtertool

Kirkcaldy: Old (01592 641672)
Vacant   2 Townsend Place, Kirkcaldy KY1 1HB   01592 260448

Kirkcaldy: Pathhead (H) (01592 204635 Tel/Fax) [e-mail: pathhead@btinternet.com]
John D. Thomson BD   1985   1993   73 Loughborough Road, Kirkcaldy KY1 3DD   01592 652215
[e-mail: john.d.thomson@cableinet.co.uk]
Maureen Paterson (Mrs) BSc (Aux)   1992   1994   91 Dalmahoy Crescent, Kirkcaldy KY2 6TA   01592 262300
[e-mail: m.e.paterson@talk21.com]

Kirkcaldy: St Andrew's (H)
Vacant   15 Harcourt Road, Kirkcaldy KY2 5HQ   01592 260816

Kirkcaldy: St Brycedale (H) (01592 640016) [e-mail: office@stbee.freeserve.co.uk]
Ken Froude MA BD   1979   6 East Fergus Place, Kirkcaldy KY1 1XT   01592 264480
[e-mail: jkfroude@kfroude.freeserve.co.uk]

Kirkcaldy: St John's
Samuel M. McNaught MA BD MTh   1968   1975   25 Bennochy Avenue, Kirkcaldy KY2 5QE   01592 263821

Kirkcaldy: Templehall (H)
Brock A. White LTh — 1971 — Appin Crescent, Kirkcaldy KY2 6EJ — 01592 260156

Kirkcaldy: Torbain
Ian Elston BD MTh — 1999 — 91 Sauchenbush Road, Kirkcaldy KY2 5RN — 01592 263015

Kirkcaldy: Viewforth (H) linked with Thornton
Vacant — 66 Viewforth Street, Kirkcaldy KY1 3DJ — 01592 652502
[e-mail: dc@thefree.net]

Leslie Trinity
David J. Smith BD DipMin — 1992 1997 — 4 Valley Drive, Leslie KY6 3BQ — 01592 741008

Leven: St Andrew's (H) (01333 428511)
Alexander R. Forsyth TD BA MTh — 1973 1985 — 5 Forman Road, Leven, Fife KY8 4HH — 01333 423843
[e-mail: levenparish@compuserve.com]

Leven: Scoonie Kirk (H)
Edgar J. Ogstor BSc BD — 1976 1987 — Links Road, Leven, Fife KY8 4HR — 01333 426518

Markinch
I.D. Gordon LTh — 1972 — 7 Guthrie Crescent, Markinch KY7 6AY — 01592 758264

Methil (H)
Vacant — 14 Methilbrae, Methil KY8 3LW — 01333 426255

Methilhill See Denbeath
Thornton See Kirkcaldy: Viewforth

Wemyss
Kenneth W. Donald BA BD — 1982 1999 — 33 Main Road, East Wemyss, Fife KY1 4RE — 01592 713260
[e-mail: kenneth@kdonald.freeserve.co.uk]

Name	Years	Charge	Address	Phone
Cooper, M.W. MA	1944 1979	(Kirkcaldy Abbotshall)	Applegarth, Sunny Park, Kinross KY13	01577 263204
Crawford, S.G. Victor	1980 1991	(Glasgow: Calton Parkhead)	Crofton, 65 Main Road, East Weymss KY1 4RI	01592 712325
Dick, James S. MA BTh	1988 1997	(Glasgow: Ruchazie)	1 Hawkmuir, Kirkcaldy KY1 2AN	01592 260289
Forrester, Ian L. MA	1964 1996	(Friockheim, Kinnell with Inverkeilor and Lunan)	8 Bennochy Avenue, Kirkcaldy KY2 5QE	01592 260251
Gatt, David W.	1981 1995	(Thornton)	15 Beech Avenue, Thornton KY1 4AT	01592 774328
Gibson, Ivor MA	1957 1993	(Abercorn with Dalmeny)	15 McInnes Road, Glenrothes KY7 6BA	01592 759982
Howden, Margaret (Miss) DCS		(Deaconess)	38 Munro Street, Kirkcaldy KY1 1PY	01592 205913

McAlpine, Robin J. BDS BD	1988 1997	Adviser in Mission and Evangelism	10 Seton Place, Kirkcaldy KY2 6UX [e-mail: robin.mcalpine@virgin.net]	01592 643518
McDonald, Iain J.M. MA BD	1984 1996	Chaplain, Kirkcaldy Acute Hospitals	26 Cairngorm Crescent, Kirkcaldy KY3 5RG	01592 263012
McKenzie, Donald M. TD MA	1947 1986	(Auchtertool with Burntisland)	76 Forth Park Gardens, Kirkcaldy KY2 5TD	01592 610281
MacLeod, Norman	1960 1988	(Orwell with Portmoak)	324 Muirfield Drive, Glenrothes KY6 2PZ	01592 620053
Reid, Martin R.B.C.	1960 1990	(Falkirk West)	13 Rothes Park, Leslie KY6 3LL	01334 473406
Simpson, Gordon M. MA BD	1959 1996	(Leslie Trinity)	37 Spottiswoode Gardens, St Andrews KY16 8SA	01592 205510
Sutherland, William	1964 1993	(Bo'ness Old)	88 Dunrobin Road, Kirkcaldy KY2 5YT	01592 741009
Taylor, John T.H.	1947 1983	(Glenrothes Christ's Kirk on the Green)	9 Douglas Road, Leslie KY6	01387 857431
Thomson, Gilbert L. BA	1965 1996	(Glenrothes Christ's Kirk)	3 Fortharfield, Freuchie KY15 7JJ	01592 873616
Webster, Elspeth H. (Miss) DCS		(Deaconess)	82 Broomhill Avenue, Burntisland KY3 0BP	013374 646
Young, W. Finlayson MA	1943 1979	(Kinglassie)	78 Whitecraig Road, Newburgh, Fife KY14	

KIRKCALDY ADDRESSES

Abbotshall	Abbotshall Road	Templehall	Beauly Place
Linktown	Nicol Street x High Street.	Torbain	Lindores Drive
Old	Kirk Wynd	Viewforth	Viewforth Street x Viewforth Terrace
Pathhead	Harriet Street x Church Street		
St Andrew's	Victoria Road x Victoria Gdns		
St Brycedale	St Brycedale Avenue x Kirk Wynd		
St John's	Elgin Street		

(26) ST ANDREWS

Meets alternately at Cupar, in St John's Church, and at St Andrews, in Hope Park Church, on the second Wednesday of February, March, April, May, September, October, November and December, and on the last Wednesday of June.

Clerk:	REV. PETER MEAGER MA BD CERTMGMT	7 Lorraine Drive, Cupar KY15 5DY	01334 656991

Abdie and Dunbog (H) linked with Newburgh (H)

Robert J.V. Logan MA BD	1962	1998	2 Guthrie Court, Cupar Road, Newburgh, Fife KY14 6HA [e-mail: rjvlogan@aol.com] 01337 840275 (Tel/Fax)

Anstruther

Ian A. Cathcart BSc BD	1994	The James Melville Manse, Anstruther KY10 3EX 01333 311808

Auchtermuchty (H)

Ann G. Fraser (Mrs) BD CertMin	1990	2 Burnside, Auchtermuchty KY14 7AJ 01337 828519

Charge / Minister			Address	Telephone
Balmerino (H) linked with Wormit (H) Graeme W. Beebee BD	1993		5 Westwater Place, Newport-on-Tay DD6 8NS	01382 542626
Boarhills and Dunino linked with St Andrews Martyrs' Vacant			49 Irvine Crescent, St Andrews KY16 8LG	01334 472948
Cameron linked with St Andrews: St Leonard's Alan D. McDonald LLB BD MTh	1979	1998	1 Cairnhill Gardens, St Andrews KY16 8UR	01334 472793
Carnbee linked with Pittenweem Charles G. Thrower BSc	1965	1970	Pittenweem, Fife KY10 2LR	01333 311255
Cellardyke (H) linked with Kilrenny David J.H. Laing BD DPS	1976	1999	Toll Road, Cellardyke, Anstruther KY10 3BH	01333 310810
Ceres and Springfield Matthew Z. Ross LLB BD	1998		The Manse, St Andrews Road, Ceres, Cupar KY15 5NQ [e-mail: mzross@aol.com]	01334 828233 (Tel/Fax) 07050 191367 (Mbl)
Crail linked with Kingsbarns (H) George Fairlie BD BVMS MRCVS	1971	1989	Crail, Fife KY10 3UH	01333 450358
Creich, Flisk and Kilmany linked with Monimail Mitchell Collins BD CPS	1996		Brunton, Cupar, Fife KY15 4PA	01337 870332
Cupar: Old (H) & St Michael of Tarvit Derek Browning MA BD DMin	1987		Eden Manse, Cupar, Fife KY15 4HQ [e-mail: Derek.Browning@btinternet.com]	01334 653196 (Tel/Fax)
Cupar: St John's John D. Hegarty LTh ABSC	1988	1997	23 Hogarth Drive, Cupar, Fife KY15 5YH	01334 655851
Dairsie linked with Kemback linked with Strathkinness (H) Alexander Strickland JP LTh	1971	1981	Dairsie, Cupar, Fife KY15 4RS	01334 653283
Edenshead and Strathmiglo Thomas G.M. Robertson LTh	1971	1984	Strathmiglo, Fife KY14 7QD	01337 860256
Elie (H) linked with Kilconquhar and Colinsburgh (H) Iain F. Paton BD FCIS	1980	1998	30 Bank Street, Elie, Leven KY9 1BW	01333 330685
Falkland (01337 858442) linked with Freuchie (H) John W. Jarvie BD CertMin MTh	1990		1 Newton Road, Falkland, Fife KY15 7AQ [e-mail: john.w.jarvie@usa.net]	01337 857696

Freuchie (H) See Falkland

Howe of Fife
Marion J. Paton (Miss) BMus BD   1991   1994   83 Church Street, Ladybank, Fife KY15 7ND   01337 830513
[e-mail: Marion.J.Paton@btinternet.com]

Kemback See Dairsie
Kilconquhar and Colinsburgh See Elie
Kilrenny See Cellardyke
Kingsbarns See Crail

Largo and Newburn(H) linked with Largo St David's
Rosemary Frew (Mrs) MA BD   1988   The Manse, Church Place, Upper Largo Fife KY8 6EH   01333 360286

Largo St David's See Largo and Newburn

Largoward linked with St Monans (H)
Gilbert C. Nisbet CA BD   1993   St Monans, Fife KY10 2DD   01333 730258

Leuchars: St Athernase and Guardbridge
A. Ray C. Gaston MA BD   1969   1998   7 David Wilson Park, Balmullo, Fife KY16 0NP   01334 870038 (Tel/Fax)
[e-mail: ray@gastona.freeserve.co.uk]

Monimail See Creich, Flisk and Kilmany
Newburgh See Abdie and Dunbog

Newport-on-Tay (H)
W. Kenneth Pryde DA BD   1994   57 Cupar Road, Newport-on-Tay DD6 8DF   01382 543165 (Tel/Fax)
[e-mail: wkpryde@aol.com]

Pittenweem See Carnbee

St Andrews: Holy Trinity
Charles Armour MA   1939   1949   17 Queen's Gardens, St Andrews KY16 9TA   01334 474494

St Andrews: Hope Park (H)
A. David K. Arnott MA BD   1971   1996   20 Priory Gardens., St Andrews KY16 8XX   01334 472912 (Tel/Fax)

St Andrews: Martyrs'(H) See Boarhills and Dunino
St Andrews: St Leonard's (H) See Cameron
St Monans See Largoward
Springfield See Ceres
Strathkinness See Dairsie

Tayport
Colin J. Dempster BD — 1990 — 27 Bell Street, Tayport DD6 9AP — 01382 552861

Wormit See Balmerino

Name	Years	Charge	Address	Tel.
Alexander, Jas. S. MA BD BA PhD	1966 1973	University of St Andrews	5 Strathkinness High Road, St Andrews KY16 9RP	01334 472680
Bennett, Alestair TD MA	1938 1976	(Strathkinness)	7 Bonfield Park, Strathkinness, St Andrews KY16 9SY	01334 850249
Best, Ernest MA BD PhD DD	1949 1982	(University of Glasgow)	13 Newmill Gardens, St Andrews KY16 8RY	01334 473315
Bews, James MA	1942 1981	(Dundee Craigiebank)	21 Balrymonth Court, St Andrews KY16 8XT	01334 476087
Bogie, A.P. MA FSAScot	1944 1979	(Forgan)	7 Gourlay Wynd, St Andrews KY16 8HP	
Bradley, Ian MA BD DPhil	1990 1990	Lecturer: University of Aberdeen	4 Donaldson Gardens, St Andrews KY16 9DN	01334 475389
Brown, Lawson R MA	1960 1997	Cameron with St Andrew's St Leonard's)	10 Park Street, St Andrews KY16 8AQ	01334 473413
Buchan, Alexander MA BD	1975 1992	(North Ronaldsay with Sanday)	26 Allan Robertson Drive, St Andrews KY16 8EY	01334 473875
Buchan, Isabel C. (Mrs)	1975		26 Allan Robertson Drive, St Andrews KY16 8EY	01334 473875
Cameron, James K. MA BD PhD FRHistS	1953 1989	(University of St Andrews)	Priorscroft, 71 Hepburn Gardens, St Andrews KY16 9LS	01334 473996
Casebow, Brian C. MA BD	1959 1993	(Edinburgh: Salisbury)	"The Rowans", 67 St Michael's Drive, Cupar KY15	01334 656385
Douglas, J.D. MA BD PhD	1957		2 Doocot Road, St Andrews KY16	01334 474876
Douglas, Peter C. JP	1966 1993	(Boarhills linked with Dunino)	The Old Schoolhouse, Flisk, Newburgh, Fife KY14 6HN	01337 870218
Duncan, James SDA NDA	1962 1972	Teacher: Religious Education	14 Largo Road, Lundin Links, Leven KY8 6DG	
Earnshaw, Philip BA BSc BD	1986 1996	(Glasgow: Pollokshields)	22 Castle Street, St Monans KY10 2AP	01333 730640
Edington, George L.	1952 1989	(Tayport)	646 Burghmuir Road, Perth PH1 1LH	
Galloway, Robert W.C. LTh	1970 1998	(Cromarty)	22 Haughgate, Leven KY8	
Gibson, Henry M. MA BD PhD	1960 1999	(Dundee: The High Kirk)	4 Comerton Place, Drumoig, by Leuchars, St Andrews KY16 0NQ	01382 542199
Gordon, Peter M. MA BD	1958 1995	(Airdrie West)	3 Cupar Road, Cuparmuir, Cupar KY15 5RH	01334 652341
Gordon, Fiona S. (Mrs) DCS		(Deacon)	3 Cupar Road, Cuparmuir, Cupar KY15 5RH	01334 652341
Henney, William MA DD	1957 1996	(St Andrews Hope Park)	46 Hepburn Gardens, St Andrews KY16	01334 472560
Hill, Roy MA	1962 1997	(Lisbon)	Forgan Cottage, Kinnessburn Road, St Andrews KY16	01334 472121
Howieson, R.A. JP MA	1937 1977	(Newport-on-Tay St Thomas's)	3 Baker Lane, St Andrews KY16	01334 473711
Kinnis, Robert L. MA BD	1931 1972	(Baillieston Mure Memorial)	Gibson House, St Andrews KY16	
Law, Arthur ACIB	1968 1988	(Kincardine in Menteith with Norrieston)	13 South Road, Cupar KY15 5JF	01334 654213
Learmonth, Walter LTh	1968 1997	(Ceres with Springfield)	14 Marionfield Place, Cupar KY15	01334 656290
Lithgow, Thomas MA	1945 1982	(Banchory Devenick with Maryculter)	124 Balgarvie Crescent, Cupar, Fife KY15 4EG	01334 655537
McCartney, Alexander C. BTh	1973 1995	(Caputh and Clunie with Kinclaven)	10 The Glebe, Crail KY10 3UT	01333 451194
McFadyen, Gavin J.	1963 1992	(Whiteinch)	62 Toll Court, Lundin Links, Leven, Fife KY8 6HH	01333 320434
McGregor, Duncan J. FIMA	1982 1996	(Channelkirk with Lauder Old)	14 Mount Melville, St Andrews KY16	01334 478314
Macintyre, William J. MA BD DD	1951 1989	(Crail with Kingsbarns)	Tigh a'Ghobhainn, Lochton, Crail KY10 3XE	01333 50327
McKane, William MA PhD DLitt DD FBA	1949 1990	(University of St Andrews)	51 Irvine Crescent, St Andrews KY16 8LG	01334 473797
Mackenzie, A.C. MA	1955 1995	(Biggar)	Hedgerow, 5 Sheils Avenue, Freuchie KY7 7JD	
McKenzie, Isabella (Miss) DCS		(Deacon)	2 Crescent Road, Lundin Links, Lower Largo KY8 6AF	01333 320115
Mackenzie, J.A..R. MA	1947 1987	(Largo St David's)	61 Viewforth Terrace, Kirkcaldy KY1 3PB	

Name and Qualifications			Charge / Appointment	Address	Telephone
MacLeod, J. Angus MA	1957	1995	(Keith: St Rufus and Botriphnie)	42 Braehead, St Monance KY10 2AL	01333 730081
MacNab, Hamish S.D. MA	1948	1982	(Kilrenny)	Fairhill, Northmuir, Kirriemuir DD8	01575 72564
McPhail, Peter MA BD	1940	1982	(Creich, Flisk and Kilmany)	44 Doocot Road, St Andrews KY16 8QP	01334 473093
Marshall, James S. MA PhD	1939	1979	(Edinburgh: South Leith Assoc)	25 St Mary's Street, St Andrews KY16 8AZ	01334 476136
Meager, Peter MA BD CertMgmt(Open)	1971	1998	(Elie with Kilconquhar and Colinsburgh)	7 Lorraine Drive, Cupar KY15 5DY	01334 656991
Nicol, Robert M.	1984	1996	(Jersey: St Columba's)	35 Upper Greens, Auchtermuchty, Cupar, Fife KY14 7BX	01337 828327
Ord, J.K.	1963		(Falkirk Condorrat)	24 Forth Street, St Monance KY10 2AX	01333 730461
Patterson, J.W. BA BD	1948	1989	(St Andrews Martyrs)	34 Claybraes, St Andrews KY16 8RS	01334 473606
Portchmouth, Roland John NDD ATD	1980	1989	(Bendochy)	1 West Braes, Pittenweem, Fife KY10 2FS	01333 311448
Porteous, J.K. DD	1944	1997	(Cupar St John's)	16 Market Street, St Andrews KY16	
Robb, Nigel I. FCP MA BD ThM MTh	1981	1998	Director of Educational Services, Board of Ministry	121 George Street, Edinburgh EH2 4YN [e-mail: nrobb@cofscotland.02G.uk]	0131 225 5722
Roy, Alan J. BSc BD	1960	1999	(Aberuthven with Dunning)	14 Comerton Place, Drumoig, nr Leuchars KY16 0NQ	01382 542225
Salters, Robert B. MA BD PhD	1966	1971	University of St Andrews	Vine Cottage, 119 South Street, St Andrews KY16 9UH	01334 473198
Scott, J. Miller MA BD FSAScot DD	1949	1988	(Jerusalem)	St Martins, 6 Trinity Place, St Andrews KY16 8SG	01334 479518
Shaw, D.W.D. BA BD LLB WS DD	1960	1990	(University of St Andrews)	4 Alexandra Court, St Andrews KY16 9XH	01334 477254 (Tel/Fax)
Sinclair, David I BSc BD PhD DipSW	1990	1998	(Boarhills and Dunino with St Andrews Martyrs)	42 South Road, Cupar KY15 5JF	01334 656957
Spowart, Mary G. (Mrs)	1978	1991	(Papa Westray with Westray)	Aldersyde, St Abbs Road, Coldingham, Eyemouth TD14 5NR	01890 771697
Stevenson A.L. LLB MLitt DPA FPEA	1984	1993	(Balmerino linked with Wormit)	41 Main Street, Dairsie, Fife KY16	01334 870582
Stoddart, David L.	1961	1987	(Laggan with Newtonmore)	3 Castle Street, Anstruther KY10 3DD	01333 310668
Strong, Clifford LTh	1983	1995	(Creich, Flisk and Kilmany with Monimail)		
Taylor, Ian BSc MA LTh DipEd	1983	1997	(Abdie and Dunbog with Newburgh)	60 Maryknowe, Gauldry, Newport-on-Tay DD6 8SL	01382 330445
Thomson, P.G. MA BD MTh ThD	1947	1989	(Irvine Fullarton)	Lundie Cottage, Arncroach, Fife KY10 2RN	01333 720222
Torrance, Alan MA BD Dr Theol	1984	1999	University of St Andrews	Fullarton, 2 Beech Walk, Crail KY10 3UN / St Mary's College, South Street, St Andrews KY16 9JU	01333 50423 / 01334 462851
Turnbull, James J. MA	1940	1981	(Arbirlot with Colliston)	Woodlands, Beech Avenue, Ladybank KY7 7NG	01337 30279
Walker, James B. MA BD DPhil	1975	1993	Chaplain: University of St Andrews	1 Gillespie Terrace, The Scores, St Andrews KY16 9AT [e-mail: jbw1@St-Andrews.Ac.uk]	01334 477471 (Tel) / 01334 462697 (Fax)
Watson, D.H.A.	1956	1994	(Anstruther)	Lindores, 6 Roomebay Crescent, Crail KY10	01333 450609
Whyte, James A. MA LLD DD DUniv	1945	1987	(University of St Andrews)	13 Hope Street, St Andrews KY16 9HJ	01334 472323
Wilson, Robert McL. MA BD PhD DD FBA			(University of St Andrews)	10 Murrayfield Road, St Andrews KY16 9NB	01334 474331
Wright, Lynda (Miss) BEd DCS	1946	1983	Deacon: Retreat Leader, Key House	6 Key Cottage, High Street, Falkland, Fife KY15 7BD	01337 857705

(27) DUNKELD AND MEIGLE

Meets at Pitlochry on the first Tuesday of September and December; on the third Tuesday of February, April and October, and at the Moderator's Church on the third Tuesday of June.

Clerk: REV. ALBERT B. REID BD BSc   The Manse, Dundee Road, Meigle, Blairgowrie PH12 8SB   01828 640278 (Tel/Fax)
                                                                                         [e-mail: abreid@surfaid.org]

Assistant Clerk: REV. BRUCE DEMPSEY BD   The Manse, Caddam Road, Coupar Angus, Perthshire PH13 9EF   01828 628871
                                                                                         [e-mail: dunkeld&meigle@pipex dial.com]

Aberfeldy (H) linked with Amulree and Strathbraan linked with Dull and Weem
Alexander M. Gunn MA BD   1967   1986   Taybridge Terrace, Aberfeldy, Perthshire PH15 2BS   01887 820656 (Tel/Fax)

Alyth (H)
Neil N. Gardner MA BD   1991   1998   Cambridge Street, Alyth, Perthshire PH11 8AW   01828 632104
                                                                [e-mail: nng@surfaid.org]

Amulree and Strathbraan See Aberfeldy

Ardler, Kettins and Meigle
Albert B. Reid BD BSc   1966   1993   The Manse, Dundee Road, Meigle, Blairgowrie PH12 8SB   01828 640278 (Tel/Fax)
                                                                [e-mail: abreid@surfaid.org]

Bendochy linked with Blairgowrie St Mary's South
Michael R. Philip BD   1978   1988   83 Smithfield Crescent, Blairgowrie PH10 6UE   01250 874717
                                                                [e-mail: mrphilip@onet.co.uk]]

Blair Atholl and Struan
Neil Gow BSc MEd BD   1996   Blair Atholl, Perthshire PH18 5SX   01796 481213
                                                        [e-mail: the-gows@lineone.net]

Blairgowrie: St Andrew's (H)
Robert Sloan BD   1997   Upper David Street, Blairgowrie PH10 6HB   01250 872146
                                                [e-mail: robertsloan@lineone.net]

Blairgowrie: St Mary's South See Bendochy

Braes of Rannoch linked with Foss and Rannoch (H)
David G. Hamilton MA BD   1971   1998   Kinloch Rannoch, Pitlochry PH16 5QA   01882 632381
                                                                [e-mail:dghamilton@bigfoot.com]

Caputh and Clunie (H) linked with Kinclaven (H)(T)
Linda J. Broadley (Mrs) LTh DipEd   1996   Caputh, Perth PH1 4JH   01738 710520

Coupar Angus Abbey
Bruce Dempsey BD   1997   Caddam Road, Coupar Angus, Perthshire PH13 9EF   01828 627331
[e-mail: demp01@aol.com]

Dull and Weem See Aberfeldy

Dunkeld (H)
Albert E. Smith BD FSAScot   1983   1990   Cathedral Manse, Dunkeld PH8 OAW   01350 727249
[e-mail: aesdunkeld@aol.com]

Fortingall and Glenlyon linked with Kenmore and Lawers
Anne J. Brennan BSc BD MTh   1999   Balnaskeag, Kenmore, Aberfeldy PH15 2HB   01887 830218

Foss and Rannoch See Braes of Rannoch

Grantully Logierait and Strathtay
Vacant   Strathtay, Perthshire PH9 OPG   01887 840251

Kenmore and Lawers (H) See Fortingall and Glenlyon
Kinclaven See Caputh and Clunie

Kirkmichael Straloch and Glenshee linked with Rattray (H)
Hugh C. Ormiston BSc BD MPhil PhD   1969   1998   The Manse, Alyth Road, Rattray PH10 7HF   01250 872462
[e-mail: hcormiston@aol.com]

Pitlochry (H) (01796 472160)
Malcolm Ramsay BA LLB DipMin   1986   1998   Manse Road, Moulin, Pitlochry PH16 5EP   01796 472774

Rattray See Kirkmichael Straloch and Glenshee

Tenandry
Continued Vacancy

Barbour, Robin A.S.   1954 1982   (University of Aberdeen)   Fincastle, Pitlochry PH16 5RJ   01796 473209
  KCVO MC BD STM DD
Bell, F. Routledge   1944 1983   (Caputh with Murthly)   Hawthornbank House, Wolfhill, Perth PH2 6DA   01821 650421

Name		Congregation	Address	Phone
Campbell, John A. JP FIEM	1984 1998	(Irvine: St Andrew's)	Flowerdale, Balmoral Lane, Blairgowrie PH10 7AF	01250 872795
Cassells, Alexander K. MA BD	1961 1997	(Leuchars St Athernase and Guardbridge)	Tighaness, Keltney Burn, By Aberfeldy PH15 2LS	01887 830758
Dick, Tom MA	1951 1982	(Dunkeld)	Mo Dhachaidh, Callybrae, Dunkeld PH8 OEP	01350 727338
Duncan, James BTh FSAScot	1980 1995	(Blair Atholl and Struan)	25 Knockard Avenue, Pitlochry PH16 5JE	01796 474096
Forsyth, David Stuart MA	1948 1992	(Belhelvie)	Birchlea, 38 Fonab Crescent, Pitlochry PH16 5SR	01796 473708
Fulton, Frederick H. MA	1942 1983	(Clunie, Lethendy and Kinloch)	Grampian Cottage, Chapel Brae, Braemar AB35 5YT	01339 741277
Grieve, David S.A. MA BD	1954 1991	(Arbirlot with Carmyllie with Colliston)	Dundarroch, Meigle Road, Alyth, Blairgowrie PH11 8EU	01828 632318
Henderson, John D. MA BD	1953 1992	(Cluny with Monymusk)	Aldersyde, George Street, Blairgowrie PH10 6HP	01250 875181
Knox, John W. MTheol	1992 1997	(Lochgelly: Macainsh)	Heatherlea, Main Street, Ardler, Blairgowrie PH12 8SR	01828 640731
Low, J.E. Stewart MA	1957 1997	(Tarbat)	Floral, Perth Road, Blairgowrie PH10 6QB	01250 873108
McAlister, D.J.B. MA BD PhD	1951 1989	(North Berwick Blackadder)	2 Duff Avenue, Moulin, Pitlochry PH16 5EN	01796 473591
Macartney, William M. MA	1938 1978	(Vienna)	Coutie Cottage, Coupar Angus, Pethshire PH13 9HF	01828 628152
Macdonald, James F. TD	1930 1984	(Bendochy with Kinclaven)	6 Cluny Court, Grant Road, Blairgowrie PH10 6PU	01250 875737
Macpherson, Norman J. TD	1954 1980	(Blairgowrie St Mary's South)	31 Glenburn Drive, Inverness IV2 4NE	01463 230536
MacVicar, Kenneth MBE DFC TD MA	1950 1990	(Kenmore with Lawers with Fortingall & Glenlyon)	Illeray, Kenmore, Aberfeldy PH15 2HE	01887 830514
Martin, Francis BL	1956 1991	(Pitlochry East)	58 West Moulin Road, Pitlochry PH16 5EQ	01796 472619
Shannon, W.G.H. MA BD	1955 1998	(Pitlochry)	19 Knockard Road, Pitlochry PH16 5HJ	01796 473533
Stewart, Walter T.A.	1964 1999	(Barry)	7A Tummel Crescent, Pitlochry PH16 5DF	01796 473422
Tait, Thomas W. ED	1972 1997	(Rattray)	20 Cedar Avenue, Blairgowrie PH10 6TT	01250 874833
Young, G. Stuart	1961 1996	(Blairgowrie: St Andrew's)	7 James Place, Stanley PH1 4PD	01738 828473

(28) PERTH

Meets at Scone: Old, at 7.00pm, in the Elizabeth Ashton Hall, on the second Tuesday of every month except January, July and August, when there is no meeting, and on the last Tuesday of June when it meets in the church of the incoming Moderator

Clerk:	Rev. ALEX. M. MILLAR MA BD MBA		Scone: New Church, Angus Road, Scone, Perth PH2 6QU	01738 553605 (Tel)
Presbytery Office:			[e-mail: perth@dial.pipex.com]	01738 553607 (Fax)

Aberdalgie and Dupplin linked with Forteviot

Colin R. Williamson LLB BD	1972 1984	Aberdalgie, Perth PH2 0QD	01738 625854

Abernethy and Dron linked with Arngask

Kenneth G. Anderson MA BD	1967 1988	Abernethy, Perth PH2 9JP	01738 850607

Aberuthven linked with Dunning

Vacant		The Manse, Dunning, Perth PH2 0SL	01764 684223

Almondbank Tibbermore
Donald Campbell BD — 1998 — Pitcairngreen, Perth PH1 3LT — 01738 583217

Ardoch (H) linked with Blackford (H)
Hazel Wilson (Ms) MA BD DipEd DMS — 1991 — Braco, Dunblane FK15 9RE — 01786 880217

Arngask See Abernethy and Dron

Auchterarder (H)
Michael R.R. Shewan MA BD CPS — 1985 1998 — 24 High Street, Auchterarder, Perth PH3 1DF — 01764 662210

Auchtergaven and Moneydie
William McGregor LTh — 1987 — Bankfoot, Perth PH1 4BS — 01738 787235

Blackford See Ardoch

Cargill Burrelton linked with Collace
Robert J. Watt BD — 1994 — Woodside, Blairgowrie PH13 9NQ — 01828 670352
[e-mail: rjw@tesco.net]

Cleish (H) linked with Fossoway St Serf's and Devonside
A. David Macleod MA BD — 1993 1994 — Cleish, Kinross KY13 7LR — 01577 850231 (Tel/Fax)

Collace See Cargill and Burrelton

Comrie and Strowan (H) linked with Dundurn (H)
P.D. Thomson MA BD — 1968 1978 — Comrie, Perthshire PH6 2HE — 01764 670269
[e-mail: revpdt@the-manse.freeserve.co.uk]

Crieff (H)
Bruce Ritchie BSc BD — 1977 1987 — 8 Strathearn Terrace, Crieff PH7 3AQ — 01764 653907

Dunbarney (H) linked with Forgandenny
W. Duncan Stenhouse MA BD — 1989 — Dunbarney Manse, Bridge of Earn, Perth PH2 9DY — 01738 812463

Dundurn See Comrie and Strowan
Dunning See Aberuthven

Errol (H) linked with Kilspindie and Rait
John M. Pickering BSc BD — 1997 — Errol, Perth PH2 7PZ — 01821 642279

Forgandenny See Dunbarney

Forteviot See Aberdalgie and Dupplin
Fossoway St Serf's and Devonside See Cleish

Fowlis Wester linked with Madderty linked with Monzie
Alexander F. Bonar LTh LRIC   1988   1996   Beechview, Abercairney, Crieff PH7 3NF   01764 652116

Gask (H) linked with Methven and Logiealmond (H)
Brian Bain LTh   1980   1986   Methven, Perth PH1 3QD   01738 840274 (Tel/Fax)
brian@methvenmanse.freeserve.co.uk]

Kilspindie and Rait See Errol

Kinross (H)
John P.L. Munro MA BD PhD   1977   1998   15 Station Road, Kinross KY13 7TG   01577 862952

Madderty See Fowlis Wester
Methven and Logiealmond See Gask
Monzie See Fowlis Wester

Muthill (H) linked with Trinity Gask and Kinkell
Elinor J. Gordon (Miss) BD   1988   1994   Muthill, Perthshire PH5 2AR   01764 681205

Orwell (H) linked with Portmoak (H)
Una B. Stewart (Miss) BD DipEd   1995   3 Perth Road, Milnathort, Kinross KY13 9XU   01577 863461

Perth: Craigend Moncreiffe linked with Rhynd (T)
Isobel Birrell (Mrs) BD   1994   1999   Wester Tarsappie, Rhynd, Perth PH2 8QL   01738 625694

Perth: Craigie (H)
William Jackson BD CertMin   1994   1998   46 Abbot Street, Perth PH2 OEE   01738 623748

Perth: Kinnoull (H)
John F. Ferguson MA BD   1987   1993   1 Mount Tabor Avenue, Perth PH2 7BT   01738 626046

Perth: Letham St Mark's (H)
James C. Stewart BD   1997   35 Rose Crescent, Perth PH1 1NT   01738 624167
Kenneth McKay DCS   11F Balgowan Road, Perth PH1 2JG   01738 621169

Perth: North (01738 622298)
David W. Denniston BD   1981   1996   127 Glasgow Road, Perth PH2 OLU   01738 625728
[e-mail: david.denniston@virgin.net]
Patricia Munro (Miss) BSc DCS   4 Hewat Place, Perth PH1 2UD   01738 627549
[e-mail: patm@tesco.net]

Perth: St Andrew's and St Stephen's
Alfred G. Drummond BD   1991   44 Hay Street, Perth PH1 5HS   01738 621305
John Buchanan DCS   22 Brora Court, North Muirton, Perth PH1 3DQ   01738 631697

Perth: St John the Baptist's (H) (01738 626159)
David D. Ogston MA BD   1970   15 Comely Bank, Perth PH2 7HU   01738 621755
Elizabeth Brown (Mrs) SRN (Aux)   1996   25 Highfield Road, Scone PH2 6RN   01738 552391 (Tel/Fax)

Perth: St Leonard's-in-the-Fields and Trinity (H) (01738 632238)
Gordon G. Stewart MA   1961   1970   5 Strathearn Terrace, Perth PH2 OLS   01738 621709

Perth: St Matthew's (01738 627708)
Ewen J. Gilchrist BD DipMin DipComm   1982   1988   23 Kincarrathie Crescent, Perth PH2 7HH   01738 626828

Portmoak   See Orwell

Redgorton linked with Stanley
Derek G. Lawson LLB BD   1998   22 King Street, Stanley, Perth PH1 4ND   01738 828247
[e-mail: lawson@stanley9835.freeserve.co.uk]

Rhynd   See Perth Craigend Moncreiffe

St Madoes and Kinfauns
Vacant   Glencarse, Perth PH2 7NF   01738 860837)

St Martin's linked with Scone New (H) (01738 553900)
Alexander M. Millar MA BD MBA   1980   1987   24 Victoria Road, Scone PH2 6JW   01738 551467
[e-mail: millar@amillar62.freeserve.co.uk]

Scone: New   See St Martin's

Scone: Old (H)
J. Bruce Thomson JP MA BD   1972   1983   Burnside, Scone, Perth PH2 6LP   01738 552030
[e-mail: bruce@agape45.freeserve.co.uk]

Stanley   See Redgorton
Trinity Gask and Kinkell   See Muthill

Alexander, William M. BD   1971   1998   (Berriedale and Dunbeath with Latheron)   23 Muirend Avenue, Perth PH1 1JL
Barr, George K. ARIBA BD PhD   1967   1993   (Uddingston: Viewpark)   7 Tay Avenue, Comrie PH6 2PE   01764 670454
Barr, John BSc PhD BD   1958   1979   (Kilmacolm: Old)   5 Abbey Park, Auchterarder PH3 1EN   01764 663056
Barr, T. Leslie LTh   1969   1997   (Kinross)   10 Auld Mart Lane, Milnathort KY13 7FP   01577 861192

Name			Role	Address	Tel
Bertram, Thomas A.	1972	1995	(Patna Waterside)	The Hydro, Crieff PH7 3LQ	01764 655555
Birrell, John M. MA LLB BD	1974	1996	Hospital Chaplain, Perth Royal Infirmary	Wester Tarsappie, Rhynd, Perth PH2 8QL	01738 625694
Bonomy, William MA BD	1946	1987	(Inverkip)	16 Juniper Place, Perth PH1 1EZ	01738 623803
Brown, R. Russell MA	1940	1986	(Perth Kinnoull)	Gowanbank, Isla Road, Perth PH2 7HQ	01738 632469
Carr, W. Stanley MA	1951	1991	(Largs: St Columba's)	11 College Place, Methven PH1 3QN	01738 840455
Cowie, J.L. MA	1950	1977	(Edinburgh: Richmond Craigmillar)	16 Curate Wynd, Kinross KY13 7DX	01577 864762
Donaldson, Robert B. BSocSc	1953	1997	(Kilchoman with Portnahaven)	11 Strathearn Court, Crieff PH7 3DS	01764 654976
Galbraith, W. James L. Bsc BD MICE	1973	1996	(Kilchrenan and Dalavich with Muckairn)	19 Mayfield Gardens, Kinross KY13 7GD	01577 863887
Gilchrist, Kay (Miss) BD	1996		Chaplain, Rachel House	45 Hawthorn Drive, Craigneuk, Airdrie ML6 8AP	
Gregory, J.C. LTh	1968	1992	(Blantyre St Andrew's)	2 Southlands Road, Auchterarder PH3 1BA	01764 664594
Grimson, John A. MA	1950	1986	(Glasgow Wellington: Associate)	29 Highland Road, Turret Park, Crieff PH7 4LE	01764 653063
Halliday, Archibald R. BD	1964	1999	(Duffus with Forres: St Leonard's with Rafford)	2 Pittenzie Place, Crieff PH7 3JL	01764 681275
Henry, Malcolm N. MA BD	1951	1987	(Perth Craigie)	Kelton, Castle Douglas DG7 1RU	01556 4144
Hill, Robert S. BA	1967	1973	(Glenshee and Glenericht)	16 Highland Crescent, Crieff PH7 4LH	01764 652975
Houston, Alexander M.	1939	1977	(Tibbermore)	120 Glasgow Road, Perth PH2 OLU	01738 628056
Kelly, T. Clifford	1973	1995	(Ferintosh)	7 Bankfoot Park, Scotlandwell, Kinross KY13 7JP	01592 840387
Lawson, Ronald G. MA BD	1964	1999	(Greenock: Wellpark Mid Kirk)	6 East Brougham Street, Stanley PH1 4NJ	01738 828871
Leckie, Joseph L. MA MPhil	1954	1996	(Fowlis Wester wt Madderty wt Monzie)	"Caddam", Perth Road, Crieff PH7 3EQ	01764 652506
Longmuir, T. Graeme MA BEd	1976	1984	School Chaplain	The Manse, Strathallan School, Forgandenny, Perth PH2 9HP	01738 812110
McCormick, Alastair F.	1962	1998	(Creich with Rosehall)	14 Balmanno Park, Bridge of Earn PH2 9RJ	01738 813588
McDonald, John A. MA BD	1978	1997	(Cumbernauld: Condorrat)	22 Commissioner Street, Crieff PH7 3AY	01764 653647
Macdonald, W.U. JP MA	1939	1984	(Aberdalgie and Dupplin with Forteviot)	30 Muircroft Terrace West, Perth PH1 1DY	01738 627948
MacKenzie, Donald W. MA	1941	1983	(Auchterarder The Barony)	81 Kingswell Terrace, Perth PH1 2DA	01738 633716
MacLean, Nigel R. MA BD	1940	1986	(Perth St Paul's)	9 Hay Street, Perth PH1	01738 626728
McLeish, D. Nairn MA	1938	1977	(Fisherton)	Wardside House, Muthil, Crieff PH5 2AS	01764 681275
Macleod, Donald A. MA	1955	1987	(Inveraven and Glenlivet)	Flat 3, Ardchoille House, Strathmore Street, Perth PH2 7HP	01738 630939
MacMillan, Riada M. (Mrs) BD	1991	1998	(Perth: Craigend Moncreiffe with Rhynd)	73 Muirend Gardens, Perth PH1 1JR	01738 628867
McNaughton, David J.H. BA CA	1976	1995	(Killin and Ardeonaig)	30 Hollybush Road, Crieff PH7 3HB	01764 653028
MacPhee, Duncan P.	1951	1980	(Braemar with Crathie: Associate)	Braemar Cottage, Ben Alder Place, Kirkcaldy KY2 5RH	01592 201984
McQuilken, John E. MA BD	1969	1992	(Glenaray and Inveraray)	18 Clark Terrace, Crieff PH7 3QE	01764 655764
Millar, Archibald E. DipTh	1965	1991	(Perth St Stephen's)	7 Maple Place, Perth PH1 1RT	01738 621813
Millar, Jennifer (Mrs) BD DipMin	1986	1995	Teacher, Religious Education	24 Victoria Road, Scone PH2 6JW	01738 551467
Rutherford, David W. MC MA BD	1935	1975	(Aberdour St Fillan's)	152 Glasgow Road, Perth PH2 OLX	01738 621404
Shirra, James MA	1945	1987	(St Martin's with Scone New)	17 Dunbarney Avenue, Bridge of Earn, Perth PH2 9BP	01738 812610
Stewart, Anne (Mrs) BD CertMin	1998		Hospital Chaplain	35 Rose Crescent, Perth PH1 1NT	01738 624167
Stewart, Robin I. MA BD STM	1959	1995	(Orwell with Portmoak)	Oakbrae, Perth Road, Murthly PH1 4HF	01738 710220
Tait, H.A.G. MA BD	1966	1997	(Crieff: South and Monzievaird)	14 Sheiling Hill Place, Crieff PH7 4ER	01764 652325
Taylor, A.H.S. MA BA BD	1957	1992	(Hoddam with Brydekirk)	41 Anderson Drive, Perth PH1 1LF	01738 626579
Urquhart, J. MacNeill MA	1942	1980	(Kilspindie and Rait with Kinfauns)	4 Afton Drive, Denny FK6 5PD	01324 815380
Varwell, Adrian P.J. BA BD PhD	1983	1998	Director, St Ninian's Centre, Crieff	St Ninian's Centre, Crieff PH7 4BG	(Tel) 01764 653766 (Fax) 01764 655824
Whitson, William S. MA	1959	1999	(Cumbernauld: St Mungo's)	6 Latch Burn Wynd, Dunning, Perthshire PH2 0SP	01764 684272

PERTH ADDRESSES

Craigend Moncreiffe	Glenbruar Crescent	
Craigie	Abbot Street	
Kinnoull	Dundee Rd near Queen's Bridge	
Letham St Mark's	Rannoch Road	
North	Mill Street near Kinnoull Street.	St John's Street
St Andrew's and	Atholl Street and	St John's
St Stephen's	Atholl Street and	St Leonard's-in-the-Fields and Trinity	Marshall Place
	Balhousie Street (North end)	St Matthew's	Tay Street

(29) DUNDEE

Meets at Dundee, Meadowside St Paul's Church Halls, Nethergate, on the second Wednesday of February, March, May, September, October, November and December and on the fourth Wednesday of June.

Clerk:	REV. JAMES A. ROY MA BD	Nicoll's Lane, Dundee DD2 3HG	01382 611415
Presbytery Office:		[e-mail: a2103475@infotrade.uk.7]	

Abernyte linked with Inchture and Kinnaird linked with Longforgan (H)

J.A.P. Jack BSc BArch BD	1989		Longforgan DD2 5EU [e-mail: jpa@jpaj.demon.co.uk]	01382 360238
Elizabeth Kay (Miss) DipYCS (Aux)	1993	1999	1 Kintail Walk, Inchture PH14 9RY	01828 686029

Auchterhouse (H) linked with Murroes and Tealing (T)

Sydney S. Graham DipYL MPhil	1987	1995	The Manse, Balgray, Tealing DD4 0QZ [e-mail: graythom@sol.co.uk]	01382 380224

Dundee: Albany-Butterburn linked with St David's North

Gideon G. Scott MA BD ThM	1963	1973	2 Anstruther Road, Dundee DD4 7EA	01382 456579

Dundee: Balgay (H)

George K. Robson LTh DPS	1983	1987	150 City Road, Dundee DD2 2PW	01382 668806

Dundee: Barnhill St Margaret's (H)

Gordon D. Jamieson MA BD	1974	1986	Invermark Terrace, Barnhill DD5 2QU	01382 779278

Dundee: Broughty Ferry East (H) (01382 738264)

Alan H. MacKay BD	1974	1984	8 West Queen Street, Broughty Ferry DD5 1AR	01382 778972

Dundee: Broughty Ferry St Aidan's (T)(H)

Caroline Jackson (Mrs) MA BD	1995		63 Collingwood Street, Barnhill DD5 2UF	01382 736828

Charge / Minister		Address	Phone
Dundee: Broughty Ferry St James' (H)			
Thomas P. Robertson	1963	95 Seafield Road, Broughty Ferry DD5 3AP	01382 779803
Dundee: Broughty Ferry St Luke's and Queen Street			
Vacant	1970	22 Albert Road, Broughty Ferry DD5 1AZ	01382 779212
Dundee: Broughty Ferry St Stephen's and West (H)			
John U. Cameron BA BSc PhD BD ThD	1974	33 Camperdown Street, Broughty Ferry DD5 3AA	01382 477403
Dundee: Camperdown (H) (01382 623958)			
Sheila Craik (Mrs) BD	1989	Camperdown Manse, Myrekirk Road, Dundee DD2 4SF	01382 621383
James H. Simpson BSc (Aux)	1996 1999	11 Claypotts Place, Broughty Ferry DD5 1LG	01382 776520
Dundee: Chalmers Ardler (H)			
Kenneth D. Stott MA BD	1989	The Manse, Turnberry Avenue, Dundee DD2 3TP	01382 827439
Jane Martin (Miss) DCS	1997	12A Carnoustie Court, Ardler, Dundee DD2 3RB	01382 813786
Dundee: Clepington			
A.A. Christie BD	1997	17A Claypotts Road, Broughty Ferry DD5 1BS	01382 730085
Dundee: Craigiebank (H) (01382 457951) linked with Douglas and Angus (01382 739884)			
Michael V.A. Mair MA BD	1967 1998	244 Arbroath Road, Dundee DD4 7SB	01382 452337
Edith F. McMillan (Mrs) MA BD (Assoc)	1981 1999	19 Americanmuir Road, Dundee DD3 9AA	01382 812423
Dundee: Douglas and Angus (01382 739884) See Dundee: Craigiebank			
Dundee: Downfield South (H) (01382 810624)			
Vacant		15 Elgin Street, Dundee DD3 8NL	01382 889498
Dundee: Dundee (St Mary's) (H) (01382 226271)			
Keith F. Hall MA BD	1980	33 Strathern Road, West Ferry, Dundee DD5 1PP	01382 778808
Dundee: Fairmuir (H)			
David C. McLeod BSc MEng BD	1969	6 Carseview Gardens, Dundee DD2 1NE	01382 641371
Dundee: Lochee Old and St Luke's (T)			
Elisabeth G.B. Spence (Miss) BD	1995	16 Coupar Angus Road, Dundee DD2 3HN [e-mail: elis.spence@mailcity.com]	01382 611440
Dundee: Lochee West			
James A. Roy MA BD	1965 1973	Beechwood, 7 Northwood Terrace, Wormit DD6 8PP [e-mail: a2103475@infotrade.uk]	01382 543578

Dundee: Logie and St John's Cross (H)
David S. Scott MA BD — 1987 1999 — 7 Hyndford Street, Dundee DD2 1HQ — 01382 641572

Dundee: Mains (H) (01382 812166)
Michael S. Goss BD DPS — 1991 — 9 Elgin Street, Dundee DD3 8NL [e-mail:gossdundee@aol.com] — 01382 825562
Jean Allan (Mrs) DCS — 12C Hindmarsh Avenue, Dundee DD3 7LW — 01382 827299

Dundee: Mains of Fintry (01382 508191)
Peter M. Humphris BSc BD — 1976 1977 — 4 Clive Street, Dundee DD4 7AW [e-mail: humphris@xc.org] — 01382 458629

Dundee: Meadowside St Paul's (H) (01382 225420)
Maudeen I. MacDougall (Miss) BA BD — 1978 — 36 Blackness Avenue, Dundee DD2 1HH — 01382 668828

Dundee: Menzieshill
Harry J. Brown LTh — 1991 1996 — The Manse, Charleston Drive, Dundee DD2 4ED [e-mail: harrybrown@aol.com] — 01382 667446
Sarah Hankey (Miss) DCS — 9 Earn Crescent, Dundee DD2 4BS — 01382 641549

Dundee: Mid Craigie (T) (01382 506147)
Colin A. Strong BSc BD — 1989 1992 — 96 Forfar Road, Dundee DD4 7BG [e-mail: colinstrong@bigfoot.com] — 01382 453926
Fay M. Lamont (Miss) DCS — St Ninian's Church House, Kingsway East, Dundee DD4 7RW — 01382 453818

Dundee: St Andrew's (H) (01382 224860)
Ian D. Petrie MA BD — 1970 1986 — 77 Blackness Avenue, Dundee DD2 1JN — 01382 641695

Dundee: St David's North See Dundee: Albany Butterburn

Dundee: Steeple (H) (01382 223880)
Vacant — 128 Arbroath Road, Dundee DD4 7HR — 01382 455411

Dundee: Stobswell (H)
Jane Barron (Mrs) BA DipEd BD MTh — 1999 — 23 Shamrock Street, Dundee DD4 7AH — 01382 459119

Dundee: Strathmartine (H) (01382 825817)
Stewart McMillan BD — 1983 1990 — 19 Americanmuir Road, Dundee DD3 9AA — 01382 812423

Dundee: The High Kirk (H) (01382 224433)
Vacant — 6 Adelaide Place, Dundee DD3 6LF — 01382 322955

Dundee: Trinity (H) (01382 459997)

James L. Wilson BD CPS	1986	1993	75 Clepington Road, Dundee DD4 7BJ	01382 457430

Dundee: West

Vacant			22 Hyndford Street, Dundee DD2 1HX	01382 646586

Dundee: Whitfield (E) (H) (01382 503012)

Vacant			13A Hill St Broughty Ferry DD5 2JP	01382 778636

Fowlis and Liff linked with Lundie and Muirhead of Liff (H) (01382 580550)

Martin R.H. Thomas CEng MIStructE	1987		149 Coupar Angus Road, Muirhead of Liff, Angus DD2 5QN	01382 580210
K.I. Malcolm BD ACIS ACIB (Aux)	1994	1995	1 Cloan Road, Dundee DD3 9DB	

Inchture and Kinnaird See Abernyte

Invergowrie (H)

Robert J. Ramsay LLB NP BD	1986	1997	2 Boniface Place, Invergowrie, Dundee DD2 5DW	01382 561118

Longforgan See Abernyte
Lundie and Muirhead of Liff See Fowlis and Liff

Monifieth: Panmure (H)

David B. Jamieson MA BD STM	1974		8A Albert Street, Monifieth DD5 4JS	01382 532772

Monifieth: St Rule's (H)

Vacant			Church Street, Monifieth DD5 4JP	01382 532607

Monifieth: South

Donald W. Fraser MA	1958	1959	Queen Street, Monifieth DD5 4HG	01382 532646

Monikie and Newbigging

Gordon R. Mackenzie BScAgr BD	1977	1985	59B Broomwell Gardens, Monikie DD5 3QP	01382 370200

Murroes and Tealing See Auchterhouse

Chisholm, W. Douglas MA	1943	1983	(Monifieth North and Newbigging with Monikie)	8 Musgrave Road, Chinnor, Oxon OX9 4TF	01844 352029
Clarkson, Robert G.	1950	1989	(Dundee Strathmartine)	320 Strathmartine Road, Dundee DD3 8QG	01382 825380
Craig, Iain R. MA	1948	1988	(Invergowrie)	Hope View, Burton Row, Brent Knoll, Highbridge, Somerset TA9 4BX	01278 760719
Cramb, Erik M. LTh	1973	1989	Industrial Mission Organiser	65 Clepington Road, Dundee DD4 7BQ	01382 458764

Name			Charge/Position	Address	Tel.
Doig, David M. BA BD	1972	1986	(Dundee Mid-Craigie)	13 Balmoral View, Rattray, Blairgowrie PH10 7LJ	01250 875592
Douglas, Fiona C. (Miss) MA BD PhD	1989	1997	Chaplain: University of Dundee	10 Springfield, Dundee DD1 4JE	01382 344157
Gammack, George BD	1985	1999	(Dundee: Whitfield)	13A Hill Street, Broughty Ferry, Dundee DD5 2JP	01382 503012
Hamilton, James BA BD	1939	1982	(Auchterhouse)	Ivydene, Blair Logie FK9 5PX	01259 761633
Hawdon, John E. BA MTh AICS	1961	1995	(Dundee: Clepington)	12 Rosewood Terrace, Dundee DD2 1NS	01382 646212
Hudson, J. Harrison DipTh MA BD	1961	1999	(Dundee: St Peter's McCheyne)	22 Hamilton Avenue, Tayport DD6 9BW	01382 736400
Ingram, J.R.	1954	1978	(Chaplain: RAF)	48 Marlee Road, Broughty Ferry DD5 3EX	01382 477458
Laidlaw, John J. MA	1964	1973	(Adviser in Religious Education)	14 Dalhousie Road, Barnhill DD5 2SQ	01382 668655
Macdonald, John AEA MA	1949	1985	(Lochee Old)	12 Hyndford Street, Dundee DD2 1HQ	01382 668491
Mackenzie, George R.R. MA BD	1942	1987	(Dundee Logie and StJohn's Cross)	39 Middlebank Crescent, Dundee DD2 1HZ	01382 224803
McMillan, Hector G.	1964		(Hamilton North)	6 Kinghorne Terrace, Dundee DD3 6HX	01382 456196
Macnab, S.G. BD	1938	1994	(Broughty Ferry: St Luke's)	58 Kenilworth Avenue, Dundee DD4 6LG	01382 462495
Malvenan, Dorothy DCS	1964	1990	The Deaf Association, Dundee	Flat 19, 6 Craigie Street, Dundee DD4 6PF	01382 320407
Miller, Charles W. MA	1953	1994	(Fowlis and Liff)	"Palm Springs", Parkside, Auchterhouse DD3 0RS	01241 856654
Milroy, Tom	1960	1992	(Monifieth: St Rule's)	9 Long Row, Westhaven, Carnoustie DD7 6BE	01382 642301
Mitchell, Jack MA BD CTh	1987	1996	(Dundee: Menzieshill)	10 Invergowrie Drive, Dundee DD2 1RF	01382 566013
Mowat, Gilbert M. MA	1948	1986	(Dundee Albany Butterburn)	7 Dunmore Gardens, Dundee DD2 1PP	01575 572503
Powrie, James E. LTh	1969	1995	(Dundee: Chalmers Ardler)	3 Kirktonhill Road, Kirriemuir DD8 4HU	01382 450158
Rae, Robert LTh	1968	1983	Chaplain: Dundee Acute Hospitals	47 Mains Loan, Dundee DD4 7AJ	01382 506162
Rogers, James M. BA DB DCult	1955	1996	(Gibraltar)	24 Mansion Drive, Dunclaverhouse, Dundee DD4 9DD	01382 739354
Scroggie, John C.	1951	1985	(Mains)	4 Bell Tree Gardens, Balmossie DD5 2LJ	01382 500052
Smith, Lilian MA DCS			(Deaconess)	6 Fintry Mains, Dundee DD4 9HF	

DUNDEE ADDRESSES

Church	Address	Church	Address	Church	Address
Albany Butterburn	2 Hill Street	Douglas and Angus	Balbeggie Place	Menzieshill	Charleston Drive, Lochee
Balgay	200 Lochee Road	Downfield South	Haldane Street off Strathmartine Road.	Mid Craigie	Longtown Terrace
Barnhill St Margaret's	10 Invermark Terrace	Dundee (St Mary's)	Nethergate.	Roseangle Ryehill	130 Perth Road.
Broughty Ferry		Fairmuir	329 Clepington Road	St Andrew's	2 King Street.
East	370 Queen Street.	High Kirk	119A Kinghorne Road	St David's North	273 Strathmore Avenue
St Aidan's	408 Brook Street	Lochee		Steeple	Nethergate.
St James'	5 Fort Street	Old and St Luke's	Bright Street, Lochee	Stobswell	Top of Albert Street
St Luke's and Queen Street	5 West Queen Street	West	191 High Street, Lochee	Strathmartine	315 Strathmartine Road.
St Stephen's and West	96 Dundee Road	Logie and		Trinity	73 Crescent Street
Camperdown	Brownhill Road.	St John's (Cross)	Shaftsbury Rd x Blackness Ave	Whitfield	Haddington Crescent.
Chalmers Ardler	Turnberry Avenue	Mains	Foot of Old Glamis Road		
Clepington	Isla Street x Main Street	Mains of Fintry	Fintry Road x Fintry Drive.		
Craigebank	Craigie Avenue at Greendyke Road.	Meadowside St Paul's	114 Nethergate.		

(30) ANGUS

Meets at Forfar in St Margaret's Church Hall, on the first Tuesday of each month, except June when it meets on the last Tuesday, and January, July and August when there is no meeting.

Clerk:	REV. MALCOLM I.G. ROONEY DPE BEd BD	
DeputeClerk:	MRS HELEN McLEOD MA	
Presbytery Office:	St Margaret's Church, West High Street, Forfar DD8 1BJ [e-mail: Angus Presbytery@compuserve.com]	01307 464224 (Tel) 01307 465589 (Fax)

Aberlemno linked with Guthrie and Rescobie
Brian Ramsay BD DPS   1980   1984   The Manse, Guthrie, Forfar DD8 2TP   01241 828243

Airlie Kingoldrum and Ruthven linked with Glenisla (H) linked with Kilry linked with Lintrathen
Leslie Barrett BD FRICS   1991   1999   Balduff House, Kilry, Blairgowrie PH11 8HS   01575 560260

Arbirlot linked with Carmyllie linked with Colliston
Kenneth Brown BD CPS MLitt   1991   The Manse, Arbirlot, Arbroath DD11 2NX   01241 875118 (Tel/Fax)
[e-mail: 100703.2136@compuserve.com]

Arbroath: Knox's (H) linked with Arbroath: St Vigeans (H)
Ian G. Gough MA BD MTh   1974   1990   The Manse, St Vigeans, Arbroath DD11 4RD   01241 873206

Arbroath: Old and Abbey (H)
Valerie L. Allen (Miss) BMus MDiv   1990   1996   51 Cliffburn Road DD11 5BA   01241 872196 (Tel/Fax)
[e-mail: vl2allen@aol.com]

Arbroath: St Andrew's (H)
Martin Fair BA BD   1992   Albert Street, Arbroath DD11 1RA   01241 873238 (Tel/Fax)

Arbroath: St Vigeans See Arbroath: Knox's

Arbroath: West Kirk (H)
Alasdair G. Graham BD   1981   1986   1 Charles Avenue, Arbroath DD11 2EY   01241 872244
[e-mail:alasdair.graham@lineone.net]

Barry
Vacant   The Manse, Barry, Carnoustie DD7 7RP   01241 852371

Brechin: Cathedral (H)
James A. Simpson BSc BD STM DD — 1960 — 1998 — Chanonry Wynd, Brechin DD9 6JS — 01356 622783

Brechin: Gardner Memorial (H)
Vacant — 36 Park Road, Brechin DD9 7AP — 01356 622789

Carmyllie See Arbirlot

Carnoustie
J. Colin Caskie BA BD — 1977 — 1983 — 44 Terrace Road, Carnoustie DD7 7AR — 01241 852289

Carnoustie Panbride
Matthew S. Bicket BD — 1989 — 8 Arbroath Road, Carnoustie DD7 6BL
[e-mail: matthew@bicket.freeserve.co.uk] — 01241 854478 (Tel) / 01241 855088 (Fax)

Colliston See Arbirlot

Dun linked with Hillside
Christine Houghton (Mrs) — 1997 — 4 Manse Road, Hillside, Montrose DD10 9FB — 01674 830288

Dunnichen, Letham and Kirkden
Allan F. Webster MA BD — 1978 — 1990 — 7 Braehead Road, Letham, Forfar DD8 2PG
[e-mail: allanweb@globalnet.co.uk] — 01307 818916

Eassie and Nevay linked with Newtyle
Carleen Robertson (Miss) BD — 1992 — 2 Kirkton Road, Newtyle, Blairgowrie PH12 8TS — 01828 650461

Edzell Lethnot (H) linked with Fern, Careston and Menmuir linked with Glenesk
Vacant — The Manse, Edzell, Brechin, Angus DD9 7TJ — 01356 647251

Farnell linked with Montrose St Andrew's
Iain M. Douglas MA BD MPhil DipEd — 1960 — 1980 — 49 Northesk Road, Montrose DD10 8TQ — 01674 672060

Fern, Careston and Menmuir See Edzell Lethnot

Forfar: East Old (H)
Graham Norrie MA BD — 1967 — 1978 — Lour Road, Forfar DD8 2BB — 01307 464303

Forfar: Lowson Memorial (H)
Robert McCrum BD — 1982 — 1992 — 1 Jamieson Street, Forfar DD8 2HY
[e-mail: robertmccrum@bigfoot.com] — 01307 462248

Forfar: St Margaret's (T)(H) Jean B. Montgomerie (Miss) MA BD	1973	1998	15 Potters Park Crescent, Forfar DD8 1HH	01307 466390 (Tel/Fax)
Friockheim Kinnell linked with Inverkeilor and Lunan David Taverner BD		1996	18 Middlegate, Friockheim DD11 4TS	01241 828781
Glamis, Inverarity and Kinnettles (T) Vacant			The Manse, Glamis, Forfar, Angus DD8 1RT [e-mail: revjohnmurdoch@email.msn.com]	01307 840206 (Tel) 01307 840724 (Fax)
Glenesk See Edzell Lethnot				
Glenisla See Airlie Kingoldrum and Ruthven				
Glens, The and Kirriemuir Old Malcolm I.G. Rooney DPE BEd BD	1993	1999	20 Strathmore Avenue, Kirriemuir DD8 4DJ [e-mail: malcolmrooney@compuserve.com]	01575 573724 0403 196091 (Mbl)
Guthrie and Rescobie See Aberlemno				
Hillside See Dun				
Inchbrayock linked with Montrose Melville South David S. Dixon MA BD	1976	1994	The Manse, Ferryden, Montrose DD10 9SD	01674 672108
Inverarity and Kinnettles See Glamis				
Inverkeilor and Lunan See Friockheim Kinnell				
Kilry See Airlie Kingoldrum and Ruthven				
Kirriemuir: Old (H) (01575 572819) See The Glens				
Kirriemuir: St Andrew's linked with Oathlaw Tannadice William McCulloch BD		1997	26 Quarry Park, Kirriemuir DD8 4DR	01575 575561
Lintrathen See Airlie Kingoldrum and Ruthven				
Montrose: Melville South See Inchbrayock				
Montrose: Old Laurence A.B. Whitley MA BD PhD	1975	1985	2 Rosehill Road, Montrose DD10 8ST	01674 672447
Montrose: St Andrew's See Farnell				
Newtyle See Eassie and Nevay				
Oathlaw Tannadice See Kirriemuir St Andrew's				

Name			Charge	Address	Tel
Anderson, James W. BSc MTh	1986	1997	(Kincardine O'Neil with Lumphanan)	47 Glebe Road, Arbroath DD11 4HJ	01241 872201
Becke, John C. MA	1951	1970	(Genoa)	East Woodrae, Aberlemno, Forfar DD8 3PF	01307 830278
Brodie, James BEM MA BD STM	1955	1974	(Hurlford)	Kinloch Terrace, 25A Keptie Road, Arbroath DD11 3ED	01241 873298
Brownlie, Gavin D. MA	1955	1990	(Arbroath Ladyloan St Columba's)	12 Cliffburn Road, Arbroath DD11 5BB	01241 873062
Bruce, William C. MA BD	1961	1995	(Motherwell: Dalziel)	31 Kirkton Terrace, Carnoustie DD7 7BZ	01241 411078
Butters, David	1964	1998	(Turriff: St Ninian's and Forglen)	8A Millgate, Friockheim, Arbroath DD11 4TN	01241 828030
Dyrsdale James P.R.	1967	1999	(Brechin Gardner Memorial)	51 Airlie Street, Brechin DD9 6JX	01356 625201
Finlay, Quintin BA BD	1975	1996	(North Bute)	1 Brougham Square, Northesk Road, Montrose DD10 8TD	01674 675522
Henderson, David C. CBE DD	1938	1981	(Glamis)	Isla View, Glenisla, Alyth PH11 8PH	01575 582256
Hodge, William N.T.	1966	1995	(Longside)	"Tullochgorum" 61 South Street, Forfar DD8 2BS	01307 461944
Jones, William	1952	1987	(Kirriemuir St Andrew's)	14 Muir Street, Forfar DD8 3JY	01307 463193
Keith, Donald MA BD	1971	1998	Chaplain RN	Comacchio Group Royal Marines, RM Condor, Arbroath DD11 3JS	
McKenzie, M.G. BA LLB	1978	1993	(South Ronaldsay and Burray)	18 Pearse Street, Brechin DD9 6JR	01356 623812
MacKinnon, A.W.	1951	1986	(Fern, Careston and Menmuir with Oathlaw Tannadice)	19 Gallowhill, Brechin DD9 6BL	01356 625599
MacLeod, Ian I.S. MA BD	1954	1991	(Arbroath St Andrew's)	13 Trinity Fields Crescent, Brechin DD9 6YF	
Milton, Eric G.	1963	1994	(Blairdaff)	16 Bruce Court, Links Parade, Carnoustie DD7 7JE	01241 854928
Perry, Joseph B.	1955	1989	(Farnell)	19 Guthrie Street, Letham, Forfar DD8 2PS	01307 818741
Russell, A.C. CMG ED MA	1959	1976	(Aberlemno)	Balgavies Lodge, by Forfar DD8 2TH	01307 818571
Shackleton, Scott J.S.	1993	1993	Chaplain: 45 Commando Unit, RM Condor	31 Condor Drive, Arbroath DD11 3ER	01241 879481
Smith, Hamish G.	1965	1993	(Auchterless with Rothienorman)	11A Guthrie Street, Letham, Angus DD8 2PS	01307 818973
Stevens, David MA	1935	1972	(Glenesk)	2 Rowan Cottages, Tarfside, Brechin, Angus DD9 7YU	01356 670241
Tyre, Robert	1960	1998	(Aberdeen: St Ninian's with Stockethill)	8 Borrowfield Crescent, Montrose DD10 9BR	01674 676961
Warnock, Dennis MA	1952	1990	(Kirkcaldy Torbain)	19 Keptie Road, Arbroath DD11 3ED	01241 872740
Weatherhead, James L. CBE MA LLB DD	1960	1996	(Principal Clerk)	59 Brechin Road, Kirriemuir DD8 4DE	01575 572237
Youngson, Peter	1961	1996	(Kirriemuir St Andrew's)	Coreen, Woodside, Northmuir, Kirriemuir DD8 4PG	01575 572832

ANGUS ADDRESSES

Arbroath
Abbey — West Abbey Street
Knox's — Howard Street
St Andrew's — Hamilton Green
West Kirk — Keptie Street

Brechin
Cathedral — Bishops Close
Gardner Memorial — South Esk Street

Carnoustie
Carnoustie — Dundee Street
Panbride — Arbroath Road

Forfar
East: Old — East High Street
Lowson Memorial — Jamieson Street
St Margaret's — West High Street

Kirriemuir
Old — High Street
St Andrew's — Glamis Road

Montrose
Melville South — Castle Street
Old — High Street
St Andrew's — George Street

(31) ABERDEEN

Meets at St Mark's Church, Rosemount Viaduct, Aberdeen, on the first Tuesday of February, March April, May, September, October, November and December and on the fourth Tuesday of June.

Clerk:	REV. ANDREW M. DOUGLAS MA		
Presbytery Office:		Mastrick Church, Greenfern Road, Aberdeen AB16 6TR	01224 690494 (Tel/Fax)
Hon. Treasurer:	MR A. SHARP	27 Hutchison Terrace, Aberdeen AB10 7NN	01224 315702

Aberdeen: Beechgrove (H) (01224 632102)
| T.D. Allsop MA BD | 1959 | 1977 | 156 Hamilton Place AB15 5BB | 01224 642615 |

Aberdeen: Bridge of Don Oldmachar(E) (01224 709244)
| Vacant | | | 60 Newburgh Circle AB22 8QZ | 01224 705060 |

Aberdeen: Cove (E)
| Fyfe Blair BA BD | 1989 | 1998 | 4 Charleston Way, Cove, Aberdeen AB12 3FA | 01224 898030 |

Aberdeen: Craigiebuckler (H) (01224 311367)
| Kenneth L. Petrie MA BD | 1984 | 1999 | 185 Springfield Road AB15 8AA | 01224 315125 |

Aberdeen: Denburn (H)
| Lesley Risby (Mrs) BD | 1994 | 1999 | 122 Deswood Place AB15 4DQ | 01224 642845 |

Aberdeen: Ferryhill (H) (01224 583070)
| John H.A. Dick MA MSc BD | 1982 | | 54 Polmuir Road AB11 7RT | 01224 586933 |

Aberdeen: Garthdee (H)
| James Weir BD | 1991 | | 27 Ramsay Gardens AB10 7AE | 01224 317452 |
| Scott C. Blythe BSc BD ThM | 1997 | | 8 Thistle Place AB10 1UZ | 01224 636856 |

Aberdeen: Gilcomston South (H) (01224 616144)
| D. Dominic Smart BSc BD MTh | 1988 | | 37 Richmondhill Road AB15 5EQ [e-mail: smartdd@aol.com] | 01224 314326 |

Aberdeen: Greyfriars John Knox (T) (01224 644719)
| S. Ian Dennis BD | 1992 | 1997 | 41 Gray Street AB10 6JD | 01224 584594 |

Charge / Minister		Address	Tel
Aberdeen: High Hilton (H) (01224 494717) A. Peter Dickson BSc BD	1996	24 Rosehill Drive AB24 4JJ	01224 484155
Aberdeen: Holburn Central (H) (01224 580967) George S. Cowie BSc BD	1991	6 St Swithin Street AB10 6XE	01224 593302
Aberdeen: Holburn West (H) (01224 571120) Duncan C. Eddie MA BD	1992 1999	31 Cranford Road AB10 7NJ	01224 318527
Aberdeen: Mannofield (H) (01224 310087) John F. Anderson MA BD FSAScot	1966 1975	21 Forest Avenue AB15 4TU	01224 315748
Aberdeen: Mastrick (H) (01224 694121) Brian C. Rutherford BSc BD	1977 1990	13 Beechgrove Avenue AB15 5EZ	01224 638011
Aberdeen: Middlefield (H) Vacant		73 Manor Avenue AB16 7UT	01224 685214
Aberdeen: Nigg (01224 894599) Vacant		7 Redmoss Avenue AB12 3JR	01224 871168
Aberdeen: North of St Andrew (T) (01224 643567) Graeme W.M. Muckart MTh MSc FSAScot	1983 1987	51 Osborne Place AB25 2BX	01224 646429
Aberdeen: Northfield Scott Guy BD	1989	28 Byron Crescent AB17EX	01224 692332
Duncan Ross DCS	1999	64 Stewart Crescent AB16 5SR	01224 692519
Aberdeen: Queen's Cross (H) (01224 644742) Robert F. Brown MA BD ThM	1971 1984	1 St Swithin Street AB10 6XH	01224 322549
Aberdeen: Rosemount (H) (01224 620111) A. David M. Graham BA BD	1971 1983	22 Osborne Place AB25 2DA	01224 648041
Aberdeen: Rubislaw (H) (01224 645477) Andrew G.N. Wilson MA BD	1977 1987	45 Rubislaw Den South AB15 4BD	01224 314878
Aberdeen: Ruthrieston South (H) (01224 211730) Hugh F. Kerr MA BD	1968 1985	39 Gray Street AB10 6JD	01224 586762
Aberdeen: Ruthrieston West (H) Sean Swindells BD DipMin	1996	451 Great Western Road AB10 6NL	01224 313075

Aberdeen: St Columba's Bridge of Don (H) (01224 825653)
Louis Kinsey BD — 1991 — 151 Jesmond Avenue AB22 8UG — 01224 705337

Aberdeen: St George's Tillydrone (H) (01224 482204)
Shirley A. Fraser (Miss) MA BD — 1992 — 127 Clifton Road AB24 3RH — 01224 483976

Aberdeen: St John's Church for Deaf People (H) (01224 494566)
John R. Osbeck BD — 1979 1991 — 5 Leven Avenue, Ellon AB41 9GF — 01358 21479

Aberdeen: St Machar's Cathedral (H) (01224 485988)
Richard E. Frazer BA BD — 1986 1993 — 18 The Chanonry, Old Aberdeen AB24 1RQ — 01224 483688

Aberdeen: St Mark's (H) (01224 640672)
John M. Watson LTh — 1989 — 65 Mile-end Avenue AB15 5PU — 01224 632028

Aberdeen: St Mary's (H) (01224 487227)
Michael S.M. Crawford LTh — 1966 1967 — 456 King Street AB24 3DE — 01224 633778

Aberdeen: St Nicholas, Kirk of (H) (01224 643494)
James C. Stewart MA BD STM — 1960 1980 — 48 Gray Street AB10 6JE — 01224 314056

Aberdeen: St Nicholas South of Kincorth
W.E. Wilkie LTh — 1978 — Kincorth Circle AB12 5NX — 01224 872820

Aberdeen: St Ninian's (T) (01224 319519)
Vacant — 12 Carlton Place AB15 4BQ — 01224 640525

Aberdeen: St Stephen's (H) (01224 624443)
James M. Davies BSc BD — 1982 1989 — 6 Belvidere Street AB25 2QS — 01224 635694

Aberdeen: Stockethill (New Charge Development)
Ian Aitken — 1999 — 52 Ashgrove Road West AB16 5EE — 01224 682617

Aberdeen: Summerhill
Ian A. McLean BSc BD — 1981 — 36 Stronsay Drive AB15 6JL — 01224 324669

Aberdeen: Torry St Fittick's (H)
Iain C. Barclay TD MA BD MTh MPhil — 1976 1999 — 11 Devanha Gardens East AB11 7UH [e-mail: i.c.barclay@abdn.ac.uk] — 01224 588245
Ann V. Lundie (Miss) DCS — 20 Langdykes Drive, Cove, Aberdeen AB12 3HW — 01224 898416

Aberdeen: Woodside (H) (01224 277249)
Alistair Murray BD — 1984 1990 — 322 Clifton Road AB24 4HQ — 01224 484562

Bucksburn Stoneywood (H) (01224 712411)
Nigel Parker BD MTh | 1994 | 25 Gilbert Road, Bucksburn, Aberdeen AB21 9AN | 01224 712635

Cults: East (T)(H) (01224 869028)
Flora J. Munro (Mrs) BD | 1993 | Cults, Aberdeen AB15 9TD | 01224 867587

Cults: West (H) (01224 869566)
Thomas C. Richardson LTh ThB | 1971 1978 | 3 Quarry Road, Cults, Aberdeen AB15 9EX [e-mail: richardson-tc@msn.com] | 01224 867417

Dyce (H) (01224 771295)
Russel Moffat BD MTh | 1986 1998 | 144 Victoria Street, Dyce, Aberdeen AB21 7BE | 01224 722380

Kingswells
Harvey L. Grainger LTh | 1975 1989 | Lang Stracht, Aberdeen AB15 8PL [e-mail: harvey.grainger@talk21.com] | 01224 740229

Newhills (H) (01224 716161 Tel/Fax)
Norman Maciver MA BD | 1976 | Bucksburn, Aberdeen AB21 9SS [e-mail: newhillsnm@aol.com] | 01224 712655

Peterculter (H) (01224 735845)
John A. Ferguson BD DipMin | 1988 1999 | 7 Howie Lane, Peterculter, Aberdeen AB14 0LJ | 01224 735041

Name	Year	Year	Position	Address	Phone
Aitchison, James W.	1993		Chaplain: Army	35 Redford Bank, Edinburgh EH13 0AJ	0131 441 7593
Ballantyne, Samuel MA BD	1941	1982	(Rutherford)	26 Cairncry Road, Aberdeen AB16 5DP	01224 483049
Blythe, Scott C. BSc BD	1997	1999	Chaplain: Robert Gordon University	8 Thistle Place, Aberdeen AB10 1UZ	01224 636856
Bryden, Agnes Y. (Mrs) DCS			(Deaconess)	9 Rosewell Place, Aberdeen AB15 6HN	01224 315042
Campbell, W.M.M. BD CPS	1970	1986	Hospital Chaplain	43 Murray Terrace, Aberdeen AB21 7SA	01224 591174
Coutts, Fred MA BD	1973	1989	Hospital Chaplain	9A Millburn Street, Aberdeen, AB11 6SS	01224 583805
Deans, John Bell	1951	1986	(Hospital Chaplain)	14 Balmoral Avenue, Ellon AB41 9EN	01358 721539
Dickson, John C. MA	1950	1987	(Aberdeen St Fittick's)	56 Countesswells Road, Aberdeen AB15 7YE	01224 314488
Douglas, Andrew M. MA	1957	1995	(High Hilton)	49 Hopetoun Avenue AB21 9QU	01224 713882
Falconer, James B.	1982	1992	Hospital Chaplain	3 Brimmond Walk, Westhill, Skene AB32 6HX	01224 744621
Ferguson, David A.S. MA BD DPhil	1984	1990	University of Aberdeen	44 Ashley Road, Aberdeen AB10 6RJ	01224 583817
Finlayson, Ena (Miss) DCS			(Deaconess)	13 Chapman Place, Aberdeen AB16 7DH	01224 695293
Goldie, George D. ALCM	1953	1995	(Greyfriars)	27 Broomhill Avenue, Aberdeen AB10 6JL	01224 322503
Gordon, Laurie Y.	1960	1995	(John Knox)	1 Alder Drive, Portlethen, Aberdeen AB12 4WA	01224 782703
Grant, A. Rae MA BD	1923	1966	(Cults West)	10 Crown Circus, Inverness IV2 3NQ	01463 237764
Gray, John MA BD PhD DD	1939	1980	(University of Aberdeen)	Tanlaw Cottage, Hendersyde Park, Kelso TD5 7ST	01573 224374
Haddow, Angus BSc	1963	1990	(Methlick)	25 Lerwick Road, Aberdeen AB16 6RF	01224 696362
Hutchison, A. Scott MA BD DD	1957	1991	(Hospital Chaplain)	Ashfield, Drumoak, Banchory AB31 5AG	01330 811309

Name			Role	Address	Phone
Hutchison, Alison (Mrs) M. BD DipMin	1988	1988	Hospital Chaplain	Ashfield, Drumoak, Banchory AB31 5AG	01330 811309
Hutchison, David S BSc BD ThM	1991	1999	(Aberdeen: Torry St Fittick's)	71 University Road, Aberdeen AB24 3DR	01224 316022
Johnstone, William MA BD	1963	1963	University of Aberdeen	37 Rubislaw Den South, Aberdeen AB15 6BD	01224 486240
McCallum, Moyra (Miss) MA BD DCS			(Deaconess)	176 Hilton Drive, Aberdeen AB24 4LT	01224 868082
Mackay, Murdoch M. MA			(Hospital Chaplain)	17 Hillview Terrace, Cults, Aberdeen AB15 9HJ	01224 484271
Maclean, Gillean P. (Ms) BD	1941	1986	Chaplain: University of Aberdeen	University Manse, 48 Don Street, Old Aberdeen AB24 1UU	01651 806773
Main, Alan TD MA BD STM PhD	1994	1996	University of Aberdeen	Kirkfield, Barthol Chapel, Inverurie AB51 8TD	01224 638851
Mirrilees, J.B. MA BD	1963	1980	(High Hilton)	22 King's Gate, Aberdeen AB15 4EJ	
Munro, Gillian (Miss) BSc BD	1937	1977	Chaplain's Assistant:		
	1989	1995	Aberdeen Royal Infirmary		
Russell, Andrew M. MA BD	1940	1976	(Woodside North)	685 George Street, Aberdeen AB25 3XP	01259 213115
Sefton, Henry R. MA BD STM PhD	1957	1992	(University of Aberdeen)	3 Hill Place, Alloa FK10 2LP	01224 572305
Skakle, George S. MA	1945	1987	(Aberdeen Powis)	25 Albury Place, Aberdeen AB11 6TQ	01224 646478
Smith, Angus MA LTh	1965	1991	Industrial Chaplain	30 Whitehall Terrace, Aberdeen AB25 2RY	01339 883395
Swindells, Alison J. (Mrs) LLB BD	1998		Assistant Chaplain,	1 Fa'burn Terace, Lumphanan AB31 4AG	01224 313075
			Aberdeen Royasl Infirmary	451 Great Western Road, Aberdeen AB10 6NL	
Swinton, John BD PhD	1999		University of Aberdeen	4 Whitestairs Close. Bridge of Don, Aberdeen AB22 8WE	01224 825637
Torrance, Iain R. TD MA BD DPhil	1982	1993	University of Aberdeen (01224 272274)	Concraig Smiddy, Clinterty, Kingswells, Aberdeen AB15 8RN	01224 790902
Walton, Ainslie MA MEd	1954	1995	(University of Aberdeen)	41 Gray Street, Aberdeen AB10 6JD	01224 584594
Watt, William G.	1970	1977	(South of St Nicholas Kincorth)	12 Eriskay Drive, Lang Stracht, Aberdeen AB16 6FJ	01224 697014
Welsh, Jessie R. (Miss) DCS			(Deaconess)	40 Thomson Atreet, Aberdeen AB25 2QP	01224 632323
Wood, James L.K.	1967	1995	(Ruthrieston West)	1 Glen Drive, Dyce, Aberdeen AB21 7EN	01224 722543
Young, Henry J.	1953	1980	(Edinburgh Dean)	Bank House, 1 Stewarton Road, Dunlop KA3 4AA	01560 484669

ABERDEEN ADDRESSES

Church	Address	Church	Address	Church	Address
Beechgrove	Beechgrove Avenue	Mannofield	Great Western Road x Craigton Road	St George's	Hayton Road, Tillydrone
Bridge of Don		Mastrick	Greenfern Road	St John's for the Deaf	Smithfield Road
Old Machar	Ashwood Park	Middlefield	Manor Avenue	St Machar's	The Chanory
Cove	Loirston Primary School, Loirston Avenue	Nigg	Kirk Road, Nigg	St Mark's	Rosemount Viaduct
Craigiebuckler	Springfield Road	North Church of St Andrew	Queen Street	St Mary's	King Street
Denburn	Summer Street	Northfield	Byron Crescent	St Nicholas, Kirk of	Union Street
Ferryhill	Fonthill Road x Polmuir Road	Queen's Cross	Queen's Cross	St Nicholas, South of Kincorth	
Garthdee	Ramsay Gardens	Rosemount	Rosemount Place	St Ninian's	Kincorth Circle
Gilcomston South	Union Street x Summer Street	Rubislaw	Queen's Cross	St Stephen's	Mid-Stocket Road
Greyfriars John Knox	Broad Street	Ruthrieston		Stockethill	Powis Place
High Hilton	Hilton Drive	South	Holburn Street	Summerhill	Castleton Crescent
Holburn		West	Broomhill Road	Torry St Fittick's	Stronsay Drive
Central	Holburn Street	St Columba's	Braehead Way, Bridge of Don	Woodside	Walker Road
West	Great Western Road				Church Street, Woodside

(32) KINCARDINE AND DEESIDE

Meets at Banchory on the first Tuesday of February, March, November and December, and at Stonehaven, the first Tuesday of May, September and October and the last Tuesday of June.

Clerk: REV. J.W.S. BROWN BTh   10 Forestside Road, Banchory AB31 5ZH   01330 824353

Congregation / Minister	Year	Year	Address	Phone
Aberluthnott linked with Laurencekirk (H) Peter A.D.Berrill MA BD	1983		Aberdeen Road, Laurencekirk AB30 1AJ	01561 378838
Aboyne - Dinnet (H) David Deveney BD	1997		St Eunan's Road, Aboyne AB34 5HH	01339 886447
Arbuthnott linked with Bervie Alastair McKillop BD DipMin	1995		10 Kirkburn, Inverbervie, Montrose DD10 0RT	01561 362633
Margaret M.W. Benton (Mrs) MA BD (Licentiate: Assoc)			12 Woodlands Place, Inverbervie, Montrose DD10 0SL	01561 362964
Banchory-Devenick linked with Maryculter and Cookney Andrew C. Christie LTh	1975	1990	The Manse, Kirkton of Maryculter, Aberdeen AB12 5FS	01224 735776
Banchory Ternan: East (H) Hamish K. Fleming MA	1966	1986	East Manse, Banchory, Kincardineshire AB31 5YP	01330 822481
Banchory Ternan: West (H) Donald K. Walker BD	1979	1995	2 Wilson Road, Banchory AB31 5UY	01330 822811
Benholm and Johnshaven See Mearns Coastal				
Bervie See Arbuthnott				
Birse and Feughside Jack Holt BSc BD	1985	1994	Finzean, Banchory AB31 6PB	01330 850237
Braemar linked with Crathie Robert P. Sloan MA BD	1968	1996	Crathie, Ballater AB35 5UL	01339 742208
Cromar Regine U. Cheyne (Mrs) MA BSc BD	1988	1996	Aberdeen Road, Tarland, Aboyne AB34 4UA	01339 881464
Dinnet See Aboyne - Dinnet				
Drumoak (H) linked with Durris (H) James Scott MA BD	1973	1992	The Manse, Durris, Banchory AB31 6BU	01330 844557

Fettercairn   See West Mearns
Finzean   See Birse and Feughside
Fordoun   See West Mearns
Garvock   St Cyrus   See Mearns Coastal
Glenbervie   See West Mearns

Glenmuick (Ballater) (H) Anthony Watts BD	1999	5 Netherley Place, Ballater, Aberdeenshire AB35 5QE	01339 755329
Kincardine O'Neil linked with Lumphanan Norma P. Robertson (Miss) BD	1993 1998	Lumphanan, Banchory AB31 4PR	01339 883249
Kinneff linked with Stonehaven South (H) Vacant		Cameron Street, Stonehaven AB39 2HE	01569 762576

Laurencekirk   See Aberluthnott
Lumphanan   See Kincardine O'Neill
Maryculter and Cookney   See Banchory-Devenick

Mearns Coastal George I Hastie MA BD	1971 1998	The Manse, Kirkton, St Cyrus, Montrose DD10 0BW	01674 850880 (Tel/Fax)
Newtonhill Christine M. Creegan (Mrs) MTh	1993	39 St Ternans Road, Newtonhill, Stonehaven AB39 3PF	01569 730143
Portlethen (H) (01224 782883) John R. Notman BSc BD	1990 1997	18 Rowanbank Road, Portlethen, Aberdeen AB12 4QY	01224 780211
Stonehaven: Dunnottar (H) Gordon Farquharson MA BD DipEd	1998	Dunnottar Manse, Stonehaven AB39 2XL	01569 762874
Stonehaven: Fetteresso (H) Graham S. Finch MA BD	1977 1983	13 Bath Street, Stonehaven AB39 2DH	01569 762876

Stonehaven: South   See Kinneff
Strachan   See Birse and Feughside

Torphins Peter R. Taylor JP BD	1977 1987	Torphins, Banchory AB31 4GQ	01339 882276
West Mearns David Jack LTh	1984 1988	Fettercairn, Laurencekirk AB30 1YE	01561 340203

Name		Year	Year	Address	Phone
Angus, J.A. Keith LVO TD MA	(Braemar with Crathie)	1955	1995	Darroch Den, Hawthorn Place, Ballater AB35 5QH	01339 756260
Beattie, Walter G. MA BD	(Arbroath Old and Abbey)	1956	1995	25 St Aidan Crescent, Banchory AB31 5XY	01330 824051
Brown, Alastair BD	(Glenmuick, Ballater)	1986	1992	52 Henderson Drive, Kintore, Inverurie AB51 0FB	01467 632787
Brown, J.W.S. BTh	(Cromar)	1960	1995	10 Forestside Road, Banchory AB31 5ZH	01330 824353
Caie, Albert LTh	(Glenmuick [Ballater])	1983	1997	16 Swann Place, Ballater AB35 5RW	01339 755787
Campbell, Donald MA	(Bervie)	1934	1979	Clashfarquar House, Robert Street, Stonehaven AB3 2DJ	01569 762438
Cheyne, Magnus	(Community Minister: Shetland)	1963	1996	Aberdeen Road, Tarland, Aboyne AB34 4UA	01339 881464
Collie, Joyce P. (Miss) MA PhD	(Corgarff Strathdon and Glenbuchat Towie)	1966	1994	28 Queen Victoria Park, Inchmarlo, Banchory AB31 4AL	01330 824981
Forbes, John W.A. BD	(Edzell Lethnot with Fern, Careston and Menmuir with Glenesk)	1973	1999	Mid Clune, Finzean, nr Banchory AB31 6PL	01330 850283
Gray, Robert MA BD	(Stonehaven Fetteresso)	1942	1982	4 Park Drive, Stonehaven AB39 2NW	01569 767027
Hood, E.C.P. MA	(Methlick)	1946	1989	1 Silver Gardens, Stonehaven AB39 2LH	
Kinniburgh, Elizabeth B.F. MA BD	(Birse with Finzean with Strachan)	1970	1986	7 Huntly Cottages, Aboyne AB31 5HD	01339 886757
MacLeod, Kenneth	(Bourtreebush with Portlethen)	1950	1986	30 Woodlands Place, Inverbervie, Montrose DD10 0SL	01561 362414
Nicholson, William	(Banchory Ternan East with Durris)	1949	1986	10 Pantoch Gardens, Banchory AB31 5ZD	01330 823875
Rennie, Donald B. MA	(Industrial Chaplain)	1956	1996	Memis Howe, Inverurie Street, Auchenblae, Laurencekirk AB30 1XS	01561 320622
Skinner, Silvester MA	(Lumphanan)	1941	1979	29 Silverbank Gardens, Banchory AB31 3YZ	01330 823032
Smith, J.A. Wemyss MA	(Garvock St Cyrus)	1947	1983	30 Greenbank Drive, Edinburgh EH10 5RE	0131 447 2205
Tierney, John P. MA	(Peterhead West Associate)	1945	1985	3 Queenshill Drive, Aboyne AB34 5DG	01339 886741
Urie, D.M.L. MA BD PhD	(Kincardine O'Neil)	1940	1980	Cochrane Cottage, North Deeside Road, Kincardine O'Neil AB34 5AA	01339 884204
Watt, William D. LTh	(Aboyne - Dinnet)	1978	1996	2 West Toll Crescent, Aboyne AB34 5GB	01339 886943

(33) GORDON

Meets at various locations on the first Tuesday of February, March, April, May, September, October, November and December, and on the fourth Tuesday of June.

Clerk: REV. IAIN U. THOMSON MA BD   The Manse, Skene AB32 6LX   **01224 743277**

Alford See Howe Trinity
Auchindoir and Kildrummy See Upper Donside

Barthol Chapel linked with Tarves
Vacant   Tarves, Aberdeenshire AB41 0JU   01651 851250

Belhelvie (H)
Daniel Hawthorn MA BD   1965   1998   Balmedie, Aberdeenshire AB23 0YB   01358 742227

Blairdaff linked with Chapel of Garioch Vacant		Chapel of Garioch, Inverurie AB51 9HE	01467 681619
Chapel of Garioch See Blairdaff			
Cluny linked with Monymusk G. Euan D. Glen BSc BD	1992	26 St Ninian's, Monymusk, Inverurie AB51 7HF	01467 651470
Corgarff and Strathdon See Upper Donside			
Culsalmond and Rayne linked with Daviot Mary M. Cranfield (Miss) MA BD	1989	Daviot, Inverurie AB51 0HY	01467 671241
Daviot See Culsalmond and Rayne			
Drumblade linked with Huntly Strathbogie Neil MacGregor	1995	Deveron Road, Huntly AB54 5DU	01466 792702
Echt linked with Midmar (T) David I. Souter	1996	Echt, Aberdeenshire AB32 7AB	01330 860533
Ellon Eleanor MacAlister (Mrs) BD	1994 1999	The Manse, Ellon, Aberdeenshire AB41 9BA	01358 720476
Fintray and Kinellar linked with Keithhall Margaret J. Garćen (Miss) BD	1993	Keithhall, Inverurie AB51 0LJ	01467 620435
Foveran John A. Cook MA BD	1986	Foveran, Ellon, Aberdeenshire AB41 6AP	01358 789288
Glenbuchat Towie See Upper Donside			
Howe Trinity Vacant			
Huntly Cairnie Glass Thomas R. Calder LLB BD WS	1994	Queen Street, Huntly AB54 %EB	01466 792630
Huntly Strathbogie See Drumblade			
Insch-Leslie-Premnay-Oyne Robert S. M'Leish LTh	1970 1984	Insch, Aberdeenshire AB52 6JR	01464 820914

Inverurie: St Andrew's Iain J.M. Telfer BD DPS	1978	1989	1 Ury Dale, Inverurie, Aberdeenshire AB51 3XW	01467 620468
Inverurie: West Ian B. Groves BD CPS		1989	West Manse, Westfield Road,Inverurie, Aberdeenshire AB51 3YS	01467 620285
Keig See Howe Trinity **Keithhall** See Fintray and Kinellar				
Kemnay John P. Renton BA LTh	1976	1990	Kemnay, Inverurie AB51 9ND	01467 642219
Kintore (H) Alan Greig BSc BD	1977	1992	6 Forest Road, Kintore AB51 0XG [e-mail: greig@kincarr.free-online.co.uk]	01467 632219 (Tel/Fax)
Leochel Cushnie and Lynturk linked with Tough G. Alan S. Stirling MA	1960	1992	The Manse, Muir of Fowlis, Aberdeenshire AB33 8JU	01975 581239
Meldrum and Bourtie A. Grainger Stoddart	1975	1988	Old Meldrum, Aberdeenshire AB51 0EQ	01651 872250
Methlick Vacant			Methlick, Aberdeenshire AB41 0DS	01651 806215
Midmar See Echt **Monymusk** See Cluny				
New Machar Ian Dryden MA DipEd	1988		Newmachar, Aberdeenshire AB2 0RD	01651 862278
Noth John M'Callum BD DipPTh	1989		Kennethmont AB54 4NP	01464 831244
Skene (H) Iain U. Thomson MA BD Marion G. Stewart (Miss) DCS	1970	1972	Skene, Westhill, Aberdeenshire AB32 6LX Kirk Cottage, Kirkton of Skene, Westhill, Aberdeenshire AB32 6XX	01224 743277 01224 743407
Tarves See Barthol Chapel **Tough** See Leochel Cushnie and Lynturk **Tullynessle and Forbes** See Howe Trinity				

Udny and Pitmedden
George R. Robertson LTh — 1985 — Udny, Aberdeenshire AB41 0RS — 01651 842052

Upper Donside (H)
Richard Darroch BD MTh — 1993 — Lumsden, Huntly AB54 4GQ — 01464 861757
John C. Mack JP (Aux) — 1985 — The Willows, Auchleven, Insch AB52 6QD — 01464 820387

Name	Ord.	Ind.	Charge / Note	Address	Tel
Andrew, John MA 3D DipRE DipEd	1961	1972	Teacher: Religious Education	Carter's Croft, Midmar, Inverurie AB51 7NJ	01330 833208
Bowie, Alfred LTh	1974	1998	(Alford with Keig with Tullynessle Forbes)	17 Stewart Road, Alford AB33 8UD	01975 563824
Collie, Jeannie P. (Miss) DCS			(Deaconess)	3 Formartindale, Udny Station, Ellon AB41 6QJ	01651 842575
Davidson, James M. MA	1947	1989	(Inverurie St Andrew's)	Ardlair, Montgarrie Road, Alford AB33 8LY	01975 563471
Jones, Robert A. LTh CA	1966	1997	(Marnoch)	13 Gordon Terrace, Inverurie AB51 4GT	01467 622691
Ledgard, J. Christopher BA	1993	1998	(Upper Donside)	Sheonshalh, South Road, Rhynie, Huntly AB54 4ND	01464 861429
Lister, Douglas	1945	1986	(Largo and Newburn)	Gowanbank, Port Elphinstone, Inverurie AB51 3UN	01467 621262
Macallan, Gerald E.	1954	1992	(Kintore)	82 Angusfield Avenue, Aberdeen AB15 6AT	01224 316125
Matthews, Lawrence J. BA BD	1958	1985	(Aberdeen Nigg)	23 Lower Granton Road, Edinburgh EH5 3RS	0131 552 7616
Mellis, Robert J. BTh CA	1982	1998	(Shapinsay)	81 Western Avenue, Ellon AB41 9EX	01358 721929
Milligan, Rodney	1949	1985	(Culsalmond with Rothienorman)	Cameron House, Culduthel Road, Inverness IV2 4YG	01463 243241
Murray, John MA	1932	1972	(Slains and Forvie)	Mayfield Nursing Home, Fonthill Road, Aberdeen AB1 4UN	01224 588034
Rennie, James B. MA	1959	1992	(Leochel Cushnie and Lynturk linked with Tough)		
Rodger, Matthew A. BD	1978	1999	(Ellon)	11 Westfield Avenue, Inverurie AB51 9RD	01467 622069
Scott, Allan D. BD	1977	1989	(Culsalmond with Daviot with Rayne)	57 Eilean Rise, Ellon AB41 9NF	01358 724556
Skinner, Alistair BD	1964	1989	(Edinburgh Priestfield)	20 Barclay Road, Inverurie AB51 9QP	01467 625161
Stewart, George C. MA	1952	1995	(Drumblade with Huntly Strathbogie)	36 Hillhead Drive, Ellon AB41 9WB	01358 720890
Wallace, R.J. Stuart MA	1947	1986	(Foveran)	104 Scott Drive, Huntly AB54 5PF	
				Manse View, Manse Road, Methlick, Ellon AB41 7DW	01651 806843

(34) BUCHAN

Meets at Cuminestown on the first Tuesday of February, March, April, June, September, October, November, and December.

Clerk: REV. R. NEILSON JP BSc BD — Hatton, Peterhead AB42 0QQ [e-mail: rneilson@compuserve.com] — 01779 841229 (Tel) 01779 841822 (Fax)

Aberdour linked with New Pitsligo
Robert W. Massie LTh — 1989 — 137 High Street, New Pitsligo, Fraserburgh AB43 6NH — 01771 653256

Auchaber United linked with Auchterless
Vacant — Auchterless, Turriff AB53 8BA — 01888 511217

Auchterless See Auchaber United

Banff linked with King Edward
Alan Macgregor BA BD — 1992 — 7 Colleonard Road, Banff AB45 1DZ — 01261 812107 (Tel), 01261 818526 (Fax)
[e-mail: alan.macgregor@banff98.freeserve.co.uk]
James Cook MA MDiv (Assoc) — 1999 1999 — 3B St Catherine Street, Banff AB45 1HT — 01261 815512

Crimond linked with St Fergus
James E. Lyall BD — 1993 — Crimond, Fraserburgh AB43 8QJ — 01346 532431 (Tel), 01346 532175 (Fax)

Cruden
Rodger Neilson JP BSc BD — 1972 1974 — Hatton, Peterhead AB42 0QQ — 01779 841229 (Tel), 01779 841822 (Fax)
[e-mail: rneilson@compuserve.com]

Deer(H)
James Wishart JP BD — 1986 — Old Deer, Peterhead AB42 5JB — 01771 623582

Fordyce
David Anderson MA BD — 1975 1997 — Portsoy, Banff AB45 2QB — 01261 842272

Fraserburgh: Old
Douglas R. Clyne BD — 1973 — 97 Saltoun Place, Fraserburgh AB43 9RY — 01346 518536

Fraserburgh: South (H) linked with Inverallochy and Rathen East
Ronald F. Yule — 1982 — 15 Victoria Street, Fraserburgh AB43 9PJ — 01346 518244 (Tel), 01346 511921 (Fax)

Fraserburgh: West
B. Andrew Lyon LTh — 1971 1978 — 23 Strichen Road, Fraserburgh AB43 9SA — 01346 513303 (Tel), 01346 512398 (Fax)
[e-mail: rex@balyon.demon.co.uk]

Fyvie linked with Rothienorman
Vacant — Fyvie, Turriff AB53 8RD — 01651 891230

Gardenstown
Donald N.Martin BD — 1996 — The Manse, Fernie Brae, Gardenstown, Banff AB45 3YL — 01261 851256 (Tel), 01261 851022 (Fax)
[e-mail: d.n.martin@virgin.net]

Inverallochy and Rathen East See Fraserburgh South

King Edward See Banff

Longside
Norman Smith MA BD — 1997 — 9 Anderson Drive, Longside, Peterhead AB42 4XG [e-mail: normsmith@aol.com] — 01779 821224

Lonmay linked with Rathen West
G.M. Allan Fawkes JP BA BSc — 1979 — Lonmay, Fraserburgh AB43 8UJ [e-mail: allan@fawkes.swinternet.co.uk] — 01346 532227 (Tel) / 01346 532733 (Fax)

Macduff
David J. Randall MA BD ThM — 1971 — Macduff, Banff AB45 3QL [e-mail: djrandall@macduff.force9.co.uk] — 01261 832316 (Tel) / 01261 832301 (Fax)

Marnoch
Rosemary Legge (Mrs) BSc BD MA — 1992 1997 — Aberchirder, Huntly AB54 7TS — 01466 780276

Maud and Savoch linked with New Deer
Alastair Donald MA PhD BD — 1999 — Fordyce Terrace, New Deer, Turriff AB52 6TD [e-mail: alistair@donalds99 freeserve.co.uk] — 01771 644216

Monquhitter and New Byth
Vacant — 10 Teuchar Road, Cuminestown, Turriff AB53 5YD — 01888 544279

New Deer St Kane's See Maud and Savoch
New Pitsligo See Aberdour

Ordiquhill and Cornhill (H) linked with Whitehills
Gordon Henig BSc BD — 1997 — 6 Craigneen Place, Whitehills, Banff AB45 2NE — 01261 861671

Peterhead: Old
David S. Ross MSc PhD BD — 1978 — 1 Hawthorn Road, Peterhead AB42 2DW — 01779 472618 (Tel/Fax)

Peterhead: St Andrew's (H)
David G. Pitkeathly LLB BD — 1996 — 1 Landale Road, Peterhead AB42 1QN — 01779 472141

Peterhead: Trinity
L. Paul McClenaghan BA — 1973 1996 — 18 Landale Road, Peterhead AB42 1QP [e-mail: paul.mcclenaghan@virgin.net] — 01779 472405

Pitsligo linked with Sandhaven
Ian G. Thom BSc PhD BD — 1990 — 49 Pitsligo Street, Rosehearty, Fraserburgh AB43 7JL — 01346 571237

Rathen West See Lonmay
Rothienorman See Fyvie
St Fergus See Crimond
Sandhaven See Pitsligo

Strichen linked with Tyrie
Stephen A. Blakey BSc BD   1977   1994   Kingsville, Strichen, Fraserburgh AB43 6SQ   [e-mail: sablakey@aol.com]   01771 637365

Turriff: St Andrew's
Donald B.C. Inglis MA MEd BD   1975   1983   Balmellie Road, Turriff AB53 4DP [e-mail: dbcinglis@aol.com]   01888 563240 (Tel) 01888 569071 (Fax)

Turriff: St Ninian's and Forglen
Bruce K. Gardner MA BD PhD   1988   1998   "Balloch":, Station Road, Turriff AB53 4ER [e-mail: bruce@globalnet.co.uk]   01888 563383

Tyrie See Strichen
Whitehills see Ordiquhill and Cornhill

Name			Former charge	Address	Telephone
Bell, Douglas W. MA LLB	1975	1993	(Alexandria: North)	76 Burnside Road, Mintlaw AB42 5PE	01771 623299
Birnie, Charles J. MA	1969	1995	(Aberdour and Tyrie)	"The Dookit", 23 Water Street, Strichen AB43 6ST	01771 637775
Blaikie, James BD	1972	1997	(Berwick-on-Tweed: St Andrew's Wallace Green and Lowick)	57 Glenugie View, Peterhead AB42 2BW	01779 490625
Brown, William H.	1953	1990	(Peterhead St Andrew's)	11 Henderson Park, Peterhead AB42 2WR	01779 472592
Douglas, Ian P. LTh	1974	1998	(Aberdeen: Craigiebuckler)	1 Tortorston Drive, Peterhead	
Dunlop, M. William B. LLB BD	1981	1995	(Peterhead St Andrew's)	18 Iona Avenue, Peterhead AB42 1NZ	01779 479189
Jaffray, Alison (Mrs) MA BD	1990	1995	(Forth St Paul's)	Gight Lodge, Fetterletter, Fyvie AB53 8LX	01651 806333
Jeffrey, Stewart D. BSc BD	1962	1997	(Banff with King Edward)	8 West End, Whitehills, Banff AB42 2NL	01261 861523
Mackenzie, Seoras L. BD	1996	1998	Chaplain, Army	1 RHF BFPO 38	
Scott, W.D.	1956	1989	(Maud with Savoch)	2 Thistle Gardens, Mintlaw AB42 5FG	01771 622258
Shaw, Andrew BSc FRIC	1964	1985	(Gardenstown)	39 Bridge Street, Banff AB45 1HD	01261 812949
Strachan, Ian M. MA BD	1959	1994	(Ashkirk with Selkirk)	20 Westfield Road, Turriff AB53 4AF	01888 568403
Taylor, William MA MEd	1984	1996	(Buckie North)	23 York Street, Peterhead AB42 6SN	01779 481798
Walker, Colin D.	1977	1982	(Auchindoir and Kildrummy)	The Old Manse, Alvah, Banff AB54 3US	01261 821656

(35) MORAY

Meets at St Andrew's Lhanbryde and Urquhart on the first Tuesday of February, March, April, May, September, October, November, December and the fourth Tuesday of June.

Clerk:	REV. G. MELVYN WOOD MA BD			Seafield Place, Cullen, Buckie, Banffshire AB56 4UU [e-mail: melvynwood@cullenmanse.freeserve.co.uk]	01542 841851 01542 841991 0797 409 5840	(Tel) (Fax) (Mbl)

Aberlour (H)
| Elizabeth M. Curran (Miss) BD | 1995 | 1998 | Mary Avenue, Aberlour, Banffshire AB38 9QZ | 01340 871027 |

Alves and Burghead linked with Kinloss and Findhorn
| John C. Beck BD | 1975 | 1995 | The Manse, Dunbar Street, Burghead, Elgin, Moray IV30 2XB | 01343 830365 |

Bellie linked with Speymouth
| David J. Ferguson | 1966 | 1982 | 11 The Square, Fochabers, Moray IV32 7DG
[e-mail: bellierev@aol.com] | 01343 820256
01343 820256 | (Tel)
(Fax) |

Birnie linked with Pluscarden
| Ronald J. Scotland BD | | 1993 | The Manse, Birnie, Elgin IV30 3SU | 01343 542621 |

Buckie: North (H)
| Robert P. Boyle LTh | 1990 | 1996 | 14 St Peter's Road, Buckie AB56 1DL | 01542 831328 |

Buckie: South and West (H) linked with Enzie
| Eric W. Foggitt MA BSc BD | | 1991 | East Church Street, Buckie AB56 1ES
[e-mail: ericleric@compuserve.com] | 01542 832103 (Tel/Fax) |

Cullen and Deskford
| G. Melvyn Wood MA BD | 1982 | 1997 | Seafield Place, Cullen, Buckie, Banffshire AB56 4UU
[e-mail: melvynwood@cullenmanse.freeserve.co.uk] | 01542 841851
01542 841991
0797 409 5840 | (Tel)
(Fax)
(Mbl) |

Dallas linked with Forres St Leonard's (H) linked with Rafford
| Vacant | | | Nelson Road, Forres IV36 ODR | 01309 672380 |

Duffus, Spynie and Hopeman (H)
| Vacant | | | Duffus, Elgin IV30 2QP | 01343 830276 |

Dyke linked with Edinkillie
Ann McColl Poole (Mrs) DipEd ACE LTh   1983   Brodie, Forres IV36 OTD   01309 641239

Edinkillie See Dyke

Elgin: High
Charles D. McMillan LTh   1979   1991   5 Forteath Avenue, Elgin IV30 1TQ   01343 542449

Elgin: St Giles' (H) and St Columba's South (01343 551501)   (Office and Church Halls: Greyfriars Street, Elgin IV30 1LF)
George B. Rollo BD   1974   1986   18 Reidhaven Street, Elgin IV30 1QH   01343 547208
James M. Thomson BA (Assoc)   1952   1992   48 Mayne Road, Elgin IV30 1PD   01343 547664

Enzie See Buckie South and West

Findochty linked with Portknockie linked with Rathven(T)
Graeme Austin BD   1997   20 Netherton Terrace, Findochty, Buckie AB56 2QD   01542 833484

Forres: St Laurence (H)
Barry Boyd LTh DPS   1993   12 Mackenzie Drive, Forres IV36 0JP   01309 672260

Forres: St Leonard's See Dallas

Grange linked with Rothiemay
Vacant   Rothiemay, Huntly AB54 5NE   01466 711334

Keith: North, Newmill and Boharm (H) (01542 886390)
Michael G. Lyall BD   1993   Keith, Banffshire AB55 3BR   01542 882559

Keith: St Rufus and Botriphnie (H)
Ranald S.R. Gauld MA LLB BD   1991   1995   The Manse, Keith, Banffshire AB55 3BR   01542 882799
Kay Gauld (Mrs) BD STM PhD   1999   The Manse, Keith, Banffshire AB55 3BR   01542 882799

Kinloss and Findhorn See Alves and Burghead

Knockando, Elchies and Archiestown (H) linked with Rothes
Vacant   Manse Brae, Rothes AB38 7AA   01340 831381

Lossiemouth: St Gerardine's High (H)
Duncan Murray BTh   1986   St Gerardine's Road, Lossiemouth IV31 6RA   01343 813146

Lossiemouth: St James'
George L. Cordiner BD   1973   Prospect Terrace, Lossiemouth IV31 6JS   01343 813135

Mortlach and Cabrach (H)
Hugh M.C. Smith LTh   1973   1982   Dufftown, Keith AB55 4AR   01340 820380

Pluscarden See Birnie
Portknockie See Findochty
Rafford See Dallas
Rathven See Findochty linked with Portknockie
Rothes See Knockando, Elchies and Archiestown
Rothiemay See Grange

St Andrew's Lhanbryde (H) and Urquhart
Vacant   St Andrews Road, Lhanbryde, Elgin IV30 3PU   01343 842208

Speymouth See Bellie

Name				Address	Phone
Cowie, Gordon S. MA LLB	1986	1992	(Birnie with Pluscarden)	Strathspey, Lower Inchberry, Orton, Fochabers IV32 7QH	01343 88377
Davidson, A.A.B. MA BD	1960	1997	(Grange with Rothiemay)	9 Woodlands Park, Rosemount, Blairgowrie PH10	01250 875957
Diack, Peter MA	1951	1994	(Elgin South)	3A Gordon Street, Elgin	
Douglas, Christina A. (Mrs)	1987	1993	(Inveraven and Glenlivet)	The Shieling, Dyke, Forres IV36 0SP	01309 641221
Evans, John W. MA BD	1945	1984	(Elgin High)	15 Weaver Place, Elgin IV30 1HB	
Fraser, Donald R. MA BD	1944	1985	(Kinloss and Findhorn)	Brisbane, Orchard Road, Forres IV36 OLG	01309 672596
Greaves, Andrew T. BD	1985	1997	Chaplain, Gordonstoun		
Macaulay, Alick Hugh MA	1943	1981	(Bellie with Speymouth)	5 Duke Street, Fochabers IV32 7DN	01343 820726
Miller, W.B.	1950	1987	(Cawdor with Croy and Dalcross)	10 Kirkhill Drive, Lhanbryde, Elgin IV30 3QW	01343 842368
Porter, John C.	1962	1987	(Forres St Leonard's)	17 Coppice Court, Grantown-on-Spey PH26 3LF	01479 873082
Robertson, John T. FPhS	1961	1993	(Keith: North, Newmill and Boharm)	43 Nelson Terrace, Keith AB55 3EF	01542 886339
Shaw, Duncan LTh CPS	1984		Chaplain RAF	37 Hebenten Road, Bishopmill, Elgin IV30 2EP	01343 549384
Spence, Alexander	1944	1989	(Elgin St Giles': Associate)	20 Back Braes, Brechin, Angus	
Stuart, John T. MA	1958	1993	(Duffus, Spynie and Hopeman)	1 Seaview Farm Paddock, Cummingston, Elgin IV30 2XY	01343 830890
Watt, H. Forbes	1950	1976	(Lossiemouth St Gerardine's High)	25 South Covesea Terrace, Lossiemouth IV31 6NA	01343 812975
Whiteford, Robert S. MA	1945	1986	(Shapinsay)	Lochinver Croft, Mosstowie, Elgin IV30 3TT	01343 541438
Wright, David L. MA BD	1957	1998	(Stornoway: St Columba)	84 Wyvis Drive, Nairn IV12	01667 451613

(36) ABERNETHY

Meets at Boat of Garten on the first Tuesday of February, March, April, June, September, October, November and December.

Clerk:　　REV. JAMES A.I. MACEWAN MA BD　　The Manse, Nethy Bridge　PH25 3DG　　01479 821280

Abernethy (H) linked with Cromdale (H) and Advie
James A.I. MacEwan　MA BD　　1973　1980　　Nethy Bridge, Inverness-shire　PH25 3DG　　01479 821280

Alvie and Insh (T)(H)
Vacant　　Kincraig, Kingussie, Inverness-shire　PH21 1NA　　01540 651221

Boat of Garten (H) and Kincardine linked with Duthil (H)
David W. Whyte　LTh　　1993　1999　　Deshar Road, Boat of Garten, Inverness-shire　PH24 3BN　　01479 831252

Cromdale and Advie　See Abernethy

Dulnain Bridge linked with Grantown-on-Spey (H)
Morris Smith　BD　　1988　　Golf Course Road, Grantown-on-Spey, Moray　PH26 3HY　　01479 872084

Duthil　See Boat of Garten and Kincardine
Grantown-on-Spey　See Dulnain Bridge

Inveraven and Glenlivet
Margaret A. Muir (Miss)　MA LLB BD　　1989　1993　　Ballindalloch, Banffshire　AB37 9EB　　01807 500311

Kingussie (H)
Norman R. Macaskill　MA　　1962　1991　　Kingussie, Inverness-shire　PH21 1HA　　01540 661311

Kirkmichael and Tomintoul (H)
Sven S. Bjarnason　Cand.Theol　　1975　1992　　Tomintoul, Ballindalloch, Banffshire　AB37 9HA　　01807 580254

Laggan linked with Newtonmore (H)
Irene C. Gillespie (Mrs)　BD　　1991　　Newtonmore, Inverness-shire　PH20 1DT　　01540 673238

Newtonmore　See Laggan

Rothiemurchus and Aviemore (H)
Ron C. Whyte　BD CPS　　1990　　Rothiemurchus, Aviemore, Inverness-shire　PH22 1QH　　01479 810280

Livesley, Anthony LTh   1979 1997   (Kilearn)   87 Beech Avenue, Nairn IV12 4SJ   01667 455126
Stewart, Matthew S. LTh   1981 1998   (Boat of Garten and Kincardine with Duthil)   2 Ruarden Court, Grantown-on-Spey PH26 3DA   01479 872210

(37) INVERNESS

Meets at Inverness, in the Dr Black Memorial Hall, on the first Tuesday of February, March, April, May, September, October, November and December and at the Moderator's Church on the fourth Tuesday of June.

Clerk: REV. ALASTAIR S. YOUNGER BScEcon ASCC   3 Elm Park, Inverness IV2 4WN   01463 232462 (Tel/Fax)

Ardclach linked with Auldearn and Dalmore
John L. Waugh LTh   1973   1993   Auldearn, Nairn IV12 5SX   01667 453180

Ardersier (H) linked with Petty
Alexander Whiteford LTh   1996   Ardersier, Inverness IV2 7QU   01667 462224

Auldearn and Dalmore See Ardclach

Cawdor linked with Croy and Dalcross (H)
Matthew Robertson LTh   1968   1994   Croy, Inverness IV25PH   01667 493217

Croy and Dalcross See Cawdor

Culloden The Barn (H)
James H. Robertson BSc BD   1975   1994   45 Oakdene Court, Culloden IV2 7XL   01463 790504

Daviot and Dunlichity linked with Moy, Dalarossie and Tomatin
Lilian M. Bruce (Miss) BD ThM   1971   1986   Daviot, Inverness IV2 5XL   01463 772242

Dores and Boleskine
James Christie LTh   1993   1993   The Manse, Foyers, Inverness IV2 6XU   01456 486206

Inverness: Crown (H) (01463 238929)
Peter H. Donald MA PhD BD   1991   1998   39 Southside Road, Inverness IV2 4XA   01463 231140

Inverness: Dalneigh and Bona (GD)(H)
Fergus A. Robertson MA BD   1971   1999   9 St Mungo Road, Inverness IV3 5AS   01463 232339

Inverness: East (H)
Aonghas I. MacDonald MA BD — 1967 — 1981 — 2 Victoria Drive, Inverness IV2 3QD — 01463 231269

Inverness: Hilton (T)
Duncan MacPherson LLB BD — 1994 — 4 Tomatin Road, Inverness IV2 4UA — 01463 231417

Inverness: Kinmylies (E) (H)
Fraser M.C. Stewart BSc BD — 1980 — 1992 — 2 Balnafettack Place, Inverness IV3 8TQ — 01463 712479

Inverness: Ness Bank (H)
S. John Chambers OBE BSc — 1972 — 1998 — 15 Ballifeary Road, Inverness IV3 5PJ — 01463 234653

Inverness: St Columba High (H)
Alastair S. Younger BScEcon ASCC — 1969 — 1976 — 3 Elm Park, Inverness IV2 4WN — 01463 232462 (Tel/Fax)

Inverness: St Stephen's linked with The Old High (1st charge) (H)
Colin M. Anderson BA BD STM MPhil — 1968 — 1994 — 24 Damfield Road, Inverness IV2 3HU — 01463 237129

Inverness: The Old High See Inverness: St Stephen's

Inverness: Trinity (H)
Norman I. MacRae LTh — 1966 — 60 Kenneth Street, Inverness IV3 5PZ — 01463 234756

Inverness: West (2nd Charge) (T)(H)
Alistair Malcolm BD DPS — 1976 — 1992 — 52 Crown Drive, Inverness IV2 3QG — 01463 237420

Kilmorack and Erchless
George Duthie BSc Msc PhD BD — 1998 — "Roselynn", Croyard Road, Beauly, Inverness-shire IV4 7DJ — 01463 782260

Kiltarlity linked with Kirkhill
Campbell Mackinnon BSc BD — 1982 — Kirkhill, Inverness IV5 7PX — 01463 831662

Kirkhill See Kiltarlity
Moy, Dalarossie and Tomatin See Daviot and Dunlichity

Nairn: Old (H)
Ian W.F. Hamilton BD LTh ALCM AVCM — 1978 — 1986 — 3 Manse Road, Nairn IV12 4RN — 01667 452203

Nairn: St Ninian's (H)
William B. Whyte BD — 1973 — 1975 — Queen Street, Nairn IV12 4AA — 01667 452202

Petty See Ardersier

Urquhart and Glenmoriston (H)

Hugh F. Watt BD DPS	1986	1996	Blairbeg, Drumnadrochit, Inverness-shire IV3 6UG	01456 450231

Black, Archibald T. BSc	1964	1997	(Inverness: Ness Bank)	16 Elm Park, Inverness IV2 4WN	01463 230588
Brown, Derek G. BD DipMin	1989	1994	Chaplain: Raigmore Hospital and Highland Hospice	Cathedral Manse, Cnoc-an-Lobht, Dornoch IV25 3HN	01862 810296
Buell, F. Bart BA MDiv	1980	1995	(Urquhart and Glenmoriston)	6 Towerhill Place, Cradlehall, Inverness IV1 2FN	01463 794634
Charlton, George W.	1952	1992	(Fort Augustus with Glengarry)	61 Drumfield Road, Inverness IV2 4XL	01463 242802
Chisholm, Archibald F. MA	1957	1997	(Braes of Rannoch with Foss and Rannoch)	32 Seabank Road, Nairn IV12 4EU	01667 452001
Donn, Thomas M. N/A	1932	1969	(Duthil)	6 Cawdor Road, Inverness IV2 3NR	01463 236410
Edgar, William M.G. MA	1937	1976	(Auchindoir and Kildrummy)	19 Maclean Court, Nairn IV124HZ	01667 453676
Gibbons, Richard BD		1997	Adviser in Mission and Evangelism	3 Holm Burn Place, Inverness IV2 6WT	01463 226889
Gibson, A. Cameron MRCVS	1962	1990	(Eskdalemuir with Hutton and Corrie with 'Tundergarth)	Langleigh, 10 Rowan Place, Nairn IV12 4TL	01667 455413
Gilmour, Robert M. MA BD	1942	1981	(Kiltarlity)	16/22 Culburnie, Kiltarlity, Inverness-shire IV4 7JJ	01463 741229
Graham, John	1950	1984	(Edinburgh St Andrew's Clermiston)	1 Edington Road, Milton of Culcaboc, Inverness IV2 3DB	01463 242426
Henderson, Roderick B.	1973	1982	(Kingswells)	5 Holmpark, Inverness IV2 4XT	01463 224022
Macaskill, Duncan	1952	1974	(Lochs-in-Bernera)	71 Smithton Park, Inverness IV2 7PD	01463 791376
Macdonald, Alexander	1957	1991	(Cross Ness)	45 Drumfield Road, Inverness IV2 4XL	01463 239894
Macfarlane, Donald MA	1940	1980	(Inverness East)	8 Muirfield Gardens, Inverness IV2 4HF	01463 231977
Macritchie, Ian M. BSc BD STM PhD	1987	1998	Hospital Chaplain: Inverness Hospitals	7 Merlin Crescent, Inverness IV2 3TE	01463 235204
Morrison, Hector BSc BD MTh	1981	1994	Lecturer: Highland Theological College	24 Oak Avenue, Inverness IV2 4NX	01463 238561
Selfridge, John BTh BREd	1969	1991	(Eddrachillis)	43 Highfield Avenue, Inverness IV3 8RW	01463 238905
Wilson, Ian M.	1988	1993	(Cawdor with Croy and Dalcross)	3 Kilravock Crescent, Nairn IV12 4QZ	01667 452977
Wilson, John M. MA	1964	1979	(Adviser: Religious Education)	25 Crown Drive, Inverness IV2 3QF	01463 240855

INVERNESS ADDRESSES

Inverness

Crown	Kingsmills Road x Midmills Road.
Dalneigh and Bona	St Mary's Avenue
East	Academy Street x Margaret Street
Hilton	Druid Road x Tomatin Road
Kinmylies	Kinmylies Way
Ness Bank	Ness Bank x Castle Road
St Columba High	Bank Street x Fraser Street
St Stephen's	Old Edinburgh Road x Southside Road
Old High	Church Street x Church Lane
Trinity	Huntly Place x Upper Kessock Street
West	Huntly Street x Greig Street

Nairn

Old	Academy Street x Seabank Road
St Ninian's	High Street x Queen Street

(38) LOCHABER

Meets at Caol, Fort William, in Kilmallie Church Hall, on the first Tuesday of each month except January, May, July and August when there is no meeting.

Clerk: REV. ALAN RAMSAY MA   MacIntosh Manse, 26 Riverside Park, Lochyside, Fort William   PH33 7RB   01397 702054

Charge / Name			Address	Phone
Acharacle (H) linked with Ardnamurchan				
Thomas Moffat BSc BD	1976	1987	Acharacle, Argyll PH36 4JU	01967 431665
Ardgour linked with Strontian				
James A. Carmichael LTh	1976		Ardgour, Fort William PH33 7AH	01855 841230
Ardnamurchan See Acharacle				
Arisaig and the Small Isles				
Vacant			Mid Road, Arisaig, Inverness-shire PH39 4NJ	01687 450227
Duror (H) linked with Glencoe St Munda's (H)				
Anne M. Jones (Mrs) BD			Ballachulish, Argyll PA39 4JG	01855 811998
Fort Augustus linked with Glengarry				
Moses Donaldson	1972	1993	Fort Augustus, Inverness-shire PH32 4BH	01320 366210
Alan H.W. Lamb BA MTh (Assoc)	1959	1992	Millfield Cottage, Market Hill, Fort Augustus PH32 4DS	01320 366605
Fort William: Duncansburgh (H) linked with Kilmonivaig				
Donald A. MacQuarrie BSc BD	1979	1990	Fort William, Inverness-shire PH33 6BA	01397 702297
Fort William: MacIntosh Memorial (H)				
Alan Ramsay MA	1967		26 Riverside Park, Lochyside, Fort William PH33 7NY	01397 702054
Glencoe St Munda's See Duror				
Glengarry See Fort Augustus				
Kilmallie				
James A. Munro BD DMS	1979	1994	Corpach, Fort William PH33 7JS	01397 772210
Kilmonivaig See Fort William Duncansburgh				
Kinlochleven (H) linked with Nether Lochaber (H)				
Vacant			Kinlochleven, Argyll PA40 4QW	01855 831227

Mallaig St Columba and Knoydart

Ben Johnstone MA BD   1973   1989   Mallaig, Inverness-shire PH41 4RG   01687 462256

Morvern

Alicia Ann Winning MA BD   1984   Lochaline, Morvern, by Oban PA34 5UU   01967 421267

Nether Lochaber See Kinlochleven
Strontian See Ardgour

Anderson, David M. MSc FBCO	1984 1995	Auxiliary	1 Dumfries Place, Fort William PH33 6UQ	01397 702091
Beaton, Jamesina (Miss) DCS		(Deaconess)	"Fairhills", Fort Augustus PH32 4DS	01320 366252
Gillies, Hugh M. MA JP	1939 1980	(Fort Augustus)	4 Broadstone Park, Inverness IV2 3LA	
MacLean, Hector A.M. MA	1937 1978	(Duror with Glencoe)	Gearra Beag, Duror, Argyll PA38 4BW	01631 74215
Millar, John L. MA BD	1981 1990	(Fort William Duncansburgh with Kilmonivaig)		

7 Orchard Gardens, Strathaven ML10 6UN

LOCHABER Communion Sundays

Acharacle	1 Mr., Je., Sp., Dc.	Fort William	1 Ap., Je., Oc.	Kilmonivaig	1 My., Nv.	
Ardgour	1 Je., Sp., Dc., E.	Duncansburgh	1 Mr., Je., Sp., Dc.	Kinlochleven	1 Fb., Ap., Je., Oc., Dc.	
Ardnamurchan	1 Ap., Au., Dec.	M'Intosh Memorial	1 Ap., Oc.	Mallaig	4 My., 3 Nv.	
Arisaig and Moidart	1 My., Nv.	Glencoe	1 Ja., Ap., Jl., Oc.	Morvern	E., 1 Jl., 4 Sp., 1 Dc.	
Duror	2 Jn., 3 Nv.	Glengarry	3 Mr., My., Sp., 1 Dc.	Nether Lochaber	1 Ap., Oc.	
Fort Augustus	2 My., 4 Oc.	Kilmallie		Strontian	1 Je., Sp. Dc.	

(39) ROSS

Meets in Dingwall on the first Tuesday of each month, except January, May, July and August.

Clerk: REV. R.M. MACKINNON LTh   27 Riverford Crescent, Conon Bridge, Ross-shire IV7 8HL   01349 866293

Alness

Ronald Morrison BD   1996   27 Darroch Brae, Alness, Ross-shire IV17 OSD   01349 882238

Avoch linked with Fortrose and Rosemarkie

Samuel Torrens BD   1995   5 Nessway, Fortrose IV10 8SS   01381 620068
Alexander Glass OBE MA (Aux)   1998   "Craigton", Tulloch Avenue, Dingwall IV15 9TU   01349 863258

Charge / Minister			Address	Telephone
Contin Thomas M. McWilliam MA BD	1964	1997	Contin, Strathpeffer, Ross-shire IV14 9ES	01997 421380
Cromarty John Tallach MA MLitt	1970	1999	Cromarty, Ross-shire IV11 8YT	01381 600802
Dingwall: Castle Street (H) Grahame M. Henderson BD	1974	1987	16 Achany Road, Dingwall, Ross-shire IV15 9JB	01349 863167
Dingwall: St Clement's (H) Russel Smith BD	1994		8 Castle Hill Road, Dingwall	01349 861011
Fearn Abbey and Nigg Chapelhill James Forsyth LTh	1970	1994	Fearn, Ross-shire IV20 1TN	01862 832626
Ferintosh Daniel J.M. Carmichael MA BD	1994		Conon Bridge, Ross-shire IV7 8BE	01349 861275
Fodderty and Strathpeffer Ivan C. Warwick MA BD	1980	1999	Strathpeffer, Ross-shire IV14 9DL	01997 421398
Fortrose and Rosemarkie See Avoch				
Invergordon Vacant			Cromlet Drive, Invergordon, Ross-shire IV18 OBA	01349 852273
Killearnan with Knockbain Vacant			Killearnan, Muir of Ord, Ross-shire IV6 7SQ	01463 870234
Kilmuir and Logie Easter Kenneth J. Pattison MA BD STM	1967	1996	Delny, Invergordon, Ross-shire IV18 0NW	01862 842280
Kiltearn (H) Donald A. MacSween BD	1991	1998	Evanton, Ross-shire IV16 9UY	01349 830472
Knockbain See Killearnan				
Lochbroom and Ullapool (GD) James Gemmell MA LTh	1999		Ullapool, Ross-shire IV26 3SX	01854 612050
Resolis and Urquhart (T) Alasdair J. MacLennan BD DCE	1979	1994	The Manse, Culbokie, Conon Bridge IV7 8JN	01349 877452

Rosskeen				
Robert Jones BSc BD	1990		Alness, Ross-shire IV17 OSX	01349 882265
Tain				
Douglas A. Horne BD	1977		14 Kingsway Ave, Tain, Ross-shire IV19 1BN	01862 894140
Tarbat (T)				
Iain Mackenzie MA BD	1967	1998	Castle Street, Portmahomack, Tain, Ross-shire IV20 1YE	01862 871652
Urray and Kilchrist				
Vacant			Muir of Ord, Ross-shire IV6 7TL	01463 870259
Bolster, Richard F. JP	1956	1984	(Killearnan)	c/o 8 Craigray, Kessock, by Inverness IV1 1XH	01463 731337
Buchan, John BD MTh	1968	1993	(Fodderty and Strathpeffer)	"Faithlie", 45 Swanston Avenue, Inverness IV3 6QW	01463 713114
Dupar, Kenneth W. BA BD PhD	1965	1993	(Christ's College, Aberdeen)	The Old Manse, The Causeway, Cromarty IV11 8XJ	01381 600428
Harries, David A.	1950	1990	(British Sailors' Society)	17 Chanonry Crescent, Fortrose IV10 8RH	
Holroyd, Gordon B.Th FPhS FSAScot	1959	1993	(Dingwall: St Clements)	22 Stuarthill Drive, Maryburgh, Dingwall IV15 9HU	01349 863379
Howe, Andrew Y. BTh	1957	1989	(Rosskeen)	Bredon Cottage, Stringfield Road, Alness IV17	01349 882302
Liddell, Margaret (Miss) BD DipTh	1987	1997	(Contin)	20 Wyvis Crescent, Conon Bridge IV7 8BZ	01349 865997
MacAlpine, A.G. MA BD STM	1935	1975	(Tain)	Maybank, St Catherine's Road, Forres IV36 0LL	01309 672027
Macdonald, Norman MA BD	1937	1970	(Aberdeen Trinity)	44 Alder Drive, Perth PH1 3EU	
Mackenzie, A. Ian	1945	1986	(Glenelg with Glenshiel with Kintail)	4 St Mary's Well, Tain IV19 1LS	01862 89305
McGowan, Andrew T.B. BD STM PhD	1979	1994	Highland Theological College	6 Kintail Place, Dingwall IV15 9RL	
Mackinnon, R.M. LTh	1968	1995	(Kilmuir and Logie Easter)	27 Riverford Crescent, Conon Bridge, Ross-shire IV7 8HL	01349 866293
Maclennan, William	1952	1981	(Lochbroom and Ullapool)	8 Firthview Road, Inverness IV3 8LZ	01463 225253
Macleod, Donald R. MA	1953	1986	(Ferintosh)	1 Top Street, Connon Bridge IV7 8BH	01349 863160
Macleod, John MA	1959	1993	(Resolis and Urquhart)	"Benview" 19 Balvaird, Muir of Ord	01463 871286
Niven, William W. BTh	1982	1995	(Alness)	4 Obsdale Park, Alness IV17 0XG	01349 882427
Orr, William LTh	1972	1987	(Tarbat)	Tigh-Glas, Tarbatness Road, Portmahomack, Fearn IV20	01862 87294
Rutherford, Ellon B. (Miss) MBE DCS			(Deaconess)	41 Duncanston, Conon Bridge IV7 8JB	01349 877439

(40) SUTHERLAND

Meets at Lairg on the first Tuesday of March, May, September, November and December and on the first Tuesday of June at the Moderator's Church.

Clerk: REV. J.L. GOSKIRK LTh   The Manse, Lairg, Sutherland IV27 4EH   01549 402373

Congregation / Minister			Address	Tel
Altnaharra and Farr John M. Wilson MA BD	1965	1998	Bettyhill,by Thurso, Sutherland KW14 7SS	01641 521208
Assynt and Stoer Frederick R. Hurst MA	1965	1971	Lochinver, by Lairg, Sutherland IV27 4LH	01571 844342
Clyne (H) Ian W. McCree BD	1971	1987	Golf Road, Brora, Sutherland KW9 6QS	01408 621239
Creich linked with Rosehall Olsen, Heather C. (Miss) BD	1978	1999	Bonar Bridge, Ardgay, Sutherland IV24 3EB	01863 766256
Dornoch Cathedral (H) Susan M. Brown (Mrs) BD DipMin	1985	1998	Dornoch, Sutherland IV25 3HN	01862 810296
Durness and Kinlochbervie John T. Mann BSc BD	1990	1998	Kinlochbervie, by Lairg, Sutherland IV27 4RG	01971 521287
Eddrachillis John MacPherson BSc BD	1993		Scourie, by Lairg, Sutherland IV27 4TQ	01971 502431
Golspie George M. Donaldson MA BD	1984	1989	Fountain Road, Golspie, Sutherland KW10 6TH	01408 633295
Kildonan and Loth Helmsdale (H) Melvyn James Griffiths BTh.DipTheol	1978	1996	Helmsdale, Sutherland KW8 6HT	01431 821674
Kincardine Croick and Edderton Alan Watt MTh	1996		Ardgay, Sutherland IV24 3BG	01863 766285
Lairg (H) linked with Rogart (H) J.L. Goskirk LTh	1968		Lairg, Sutherland IV27 4EH	01549 402373

Melness and Tongue (H)
Vacant — Tongue, by Lairg, Sutherland IV27 4XL — 01847 611230

Rogart See Lairg
Rosehall See Creich

Rettie, James A. BTh — 1981 1999 — 2 Trentham Drive, Westhill, Inverness IV2 — 01641 521208
Wilson, Mary D. (Mrs) RGN SCM DTM — 1990 1998 — The Manse, Bettyhill, Thurso KW14 7SS

(41) CAITHNESS

Meets alternately at Wick and Thurso on the first Tuesday of Feburary, March, May, September, November and December, and the third Tuesday of June.

Clerk: REV. MICHAEL G. MAPPIN BA — Mundays, Banks Road, Watten KW1 5YN — 01955 621720

Berriedale and Dunbeath linked with Latheron
Vacant — Ross Manse, Dunbeath, Caithness KW6 6EA — 01593 731228

Bower linked with Watten
C.J. Grant Bell — 1983 1999 — Watten, Caithness KW1 5YN — 01955 621220

Canisbay linked with Keiss
Iain Macnee LTh BD MA PhD — 1975 1998 — Canisbay, Wick, KW1 4YH — 01955 611309

Dunnet linked with Olrig
Vacant — Olrig, Castletown, Thurso KW14 8TP — 01847 821221

Halkirk and Westerdale
Kenneth Warner BD DA DipTD — 1981 — Abbey Manse, Halkirk, KW12 6UU — 01847 831227

Keiss See Canisbay
Latheron See Berriedale and Dunbeath

Lybster and Bruan (T)
Iain A. Sutherland BSc BD — 1996 — Central Manse, Lybster, Caithness KW3 6BN — 01593 721231

Olrig See Dunnet

Reay linked with Strathy and Halladale (H)
James S. Dewar MA BD — 1983 1994 — Reay, Thurso, KW14 7RE — 01847 811272

Strathy and Halladale See Reay

Thurso: St Peter's and St Andrew's (H)
Kenneth S. Borthwick MA BD — 1983 1989 — 46 Rose Street, Thurso KW14 7HN — 01847 895186

Thurso: West (H)
Ronald Johnstone BD — 1977 1984 — Thorkel Road, Thurso KW14 7LW — 01847 892663

Watten See Bower

Wick: Bridge Street
A.A. Roy MA BD — 1955 — Mansefield, Miller Avenue, Wick KW1 4DF — 01955 602822

Wick: Old (H)(L)
R. Stewart Frizzell BD — 1961 1988 — Miller Avenue, Wick, KW1 4DF — 01955 604252

Wick: Pulteneytown (H) and Thrumster
William F. Wallace BDS BD — 1968 1974 — Coronation Street, Wick KW1 5LS — 01955 603166

Alexander, Dugald C. MA BD — 1945 1977 — (Dunscore) — WAAS, 1 Robertson's Lane, Thurso KW14 7DF — 01847 894938
Mappin, Michael G. BA — 1961 1998 — (Bower with Watten) — Mundays, Banks Road, Watten, by Wick KW1 5YL — 01955 621720

CAITHNESS –
Communion Sundays

Berriedale and Dunbeath	2 Mr., Je., Sp., Dc.
Bower	1 Jl., Dc.
Canisbay	1 Je., Nv.
Dunnet	last My., Nv.
Halkirk	Oct., Ap., Jl.
Westerdale	Ap., Oc., 4 Dc.
Keiss	1 My., 3 Nv.
Latheron	1 Jl., 2 Sp., 1 Dec., 2 Mr.
Lybster and Bruan	3 Je., Nv., E.
Olrig	last My., Nv.
Reay	last Ap., Sp.
Strathy and Halladale	1 Jn., last Nv.
Thurso	
St Peter's and St Andrew's	1 Fb., Ap., Je., Sp., Nv.
West	4 Mr., Je., Nv.
Watten	1 Jl., Dc.
Wick	
Bridge Street	1 Ap., Oc.
Old	4 Ap., Sp.
Pulteneytown and Thrumster	1 Mr., Je., Sp., Dc.

(42) LOCHCARRON – SKYE

Meets in Kyle on the first Tuesday of each month except January, May, July and August.

Clerk: REV. ALLAN J. MACARTHUR BD   High Barn, Croft Road, Lochcarron, Ross-shire IV54 8YDA   01520 722278 (Tel)
[e-mail: a.macarthur@btinternet.com]   01520 722674 (Fax)

Applecross, Lochcarron and Torridon (GD)
Vacant
David Scott BTh (Assoc)   1994   Lochcarron, Ross-shire IV54 8YD
                                    Applecross, Ross-shire IV54 8LU   01520 744263

Bracadale and Duirinish (GD)
Vacant   Dunvegan, Isle of Skye IV55 8WQ   01470 521457

Gairloch and Dandonnell
Vacant   Gairloch, Ross-shire IV21 2BT   01445 712053 (Tel/Fax)

Glenelg and Kintail
Donald Beaton MA BD MTh   1961   1988   Inverinate, Kyle, Ross-shire IV40 8HE   01599 511245

Kilmuir and Stenscholl (GD)
Vacant   Staffin, Isle of Skye IV51 9JX   01470 562201 (Tel/Fax)

Lochalsh
Allan B. Brown BD MTh   1995   Kyle, Ross-shire IV40 8DA   01599 534294

Lochcarron and Sheildaig See Applecross

Portree (GD)
John Ferguson LTh BD DD   1973   1980   Viewfield Road, Portree, Isle of Skye IV51 9ES   01478 612019 (Tel/Fax)

Snizort (H) (GD)
Donald MacLeod LTh   1988   Snizort, Portree, Isle of Skye IV51 9XE   01470 532260 (Tel/Fax)

Torridon and Kinlochewe See Applecross

Strath and Sleat (GD)
Iain M.A. Reid BD   1990   Broadford, Isle of Skye IV49 9AA   01471 822538 (Tel/Fax)
John Nicolson BD DipMin (Assoc)   1997   Loch Nevis, 13 Calliparry, Ardvasar, Sleat, Isle of Skye IV45 8RS   01471 844469

McCulloch, Alan J.R.	1990	1995	Chaplain: Army	IRHF, BFPO 38	01520	722433
MacDonald, Kenneth	1965	1992	(Associate: Applecross l/w Lochcarron...)	Tigharry, Main Street, Lochcarron, Ross-shire IV54		
MacDougall, Angus	1940	1982	(Sleat)	The Old Manse, Kilmore Street, Isle of Skye IV44 8RG	01471	844238
Mackinnon, Duncan	1956	1989	(Plockton and Kyle)	7 Garth Road, Inverness IV2 4DA	01463	230971
MacLeod, R. BA MBA BD	1994	1998	Chaplain: Royal Navy	15 Burnshill Drive, Norton, Fitzwarren, Taunton TA2 6QF		
Matheson, James G. MA BD DD	1936	1979	(Portree)	10 Husabost, Dunvegan, Isle of Skye IV49	01470	511335
Ritchie, Walter M.	1973	1999	(Uphall South)	"Strathardle", Fernilea, Carbost, Isle of Skye IV47 8SJ	01478	640458
Williamson, Tom MA BD	1941	1982	(Dyke with Edinkillie)	16 Cove, Inverasdale, Poolewe, Achnasheen IV22 2LT	01445	781423

LOCHCARRON – SKYE
Communion Sundays

Applecross	1 Jl.	Kilmuir	1 Mr., Sp.	Portree	E., P., X., 2 Mr., Au., 1 Nv.
Bracadale	3 Mr., Sp.	Kintail	3 Ap., Jl.	Sleat	2 Je., Dc.
Duirinish	3 Ja., E., 2 Je., 3 Sep.	Lochalsh and Stromeferry	4 Je., Sp., X., E.	Snizort	1 Je., Dc.
Dundonnell	4 Je.	Lochcarron and Shieldaig	E., 3 Je., 1 Oc.	Stenscholl	1 Je., Dec.
Gairloch	3 Je., Nv.	Plockton and Kyle	2 My., 1 Oc.	Strath	1 Mr., Au.
Glenelg	2 Je., Nv.			Torridon and Kinlochewe	2 My
Glenshiel	1 Jl.				

(43) UIST

Meets on the fourth Wednesday of January, March, September and November in Lochmaddy and the fourth Wednesday of June in Leverburgh.

Clerk: REV. MURDO SMITH MA BD   Scarista, Isle of Harris HS3 3HX   01859 550200

Barra (GD)
Vacant   Cuithir, Castlebay, Isle of Barra HS9 5XD   01871 810230

Benbecula (GD)(H)
Kenneth J. Macpherson BD   1988   1998   Griminish, Isle of Benbecula HS7 5QA   01870 602180

Bernera (GE) (H)
Vacant   Isle of Berneray, Lochmaddy, Isle of North Uist HS6 5BD   01876 540234

Carinish (GD) (H)

Thomas J.R. MacKinnon LTh DipMin	1996	1998	Clachan, Isle of North Uist HS6 5HD	01876 580219

Kilmuir and Paible (GE)

Vacant			Paible, Isle of North Uist HS6 5ED	01876 510310

Lochmaddy and Trumisgarry (GD)

Angus MacDonald BSc BD	1995		Lochmaddy, Isle of North Uist HS6 5AA	01876 500414

Manish-Scarista (GD) (H)

Murdo Smith MA BD	1988		Scarista, Isle of Harris HS3 3HX	01859 550200

South Uist (GD)

James B. Lawson MA BD	1961	1998	Daliburgh, Isle of South Uist HS8 5SS	01878 700265

Tarbert (GE) (H)

Norman MacIver BD	1976	1988	Tarbert, Isle of Harris HS3 3DF	01859 502231

(Amhuinsuidhe)

			Mission House, Amhuinsuidhe, Tarbert, Isle of Harris HS3 3AS	01859 560201

MacInnes, David MA BD	1966	1999	(Kilmuir and Paible)	9 Golf View Road, Kinmylies, Inverness IV3 8SZ	01859 502310
Macrae, D. A. JP MA	1942	1988	(Tarbert)	5 Leverhulme Road, Tarbert, Isle of Harris HS3 3DD	01859 540288
Macrae, William DCS			(Deacon)	6 Park View Terrace, Isle of Scalpay, Tarbert, Isle of Harris HS4 3XX	
Muir, Alexander MA BD	1982	1996	(Carinish)	14 West Mackenzie Park, Inverness IV2 3ST	01463 712096
Smith, John M.	1956	1992	(Lochmaddy)	Hamersay, Clachan, Isle of North Uist HS6 5HD	01876 580332

UIST –
Communion Sundays

Barra	Easter, Pentecost, Christmas
Benbecula	2 Mr., Sp.
Bernera	2 Jl. Nv.
Carinish	4 Mr., Au.

Kilmuir and Paible	1 Jn., 3 Nv.
Lochmaddy and Trumisgarry	4 Jn., Oc.
Manish-Scarista	3 Ap., 1 Oc.

South Uist – Iochdar	1 Mr.
Howmore	1 Jn.
Daliburgh	1 Sp.
Tarbert	2 Mr., 3 Sp.

(44) LEWIS

Meets at Stornoway, in St Columba's Church Hall, on the first Tuesday of February, March, April, June, September, November and December.

Clerk:　REV. THOMAS S. SINCLAIR MA BD — Martin's Memorial Manse, Matheson Road, Stornoway, Isle of Lewis HS1 2LR [e-mail:tssinclair@lineone.net] — 01851 702206 (Tel/Fax) / 04325 166038 (Pager)

Charge / Minister		Address	Tel
Barvas (GD) (H) Ivor MacDonald BSc MSc BD	1993	Barvas, Isle of Lewis HS2 0QY [e-mail: ivormacd@aol.com]	01851 840218
Carloway (GD) (H) Murdo M. Campbell BD DipMin	1997	Carloway, Isle of Lewis HS2 9AU [e-mail: cam204576@aol.com]	01851 643255
Cross Ness (GE) (H) Vacant		Swainbost, Ness, Isle of Lewis HS2 0TB	01851 810375
Kinloch (GE) (H) Donald Angus MacLennan	1975　1989	Laxay, Lochs, Isle of Lewis HS2 9LA	01851 830218
Knock (GE) (H) James Macdonald LTh CPS	1984	Garrabost Point, Isle of Lewis HS2 0PW	01851 870917
Lochs-in-Bernera (GD) (H) Kenneth Donald Macleod BD CPS	1989	Bernera, Isle of Lewis HS2 9LU	01851 612371
Lochs-Crossbost (GD) Andrew W.F. Coghill BD DPS	1993	Leurbost, Lochs, Isle of Lewis HS2 9NS [e-mail: andcoghill@aol.com]	01851 860243
Stornoway: High (GE) (H) William B. Black MA BD	1972　1998	Goathill Road, Stornoway HS1 9NJ	01851 703106
Stornoway: Martin's Memorial (H) Thomas Suter Sinclair MA BD	1966　1976	Matheson Road, Stornoway HS1 2LR [e-mail: tssinclair@lineone.net]	01851 702206 (Tel/Fax) / 04325 166038 (Pager)
Stornoway: St Columba (GD) (H) Vacant		Lewis Street, Stornoway HS1 2JF	01851 703350

Uig (GE)
William Macleod   1957 1964   Miavaig, Uig, Isle of Lewis HS2 9HW   01851 672216 (Tel/Fax)

Macaulay, Donald OBE JP	1968	1992	(Park)	6 Kirkibost, Bernera, Isle of Lewis HS2 9RD	01851 612341
Macdonald, William	1952	1982	(Knock)	13 Laxay, Lochs, Isle of Lewis HS2 9PJ	01851 830231
MacRitchie, Murdanie	1958	1969	(Acharacle)	15A New Garrabost, Isle of Lewis HS2 OPR	01851 870763
MacSween, Norman	1952	1986	(Kinloch)	7 Balmerino Drive, Stornoway, Isle of Lewis HS1 2TD	01851 703369
Morrison, Alexander	1952	1973	(Barvas)	Ceol Mara, Marig, Isle of Harris HS3 3AG	01859 502667

LEWIS
Communion Sundays

Barvas	3 Mr., Sp.	Lochs-Crossbost	4 Mr., Sp.	
Carloway	1 Mr., last Sp.	Stornoway		
Cross, Ness	2 Mr., Oc.	Stornoway	St Columba	3 Fb., last Au.,
Kinloch	3 Mr., 2 Je., 2 Sp.	High	3 Fb., last Au.	Thurs before Easter,
Knock	1 Ap., Nv.	Martin's Memorial	3 Fb., last Au.	and before Remembrance
Lochs-in-Bernera	1 Ap., 2 Sp.	Uig	3 Je., 1 Sp.	

(45) ORKNEY

Meets at Kirkwall, in the Town Hall, on the first Tuesday of September and February, on the second Tuesday of October, on the fourth Tuesday of November and April, and on the last Tuesday in June.

Clerk:	REV. TREVOR G. HUNT BA BD	The Manse, Finstown, Orkney KW17 2EG	01856 761328 (Tel/Fax)
		[e-mail: TghOrkney@aol.com]	0467 602598 (Mbl)
		[Internet: http://members.aol.com/OrkneyPrsb/index.htm]	

Birsay linked with Harray and Sandwick
Lynn Brady (Miss) BD DipMin   1996   Quoyloo, Sandwick, Orkney KW17 2SD   01856 841506

Deerness linked with Holm linked with St Andrews
Joan H. Craig (Miss) MTheol   1986   1993   Holm, Orkney KW17 2SD   01856 781422 (Tel/Fax)
[e-mail: JoanHCraig@compuserve.com]

Eday linked with Stronsay Moncur Memorial (H)
Joyce Keyes (Mrs)   1996   Stronsay, Orkney KW17 2AF   01857 616311

Evie linked with Firth linked with Rendall
Trevor G. Hunt BA BD — 1986 — Finstown, Orkney KW17 2EG / [e-mail: TghOrkney@aol.com] / [Internet: http://members.aol.com/OrkneyEFR/index.htm] — 01856 761328 (Tel/Fax) / 0467 602598 (Mbl)

Firth See Evie

Flotta linked with Hoy and Walls (T)
Vacant — South Isles Manse, Longhope, Stromness, Orkney KW16 3PG — 01856 701325

Harray and Sandwick See Birsay
Holm See Deerness
Hoy and Walls See Flotta

Kirkwall: East
Allan McCafferty BSc BD — 1993 — Thom Street, Kirkwall, Orkney KW15 1PF / [e-mail: 106611.440@compuserve.com] — 01856 875469

Kirkwall: St Magnus Cathedral (H)
Ronald Ferguson MA BD ThM — 1972 — Berstane Road, Kirkwall, Orkney KW15 1NA / [e-mail: ronferguson@clara.co.uk] — 01856 873312 (Tel/Fax)
[Eleanor Morson (Mrs) (Assist) — 1990 — The Rectory, Dundas Crescent, Kirkwall , Orkney KW15 1JQ] — 01856 872024]
Scottish Episcopal Church

North Ronaldsay linked with Sanday (H)
James Daniel Gibb BA LTh — 1994 — Sanday, Orkney KW17 2BW / [e-mail: danny@mgibb.freeserve.co.uk] — 01857 600429 (Tel/Fax) / 0374 632492 (Mbl)

Orphir (H) linked with Stenness (H)
Thomas L. Clark BD — 1985 — Stenness, Stromness, Orkney KW16 3HH — 01856 761331

Papa Westray linked with Westray
Iain D. MacDonald BD — 1993 — The Manse, Rapness, Westray, Orkney KW17 2DE / [e-mail: macdonald@rapnessmanse.freeserve.co.uk] — 01857 677357 (Tel/Fax) / 041 0443780 (Mbl)

Rendall See Evie

Rousay
Vacant

St Andrew's See Deerness
Sanday See North Ronaldsay

Shapinsay
Joyce Lynn (Mrs) MIPM BD   1995   1999   Shapinsay, Balfour, Orkney KW17 2EA   01856 711332

South Ronaldsay and Burray
Maria A.G. Plate (Miss) LTh BA   1983   1994   St Margaret's Hope, Orkney KW17 2RN   01856 831288

Stromness (H)
Fiona L. Lillie (Mrs) BA BD MLitt   1995   1999   5 Manse Lane, Stromness, Orkney KW16 3AP   01856 850203

Stronsay See Eday
Westray See Papa Westray

Brown, R. Graeme BA BD	1961	1998	(Birsay with Rousal)	Brihg Deeps, Orphir, Orkney KW17 2LX	(Tel/Fax) 01856 811707
Cant, H.W.M. MA BD STM	1951	1990	(Kirkwall St Magnus Cathedral)	Quoylobs, Holm KW17 2RY	01856 781300
Fox, Edward P.G.	1950	1983	(Eday with Stronsay Moncur Memorial)	Old Schoolhouse, Stronsay	01857 616388
Ward, Michael J. BSc BD PhD	1983	1999	Community Minister	Ploverhall, Deerness, Orkney KW17 2QJ	01856 741349
				[e-mail: revmv@aol.com]	(Mbl) 0370 895543

(46) SHETLAND

Meets at Lerwick on the first Tuesday of March, April, June, September, October, November and December.

Clerk: REV. NORMAN R. WHYTE BD DipMin   Park Neuk, Meadow Field Place, Scalloway ZE1 0UE   **01595 880865**
[e-mail: burraman@msm.com]

Burra Isle linked with Tingwall
Norman R. Whyte BD DipMin   1982   1995   Park Neuk, Meadow Field Place, Scalloway ZE1 0UE   01595 880865
[e-mail: burraman@msn.com]

Delting linked with Nesting and Lunnasting
Winnie Munson (Ms) BD   1996   The Manse, Grindwell, Brae, Shetland ZE2 9QJ   01806 522219

Dunrossness and St Ninians inc Fair Isle linked with Sandwick Cunningsburgh and Quarff
Charles H.M. Greig MA BD   1976   1997   Sandwick, Shetland ZE2 9HW   01950 431244

Fetlar linked with Yell
Magnus J.C. Williamson   1992   Mid Yell, Shetland ZE2 9BN   01957 702283

Lerwick and Bressay
James A.M. Dowswell — 1991 — The Manse, St Olaf Street, Lerwick, Shetland ZE1 0ES — 01595 692125

Nesting and Lunnasting See Delting

Northmavine
Alice H. Kirkpatrick (Miss) MA BD FSAScot — 1987 — Northmavine Manse, Hillswick, Shetland ZE2 9RW — 01806 503223

Sandsting and Aithsting linked with Walls and Sandness
William J. McMillan CA LTh BD — 1969 1997 — Westside Manse, Effirth, Bixter, Shetland ZE2 9LY — 01595 810386

Sandwick, Cunningsburgh and Quarff See Dunrossness and St Ninian's
Tingwall See Burra Isle

Unst
John L. McNab MA BD — 1997 — Baltasound, Unst, Shetland ZE2 9DZ — 01957 711335

Walls See Sandsting and Aithsting

Whalsay and Skerries
Irene A. Charlton (Mrs) BTh — 1994 1997 — The Manse, Marrister, Whalsay, Shetland ZE2 9AE — 01806 566767

Yell See Fetlar

Fox, Edward P.G. — 1950 1983 — (Eday with Stronsay Moncur Memorial) — Old Schoolhouse, Stronsay — 01857 616388
Blair, James N. — 1962 1986 — (Sandsting and Aithsting with Walls) — 2 Swinster, Sandwick, Shetland
Smith, Catherine (Mrs) DCS — 1964 1998 — Presbytery Assistant — 21 Lingero, Bixter, Shetland — 01595 810207
Wilson, W. Stewart DA — 1980 1997 — (Kirkcudbright) — Aesterhoull, Fair Isle ZE2 9JU

(47) ENGLAND

Meets at London, in Crown Court Church, on the second Tuesday of March and December and at StColumba's Pont Street on the second Tuesday of June and October.

Clerk: REV. W.A. CAIRNS BD — St Columba's Church, Pont Street, London SW1X OBD
0207 584 2321
0207 373 1823 (Home)
0207 584 5446 (Fax)

Corby: St Andrew's (H)
John F. Mackie BD — 1979 1983 — 6 Honiton Gardens, Corby NN18 8BW — 01536 203175

Corby: St Ninian's (H) (01536 265245)
Alan Sharp BSc BD — 1980 1989 — 46 Glyndebourne Gardens, Corby NN18 0PZ — 01536 741179

Guernsey: St Andrew's in the Grange (H)
Vacant — The Manse, Le Villocq, Castel Guernsey — 01481 57345

Jersey: St Columba's (H)
James G. Mackenzie BA BD — 1980 1997 — 18 Claremont Avenue, St Saviour, Jersey — 01534 30659

Liverpool: St Andrew's
Continued Vacancy
Session Clerk: E. Graham (Mr) — 0151 525 4496

London: Crown Court (H) (0207 836 5643)
H. Stanley C. Hood MA BD — 1966 1991 — 53 Sidmouth Street, London WC1H 8JB — 0207 278 5022
Timothy Fletcher BA FCMA (Aux) — 1998 — 37 Hareston Valley Road, Caterham, Surrey CR3 6HN — 01883 340826

London: St Columba's (H) linked with Newcastle St Andrew's (H)
J.H. McIndoe MA BD STM — 1966 1988
W.A. Cairns BD (Assoc) — 1978 1980 — St Columba's, Pont Street, London SW1X OBD — 0207 584 2321
[Easter Smart MDiv (Assist)]

Bayes, Muriel (Mrs) DCS — (Deaconess) — 6 Blenheim Close, Rushdean, Northants NN10 9JA
Bowie, A. Glen CBE BA BSc — 1954 1984 — (Principal Chaplain: RAF) — 16 Weir Road, Hemingford Grey, Huntingdon PE18 9EH — 01480 381425

Name	Position			Address	Tel
Brown, Scott J. BD	Chaplain: RN	1993		30 Lovage Road, Whitely, Hants PO15 7LD	
Cameron, R.N.	Chaplain: Community	1975	1981	The Church Centre, Rheine Area Support Unit, BFPO 40	0049 2161 472770
Coulter, David G. BA BD	Chaplain: Army	1989	1994	21 Godley Road, salisbury, Wilts SP2 8EQ	01722 330436
Craig, Gordon W. MBE MA BD	Chaplain: RN	1972	1972	42 CDORM, Bickleigh Barracks, Plymouth PL6 7AJ	(Tel) 01752 727027 (Fax) 01752 839320
Davison, Charles F. MA	(Guernsey St Andrew's in the Grange)	1947	1987	Maryfield, Green Lanes, St Peter Port, Guernsey C1	01481 27446
Drummond, J.S. MA	(Corby St Ninian's)	1946	1978	77 Low Road, Hellesdon, Norwich NR6 5AG	01603 417736
Duncan, Denis M. BD PhD	(Editor: *The British Weekly*)	1944	1986	1 Cranbourne Road, London N10 2BT	0208 883 1831
Fyall, Robert S. MA BD	Tutor: St John's College, Durham	1986	1989	7 Briardene, Durham DH1 4QU	
Hughes, O. Tudor MBE BA	(Guernsey St Andrew's in the Grange)	1934	1976	4 Belcher Court, Dorchester on Thames, Oxon	
Jolly, Andrew J. BD	Chaplain: RAF	1989	1996	Chaplaincy and Welfare Centre, RAF Bruggen BFPO 25	
Lugton, George L. MA BD	(Guernsey St Andrew's in the Grange)	1955	1997	6 Clos de Beauvoir, Rue Cohu, Guernsey GY5 7TE	01481 54285
MacDonald, James W. BD	Principal Chaplain: British Sailors' Society	1976	1990	43 Beattie Rise, Hedge End, Southampton SO3 4OJ	01489 790106
McEnhill, Peter BD PhD	Lecturer	1992	1996	Westminster College, Madingley Road, Cambridge CB3 0AA	01223 353997
Macfarlane, Peter T. BA LTh	(Chaplain: Army)	1970	1994	Caen na Coille, 42 Muirs, Kinross KY13 7AU	01762 391027
Majcher, Philip L. BD	Chaplain: Army	1982	1987	HQ 3rd Infantry Brigade BFPO 809	01504 40507
Martin, A.M. BA BD	Chaplain: Army	1989	1989	HQ 20th Armoured Brigade BFPO 16	
Mills, Peter W. BD CPS	Chaplain: RAF	1984		Chaplaincy Services RAF, HQ PTC, Insworth, Glos GL3 1EZ	01452 712612
Morrison, James G. MBE MA	(Rotterdam)	1942	1980	8 Ecton Hall, Ecton, Northants NN6 0QE	01604 785158
Richmond, James MA BD PhD	(Lancaster University)	1956	1994	10 Wallace Lane, Forton, Preston, Lancs PR3 0BA	01524 791705
Ross, Hector C. MA	(Gillingham, St Margaret's)	1949	1988	48 Copenhagen Road, Gillingham, Kent ME7 4RV	01634 306981
Stewart, Charles E. BSc BD PhD	Chaplain of the Fleet	1976	1976	Room 205, Victory Building, HM Naval Base, Portsmouth PO1 3LS	01705 727901
Wallace, Donald S.	(Chaplain: RAF)	1950	1980	7 Dellfield Close, Watford, Herts WD1 3BL	01923 223289
White, Earlsley M. BA	(Uddingston: Park)	1957	1998	27 North Lodge, Epsom Cottage, Epsom, Surrey KT17 4JH	01372 821227

ENGLAND – Town Addresses

Corby
St Andrew's   Occupation Road
St Ninian's   Beanfield

Liverpool   The Western Rooms, Anglican Cathedral
Newcastle   Sandyford Road

London
Crown Court   Crown Court WC2
St Columba's   Pont Street SW1

(48) EUROPE

Clerk: REV. JAMES W. McLEOD MA	6 Chemin Taverney, 1218 Grand Saconnex, Geneva, Switzerland [e-mail: cofsg@pingnet.ch]			00 41 22 798 29 09 (Tel/Fax)
Amsterdam John A. Cowie BSc BD	J.W. Brouwersstraat 9, 1071 LH Amsterdam, The Netherlands [e-mail: john.cowie@tip.nl]	1983	1989	00 31 20 672 2288
Brussels Thomas C. Pitkeathly MA CA BD	23 Square des Nations, 1000 Brussels, Belgium [e-mail:Pitkeathly@compuserve.com]	1984	1991	00 32 2 672 40 56
Diana Townsend (Mrs) MA DipEd DipCPC (Aux)	Amendijiaan 2, 1933 Sterrebeek, Belgium	1996		00 32 2 731 96 25
Budapest Kenneth I MacKenzie BD CPS	St Columba'a Scottish Mission, Vorosmarty utca 51, 1064 Budapest, Hungary [e-mail:rch@mail.elender.hu]	1990	1999	00 36 1 343 8479
Costa del Sol linked with Gibraltar John R. Page ED DipMin	11 Calle Margarita Blanca, Fuengirola, Spain	1988	1996	00 34 5 258 8394
Geneva James W. McLeod MA	6 Chemin Taverney, 1218 Grand Saconnex, Geneva, Switzerland [e-mail:cofsg@pingnet.ch]	1965	1994	00 41 22 798 29 09
Gibraltar linked with Costa del Sol John R. Page BD DipMin	29 Scud Hill, Gibraltar	1988	1996	00 350 77040
Lausanne Douglas R. Murray MA BD	26 Avenue de Rumine, 1005 Lausanne, Switzerland	1965	1994	00 41 21 323 98 28
Lisbon Gordon Oliver BD	Rua da Arriaga 11, 1200 - 608 Lisbon	1979	1998	00 351 1 3995 7677
Malta Colin A. Westmarland MBE BD	206/3 Old Bakery Street, Valletta, Malta	1971	1975	00 356 222 643

Name			Address	Telephone
Paris				
William M. Reid MA BD	1966	1993	10 Rue Thimmonier, 75009 Paris, France	00 33 1 48 78 47 94
Rome St Andrew's				
David F. Huie MA BD	1962	1991	Via XX Settembre 7, 00187 Rome, Italy [e-mail:david.huie@flashnet.it]	(Tel) 00 39 06 482 7627 (Fax) 00 39 06 487 4370
Rotterdam				
Robert A. Calvert BSc BD	1983	1995	Gelebrem 59, 3068 TJ Rotterdam, The Netherlands [e-mail:Scots-International-Church-@compuserve.com]	00 31 10 220 4199
Joost Pot BSc (Aux)	1992		Rijksstraatweg 12, 2988 BJ Ridderkerk, The Netherlands	00 31 18 042 0894
With Romanian Reformed Church				
Celia G. Kenny (Mrs) MA MTh	1995	1998	Protestant Theological Institute, RO-3400 Cluj, Piata Avram Lancu 13, Romania	
Conference of European Churches				
Stewart J. Lamont BSc BD	1972	1999	Church and Society Commission, Ecumenical Centre, 174 Rue Joseph II, B-1000 Brussels, Belgium [e-mail: eeccs@skypro.be] Avenue de Broqueville 140, 1200 Brussels, Belgium (Home)	(Tel) 00 32 2 230 17 32 / 00 32 2 231 14 13 (Fax) 00 32 2 772 71 22
World Alliance of Reformed Churches				
Paraic Raemonn BA BD	1982	1993	WARC, 150 Route de Ferney, 1211 Geneva 2, Switzerland [e-mail:par@warc.ch]	00 41 22 791 62 43
World Council Secretariat				
Alan D. Falconer MA BD DLitt	1972	1995	WCC, 150 Route de Ferney, 1211 Geneva 2, Switzerland [e-mail:af@wcc-coe.org]	00 41 22 791 63 37

CORRESPONDING MEMBERS

Name			Address	Telephone
James M. Brown MA BD	1982		Neustrasse 15, D-4630 Bochum, Germany	
Claus W. Clausen	1986	1993	Kleingemuender Strasse 59, D-69118, Heidelberg-Zeigelhausen, Germany	00 49 234 133 65
R. Graeme Dunphy	1988	1993	Institut fur Angelistik, Universitatsstrasse 31, D-93053 Regensburg, Germany	
Rhona Dunphy (Mrs)				
Professor A.I.C. Heron BD DTheol	1975	1987	University of Erlangen, Kochstrasse 6, D-91054, Erlangen, Germany	00 49 9131 85 2202

Jane Howitt (Miss)

Scripture Union, PO Box 476, LV 1050 Riga, Latvia
[e-mail:janesu@com.latnet.lv]

00 371 7 220877

(Brussels)	A.J. Macleod MA BD	1943	(1974)	27A Cathcart Road, London SW10
(Brussels)	Charles C. McNeill OBE BD	1962	(1991)	17 All Saints Way, Beachamwell, Swaffham, Norfolk PE37 8BU
(Gibraltar)	D. Stuart Philip MA	1952	(1990)	6 St Bernard's Crescent, Edinburgh EH4 1NP 0131 332 7499
(Paris)	Bruce Robertson MA BD	1953	(1992)	Old Dairy Cottage, School Lane, Winfrith Newburgh, Dorset DT2 8JX 01305 852050

(49) JERUSALEM

Jerusalem: St Andrew's
Maxwell D.Craig BD ThM (Locum)   1966   1998   PO Box 8619, 91 086 Jerusalem, Israel   (Tel) 00 972 2 673 2401
(Fax) 00 972 2 673 1711

Tiberias: St Andrew's
Frederick W. Hibbert BD   1986   1995   Sea of Galilee Centre, PO Box 104, 14 100 Tiberias, Israel   (Tel) 00 972 6 672 1165
[e-mail: scottie@rannet.com]   (Fax) 00 972 6 679 0145

SECTION 6

Additional Lists
of Personnel

A	Auxiliary Ministers
B	Chaplains to HM Forces
C	Chaplains, Hospital
D	Chaplains, Full-time Industrial
E	Chaplains, Prison
F	Chaplains, University
G	Diaconate
H	Ministers having resigned Membership of Presbytery
I	Ministers holding Ministerial Certificates
J	Mission and Evangelism Advisers
K	Overseas Appointments
L	Overseas Locations
M	Overseas Retired Mission Partners
N	Parish Assistants and Project Workers
O	Readers
P	Representatives on Local Authorities
Q	Retired Lay Agents

LIST A – AUXILIARY MINISTERS

NAME	ORD	ADDRESS	TEL	PR
Anderson, David M. MSc FBCO	1984	1 Dumfries Place, Fort William PH33 6UQ	01397 702091	38
Brown, Elizabeth (Mrs) JP RGN	1996	25 Highfield Road, Scone, Perth PH2 6RN	01738 552391	28
Cloggie, June (Mrs)	1997	8 Trossachs Road, Aberfoyle FK8 3SW	01877 382382	23
Cruikshank, Alistair A.B. MA	1991	2A Chapel Place, Dollar FK14	01259 742549	23
Davidson, David W.	1987	Grianail, Glenegedale, Port Ellen, Isle of Islay PA42 7AS	01496 302194	19
Durno, Richard C. DSW CQSW	1989	31 Springfield Road, Bishopbriggs G64 1PJ	0141 772 1052	16
Ferguson, Archibald M. MSc PhD CEng FRINA	1989	The Whins, Barrowfield, Cardross G82 5NL	01389 841517	18
Fletcher, Timothy E.G. BA FCMA	1998	37 Hareston Valley Road, Caterham, Surrey CR3 6HN	01883 340826	47
Glass, Alexander OBE MA	1998	Craigton, Tulloch Avenue, Dingwall IV15 9TU	01349 863258	39
Howie, Marion L.K. (Mrs) MA ARCS	1992	51 High Road, Stevenston KA20 3DY	01294 466571	12
Jenkinson, John J. JP LTCL ALCM DipEd DipSen	1991	8 Rosehall Terrace, Falkirk FK1 1PY	01324 625498	22
Kay, Elizabeth (Miss) Dip YCS	1993	1 Kintail Walk, Inchture, Perthshire PH14 9RY	01828 686029	29
McCann, George McD. BSc ATI	1994	Rosbeg, Parsonage Road, Galashiels TD1 3HS	01896 752055	4
MacFadyen, Anne M. (Mrs) BSc BD	1995	295 Mearns Road, Newton Mearns G77 5LT	0141 639 3605	16
Mack, Elizabeth (Miss) Dip PEd	1994	24 Roberts Crescent, Dumfries DG2 7RS	01387 264847	8
Mack, John C. JP	1985	The Willows, Auchleven, Insch AB52 6QD	01464 820387	33
Mailer, Colin	1996	Innis Chonain, Back Row, Polmont FK2 0RD	01324 712401	22
Malcolm, Kenneth I. BD ACIS ACIB	1994	1 Cloan Road, Dundee DD3 9DB	01382 858721	29
Manson, Eileen (Mrs) DCE	1994	1 Cambridge Avenue, Gourock PA19 1XT	01475 632401	15
Munro, Mary (Mrs) BA	1993	High Barbeth, Leswalt DG9 0QS	01776 870250	9
Paterson, Andrew E. JP	1994	6 The Willows, Kelty KY4 0FQ	01383 830998	24
Paterson, Maureen (Mrs) BSc	1992	91 Dalmahoy Crescent, Kirkcaldy KY2 6TA	01592 262300	25
Pot, Joost BSc	1992	Rijksstraateg 12, 2988 BJ Ridderkerk, The Netherlands	00 31 18 042 0894	48
Ramage, Alistair E. BA	1996	16 Claremont Gardens, Milngavie, Glasgow G62 6PG	0141 956 2697	18
Riddell, Thomas S. BSc CEng FIChemE	1993	4 The Maltings, Linlithgow EH49 6DS	01506 843251	2
Shaw, Catherine A.M. MA	1998	40 Marrygreen Place, Stewarton KA3 5EP	01560 483352	11
Simpson, James H. BSc	1996	11 Claypotts Place, Broughty Ferry DD5 1LG	01382 776520	29
Townsend, Diana (Mrs) MA DipEd Dip CPC	1996	Armendijlaan, 1933 Sterrebeek, Belgium	00 32 27 31 96 25	48
Wandrum, David	1993	42C Clouden Road, Kildrum, Cumbernauld G67 2EW	01236 723288	22
Watson, Jean S. (Miss) MA	1993	29 Strachan Crescent, Dollar FK14 7HL	01259 742872	23
Wilson, Mary D. (Mrs) RGN SCM DTM	1990	The Manse, Bettyhill,Thurso KW14 7SS	01641 521208	40
Wilson, Roy DA ARIBA ARIAS	1986	20 William Ure Place, Bishopbriggs G64 3BH	0141 762 4853	18
Zambonini, James LIA Dip	1997	100 Old Manse Road, Netherton, Wishaw ML2 0EP	01698 350889	17

LIST B – CHAPLAINS TO HM FORCES

NAME	ORD	COM	BCH	ADDRESS
Acklam, Clifford	1997	1997	A	1 Royal Scots, Hyderabad Barracks, Colchester, Essex CO2 7TB
Aitchison, James W.	1993	1993	A	2 Bn ITC Catterick (EP), Helles Barracks, Catterick, N Yorks DL9 4HH
Brown, Scott J. BD	1993	1993	RN	HMS Neptune, HM Naval Base Clyde, Faslane, Helensburgh G84 8HL
Cameron, R.N.	1975	1981	A	The Church Centre, Rheindahlen Support Unit BFPO 40
Connolly, Daniel BD DipTheol DipMin	1983		A	1 A and S H, Redford Barracks, Colinton Road, Edinburgh EH13 0PP
Coulter, David G. BA BD	1989	1994	A	HQ Land Command, Erskine Barracks, Wilton, Salisbury, Wilts SP2 0AG
Craig, Gordon T. BD DipMin	1988	1988	RAF	Chaplaincy Centre, RAF College, Cranwell NG34 8HB
Craig, Gordon W. MBE MA BD	1972	1972	RN	42 CDO RM, Bickleigh Barracks, Plymouth, Devon PL6 7AJ
Dailly, J.R. BD DipPS	1979	1979	A	DACG, 42 NW Bde, Fulwood Barracks, Preston PR2 8AA
Jolly, Andrew J. BD CertMin	1983	1996	RAF	Chaplaincy Centre, RAF Bruggen, BFPO 25
Keith, Donald MA BD	1971	1984	RN	Comacchio Gp RM, RM Condor, Arbroath, Angus DD11 3SJ
Kingston, David V.F. BD	1993	1993	A	1 Highlanders, Somme Barracks, Catterick Garrison, N Yorks DL9 3AQ
McCulloch, Alen J.R.	1990	1995	A	1 Black Watch, Fort George, Ardersier, Inverness IV1 2TD
McFadzean, Iair MA BD	1989	1989	RAF	Chaplains Office, RAF Leuchars, St Andrews, Fife KY16 0JX
Mackenzie, Seoras L. BD	1996	1998	A	1 RHF, BFPO 38
MacLeod, C.A.	1996	1996	A	BHQ 1 KOSB, Salamanca Barracks, BFPO 53
MacLeod, Rory A.R. BA BD MBA	1994	1998	RN	40 Cdo RM, Norton Manor Camp, Taunton, Somerset TA2 6PF
MacLeod, R.N.	1986	1992	A	Army Training Regiment, Glencorse Barracks, Penicuik EH26 0NP
Majcher, Philip L. BD	1982	1987	A	HQ 3Inf Bde, BFPO 809
Martin, A.M. BA BD	1989	1989	A	Senior Chaplain, 20 Armd Bde, BFPO 16
Mills, Peter W. BD CPS	1984	1984	RAF	Chaplaincy Services (RAF), Room F84, HQPTC Innsworth, Glos GL3 1EZ
Murning, John BD	1988	1999	A	
Norman, Alison E.P. MA BD.	1987	1992	RN	HMS Raleigh, Torpoint, Cornwall PL11 2PD
Prentice, Donald K. BSc BD	1992	1992	A	Royal Defence Medical College, Fort Blockhouse, Gosport, Hants PO12 2AB
Rae, Scott M. MBE BD CPS	1976	1981	RN	HMS Sultan, Military Road, Gosport, Hants PO12 3BY
Shackleton, Scott J.S. BD	1993	1993	RN	HMS Ocean, BFPO 350
Shaw, Duncan LTh CPS	1984	1984	RAF	CSFC Chaplains Office, RAF Lossiemouth, Morayshire IV31 6SD
Stewart, Charles E. BSc BD MTh PhD	1976	1976	RN	Chaplain of the Fleet, Room 203, Victory Building, HM Naval Base, Portsmouth PO1 3LS
Whitton, John P. MA BD	1977	1977	A	Assistant Chaplain General, Army HQ Scotland, Craigiehall, South Queensferry EH30 9TN

CHAPLAINS TO HM FORCES (retired)

NAME	ORD	RTD	BCH	ADDRESS
Blakey, Stephen A. BSc BD	1977	1994	(A)	Kingsville, Strichen, Fraserburgh AB43 6SQ
Bowie, A. Glen CBE BA BSc	1954	1984	(RAF)	16 Weir Road, Hemingford Grey, Huntingdon PE18 9EH
Brown, P. MA	1953	1987	(RN)	24 Inchmickery Drive, Dalgety Bay, Fife KY11 5NF
Edwards, Michael S. MA	1982	1996	(A)	Flat 1G, Ascot Court, Dorchester Avenue, Glasgow G12 0BE
Harkness, James CB OBE QHC MA	1961	1995	(A)	13 Saxe Coburg Place, Edinburgh EH3 5BR
Huie, David F. MA BD	1962	1991	(RN)	Via XX Settembre 7, 00187 Rome, Italy
Ingram, J.R.	1954	1978	(RAF)	48 Marlee Road, Broughty Ferry DD5 3EX
Macfarlane, Peter T. BA LTh	1970	1994	(A)	42 The Muirs, Kinross KY13 7AU
Neill, Bruce F. MA BD	1966	1996	(RN)	The Manse, Main Street, St Boswells TD6 0BB
Robertson, Matthew LTh	1968	1994	(A)	The Manse, Croy, Inverness IV1 2PH
Shedden, John QHC BD DipPSS	1971	1998	(RAF)	4 Wilton Hill Terrace, Hawick TD9 8BE
Shields, John MBE LTh	1972	1997	(A)	The Manse, Lauder, Berwickshire TD2 6QD
Wallace, Donald S.	1950	1980	(RAF)	7 Dellfield Close, Watford, Herts WD1 3LB

CHAPLAINS TO HM FORCES (Territorial Army)

NAME	ORD	COM		ADDRESS
Barclay, Iain C TD	1976	1982		Staff Chaplain, HQ Scotland (Army), Edinburgh EH30 9TN
Blakey, Stephen A.	1977	1996		32 (Scottish) Signal Regiment (V), Glasgow G20 6JU
Forsyth, Alex R. TD	1973	1983		71 Engineer Regiment (V), RAF Leuchars, Fife KY16 0JX
Gibson, James	1978	1986		205 (Scottish) Field Hospital (V), Glasgow G51 2YE
Kerr, Angus	1983	1995		Lowland Volunteers, Edinburgh EH7 4HW
Kinsey, Louis	1991	1992		205 (Scottish) Field Hospital (V), Glasgow G51 2YE
Thomson, John M.A.	1978	1992		105 Regiment, Royal Artillery (V), Edinburgh EH13 0LA
Warwick, Ivan C.	1980	1990		Highland Volunteers, Perth PH1 5BT

CHAPLAINS TO HM FORCES (Army Cadet Force)

	ORD	COM	ADDRESS
Abelado, Benjamin J.A.	1991	1998	Glasgow & Lanarkshire Bn., Glasgow G72 8YP
Almond, David M.	1996	1998	Glasgow & Lanarkshire Bn., Glasgow G72 8YP

NAME	ORD	COM	ADDRESS
Andrews, Edward	1985	1998	Lothian & Borders Bn., Broxburn EH52 5PD
Barclay, Iain C. TD	1976	1996	Black Watch (Royal Highland Regiment) Bn., Perth PH1 5BT
Campbell, Roderick D.M. TD	1975	1998	Argyll & Sutherland Highlanders Bn., Alexandria G82 2DG
Frizzell, Stewart	1961	1993	Queens Own Highlanders Bn., Inverness IV2 4SU
Goskirk, J. Leslie	1968	1985	Queens Own Highlanders Bn., Inverness IV2 4SU
Homewood, I. Max	1997	1998	Argyll & Sutherland Highlanders Bn., Alexandria G82 2DG
Swindells, Sean	1996	1998	Gordon Highlanders Bn., Aberdeen AB23 8DU
Torrance, Iain R. TD	1982	1996	Gordon Highlanders Bn., Aberdeen AB23 8DU
Whyte, Margaret A.	1988	1997	West Lowland Bn., Ayr KA8 9HX

LIST C – HOSPITAL CHAPLAINS ("Full-Time" Chaplains are listed first in each area)

LOTHIAN

EDINBURGH – LOTHIAN UNIVERSITY HOSPITALS NHS TRUST
ROYAL INFIRMARY [0131 536 3085]
Rev. Dr Ewan Kelly   29 Buckstone Crescent, Edinburgh EH10 6PJ
Rev. Douglas F. Stevenson   128 Church Street, Tranent EH33 1BL
Miss Anne Mulligan   Chaplain's Assistant   1/6 Coxfield, Edinburgh EH11 2SY
WESTERN GENERAL HOSPITAL
N.H.S. TRUST [0131 537 1000]
Rev. Melville Schofield   25 Rowantree Grove, Currie EH14 5AT
LOTHIAN PRIMARY CARE NHS TRUST
ROYAL EDINBURGH HOSPITAL [0131 537 6734]
Rev. Murray Chalmers   25 Greenbank Road, Edinburgh EH10 5RX
Mrs Alison Wagstaff   Chaplain's Assistant   27 Cambridge Gardens, Edinburgh EH6 5DH

LIVINGSTON –
WEST LOTHIAN HEALTHCARE N.H.S. TRUST [01506 419666]
Rev. Thomas Crichton   18 Carlton Terrace, Edinburgh EH7 5DD
Rev. Dr Georgina Nelson   6 Pentland Park, Craigshill, Livingston EH54 5NR

HOSPICES

MARIE CURIE CENTRE   Rev. Tom Gordon   Frogston Road West, Edinburgh EH10 7DR   (Tel) 0131 445 2141
                                                                                                            (Fax) 0131 445 5845
ST COLUMBA'S HOSPICE   Rev. Derek Murray   Challenger Lodge, 15 Boswall Road, Edinburgh EH5   0131 551 1381

0131 536 3086

Hospital	Chaplain	Address	Tel.
CITY	Rev. Harry Telfer	32 Mayfield Road, Edinburgh EH9 2NJ	0131 667 1629
CORSTORPHINE	Rev. J. William Hill	23 Belgrave Road, Edinburgh EH12 6NG	0131 334 3188
EASTERN GENERAL	Rev. John Tait	52 Pilrig Street, Edinburgh EH6 5AS	0131 554 1842
ROYAL EDINBURGH HOSPITAL	Rev. John Whitley	114 Viewforth, Edinburgh EH10 4LN	0131 229 0133
LIBERTON	Rev. Donald M. Skinner	43 Ravenscroft Street, Edinburgh EH17 8QJ	0131 664 2147
PRINCESS MARGARET ROSE	Rev. Kenneth J. Mackay	122 Sighthill Loan, Edinburgh EH11 4NT	0131 453 6921
ROYAL HOSPITAL FOR SICK CHILDREN	Rev. Andrew Ritchie	202 Colinton Road, Edinburgh EH14 1BP	0131 443 2020
ROYAL VICTORIA	Rev. D. Graham Leitch	38 Cluny Gardens, Edinburgh EH10 6BN	0131 447 8702
	Rev. Sara Embleton	20 Wilton Road, Edinburgh EH16 5NX	0131 667 3981
WESTERN GENERAL	Rev. Keith S.P. Robinson	52 Inverleith Row, Edinburgh EH3 5PX	0131 667 7258
	Rev. Ralph C.P. Smith	2 Blackford Hill View, Edinburgh EH9 3HD	0131 557 6082
	Rev. Anne T. Logan	19 Eildon Street, Edinburgh EH3 5JU	
LINLITHGOW ST MICHAEL'S	Rev. John Paterson	St Michael's Manse, Linlithgow EH49 7AL	01506 842195
BELHAVEN	Rev. Laurence H. Twaddle	7 Ashfield Place, Dunbar DH42 1NH	01368 863098
EDENHALL	Rev. Patricia Allen	1 Westgate, Dunbar EH42 1JL	01368 865711
HERDMANFLAT	Rev. William C. Thomas	11 Muirfield Crescent, Gullane EH31 2HN	01620 842415
LOANHEAD	Rev. James M. Ritchie	46 St James' Gardens, Penicuik EH26 9DU	01968 676123
	Rev. Kenneth D.F. Walker	The Manse, Athelstaneford, North Berwick EH39 5BE	01620 880378
ROODLANDS	Rev. John W. Fraser	North Manse, Penicuik EH26 8AG	01968 672213
ROSSLYNLEE	Mrs Muriel Willoughby	32 Marchburn Drive, Penicuik EH26 9HE	01968 675249

BORDERS

Hospital	Chaplain	Address	Tel.
MELROSE – BORDERS GENERAL HOSPITAL N.H.S. TRUST [01896 754333]	Rev. J. Ronald Dick	Chaplaincy Centre, Borders General Hospital, Melrose TD6 9BS	
DINGLETON	Rev. John Riddell	42 High Street, Jedburgh TD8 6NQ	01835 863223
HAY LODGE, PEEBLES	Rev. James H. Wallace	Innerleithen Road, Peebles EH45 8BD	01721 721749
KNOLL	Rev. David Hebenton	Grey Gables, Beanburn, Ayton, Eyemouth TD14 5QY	01890 781333
INCH	Rev. Robin McHaffie	Kirk Yetholm, Kelso TD5 8RD	01573 420308

DUMFRIES AND GALLOWAY

Hospital	Chaplain	Address	Tel.
DUMFRIES HOSPITALS [01387 246246]	Rev. Alexander E. Strachan	Netherwood Lodge, Glencaple Road, Dumfries DG1 4TY	01387 267585
THOMAS HOPE, LANGHOLM	Rev. W. Haisley Moore	17 Shawpark Crescent, Selkirk TD7 4EX	01750 22566
LOCHMABEN	Rev. W. Logan Kirk	The Manse, Hightae, Lockerbie DG11 1JL	01387 811499
MOFFAT			
NEW ANNAN	Rev. S.E.P. Beveridge	The Manse, Ecclefechan, Lockerbie DG11 3BU	01576 300357

CASTLE DOUGLAS			
CRESSWELL	Rev. J. Hamilton Fraser	1 Castle View, Castle Douglas DG7 1BG	01556 502171
DUMFRIES AND GALLOWAY	Rev. Mary Hutchison (Mrs)	25 Twiname Way, Heathhall, Dumfries DG1 3ST	01387 250610
ROYAL INFIRMARY			
	Rev. Mary Hutchison (Mrs)	25 Twiname Way, Heathhall, Dumfries DG1 3ST	01387 250610
	Rev. D.K.P. Bennett	Irongray Manse, Dumfries DG2 9TR	01387 720227
KIRKCUDBRIGHT	Rev. Douglas R. Irving	6 Bourtree Avenue, Kirkcudbright DG6 4AU	01557 330489
THORNHILL	Rev. John E. Gisbey	The Manse, Thornhill DG3 5DP	01848 331191
DALRYMPLE	Rev. Keith Offor	St Ninian's Manse, Stranraer DG9 9AB	01776 702443
GARRICK	Rev. Samuel McC. Harris	Linden, Leswalt Road, Stranraer DG9 OAA	01776 706387
NEWTON STEWART	Rev. Neil G. Campbell	The Manse, Newton Stewart DG8 6HH	01671 402259
AYRSHIRE AND ARRAN			
AYRSHIRE AND ARRAN PRIMARY CARE			
N.H.S. TRUST [01292 610556]			
AILSA HOSPITAL, AYR	Rev. John Banks	19 Victoria Drive, Troon KA10 6JF	01292 317758
AYRSHIRE AND ARRAN ACUTE HOSPITALS			
N.H.S. TRUST [01563 521133]			
CROSSHOUSE HOSPITAL KILMARNOCK	Rev. Judith Huggett	4 Westmoor Crescent, Kilmarnock KA1 1TX	01292 442554
AYR/BIGGART HOSPITALS [01292 610555]	Rev. Roderick H. McNidder	10 Hollow Park, Alloway KA7 4SR	
ARROL PARK	Mrs Norma Livingstone	31 Victoria Drive, Troon KA10 6JF	01292 269161
BALLOCHMYLE	Rev. A.M. McPhail	87 Forehill Road, Ayr KA7 3JR	01290 700365
	Rev. Kevin MacKenzie	The Manse, Mauchline Road, Ochiltree KA18 2PZ	01465 831282
DAVIDSON	Rev. Robert Bell	The Manse, Ballantrae, Girvan KA26 0UH	01290 420769
HOLMHEAD	Rev. John Paterson	33 Barrhill Road, Cumnock KA18 1PJ	
CROSSHOUSE	Mrs Norma Livingstone	31 Victoria Drive, Troon KA10 6JF	
KIRKLANDSIDE	Rev. Barbara Urquhart	Manse of Kilmaurs, 9 Standalane, Kilmaurs KA3 2NB	01863 538289
STRATHLEA	Rev. Carolyn Baker	10 Mauchline Road, Ochiltree KA18 2PZ	01290 700365
AYRSHIRE CENTRAL	Rev. Hugh M. Adamson	Mure Church Manse, West Road, Irvine KA12 8RE	01294 279916
	Rev. James Roy	10A Graham Terrace, Stewarton KA3 5BB	01560 484602
	Rev. Scott Robertson	31 Milgarholm Avenue, Irvine KA12 0EL	
BROOKSBY HOUSE LARGS	Rev. Stephen J. Smith	31 Douglas Street, Largs KA30 8PT	01475 672370
WAR MEMORIAL, ARRAN	Rev. Elizabeth Watson	The Manse, Whiting Bay, Isle of Arran KA27 8RE	01770 700289
LADY MARGARET, MILLPORT	Rev. Marjory MacKay	The Manse, Millport, Isle of Cumbrae KA28 0EE	01475 530460

LANARKSHIRE

WILLIAM SMELLIE AND LOCKHART	Rev. Catherine Collins	2 Friarsdene, Lanark ML11 9EJ	01555 663363
	Rev. John M.A. Thomson	32 Braxfield Road, Lanark ML11 9BS	01555 662600
CLELAND	Rev. Bruce Gordon	The Rectory, Cleghorn Road, Lanark ML11 7QT	01357 820244
KELLO	Rev. John Jackson	36 Townhead Street, Strathaven ML10 6DH	01899 220227
LADY HOME	Rev. Gavin Elliott	61 High Street, Biggar ML12 6DA	01555 851213
LAW	Rev. Lawrie I. Lennox	The Manse, Douglas, Lanark ML11 0PZ	01698 373180
	Rev. William A.F. Izett	53 Lawhill Rd, Law, Carluke ML8 5EZ	01555 892409
	Rev. David A. Young	The Manse, Kirkmuirhill, Lanark ML11	
	Rev. J. Allardyce		
	(Roadmeetings)	Congregational Manse, Rhyde Road, Wishaw ML2 7DU	
	Rev. David Collins	Greyfriars Manse, Friarsdene, Lanark ML11 9EJ	01355 663363
	Rev. Geoff McKee	Kirkstyle Manse, Church Street, Carluke ML8 4BA	
	Rev. Graeme McKay	75 Mossneuk Park, Wishaw ML2 8LX	01698 384905
STRATHCLYDE	Rev. David W. Doyle	19 Orchard Street, Motherwell ML1 3JE	01698 263472
BIRKWOOD	Rev. Sheila Mitchell	Calsay Cottage, New Trows Road, Lesmahagow ML11 0ER	01555 892445
HAIRMYRES	Rev. David E.P. Currie	1 Barr Terrace, East Kilbride G74 1AP	01355 220753
	Rev. John Brewster	21 Turnberry Place, East Kilbride G75 8TB	01355 242564
	Rev. Douglas Clark	40 Maxwell Drive, East Kilbride G74 4NG	01385 220732
	Rev. Iain Greenshields	2 Orchard Gate, Larkhall ML9 1HA	01698 882457
KIRKLANDS	Rev. James M. Gibson	The Manse, Bothwell G71 8PO	01698 853189
STONEHOUSE	Rev. James S.G. Hastie	The Manse, Quarry Road, Larkhall ML9 1HM	01698 882238
	Rev. James P. Fraser	26 Hamilton Road, Strathaven ML10 6JA	01357 522758
UDSTON	Rev. J. Stanley Cook	43 Bothwell Road, Hamilton ML3 0BB	01698 458770
	Rev. J. Mary Henderson	Overtown Manse, Wishaw ML2 0QP	01698 372330
	Rev. William M. Glencross	5 Bredin Way, Motherwell ML1 3PD	01698 282527
BELLSHILL			
COATHILL			
MONKLANDS GENERAL	Rev. James S. Salmond	Manse of Holytown, Motherwell ML1 5RU	01698 832622
	Rev. Scott McKenna	14 Holmbrae Road, Uddingston G71 6NP	01698 813113
	Rev. James Grier	47 Blair Road, Coatbridge ML5 1JQ	01236 432427
	Rev. Thomas Pollock	Clarkston Manse, Forrest Street, Airdrie ML6 7BE	01236 769676
WESTER MOFFAT	Rev. Henry J.W. Findlay	St Mark's Manse, Coltness Road, Wishaw ML2 7EX	01698 384596
HARTWOODHILL	Rev. William D. Beattie	Calderhead Manse, Kirk Road, Shotts ML7 5ET	01501 820042
MOTHERWELL –			
PSYCHIATRIC	Rev. John Handley	12 Airbles Crescent Motherwell	01698 262733
COMMUNITY MENTAL HEALTH CARE	Rev. J. Stanley Cook	43 Bothwell Road, Hamilton ML3 0BB	01698 458770
	Rev. Sharon Colvin	48 Dunrobin Road, Airdrie ML6 8LR	01236 763154
	Rev. Rosemary Smith	Blantyre Old Manse, High Blantyre G72 9UA	01698 823130

GREATER GLASGOW

NORTH GLASGOW UNIVERSITY HOSPITALS NHS TRUST

Institution	Chaplain	Address	Phone
GLASGOW ROYAL INFIRMARY [0141 211 4000/4661]	Rev. Anne J.M. Harper	122 Greenock Road, Bishopton PA7 5AS	
WESTERN INFIRMARY [0141 211 2000]	Rev. Keith Saunders	1 Beckfield Drive, Robroyston, Glasgow G33 1SR	

GREATER GLASGOW PRIMARY CARE N.H.S. TRUST

Institution	Chaplain	Address	Phone
GARTNAVEL ROYAL HOSPITAL [0141 211 3600]	Rev. Cameron H. Langlands	Flat G/1, 28 Plantation Park Gardens, Glasgow G51 1NW	

SOUTH GLASGOW UNIVERSITY HOSPITALS NHS TRUST

Institution	Chaplain	Address	Phone
SOUTHERN GENERAL HOSPITAL [0141 201 2156]	Rev. Janet P.H. Macmahon	6 Jubilee Gardens, Bearsden, Glasgow G61 2RT	
	Rev. Blair Robertson	14 Crosbie Street, Glasgow G20 0BD	
VICTORIA INFIRMARY	Rev. Christopher L. Levison	5 Deaconsbank Avenue, Stewarton Road, Glasgow G46 7UN	0141 201 5164
LIGHTBURN GERIATRIC	Rev. Patricia McDonald	11 Whithaugh Crescent, Glasgow G53 7JJ	0141 876 1408
ROYAL MATERNITY	Rev. H. Marshall Gibson	29 Broompark Drive, Glasgow G31 2JB	0141 554 0997
ROYAL INFIRMARY	Mrs Sandra Bell	62 Loganswell Road, Thornliebank, Glasgow G46 8AX	
	Rev. Patricia McDonald	11 Whithaugh Crescent, Glasgow G53 7JJ	0141 876 1408
STOBHILL	Rev. E. Gwynfai Jones	42 Melville Gardens, Bishopbriggs G64 3DE	0141 772 2848
	Rev. Elizabeth W. Sutherland	54 Etive Crescent, Bishopbriggs, Glasgow G54 1ES	0141 772 1453
	Rev. John Beaton	33 North Birbiston Road, Lennoxtown, Glasgow G65 7LZ	0141 772 2987
	Rev. John G. Fraser	17 Beauford Gardens, Bishopbriggs, Glasgow G64 2DJ	0141 647 6250
	Rev. Kenneth Coulter	8 Abbotsford Avenue, Rutherglen G73 3NX	0141 883 5618
	Miss Anne McDonald	81 Arbroath Avenue, Glasgow G52 3HJ	0141 944 8797
STOBHILL (WYNDFORD LOCKS)	Rev. Robert Owen	5 Firdon Crescent, Glasgow G15 6QQ	0141 883 5618
STOBHILL (MENTAL HEALTH)	Miss Anne McDonald	81 Arbroath Avenue, Glasgow G52 3HJ	0141 942 0507
CANNIESBURN	Rev. John W.F. Harris	61 Drymen Road, Bearsden G61 2SU	0141 951 1007
	Rev. Margaret Yule	Radnor Park Manse, Spencer Street, Clydebank G81 3AS	0141 556 2520
GARTLOCH	Rev. Ronald Anderson	97 Drumover Drive, Glasgow G31 5RP	0141 554 3640
	Rev. John Graham	87 Drumover Drive, Glasgow G31 5RR	01360 622281
LENNOX CASTLE	Rev. A.L. Walker	11 Dundas Avenue, Torrance G64 4BD	01760 312572
	Rev. D.J. Torrance	34 Glenward Avenue, Lennoxtown G65	
LEVERNDALE	Rev. Alexander Macdonald	The Manse, Neilston, Glasgow G78 3NP	0141 881 1958
	Rev. Roderick MacDonald	104 Lamington Road, Glasgow G52 2SE	0141 882 2065
	Rev. Patricia MacDonald	11 Whithaugh Crescent, Glasgow G53 7JJ	0141 876 1408
DARNLEY COURT	Rev. Colin Brown	2 Waukglen Drive, Southpark Village, Glasgow G43 7UG	
WOODILEE	Rev. Alastair MacDonald	65 Woodend Drive, Glasgow G13 1QF	0141 954 4744

VICTORIA INFIRMARY/MEARNSKIRK			
GARTNAVEL GENERAL	Rev. Alan Raeburn	110 Mount Annan Drive, Glasgow G44 4RZ	0141 632 1514
	Miss Anne McDonald	81 Arbroath Avenue, Glasgow G52 3HJ	0141 883 5618
WESTERN	Rev. Ian C. MacKenzie	1515 Maryhill Road G20 7XL	0141 946 1568
BLAWARTHILL	Rev. Marjorie Taylor	1 Kirkhill Road, Strathaven ML10 6HN	01357 520643
COWGLEN	Rev. Neil Galbraith	46 Earlbank Avenue G14 9HL	0141 954 0328
DARNLEY – CARE FOR THE ELDERLY	Rev. Michael Gibson	41 Rouken Glen Road, Thornliebank G46 7JD	0141 638 3023
GREENFIELD PARK	Rev. Patricia McDonald	11 Whithaugh Crescent, Glasgow G53 7JJ	0141 876 1408
KNIGHTSWOOD/DRUMCHAPEL	Rev. Andrew McMillan	1 Swallow Gardens, Glasgow G13 4QD	0141 959 7158
LENZIE	Rev. James Ferguson	The Manse, Larch Avenue, Lenzie G66 4HX	0141 776 3831
RUTHERGLEN TAKARE	Rev. J.W. Drummond	21 Albert Drive, Rutherglen G73 3RT	0141 643 0234
	Rev. A.M. Morrice	80 Blairbeth Road, Rutherglen G73 4JA	0141 634 4366
	Rev. Alexander Thomson	31 Highburgh Drive, Rutherglen G73 3RR	0141 647 6178
YORKHILL QUEEN MOTHER'S	Rev. Sandra Black	36 Glencairn Drive, Glasgow G41 4PN	0141 423 4000
YORKHILL SICK CHILDREN	Rev. Archibald Robertson	54 Mansewood Road, Glasgow G43 1TL	0141 632 0724
BALORNOCK AND SPRINGBURN HOMES	Rev. A.G. Allan	30 Dalrymple Street, East Kilbride G74 4LF	013552 26190
PRINCE AND PRINCESS OF WALES HOSPICE	Rev. M.H. Johnston	59 Broughton Road, Balmore View, Glasgow G23 5BP	0141 945 0860
FOURHILLS NURSING HOME	Rev. W.G. Ramsay	3 Tofthill Avenue, Bishopbriggs G64 3PN	0141 762 1844
	Rev. John Graham	121 Garthland Drive, Dennistoun G31 2SQ	

ARGYLL AND CLYDE

INVERCLYDE ROYAL HOSPITAL			
GREENOCK [01475 633777]	Rev. Elizabeth Crumlish	110 Eldon Street, Greenock PA16 7RL,	01475 721048
	Rev. William Hewitt	50 Ardgowan Street, Greenock PA16 5RP	
DYKEBAR	Rev. Alistair Morrison	36 Newtyle Road, Paisley PA1 3JX	0141 889 4279
	Rev. J.C. MacColl	The Grange, Park Road, Johnstone PA5 8LS	01505 320142
	Rev. Brian L. Farmer	27 Oakwood Avenue, Paisley PA2 9NG	0141 884 4502
	Miss Margaret McBain	33 Quarry Road, Paisley PA2 7RD	0141 854 2920
HAWKHEAD	Rev. David Palmer	19 Corsebar Drive, Paisley PA2 9QD	0141 882 2277
MERCHISTON HOUSE	Rev. Thomas Cant	18 Oldhall Road, Paisley PA1 3HL	0141 886 2896
JOHNSTONE	Rev. James Rule	6 St Andrews Road, Renfrew PA4 0SN	01505 702669
ROYAL ALEXANDRA	Rev. Arthur Sherratt	West Manse, Kilbarchan PA10 2JR	01505 320060
	Rev. James Boag	61 Auchenlodement Road, Elderslie PA5 9PN	01805 702621
	Rev. Alister W. Bull	East Manse, Church Street, Kilbarchan PA10 2JQ	0141 883 3505
	Rev. Douglas Ralph	24 Kinpurnie Road, Paisley PA1 3HM	0141 887 0884
	Rev. Ian S. Currie	9 Hawkhead Road, Paisley PA1 3ND	0141 886 2074
	Rev. E. Lorna Hood (Mrs)	North Manse, 1 Alexandra Drive, Renfrew PA4 0SN	01505 325131
	Rev. Edward Marshall	The Manse, Linwood PA3 3DL	
BRIDGE OF WEIR	Rev. Robert A. Montgomery	Quarrier's Village, Bridge of Weir PA11 3SD	01505 690498
RAVENSCRAIG	Rev. James H. Simpson	76 Finnart Street, Greenock PA16 8HJ	01475 722338

DUMBARTON JOINT

Hospital	Chaplain	Address	Telephone
VALE OF LEVEN GENERAL	Rev. Ian Miller	1 Glebe Gardens, Bonhill, Alexandria G83 9HB	01389 753039
VALE OF LEVEN GERIATRIC	Rev. Kenneth Russell	Appin House, Drymen Road, Balloch G83 8MT	01389 752734
CAMPBELTOWN	Rev. W. Bristow	Lailt, Lepenstrath, Southend, Argyll PA28 6RU	01586 830667
LOCHGILPHEAD	Rev. Robert Malloch	Church of Scotland Manse, Tayvallich, Lochgilphead PA31 8PG	01546 870611
ISLAY	Rev. Anne McIvor	The Manse, Bowmore, Isle of Islay PA43 7LH	01496 810271
DUNOON	Rev. James Watson	7 Lochan Avenue, Kirn, Dunoon PA23 8HT	01369 702851
DUNOON ARGYLL UNIT	Rev. J.A. Gray	Holyns, Ardentinny, Dunoon PA23 8TR	01369 810243
ROTHESAY			
LORN AND THE ISLANDS DISTRICT GENERAL	Rev. Archibald Lamont	8 Achlonan, Taynuilt PA35 1JJ	01866 822385

FORTH VALLEY

Hospital	Chaplain	Address	Telephone
BELLSDYKE	Rev. Colin Cameron	15 Woodlands Crescent, Falkirk FK1 5AE	01324 624600
	Rev. Henry Munroe	Viewforth, High Road, Maddiston, Falkirk FK2 OBL	01324 712446
	Rev. Robert MacLeod	13 CannonsWay, Falkirk FK2 7QG	01324 631008
BO'NESS	Rev. James Marshall	Craigmailen Manse, Braehead, Bo'ness EH51 0BZ	01506 823784
BONNYBRIDGE	Rev. Donald McCorkindale	133 Falkirk Road, Bonnybridge FK4 1BA	01324 812621
FALKIRK ROYAL INFIRMARY	Rev. Joanne Finlay	The Manse, Bowhouse Road, Grangemouth FK3 0EX	01324 471595
	Rev. John McCallum	11 Burnbrae Gardens, Falkirk FK1 5SB	
	Rev. Yvonne Hendrie	1 Valleyview Place, Falkirk FK2 7JB	01324 621087
R.S.N.H. LARBERT	Rev. Robert K. Hardie	Manse of Stenhouse, Stenhousemuir, Larbert FK5 4BU	01324 562393
	Rev. Robert Philip	Congregational Church Manse, Avonbridge FK1 2LU	01324 861252
	Rev. Duncan McCosh	Christ Church Rectory, Kerse Lane, Falkirk FK1 1RX	01324 623709
BANNOCKBURN	Rev. James Landels	Allan Manse, Bogend Road, Bannockburn FK7 8NP	01786 814692
CLACKMANNAN COUNTY	Rev. Douglas Aitken	The Manse, Clackmannan FK10 4JH	01259 214238
KILDEAN	Rev. R.W. Irvine	9 Fraser Place, Causewayhead, Stirling FK9 5RE	01786 448802
SAUCHIE	Rev. Malcolm MacRae	10b Victoria Place, Stirling FK8 2QU	01786 465547
STIRLING ROYAL INFIRMARY	Rev. James W. Benson	1 Sunnyside, Dunblane FK15 9HA	01786 822624
	Rev. Stuart Pryce	36 Forth Park, Bridge of Allan FK9 5NT	01786 831026
	Rev. Gary McIntyre	7 Randolph Road, Stirling FK8 2AJ	01786 474421

FIFE

Hospital	Chaplain	Address	Telephone
FIFE ACUTE HOSPITALS NHS TRUST QUEEN MARGARET HOSPITAL DUNFERMLINE [01383 623623] VICTORIA HOSPITAL, KIRKCALDY [01592 643355]	Rev. Isabel Whyte	34 Shandon Crescent, Edinburgh EH11 1QF	0131 337 3559
	Rev. Iain J.M. McDonald	11 James Grove, Kirkcaldy KY1 1TN	01592 253775

Hospital	Chaplain	Address	Phone
LYNEBANK	Rev. Elizabeth Fisk	51 St John's Drive, Dunfermline FK12 7TL	01383 720256
MILESMARK	Rev. Isabel Whyte	34 Shandon Crescent, Edinburgh EH11 1QF	0131 337 3559
CAMERON	Rev. James L. Templeton	Innerleven Manse, McDonald Street, Methil KY8 3AJ	01333 426310
GLENROTHES	Rev. Ian D. Gordon	7 Guthrie Crescent, Markinch KY7 6AY	01592 758264
RANDOLPH WEMYSS	Rev. Elizabeth Cranfield	9 Chemiss Road, Methilhill KY8 2BS	01592 713142
ADAMSON, CUPAR	Rev. John O. Hegarty	23 Hogarth Drive, Cupar KY15 5YH	01334 655851
NETHERLEE, NEWPORT	Rev. Graeme Beebee	5 Westwater Place, Newport-on-Tay DD6 8NS	01382 542626
STRATHEDEN, CUPAR	Rev. John W. Patterson	34 Claybraes, St Andrews KY16 8RS	01334 473606
	Miss Margaret Browning	4 Wellpark Terrace, Newport-on-Tay DD6 8HT	01382 542140
ST ANDREWS MEMORIAL	Rev. David Arnott	20 Priory Gardens, St Andrews KY16 8XX	01334 472912

TAYSIDE

TAYSIDE UNIVERSITY HOSPITALS N.H.S. TRUST

Hospital	Chaplain	Address	Phone
DUNDEE NINEWELLS HOSPITAL [01382 660111]	Rev. Robert Rae	47 Mains Loan, Dundee DD4 7AF	
PERTH ROYAL INFIRMARY [01738 473896]	Rev. John M. Birrell	5 Hewat Place, Perth PH1 2UD	
ABERFELDY	Rev. Alexander M. Gunn	The Manse, Taybridge Terrace, Aberfeldy PH15 2BS	01887 820656
BLAIRGOWRIE RATTRAY	Rev. Robert Sloan	St Andrew's Manse Upper David Street Blairgowrie PH10 6HB	01250 872146
IRVINE MEMORIAL	Rev. Christopher Brown	8 Tom Na Moan Road, Pitlochry PH16 5HN	01796 472719
CRIEFF COTTAGE	Rev. Henry A.G. Tait	14 Sheiling Hill Place, Crieff PH7 4ER	01764 652325
MACMILLAN HOSPICE	Rev. Anne Stewart	35 Rose Crescent, Perth PH1 1NT	01738 624167
MURRAY ROYAL	Rev. John F. Ferguson	1 Mount Tabor Avenue, Perth PH2 7BT	01738 626046
	Rev. Peter Meager	7 Lorraine Drive, Cupar KY15 5DY	01334 656991
ST MARGARET'S COTTAGE	Rev. Randal MacAlister	St Kessog's Rectory, High Street, Auchterarder PH3 1AD	01764 662525
ASHLUDIE	Rev. Donald W. Fraser	South Manse, Queen Street, Monifieth DD5 4HG	01382 532646
	Rev. David B. Jamieson	Panmure Manse, 8A Albert Street, Monifieth DD5 4JS	01382 532772
	Rev. Thomas P. Robertson	95 Seafield Road, Broughty Ferry, Dundee DD5 3AP	01382 779803
LIMB FITTING CENTRE	Rev. Charles W. Miller	"Palm Springs", Parkside, Auchterhouse, Dundee DD3 0QS	01382 226407
DUNDEE, ROYAL LIFF	Rev. Stewart McMillan	19 Americanmuir Road, Dundee DD3 9AA	01382 812423
ROYAL VICTORIA	Rev. Tom Milroy	9 Long Row, Westhaven, Carnoustie DD7 6BE	01241 856654
NINEWELLS	Rev. Stewart McMillan	19 Americanmuir Road, Dundee DD3 9AA	01382 812423
STRATHMARTINE	Rev. Alasdair G. Graham	1 Charles Avenue, Arbroath DD11 2EZ	01241 872244
ARBROATH INFIRMARY	Rev. James P.R. Drysdale	36 Park Road, Brechin DD9 7AP	01356 622789
BRECHIN INFIRMARY	Rev. Brian Ramsay	The Manse, Guthrie, Forfar DD8 2TP	01241 828243
FORFAR INFIRMARY AND WHITEHILLS	Rev. Graham Norrie	East Manse, Lour Road, Forfar DD8 2BB	01307 464303
LITTLE CAIRNIE	Rev. Ian G. Gough	St Vigeans Manse, Arbroath DD11 4RD	01241 873206
MONTROSE ROYAL	Rev. Iain M. Douglas	49 North Esk Road, Montrose DD10 8TQ	01674 672060
STRACATHRO	Rev. James Drysdale	51 Airlie Street, Brechin DD9 6JX	01356 625201
SUNNYSIDE ROYAL			

GRAMPIAN

GRAMPIAN UNIVERSITY HOSPITALS N.H.S. TRUST
ABERDEEN ROYAL INFIRMARY
[01224 681818 and 01224 840747]

Rev. Fred Coutts	9a Milburn Street, Aberdeen AB11 6SS
Rev. James Falconer	3 Brimmond Walk, Westhill, Skene, Aberdeenshire AB32 6XH
Rev. Gillian Munro	685 George Street, Aberdeen AB25 3XP
Rev. Alison Swindells (Chaplain's Assistant)	451 Great Western Road, Aberdeen AB10 6NL

ABERDEEN GENERAL HOSPITALS
[01224 556783]

Rev. Alan Stoddart	21 Creel Road, Bayside, Cove AB1 4BX
Rev. Alison Hutchison (part-time)	"Ashfield", Drumoak, Banchory AB31 3AA

GRAMPIAN PRIMARY CARE N.H.S. TRUST
ROYAL CORNHILL and WOODLANDS HOSPITAL
[01224 663123]

Rev. William Campbell	43 Murray Terrace, Aberdeen AB1 2SA
Mr Donald Meston (Chaplain's Assistant)	20 Rosehill Place, Aberdeen AB2 2LE
Miss Pamela Adam (Chaplain's Assistant)	409 Holburn Street, Aberdeen AB10 7GS

Hospital	Name	Address	Telephone
ABOYNE	Rev. David Devenney	The Manse, St Eunan's Road, Aboyne AB34 5HH	013398 86447
KINCARDINE COMMUNITY	Rev. Graham S. Finch	13 Bath Street, Stonehaven AB3 2DH	01569 762876
GLEN O' DEE	Rev. Donald Walker	2 Wilson Road, Banchory AB31 3UY	01330 822811
KINCARDINE O'NEIL	Rev. Peter R. Taylor	The Manse, Torphins AB31 4JS	01339 882276
KINCARDINE COMMUNITY	Rev. Kenneth L. Petrie	South Manse, Cameron Street, Stonehaven AB3 2HE	01569 762576
INVERURIE	Rev. Ian B. Groves	West Manse, Inverurie AB51 9YS	01467 620285
	Rev. Iain J.M. Telfer	St Andrew's Manse, Inverurie AB5 9XT	01467 620468
	Rev. Robert S. McLeish	The Manse, Insch AB52 6JR	01464 820914
INSCH	Rev. Thomas Calder	The Manse, Queen Street, Huntly AB54 5EB	01466 792630
JUBILEE	Rev. David Anderson	The Manse, Portsoy, Banff AB45 2QB	01261 842272
CAMPBELL	Rev. Alan Macgregor	7 Colleonard Road, Banff AB45 1DZ	01261 812107
CHALMERS	Rev. Douglas R.Clyne	97 Saltoun Place, Fraserburgh AB43 5RY	01346 518536
FRASERBURGH	Rev. Gordon Henig	6 Craigneen Place, Whitehills, Banff AB45 2NE	01261 861671
LADYSBRIDGE	Rev. Alastair Donald	1 Hawthorn Road, Peterhead AB42 6DW	01771 644216
MAUD	Rev. David S. Ross	New Deer Manse, Turriff AB53 6TG	01779 472618
PETERHEAD COTTAGE	Rev. Bruce Gardner	St Ninian's Manse, Turriff AB53 4AY	01888 563383
TURRIFF	Rev. David Pitkeathly	1 Landale Road, Peterhead AB42 1QN	01779 472141
UGIE	Rev. George B. Rollo	18 Reidhaven Street, Elgin IV30 1QH	01343 547208
BILBOHALL	Rev. George B. Rollo	18 Reidhaven Street, Elgin IV30 1QH	01343 547208
DR GRAY'S	Rev. Margaret Muir	The Manse, Ballindalloch Banffshire AB37 9EB	01807 500311
FLEMING COTTAGE			

Institution	Chaplain	Address	Telephone
LEANCHOIL	Rev. John Beck	The Manse, Dunbar Street, Burghead, Elgin IV30 2XB	01343 830365
SPYNIE	Rev. Ray Hall	21 St Peter's Road, Duffus, Elgin IV30 5QL	01343 830985
SEAFIELD	Rev. Eric Foggit	The Manse, East Church Street, Buckie AB56 1ES	01542 832103
STEPHEN AND COUNTY HOSPITALS	Rev. Hugh M.C. Smith	The Manse, Dufftown AB55 4AR	01340 820380
TURNER MEMORIAL	Rev. Michael Lyall	North Church Manse, Keith AB55 3BR	01542 882559

HIGHLAND

Institution	Chaplain	Address	Telephone
HIGHLAND ACUTE HOSPITALS NHS TRUST	Rev. Iain MacRitchie	7 Merlin Crescent, Inverness IV2 3TE	
THE RAIGMORE HOSPITAL [01463 704000]	Rev. Derek Brown	The Manse, Dornoch IV25 3HV	
IAN CHARLES	Rev. Morris Smith	Golfcourse Road, Grantown on Spey PH26 3HY	01479 872084
ST VINCENT	Rev. Norman Macaskill	The Manse, Kingussie PH21 1HA	01540 661311
CRAIG DUNAIN	Rev. William J. Campbell	c/o Craig Dunain Hospital, Inverness IV3 6JU	01463 242860
NAIRN TOWN AND COUNTY	Rev. William B. Whyte	St Ninian's Manse, Queen Street, Nairn IV12 4AA	01667 452202
BELFORD AND BELHAVEN	Rev. Donald A. MacQuarrie	Manse of Duncansburgh, Fort William PH33 6BA	01397 702297
GLENCOE	Rev. Anne Jones	The Manse, Ballachulish PA39 4JG	01885 811209
INVERGORDON COUNTY	Rev. Robert Jones	Rosskeen Manse, Alness IV17 0SX	01349 882265
LAWSON MEMORIAL			
MIGDALE			
CAITHNESS GENERAL	Rev. A.A. Roy	Mansefield, Miller Avenue, Wick KW1 4DF	01955 602822
	Rev. R. Stewart Frizzell	Old Manse, Miller Avenue, Wick KW1	01955 603286
	Rev. William Wallace	The Manse, Coronation Street, Wick KW1 5LS	01955 603166
DUNBAR	Rev. Ronald Johnstone	West Manse, Thorkel Road, Thurso KW14 7LW	01847 892663
BROADFORD MACKINNON MEMORIAL	Rev. Iain M.A. Reid	The Manse, Broadford, Isle of Skye IV49 9AA	01471 822538
GESTO	Rev. Donald MacLeod	Snizort, Portree, Isle of Skye IV51 9XE	01470 532260

WESTERN ISLES HEALTH BOARD

WESTERN ISLES

ORKNEY HEALTH BOARD

Institution	Chaplain	Address	Telephone
BALFOUR AND EASTBANK	Rev. Michael J. Ward	Hall Cottage, Tankerness, Orkney KW17 2QS	01856 861393
	Mr J. McBride	United Free Manse, 2 Morven Villa, Dounby, Orkney KW17 2HT	(Mbl) 01856 741349
	Rev. Michael J. Ward	Ploverhall, Deerness, Orkney KW17 2QJ	0370 895543

LIST D – FULL-TIME INDUSTRIAL CHAPLAINS

EDINBURGH (Edinburgh City Mission Appointment)	Mr John Hopper	26 Mulberry Drive, Dunfermline KY11 5BZ	01383 737189
EDINBURGH (Methodist Appointment)	Rev. Bill Rayne	5 Dudley Terrace, Edinburgh EH6 6QQ	0131 554 1636
EDINBURGH (part-time)	Mrs Dorothy Robertson	12 Clerwood Park, Edinburgh EH12 8PW	0131 334 5440
GLASGOW			
WEST OF SCOTLAND	Rev. Alister Goss	79 Weymouth Crescent, Gourock PA19 1HR	(Office) 0141 332 4458 01475 638944 (Office) 01475 629983
NORTH EAST	Rev. Angus Smith	1 Fa'burn Terrace, Lumphanan AB31 4AG	01339 883395 (Office) 01224 233532/3
NORTH OF SCOTLAND	Mr Lewis Rose DCS	16 Gean Drive, Blackburn AB21 0YN	01224 790145
NORTH LANARKSHIRE AND EAST KILBRIDE	Rev. John Potter	5 Eriskay Avenue, Hamilton ML3 8QB	01698 428345
TAYSIDE & NATIONAL CO-ORDINATOR	Rev. Erik Cramb	65 Clepington Road, Dundee DD4 7BQ	01382 458764

LIST E – PRISON CHAPLAINS

ABERDEEN CRAIGINCHES	Rev. David Souter Rev. Elizabeth Ross	The Manse, Echt AB32 7AB 30B Sunnybank Road, Aberdeen AB2 3NH	01330 860533 01224 488807
CASTLE HUNTLY	Rev. James Jack Rev. David MacLeod	The Manse, Longforgan DD2 5EU 6 Carseview Gardens, Dundee DD2 1NE	01382 360238 01382 641371
CORNTON VALE	Rev. Elaine MacRae	The Manse, Kippen, Stirling FK8 3DN	01786 870229
DUMFRIES	Rev. Christopher Wallace Rev. William Kelly	The Manse, Twynholm, Kirkcubright DG6 4NY The Manse, Troqueer Road, Dumfries DG2 7DF	01557 860381 01387 253043

Prison	Chaplain	Address	Telephone
DUNGAVEL	Rev. Shaw J. Paterson	15 Lethame Road, Strathaven ML10 6ND	01357 20019
	Rev. Fraser Turner	South & Quarter Manse, Limekiln Road, Hamilton ML3 7XA	01698 424511
EDINBURGH: SAUGHTON	Rev. I. David Miller	146 Craigleith Road, Edinburgh EH4 2EQ	0131 332 6378
	Rev. Max. Homewood	5 Essex Brae, Edinburgh EH4 6LN	0131 339 3884
	Miss Norma Ronald	43/26 Gillespie Crescent, Edinburgh EH10 4HY	0131 228 1008
AND SPS ADVISER IN CHAPLAINCY	Rev. R. Stuart M. Fulton	c/o Scottish Prison Service HQ, 5 Redheughs Rig, Edinburgh	0131 244 8459
GLASGOW: BARLINNIE	Rev. Edward V. Simpson	5 Langtree Avenue, Glasgow G46 7LN	0141 638 8767
	Rev. Robert J.M. Anderson	The Manse, Carmunnock, Glasgow G76 9AJ	0141 644 1578
	Rev. C. Blair Gillon	3 Dargarvel Avenue, Glasgow G41 5LD	0141 427 1282
	Rev. Russell McLarty	38 Lochview Drive, Glasgow G33 1QF	0141 770 9611
	Rev. Ian McInnes	46 Earlbank Avenue, Glasgow G14 9HL	0141 954 0328
LOW MOSS	Rev. George Cranston	26 Parkhill Drive, Glasgow G73 2PW	0141 647 6688
	Rev. David Cameron	122 Broomfield Avenue, Newton Mearns G77 5JR	0141 616 0642
GLENOCHIL	Rev. George Sherry	The Manse, Menstrie FK11 7EA	01259 761461
	Rev. Malcolm MacRae	10b Victoria Place, Stirling FK8 2QU	01786 465547
	Rev. Robert Irvine	9 Fraser Place, Stirling FK9 5RE	01786 444802
	Rev. Alan F.M. Downie	37A Claremont, Alloa FK10 2DG	01259 213872
GREENOCK	Rev. Kenneth Fisher	33 Halfway Street, West Kilbride KA23 9EQ	01294 829973
	Rev. Peter Webster	84 Forsyth Street PA16 8QY	01475 721439
INVERNESS	Rev. Colin Anderson	24 Damfield Road, Inverness IV2 4HU	01463 237129
	Rev. George Charlton	61 Drumfield Road, Inverness IV2 4LX	01463 242802
KILMARNOCK	Rev. Andrew Downie	HMP Bowhouse, Mauchline Road, Kilmarnock	
LONGRIGGEND	Rev. Ian O. Coltart	161 Kirk Road, Wishaw ML2 8LH	01698 372464
	Rev. Tom Nelson	4 Hamilton Way, Stonehouse ML9 3PU	01698 792364
	Rev. Ian Watson	The Manse, Main Street, Caldercruix ML6 7RF	01236 842279
NORANSIDE	Rev. William Hodge	61 South Street, Forfar DD8 2BS	01307 461944
PENNINGHAME	Rev. Neil Campbell	The Manse, York Road, Newton Stewart DG8 6HH	01671 402259
	Rev. Roger Dean	The Manse, Port William, Newton Stewart DG8 9QP	01988 700257
PERTH	Rev. John McQuilken	18 Clark Terrace, Crieff PH7 3QE	01764 655764
	Rev. J. Bruce Thomson	The Manse, Burnside, Scone, Perth PH2 6LP	01738 552030
	Rev. Colin Williamson	The Manse, Aberdalgie, Perth PH2 0QD	01738 625854
	Mrs Deirdre Yellowlees	Ringmill House, Gannochy Farm, Perth PH2 7JH	01738 633773
	Mrs Isobel Birrell	Wester Tarsappie, Rhynd, Perth PH2 8QL	01738 625694

PERTH: FRIARTON	Rev. Alexander Bonar	Beechview, Abercairney, Crieff PH7 3QQ	01764 652116
PETERHEAD	Rev. G.M. Allan Fawkes	The Manse, Lonmay, Fraserburgh AB43 4UJ	01346 532227
	Rev. James Lyall	The Manse, Crimond, Fraserburgh AB43 8QJ	01346 532431
POLMONT	Rev. Daniel L. Mathers	36 Thistle Avenue, Grangemouth FK3 8YQ	01324 474511
	Rev. John Fairful	The Manse, Airth, Falkirk FK2 8JQ	01324 831474
	Rev. Sheila Blount	9 Major's Loan, Falkirk FK1 5QF	01324 623063
	Rev. James Drysdale	The Manse, Shieldhill, Falkirk FK1 2EG	01324 621938
	Rev. Brian Hendrie	1 Valleyview Place, Falkirk FK2 7JB	01324 621087
SHOTTS	Rev. Andrew Campbell	70 Baron's Road, Motherwell ML1 2NB	01698 263803
	Rev. James Seath	1 Allan Avenue, Carluke ML8 5UA	01555 771644
	Rev. Derek Pope	3 Kirkland Street, Motherwell ML1 3JW	01698 266716
SHOTTS: N.I.C.	Rev. Iain Greenshields	2 Orchard Gate, Larkhall ML9 1HA	01698 882457

LIST F – UNIVERSITY CHAPLAINS

ABERDEEN	Gillean P. Maclean BD	01224 484271
ABERTAY, DUNDEE	Fiona C. Douglas BD PhD	0141 331 3823
CALEDONIAN	Iain A. Whyte BA BD STM	01382 623181 (ext 4156)
DUNDEE	Fiona Mathieson BD	0131 650 2596
EDINBURGH	Howard G. Taylor BSc BD	0141 330 5419
GLASGOW	Deryck Collingwood	0131 449 5111 (ext 4508)
HERIOT WATT	Alister W. Bull BD DipMin	0131 444 2266
NAPIER	Scott Blythe BSc BD	01505 702621
PAISLEY	James B. Walker MA BD DPhil	01224 262000 (ext 3506)
ROBERT GORDON	Alexander Horsburgh MA BD	01334 462866
ST ANDREWS	Marjory Macaskill LLB BD	01786 832118
STIRLING		0141 553 4144
STRATHCLYDE		

LIST G – THE DIACONATE

NAME	COM	APP	ADDRESS	TEL	PRES
Allan, Jean (Mrs)	1989	1988	12C Hindmarsh Avenue,, Dundee DD3 7LW	01382 827299	29
Anderson, Janet (Miss)	1979	1982	322 Gartcraig Road, Glasgow G33 2TB	0141 774 5329	16
Beaton, Margaret (Miss)	1989	1988	64 Gardenside Grove, Fernlee Gardens, Carmyle, Glasgow G32 8DS	0141 646 2297	16
Black, Linda (Miss) BSc	1993	1992	127B Spateston Road, Johnstone PA5 0SY	01505 345735	14
Buchanan, John (Mr)	1988	1994	22 Brora Court, North Munton, Perth PH1 3DQ	01738 631697	28
Buchanan, Marion (Mrs)	1983	1997	6 Hamilton Terrace, Edinburgh EH15 1NB	0131 669 5312	1
Burns, Marjorie (Mrs)	1997	1997	115 Burghley Drive, Corby, Northants NN18 8EA	01536 408158	47
Carson, Christine (Miss) MA	1992	1998	7 Kirkwood Street, Cessnock, Glasgow G51 1QQ	0141 427 2349	16
Cathcart, John (Mr)	1989	1993	Flat 2/1, 39 Broomlands Street, Paisley PA1 2NQ	0141 848 5163	14
Corrie, Margaret (Miss)	1989	1988	44 Sunnyside Street, Camelon, Falkirk FK1 4BH	01324 670656	22
Crawford, Morag (Miss)	1977	1998	118 Wester DrylawPlace, Edinburgh EH4 2TG	0131 332 2253	24
Crocker, Elizabeth (Mrs)	1985	1992	2 Gardiner Grove, Edinburgh EH4 3RT	0131 332 0227	1
Cunningham, Ian (Mr)	1994	1997	5 Forth Court, Dalgety Bay, Fife KY11 5SF	01383 823339	24
Deans, Raymond (Mr)	1994	1998	22 Garrowhill Drive, Garrowhill, Glasgow G69 6HL	0141 771 6847	17
Dickson, Carol (Miss)	1991	1996	South Lodge, Walkerton Drive, Leslie KY5 3EY	01592 743272	25
Douglas, Marilyn (Miss)	1988	1987	201 Almond Road, Abronhill, Cumbernauld G67 3LS	01236 732136	22
Dunnett, Linda (Mrs)	1976	1999	795B Argyle Street, Glasgow G3 8DS	0141 204 4800	[16]
Erskine, Morag (Miss)	1979	1986	111 Main Drive, Erskine PA8 7JJ	0141 812 6096	14
Evans, Mark (Mr)	1988	1998	Breich Valley Church Office, Longridge Parish Church, Main Street, Longridge, West Lothian EH47 8AE	01501 772020	2
Gargrave, Mary (Mrs)	1989	1998	229/2 Calder Road, Edinburgh EH11 4RG	0131 476 3493	1
Gordon, Margaret (Mrs)	1998	1997	92 Lanark Road West, Currie, Midlothian EH14 5LA	0131 449 2554	1
Gray, Greta (Miss)	1992	1991	67 Clark Avenue, Paisley	0141 884 6178	14
Hamilton, James (Mr)	1997	1995	61D Lenzie Place, Glasgow G21 3TZ	0141 558 3195	16
Hamilton, Karen (Mrs)	1995	1998	61D Lenzie Place, Glasgow G21 3TZ	0141 558 3195	16
Hankey, Sarah (Miss)	1991	1990	9 Earn Crescent, Menzieshill, Dundee DD2 4BS	01382 641549	29
Hughes, Helen (Miss)	1977	1980	Flat 2/2, 43 Burnbank Terrace, Glasgow G20 6UQ	0141 333 9459	16
Johnston, Mary (Miss)	1988	1987	19 Lounsdale Drive, Paisley PA2 9ED	0141 849 1615	14
Lamont, Fay (Miss)	1978	1988	St Ninian's Church House, Kingsway East, Dundee DD4 7RN	01382 453818	29
Low, Nan (Mrs)	1990	1995	54 Aitken Street, Airdrie ML6 6LT	01236 766493	17
Lundie, Anne V. (Miss)	1972	1992	20 Langdykes Drive, Cove, Aberdeen AB12 3HW	01224 898416	31
Lyall, Ann (Miss)	1980	1979	117 Barlia Drive, Glasgow G45 0AY	0141 631 3643	16
McBain, Margaret (Miss)	1974	1989	33 Quarry Road, Paisley PA8 7RD	0141 884 2920	14
MacDonald, Anne (Miss) BD	1980	1998	81 Arbroath Avenue, Glasgow G52 3HJ	0141 883 5618	16
MacKay, Kenneth (Mr)	1996	1995	11F Balgowan Road, Letham, Perth PH1 2JG	01738 621169	28
MacKinnon, Ronald (Mr)	1996	1995	30-4 West Pilton Gardens, Edinburgh EH4 4EG	0131 332 2688	1
McLellan, Margaret (Mrs)	1986	1997	5 Kinloch Road, Crookfur, Newton Mearns, Glasgow G77 6LY	0141 639 6853	16
McNaughton, Janette (Miss)	1982	1997	4 Dunellan Avenue, Moodiesburn, Glasgow G69 0GB	01236 870180	22

Name		Address	Telephone	
McPheat, Elspeth (Miss)	1985	11/5 New Orchardfield, Edinburgh EH6 5ET	0131 554 4143/01224 486240	1
MacPherson, James B. (Mr)	1988	13 Leslie Street, Glasgow G41 2LQ	0141 423 6868	16
McVean, M. Christine (Miss)	1969	38 Cruachan Street, Glasgow G46 8LY	0141 638 9035	16
Mair, Alex (Mr)	1988	53 Gardenside Grove, Carmyle, Glasgow G32 8DS	0141 646 2165	16
Malvenan, Dorothy (Miss)	1955	Flat 19, 6 Craigie Street, Dundee DD4 6PF	01382 462495	29
Martin, Jane (Miss)	1979	12A Carnoustie Court, Ardler, Dundee DD2 3RB	01382 813786	29
Merrilees, Ann (Miss)	1994	60 Hillend Drive, Hawick TD9 8DU	01450 370181	6
Miller, Elsie M. (Miss)	1974	30 Swinton Avenue, Rowanbank, Baillieston, Glasgow G69 6JR	0141 771 0857	22
Mitchell, Joyce (Mrs)	1994	16/4 Murrayburn Place, Edinburgh EH14 2RR	0131 453 6548	1
Morrison, Jean (Mrs)	1964	45 Corslet Road, Currie, Midlothian EH14 5LZ	0131 449 6859	
Mulligan, Anne (Miss)	1974	1/6 Coxfield, Edinburgh EH11 2SY	0131 346 7092	1
Munro, Patricia (Miss) BSc	1986	4 Hewat Place, Perth PH1 2UD	01738 627549	28
Nicholson, David (Mr)	1994	2D Doon Side, Kildrum, Cumbernauld G67 2HX	01236 732260	22
Nicol, Joyce (Mrs)	1974	93 Brisbane Street, Greenock PA16 8NY	01475 723235	18
Nicol, Senga (Miss)	1993	Flat 2/1, 160 Tollcross Road, Glasgow G31 4UX	0141 554 3028	14
Ogilvie, Colin (Mr)	1998	42 Kirkwall, The Village, Cumbernauld G67 2SQ	01236 734244	22
Rennie, Agnes M. (Miss)	1974	3/1 Craigmillar Court, Edinburgh EH16 4AD	0131 661 8475	1
Rose, Lewis (Mr)	1993	16 Gean Drive, Blackburn, Aberdeenshire AB21 0YN	01224 790145	31
Ross, Duncan (Mr)	1996	64 Stewart Crescent, Aberdeen AB16 5SR	01224 692519	31
Smith, Catherine (Mrs)	1964	21 Lingaro, Bixter, Shetland ZE2 9NN	01595 810207	46
Stewart, Marion (Miss)	1991	Kirk Cottage, Kirkton of Skene, Aberdeenshire AB32 6XX	01224 743407	33
Tait, Agnes (Mrs)	1995	2 Lennox Drive, Faifley, Clydebank G81 5JU	01389 873196	18
Teague, Yvonne (Mrs)	1965	46 Craigcrook Avenue, Edinburgh EH4	0131 536 3113	1
Urquhart, Barbara (Mrs)	1986	9 Standalane, Kilmaurs, Kilmarnock KA3 2NB	01563 538289	11
Weir, Judith (Miss)	1993	4/1 Baillie Grove, Edinburgh EH15 3BS	0131 669 7249	1
White, Joanna (Ms) BSc	1992	1B Allan Crescent, Abbeyview, Dunfermline KY11 4HE	01383 626563	24
Wilson, Glenda (Mrs)	1990	41 Colintraive Crescent, Hogganfield, Glasgow G33 1BJ	0141 770 8490	16
Wilson, Muriel (Miss)	1997	22 Well Gardens, Woodside, Glenrothes KY7 5HW	01592 753885	25
Wishart, William (Mr)	1994	17 Swift Bank, Earrock, Hamilton ML3 8PX	01698 429371	17
Wright, Lynda (Miss) BEd	1979	6 Key Cottage, High Street, Falkland KY15 7BD	01337 857705	26

THE DIACONATE (Retired List)

Name		Address	Telephone	
Anderson, Catherine B. (Mrs)	1975	13 Mosshill Road, Bellshill, Motherwell ML4 1NQ	01698 745907	17
Anderson, Mary (Miss)	1955	33 Ryehill Terrace, Edinburgh EH6 8EN	0131 553 2818	
Bayes, Muriel C. (Mrs)	1963	6 Blenheim Close, Rushden, Northants		
Beaton, Jamesina (Miss)	1953	Fairhills, Fort Augustus PH32 4DS		47
Bryden, Agnes Y. (Mrs)	1963	9 Rosewell Place, Aberdeen AB15 6HN	01320 366252	38
Cameron, Margaret (Miss)	1961	2 Rowans Gate, Paisley PA2 6RD	01224 315042	31
Campbell, Margaret M.M. (Miss)	1958	Tigh-na-Rudha, Port Ellen, Isle of Islay PA42 7DJ	0141 840 2479	14
			01496 302006	19

NAME	COM	APP	ADDRESS	TEL	PRES
Collie, Jeannie P. (Miss)	1950		3 Fortmartindale, Udny Station, Ellon AB41 6QJ	01651 842515	33
Copland, Agnes M. (Mrs) MBE	1950		3 Craigmuschat Road, Gourock PA19 1SE	01475 631870	15
Cunningham, Alison G. (Miss)	1961		23 Strathblane Road, Milngavie G62 8DL	0141 563 9232	18
Drummond, Rhoda (Miss)	1960		23 Grange Loan, Edinburgh EH9 2ER	0131 668 3631	1
Finlayson, Ellena B. (Miss)	1963		13 Chapman Place, Aberdeen AB16 7DH	01224 695293	31
Flockhart, Andrew (Mr)	1988		31 Castle Street, Rutherglen, Glasgow G73 1DY	0141 569 0716	16
Gentles, Moira (Miss)	1984		0/1 47 Crescent Road, Glasgow G13 3RY	0141 958 1465	16
Gillespie, Ann M. (Miss)	1969		Barlochan House, Palnackie, Castle Douglas DG7 1PF	01556 600378	8
Gillon, Phyllis (Miss)	1957		The Elms, 148 Whitehouse Loan, Edinburgh EH9 2EZ	0131 447 4924	
Glass, Irene (Miss)	1976		3E Falcon Road West, Edinburgh EH10 4AA	0131 447 6554	1
Gordon, Fiona S. (Mrs) MA	1958		Machrie, 3 Cupar Road, Cuparmuir, Cupar KY15 5RH	01334 652341	26
Gray, Catherine (Miss)	1969		10C Eastern View, Gourock PA19 1RJ	01475 637479	
Gray, Effie R. (Miss)	1950		8 Station Road, Edinburgh EH12 7AB	0131 334 2083	
Howden, Margaret (Miss)	1954		38 Munro Street, Kirkcaldy KY1 1PY	01592 205913	25
Hutchison, Alan E.W. (Mr)	1988		132 Lochbridge Road, North Berwick EH39 4DR	01620 894077	3
Hutchison, Maureen (Mrs)	1961		23 Drylaw Crescent, Edinburgh EH4 2AU	0131 332 8020	1
McCallum, Moyra (Miss) MA BD	1965		176 Hilton Drive, Aberdeen AB24 4LT	01224 486240	31
McCully, M. Isobel (Miss)	1974		10 Broadstone Avenue, Port Glasgow PA14 5BB	01475 742240	15
McGarva, Sadie (Miss)	1954		87 Hunter Drive, Irvine KA12 9BS	01294 271257	11
Macrae, William (Mr)	1988		6 Park View Terrace, Isle of Scalpay, Isle of Harris HS4 3XX	01859 541288	43
MacLean, Donald A. (Mr)	1988		8 Upper Barvas, Isle of Lewis PA86 0QX	01851 840454	
MacQuien, Duncan (Mr)	1988		2 Manor Crescent, Gourock PA19 1VY	01475 633407	15
MacSween, Helen (Miss)	1960		4 Craig Aonaich, Isle of Scalpay, Isle of Harris PA85 3DH		
Martin, Neil (Mr)	1988		3 Strathmiglo Place, Stenhousemuir FK5 4UQ	01324 551362	22
Mickelson, May B. (Miss)	1959		81 Milton Road East, Edinburgh EH15 2NL	0131 669 0482	1
Montgomery, Donald (Mr)	1992		17 Murray Place, Stornoway, Isle of Lewis HS1 2JB	01859 561201	44
Mortimer, Aileen (Miss)	1976		38 Sinclair Way, Knightsridge, Livingston EH54 8HW	01506 430504	2
Moyes, Sheila (Miss)	1957		158 Pilton Avenue, Edinburgh EH5 2JZ	0131 551 1731	1
Nicoll, Janet M. (Miss)	1968		74 Brucefield Avenue, Dunfermline KY11 4SY	01383 725734	24
Potts, Jean M. (Miss)	1973		28B East Claremont Street, Edinburgh EH7 4JP	0131 557 2144	1
Ramsay, Katherine (Miss) MA	1958		147 Dalkeith Road, Edinburgh EH16 5HQ	0131 667 4791	1
Ronald, Norma A. (Miss) MBE	1961		43/26 Gillespie Crescent, Edinburgh EH10 4HY	0131 228 1008	1
Rutherford, Ellen B. (Miss) MBE	1962		41 Duncanston, Conon Bridge, Dingwall IV7 8JB	01349 877439	39
Scrimgeour, Alice M. (Miss)	1950		265 Golfhill Drive, Glasgow G31 2PB	0141 564 9602	16
Sloan, Elma C. (Miss)	1957		7 Dunedin Street, Edinburgh EH7 4JB	0131 556 3496	1
Smith, Lillian (Miss)	1977		6 Fintry Mains, Dundee DD4 9HF	01382 500052	29
Steele, Jean (Miss)	1952		93 George Street, Paisley PA1 2JX	0141 889 9512	14
Stuart, Anne (Miss)	1966		19 St Colme Crescent, Aberdour KY3 0ST	01383 860049	24
Thom, Helen (Miss) BA DipEd	1959		84 Great King Street, Edinburgh EH3 6QU	0131 556 5687	1
Trimble, Robert	1988		5 Templar Rise, Livingston EH54 6PJ	01506 412504	2
Webster, Elspeth H. (Miss)	1950		82 Broomhill Avenue, Burntisland KY3 0BP	01592 873616	25

Weir, Minnie Mullo (Miss) MA	1934	37 Strathearn Court, Strathearn Terrace, Crieff PH7 3DS	01764 654189	31
Welsh, Jessie R. (Miss)	1950	40 Thomson Street, Aberdeen AB2 4QP	01224 632323	16
White, Elizabeth (Miss)	1950	17 Clincarthill Road, Rutherglen, Glasgow G73 2LF	0141 647 2683	

SUPPLEMENTARY LIST

Forrest, Janice (Mrs)	1990	11E Westercommon Road, Possilpark, Glasgow G22 5ND
Hood, Katrina (Mrs)	1988	16 Hart Synnot House, Leckford Road, Oxford
Hudson, Sandra (Mrs)	1982	10 Albany Drive, Rutherglen G73 3QN
McIntosh, Kay (Mrs)	1990	20 Braid Green, Knightsridge, Livingston EH54 8PN
McKirdy, Lorraine (Miss)	1988	29A Church Street, Bulkington, Nuneaton, Warwickshire CV12 9NL
McLaughlin, Catherine (Mrs)	1966	8 Lamlash Place, Cranhill, Glasgow G33 3XH
Muir, Alison M. (Mrs)	1969	77 Arthur Street, Dunfermline KY12 0JJ
Ramsden, Christine (Miss)	1978	52 Noel Street, Nottingham NG7 6AW
Walker, Wikje (Mrs)	1970	24 Brodie's Yard, Queen Street, Coupar Angus PH13 9RA
Wallace, Catherine (Mrs)	1987	24 Rennie Street, Falkirk FK1 5QW

LIST H – MINISTERS HAVING RESIGNED MEMBERSHIP OF PRESBYTERY
(in Terms of Act III 1992)

NAME	ORD	ADDRESS	TEL	PRES
Bailey, W. Grahame MA BD	1939	148 Craiglea Drive, Edinburgh EH10 5PU	0131 447 1663	1
Balfour, Thomas MA BD	1945	1 Dean Court, Longniddry EH32 0QT	01875 852694	3
Bogle, Michael M. MA	1936	30 Woodburn Terrace, Edinburgh EH10 4SS	0131 447 3231	1
Chirnside, Charles	1950	11 Stevenson Grove, Edinburgh EH11 2SE	0131 337 2957	23
Cooper, George MA BD	1943	8 Leighton Square, Alyth, Perthshire PH11 8AQ	01828 633746	27
Craig, Eric MA BD	1959	5 West Relugas Road, Edinburgh EH9 2PW	0131 667 8210	1
Craig, John W. MA BD	1951	83 Milton Road East, Edinburgh EH15 2NL	0131 657 2309	1
Dunlop, A. Ian TD MA BD	1939	59 Meggetland Terrace, Edinburgh EH14 1AP	0131 443 1087	1
Finlayson, D.	1943	Rhu-garbh Cottage, North Shian, Appin, Argyll PA38 4BA	01631 730416	38
Forrester-Paton, Colin MA BD	1944	Acharn, Glen Road, Peebles EH45 9AY	01721 720136	4
Gordon, Alasdair B. BD LLB	1970	2C Ashvale Court, Aberdeen	01224 571633	31
Greig, James C.G. MA BD STM	1955	St John's Croft, Sorbie, Newton Stewart DG8 8EQ	01988 850270	9
Howie, William MA BD STM	1964	26 Morgan Road, Aberdeen AB2 5IY	01224 483669	31
Inglis, C.G. MA	1944	416 Crow Road, Glasgow G11 7EA	0141 339 3078	16

NAME	ORD	ADDRESS	TEL	PRES
Lacey, Eric R. BD	1971	1 Ross Court, 96/98 Old Edinburgh Road, Inverness IV2 3HT	0131 663 1331	37
Levack, John G. MA BD	1934	5 Park Road, Dalkeith EH22 3DF	01620 823291	3
Levison, L. David MA BD	1943	47 Dunbar Road, Haddington EH41 3PJ	0131 228 3118	3
Levison, Mary I (Mrs) BA BD DD	1978	2 Gillsland Road, Edinburgh EH10 5BW	0131 668 2721	1
McCaskill, George I.L. MA BD	1953	3/5 Dun-ard Garden, Edinburgh EH9 2HZ	0131 447 9564	1
Macfarlane, Alwyn J.C. MA	1957	4/9 Belhaven Place, Edinburgh EH10 5JN		
Macfarlane, Kenneth	1963	9 Bonnington Road, Peebles	01721 723609	4
McHardy, W.D. DPhil	1947	2 Ogilvie Park, Cullen, Banff AB56 2XZ	01542 841008	35
MacLean, Ewen A. MA BD HCF	1945	27/109 West Savile Terrace, Edinburgh EH9 3DR	0131 667 0720	1
McLuskey, J. Fraser MC DD	1938	2 Richmond Court, Park Lane, Milford-on-Sea, Hants SO41 0PT	01590 645405	47
Malcolm, John W. MA BD PhD	1939	16 Abbotsford Court, Edinburgh EH10 5EH	0131 447 0326	1
Masterton, John W.G.	1941	19 Braid Avenue, Edinburgh EH10 4SR	0131 447 4157	1
Miller, Irene B. (Mrs) MA BD	1984	5 Braeside Park, Aberfeldy		27
Monro, George D. TD MA	1935	Flat 79, 303 Colinton Road, Edinburgh EH13 OHS	0131 441 7303	1
Morris, Gordon C. MA BD	1941	42 Regent Street, Edinburgh EH15 2AX	0131 669 4570	1
Murdoch, William M. BSc PhD BD STM	1980	Newton of Middlemuir, Whitecairns AB23 8XP		31
Nelson, John. MA BD	1941	7 Manse Road, Roslin EH25 9LF	0131 440 3321	3
Ogilvie, Kenneth G. MA	1953	124 Comiston Drive, Edinburgh EH10 5QU	0131 447 8909	1
Petty, P.W.P.	1962	7 Marchbank Place, Balerno, Midlothian EH14 1EU	0131 449 2123	26
Robertson, Crichton MA	1938	Robin Hill, Ludlow Road, Church Stretton, Salop SY6 6AD	01694 722046	3
Robinson, Keith S.P. MA	1950	52 Inverleith Row, Edinburgh EH3 5PX		
Ross, John H.G. OBE MA BD	1940	43 Arden Street, Edinburgh EH9 1BS	0131 447 2027	1
Scott, J. Leonard MA BD	1957	13 Cornwall Street (1 Flat L), Edinburgh EH1 2EQ	0131 229 0395	1
Shaw, Duncan JP PhD ThD Drhc	1951	4 Sydney Terrace, Edinburgh EH7 6SL	0131 669 1089	1
Stewart, Finlay J. BA BD	1936	Flat 32, 2 Hawthorn Gardens, Loanhead EH20 9EE	0131 440 4117	3
Stobie, Charles I.G.	1942	18 Market Street, St Andrews KY16 9NS	01334 476806	26
Strachan, Stanley G.	1984	The Wrens, 17 Cairns Court, Crieff PH7 3SP		28
Sutherland, Douglas G.	1946	4 Mount Melville Crescent, Strathkinness KY16 9XS	01334 850338	26
Taylor, Alexander T.H. MA BD	1938	4 The Pleasance, Strathkinness KY16 9SD	01334 850585	26
Warnock, John MA BD	1934	Glentress House, Peebles EH45 8BE	01721 720095	4
Waugh, James	1957	50 Larbert Road, Bonnybridge FK4 1EJ	01324 812276	22
Wilkie, George D. OBE BL	1948	2/37 Barnton Avenue West, Edinburgh EH4 6EB	0131 339 3973	1
Wills, William F.	1935	Sowerby House, Front Street, Sowerby, Thirsk YO7 1JP	01845 527182	12
Wylie, W. Andrew	1953	Well Rose Cottage, Peat Inn, by Cupar KY15 5LH	01334 840600	26

LIST I – MINISTERS HOLDING MINISTERIAL CERTIFICATES (UNDER ACT II 1987)

Name	Year	Address	Telephone	No.
Alexander, Helen (Miss) BD	1981	7 Polwarth Place, Edinburgh EH11 1LG	0131 346 0685	1
Arbuthnott, Joan (Mrs) MA BD	1993	23 Ladysmith Road, Edinburgh EH9 3EU	0131 667 8449	1
Archer, Nicholas D.C. BA BD	1971	c/o Thurso High School, Ormlie Road, Thurso KW14 7DS		47
Beattie, Warren	1991	33A Chancery Lane, Singapore 908554	00 1 65 256 3208	1
Black, James S. BD DPS	1976	7 Breck Terrace, Penicuik EH26 0RJ	01968 677559	3
Black, Janette M.K. (Mrs) BD	1993	5 Craigiehall Avenue, Erskine PA8 7DB	0141 812 0794	14
Black, W. Graham MA BD	1983	19 Laurel Braes, Bridge of Don, Aberdeen AB22 8XY	01224 820333	31
Blakey, Ronald S. MA BD MTh	1962	61 Orchard Brae Avenue, Edinburgh EH4 2UR	0131 343 6039	1
Bowman, Norman M. MA BD	1940	18 Eglinton Court, Eglinton Street, Saltcoats KA21 5DN	01294 463453	12
Boyd, Kenneth M. MA BD PhD	1970	1 Doune Terrace, Edinburgh EH3 6DY	0131 225 6485	1
Burnside, Alison H. (Mrs) MA BD	1991	14 Roxburgh Place, Fort William PH33	01397 701465	38
Burnside, William A.M.	1990	14 Roxburgh Place, Fort William PH33	01397 701465	38
Campbell, Roderick D.M. TD BD FSAScot	1975	22 Greenlaw Road, Newton Mearns G77 6ND	0141 639 7328	16
Campbell, Thomas R. MA BD	1986	14 Falside Avenue, Paisley PA2 6JY	01466 740274	14
Chapman, Ernest	1977	Bothwellseat, Gartly, Huntly AB54 4RL		33
Chilton, R.M.L. BD BA DipEurHum MA	1972	69 Hill Rise, Market Weighton, York YO4 3JX	01430 871147	33
Cowal, Susan G. (Miss) BA BD	1986	39 Main Street, Symington, Biggar ML12 6LL	01899 308257	
Cowie, Marion (Mrs) MA BD	1990	6 St Swithin Street, Aberdeen AB10 6XE	01224 593302	31
Currie, Gordon C.M.	1975	43 Deanburn Park, Linlithgow EH49 6HA	01506 842722	2
Davidson, John F. BSc	1970	49 Craigmill Gardens, Carnoustie DD7 6HX [e-mail: jfdavid@bcs.org.uk]	01241 855412	30
Davies, Gareth W.	1979	8 Inchcolme Drive, North Queensferry KY11 1LD	01383 418863	24
Drummond, Norman W. MA BD	1976	Ellishadder, Staffin, Isle of Skye IV51 9JE	01470 562201	42
Dungavel, William. LTh	1970	11 Churchill Road, Castleton		41
Dutch, Morris .M. BD	1998	41 Baronald Drive, Kelvindale, Glasgow G12 0HN	0141 357 2286	16
Ellis, David W. GIMechE GIProdE	1962	26 Prospect Road, Sevenoaks, Kent TN13 3UA		16
Fields, James T. MA BD STM	1988	The Bungalow, The Ridgway, Mill Hill, London NW7 1QX	0208 201 1397	47
Fleming, Thomas G.	1961	5 Glenbervie Drive, Larbert FK5 4NP	01324 552004	22
Flockhart, D. Ross OBE MA BD	1955	Longwood, Humbie EH36 5PN	01875 833208	3
Fowler, Richard C.A. BSc MSc BD	1978	4 Gardentown, Whalsay, Shetland	01806 566538	46
Fraser, Ian M. MA BD PhD	1946	Ferndale, Gargunnock FK8 3BW	01786 860612	23
Frew, John M. MA BD	1946	17 The Furrows, Walton-on-Thames KT12 3JQ		16
Galloway, Kathy (Mrs) BD	1977	20 Hamilton Park Avenue, Glasgow G12 8UU		16
Gardner, John V.	1997	24 Orange Grove, Camberwell, Victoria 3124, Australia	0061 39889 9370	1
Gunn, F. Derek BD	1986	6 Yardley Place, Falkirk FK2 7FH	01324 624938	22
Higgins G.K.	1957	150 Broughty Ferry Road, Dundee DD4 6JJ	01382 461288	29
Hood, Adam J.J.	1989	16 Hart Synot House, Leckford Road, Oxford		14

NAME	ORD	ADDRESS	TEL	PRES
Howitt, Jane (Miss)	1996	PO Box 476, LV 1050, Riga 50, Latvia		16
Ireland, Andrew BA BTh DipRD	1963	19 Glamis Gardens, Dalgety Bay, Dunfermline KY11 5TD	01383 822687	24
Johnstone, Robert MTheol	1973	59 Cliffburn Road, Arbroath, Angus DD11 5BA	01241 439292	32
Kelly, Alastair F. BL	1961	34/1 Shore Road, South Queensferry EH30 9SG	0131 319 1841	1
Kirby, Paul S. BD	1976	Flat 2, 1 Trafalgar Terrace, New St John's Road, St Helier, Jersey JE2 3LE	01534 37889	47
Lawrie, Robert M.. BD DipMin LLCM(TD)	1994	West Benview, Main Road, Langbank PA14 6XP	01475 540240	15
Liddiard, F.G.B. MA	1957	34 Trinity Fields Crescent, Brechin DD9 6BP	01356 622966	30
MacArthur, Alexander MA	1946	Luath, St Barchan's Road, Kilbarchan PA10 2AR	01505 702598	14
Maciver, Donald BD	1986	20 Withnell Road, Burnage, Manchester M19 1GH		
MacKinnon, Neil BD	1990	8 Burn Brae Terrace, Westhill, Inverness IV2 2HD	01463 791639	37
MacPherson, Gordon C.	1963	203 Capalrig Road, Patterton, Newton Mearns, Glasgow G77 6ND		11
MacQuarrie, Stuart BD BSc JP	1984	7 Stuart Avenue, Rutherglen, Glasgow G73 4JH		16
Main, Arthur W.A. BD	1954	13/3 Eildon Terrace, Edinburgh EH3 5NL		16
Mair, John BSc	1965	21 Kenilworth Avenue, Helensburgh G84 7JR	01436 671744	18
Masson, John D.	1984	5 Wheatlands, Wigton Road, Carlisle CA2 7ER		7
Matheson, Iain G. BD BMus	1985	16 New Street, Musselburgh EH21 6JP	0131 665 2128	3
Merchant, Manson C.	1992	Aberdeen		31
Mill, John Stuart MA BD	1974	11 Somerford Place, Beaconsfield, Bucks HP9 1AZ	01494 681906	47
Milloy, A. Miller DPE LTh DipTrMan	1979	3 Gleneagles Court, Brighton Road, West Sussex RH10 6AD	01444 257989	47
Mills, Archibald MA PhD	1953	32 High Street, South Queensferry EH30 9PP	0131 331 3906	1
Munro, Alexander W. MA BD	1978	Clevedon House, Ben Rhydding Drive, Ilkley, West Yorks LS 29 8BJ	01943 608515	47
Murdoch, John A.H. BA BD DPSS	1979	Priorsgate, South Street, St Andrews KY16 9QU	01334 473218	30
Neill, William G. MA BD BA DipMus	1971	76 Victoria Park Drive North, Glasgow G14 9PJ	0141 959 5835	10
Newell, Alison M. (Mrs) BD	1986	102 Copnor Road, Portsmouth PO3 5AL	01705 666535	1
Newell, J. Philip BD PhD	1982	102 Copnor Road, Portsmouth PO3 5AL	01705 666535	1
Ostler, John H. MA LTh	1975	52E Middleshot Square, Prestonpans EH32 9RJ	01875 814358	3
Owen, Catherine MTheol (Mrs)	1984	The Vicarage, St Mary's Road, Worcester Park, Surrey KT4 7JL	0208 337 5025	47
Parker, Andrew H. BSc BD	1967	25 Canton Street, London E14 6JG	0207 538 8505	47
Peat, S. William BSc BD PhD	1977	27/320 West Savile Terrace, Edinburgh EH9 3DS	0131 662 9319	1
Price, Andrea (Mrs)	1997	Mayfield House, St Ola, Kirkwall, Orkney KW15 1SU	01856 875171	45
Provan, Iain W. MA BA PhD	1991	Regent College, 5800 University Boulevard, Vancouver BC V6T 2E4, Canada	001 604 224 3245	1
Quigley, Barbara D (Mrs) MTheol ThM DPS	1979	7 Albany Terrace, Dundee DD3 6HQ	01382 223059	29
Robertson, Alan O. MA BD STM	1953	5 Southbank Court, Easter Park Drive, Edinburgh EH4 6JR	0131 312 8079	1
Ross, Robin A. MA BD	1977	Yarrow Feus, Selkirk TD7 5BL	01750 82236	4
Sawers, Hugh BA	1968	2 Rosemount Meadows, Castlepark, Bothwell G71 8EL	01698 853960	17
Scott, Donald H.	1987	11 Colebrooke Terrace, Abington ML12 6SB	01864 502732	13
Scouller, Hugh BSc BD	1985	39 Melbourne Place, North Berwick EH39 4JS	01620 893021	3
Smith, Ralph C.P. MA STM	1960	2 Blackford Hill View, Edinburgh EH9 3HD	0131 667 7258	1
Squires, J. Finlay R. MA BD	1964	16 Bath Street, Stonehaven AB39 2DH	01569 762458	32

Stewart, M.L. (Mrs)
  BSc MB ChB BD 1985 5 Main Street, Livingston Village EH54 7AF 01506 411306 2
Strachan, David G. BD DPS 1978 1 Deeside Park, Aberdeen AB15 7PQ 01224 324101 31
Strachan, Gordon MA BD PhD 1963 59 Merchiston Crescent, Edinburgh EH10 5AH 0131 229 3654 1
Thomas, W. Colville
  BTh BPhil DPS DSc 1964 11 Muirfield Crescent, Gullane EH31 2HN 01620 842415 3
Thomson, Donald M. BD 1975 1F1, 9 Brunswick Street, Edinburgh EH7 5JB 0131 557 0178 31
Tollick, Frank BSc 1958 3 Bellhouse Road, Aberdour KY3 0TL 01383 860559 24
Turnbull, Julian S.
  BSc BD MSc CEng MBCS 1980 25 Hamilton Road, Gullane EH31 2HP 01620 842958 3
Watt, John H.I. MA BD 1960 55 Union Street, Lochgilphead, Argyll PA31 8JS 01546 602143 20
Weir, Mary K. (Mrs) BD PhD 1968 RR*1, V-61 Bowen Island, BC, Vonigo, Canada 604 947 0636 1
Welsh, Alex M. BD 1979 55 Inverary Drive, Bishopbriggs, Glasgow G64 3JB   16
Wilson, Thomas F. BD 1984 55 Allison Close, Cove AB12 3WG 01224 873501 31
Winn, Fiona M.M. MA BD RGN 1994 35 Ashwood Avenue, Melbourne 3190, Australia 00 61 3 9555 2038 1
Wiseman, Ian 1993 8/4 Lochview Court, Edinburgh EH8 8AR 0131 558 9820 1
Wood, Peter MA BD 1993 c/o 3 Garronhall, Stonehaven AB39 2HF 01569 762591 32

LIST J – ADVISERS IN MISSION AND EVANGELISM

CONGREGATIONAL
DEVELOPMENT ADVISER Mr Brian Burden "Edinbane", Mid Road, Northmuir, Kirriemuir DD8 4PJ 01575 575280 (Tel/Fax)
  [e-mail: brian.burden@virgin.net]

ADVISER FOR URBAN MISSION Rev. Ian A. Moir MA BD 47 Millersneuk Drive, Lenzie G66 5JE 0141 776 1479 (Tel/Fax)
  [e-mail: ianmoir@aol.com]

REGIONAL ADVISER (EAST) Rev. Robin J. McAlpine BDS BD 10 Seton Place, Kirkcaldy KY2 6UX 01592 643518 (Tel)
  [e-mail: robinmcalpine@dial.pipex.com]
  St Brycedale Church Centre, St Brycedale Avenue, Kirkcaldy 01592 646406 (Tel/Fax)
  [e-mail: natmisskdy@dial.pipex.com]

REGIONAL ADVISER (NORTH) Rev. Richard J. Gibbons BD 3 Holm Burn Place, Inverness IV2 6WT 01463 226889 (Tel/Fax)
  [e-mail: rgibbonsIV@aol.com]
  Ness Bank Church House, 5 Ness Bank, Inverness IV2 4SF 01463 223995 (Tel/Fax)

REGIONAL ADVISER (WEST) Rev. John Campbell MA BD BSc 3 Herries Road, Glasgow G41 4DE 0141 423 3760 (Tel/Fax)
  [e-mail: campbelljohn@name.com]
  59 Elmbank Street, Glasgow G2 4PQ (Office) 0141 333 1948 (Tel/Fax)
  [e-mail: natmisnglasoffice@dial.pipex.com]

| ADVISER FOR COWAL AREA (part-time) | Mr John Anderson | 9 Berryburn, Kaimes, Tighnabruaich PA21 2BQ [e-mail: jwamission@aol.com] | 01700 811496   (Tel/Fax) |
| MISSIONS CO-ORDINATOR | Rev. Paul Beautyman MA BD | 59 Elmbank Street, Glasgow G2 4PQ (Office) [E-mail: mcpaulb@aol.com] | 0141 352 6946   (Tel/Fax) 0468 023385   (Mbl) |

LIST K – OVERSEAS APPOINTMENTS

['Not a Minister of the Church of Scotland]

NAME	ORD	APP	LOCATION
'Berger, James R.	1993		Bahamas
Burgess, Paul	1968	1994	Pakistan
Calvert, Robert	1983	1995	Rotterdam
Cowie, John A.	1983	1990	Amsterdam
'Dodman, Roy A.	1987	1983	Jamaica
*Duncan, Graham	1978	1998	South Africa
Forbes, Iain	1964	1994	Mozambique
Foreman, Anthony McLean		1995	Sri Lanka
'Fowler, Margaret	1988	1994	Jamaica
Garrity, T. Alan W.	1969	1999	Bermuda
Hibbert, Frederick W.	1986	1995	Tiberias
Huie, David	1962	1991	Rome
*Jenkins, Douglas & Janet		1997	Bahamas

NAME	ORD	APP	LOCATION
Johnston, Colin D.	1986	1994	Zambia
Lamont, Stewart J.	1972	1999	Brussels
Mackenzie, Kenneth	1990	1999	Budapest
McKinnon, Elaine	1988	1992	Kikuyu, Kenya
McLeod, James	1965	1994	Geneva
Milton, A. Leslie		1996	Mozambique
Murray, Douglas	1979	1994	Lausanne
Oliver, Gordon	1979	1997	Lisbon
Page, John	1988	1996	Gibraltar
Pitkeathly, Tom	1984	1991	Brussels
Reid, William	1966	1993	Paris
'Tamas, Bertalan	1978	1978	Budapest
Westmarland, Colin A.	1971	1975	Malta

LIST L – OVERSEAS LOCATIONS

EUROPE

| AMSTERDAM | Rev. John A. Cowie and Mrs Gillian Cowie Jan Willem Brouwersstraat 9 1071 LH, Amsterdam, The Netherlands [e-mail: john.cowie@tip.nl] The English Reformed Church, The Begijnhof (off the Spui). Service each Sunday at 10.30 am. | (Tel) 00 31 20 672 2288 (Fax) 00 31 20 676 4895 |

BRUSSELS

Rev. Thomas C. Pitkeathly and Mrs Patricia A. Pitkeathly
23 Square des Nations, 1000, Brussels, Belgium
[e-mail:pitkeathly@compuserve.com]
St Andrew's Church, Chaussée de Vleurgat 181 (off Ave Louise).   Service each Sunday at 11.00 am.

(Tel/Fax) 00 32 2 672 40 56

Rev. Stewart Lamont and Mrs Lara Lamont, Avenue de Broqueville 140, 1200 Brussels, Belgium
Office: CEC/CSC, Rue Joseph II 174, B-1000 Brussels, Belgium
[e-mail: eccs@skypro.be]

(Tel) 00 32 2 772 7122
(Tel) 00 32 2 230 1732
(Fax) 00 32 2 231 1413

BUDAPEST

Rev. Kenneth Mackenzie and Mrs Jayne Mackenzie
Scottish Mission, Vorosmarty utca 51, 1064 Budapest, Hungary
[e-mail:rch@mail.elender.hu]
Service in English and Sunday School each Sunday at 11 am.
(Rev. Bertalan Tamas (1976, held previous appointment) and Mrs Elizabeth Tamas)

(Tel/Fax) 00 36 1 343 8479

COSTA DEL SOL

Rev. John Page and Mrs Janet Page (see Gibraltar)
[e-mail:rico@maptel.es]
Services at Lux Mundi Ecumenical Centre, Fuengirola.   Service each Sunday at 10.30 am.

(Tel) 00 34 95 258 8394

GENEVA

Rev. James Macleod and Mrs Marjorie Macleod
[e-mail:cofsg@pingnet.ch]
6 Chemin Tavernay, 1218 Grand Saconnex, Geneva, Switzerland
The Calvin Auditoire, Place Taconnerie (beside Cathedral of St Pierre).   Service each Sunday 11.00 am.

(Tel/Fax) 00 41 22 798 29 09

GIBRALTAR

Rev. John Page and Mrs Janet Page
29 Scud Hill, Gibraltar
[e-mail:billsmith@gibngt.gi]
St Andrew's Church, Governor's Parade.   Service each Sunday 6.00 pm.

(Tel) 00 350 77040
(Fax) 00 350 40852

LAUSANNE

Rev. Douglas R. Murray and Mrs Sheila Murray
26 Avenue de Rumine, 1005 Lausanne, Switzerland
[e-mail: scotskirklausanne@bluewin.ch]
Service each Sunday 10.30 am; 2nd and 4th 6 pm.

(Tel/Fax) 00 41 21 323 98 28

LISBON

Rev. Gordon Oliver and Mrs Jenny Oliver
The Manse, Rua Arriaga 11, 1200-608, Lisbon, Portugal
[e-mail: gosnolisboa@mail.telepac.pt]
St Andrew's Church, Rua de Arriaga 13-15, Lisbon.   Service each Sunday 11.00 am.

00 351 1 484 4629

MALTA

Rev. Colin A. Westmarland
206/3 Old Bakery Street, Valletta, Malta

St Andrew's Church, 210 Old Bakery Street, Valletta.   Service each Sunday 11.00 am.

(Tel) 00 356 222 643
(Fax) 00 356 453 473

PARIS
Rev. William Reid and Mrs Esther Reid
10 Rue Thimmonier, 75009 Paris, France
The Scots Kirk, 17 rue Bayard (near av Montaigne, metro Roosevelt).
Service each Sunday 10.30 am.
(Tel/Fax) 00 33 1 48 78 47 94

ROME
Rev. David Huie and Mrs Margaret Huie
Via XX Settembre 7, 00187 Rome, Italy Service each Sunday 11.00 am.
[e-mail:david.huie@flashnet.it]
(Tel) 00 39 06 482 7627
(Fax) 00 39 06 487 4370

ROTTERDAM
Rev. Robert Calvert and Mrs Lesley-Ann Calvert
Gelebrem 59, 3068 TJ Rotterdam
[e-mail:scots-international-church@compuserve.com]
The Scots Kirk, Schiedamsevest 121, Rotterdam. Service each Sunday 10.30 am.
(Tel/Fax) 00 31 10 220 4199

AFRICA

KENYA

Presbyterian Church of East Africa
Dr Gordon A. McFarlane and Mrs Mary J. McFarlane (1990)   PCEA Chogoria Hospital, PO Box 35, Chogoria, Kenya
Dr Elizabeth Bevan, PCEA (1992)   Tumutumu Hospital, Private Bag, Karatina, Kenya
Rev. Elaine McKinnon (1992)   Christian Education Centre, PO Box 387, Kikuyu, Kenya
Dr Alison Wilkinson (1992)   PCEA Chogoria Hospital, PO Box 35, Chogoria, Kenya
Dr Bryson Arthur (1995) and Mrs May Arthur   St Paul's United Theological College, PO Private Bag, Limuru, Kenya
Dr Angus and Mrs Elizabeth Grant (1997)   PCEA Chogoria Hospital, PO Box 35, Chogoria, Kenya

Missionary Associates
Miss Elizabeth M. Mudie   PO Box 46464, Nairobi, Kenya
Miss Isobel Dick   PO Box 46464, Nairobi, Kenya

MALAWI
Church of Central Africa Presbyterian
Synod of Blantyre

Synod of Livingstonia
Miss Carol Finlay (1991)   CCAP Hospital, PO Box 19, Ekwendeni, Malawi
Miss M. Anne Dawson (1976)   PO Box 2, Ekwendeni, Malawi
Dr Andrew and Mrs Felicity Gaston (1997)   CCAP Hospital, PO Box 19, Ekwendeni, Malawi
Miss Lesley Thomson (1997)   CCAP Hospital, PO Box 19, Ekwendeni, Malawi

MOZAMBIQUE
Evangelical Church of Christ in Mozambique
Rev. Iain Forbes (1994, held previous appointment)   CX Postal 284, Nampula, Mozambique
and Mrs Ruth Forbes
Rev. Dr A. Leslie Milton (1996)   Ricatla Theological Seminary, CX Postal 1057, Maputo, Mozambique

SOUTH AFRICA Rev. Graham Duncan (1998, held previous appointment) and Mrs Sandra Duncan
PO Box 238, Fort Beaufort, Alice 5700, Eastern Cape, South Africa

ZAMBIA **United Church of Zambia**
Rev. Colin D. Johnston (1994)
Trinity UCZ, PO Box 30079, Lusaka, Zambia

THE CARIBBEAN, CENTRAL AND SOUTH AMERICA

BAHAMAS Rev. Dr James R. Berger (1993)
St Andrew's Manse, PO Box N1099, Nassau
[e-mail: jberger@bahamas.net.85]
(Tel) 00 1 242 322 5475
(Fax) 00 1 242 323 1960

Rev. Douglas and Rev. Janet Jenkins (1997)
Lucaya Presbyterian Kirk, PO Box F-40777, Freeport

BERMUDA Rev. T. Alan W. Garrity and Mrs Elizabeth Garrity (1999)
The Manse, PO Box PG88, Paget PGBX, Bermuda
(Tel) 00 1 441 236 0400
(Fax) 00 1 441 232 0552

JAMAICA **United Church of Jamaica and Grand Cayman**
Rev. Roy A. Dodman and Mrs Jane Dodman (1983)
8 Wishaw Drive, Kingston 8, Jamaica
[e-mail: rdodman@cwjamaica.com]
(Tel) 00 1 876 925 8491
(Fax) 00 1 876 931 5004

Rev. Margaret Fowler
PO Box 1454, 15 Westgreen Crescent, Montego Bay, Jamaica
[e-mail: revm@cwjamaica.com]
(Tel) 00 1 876 953 7646
(Fax) 00 1 876 952 0970

Ms Maureen Burke (1998)
1B Woodley Drive, Kingston 19, Jamaica
(Tel) 00 1 876 905 3106

TRINIDAD Vacant
Church of Scotland Greyfriars St Ann's, 50 Frederick Street, Port of Spain, Trinidad

ASIA

BANGLADESH **Church of Bangladesh**
Ms Gillian Rose (1996)
Bollobhpur Hospital, PC Kedargonj, DT Meherpur, Bangladesh
Mr Andrew and Mrs Rosemary Symonds (1999)
St Andrew's College, Dhaka, Bangladesh

CHINA **Together with Scottish Churches China Group**
Mr Ian Groves (1996)
Amity Foundation, Overseas Office, 4 Jordan Road, Kowloon, Hong Kong
Ms Fiona Pollard (1997)
Jiujiang Teachers' College, Jiujiang 332000, Jiangxi Province, China
Ms Julie Chrystal (1997)
Jiujiang Teachers' College, Jiujiang 332000, Jiangxi Province, China
Mr Darren Yendell (1997)
Zhenjiang Teachers' College, Zhenjiang, Jiangsu Province, China
Mr Jonathan Robinson (1997)
Zhenjiang Teachers' College, Zhenjiang, Jiangsu Province, China
Mr Mick and Mrs Anne Kavanagh (1997)
Nanping Teachers' College, 45 Guanshatian, Nanping, Fujian 353000, China
Ms Jane Thompson (1997)
Changshu Teachers' College, 98 Yuanhe Road, Changshu, Jiangsu 2185009, China

	Mr Stephen Graham (1996)	Shangrao Teachers' College, Shangrao, Jiangxi 834001, China
	Mr Richard Brunt (1998)	Tai'an Teachers' College, 56 Wenhua Road, Tai'an, Shandong 271000, China
	Mr David Conkey (1998)	Tai'an Teachers' College, 56 Wenhua Road, Tai'an, Shandong 271000, China
	Ms Pamela Gordon (1998)	Zaozhuang Teachers' College, Zaozhuang, Shandong 277160, China
	Mr Andy and Mrs Debbie Nicholson (1998)	Longyan Teachers' College, Longyan, Fujian 364000, China
	Mr David Brown (1998)	Dali Medical College, Xiaguan, Yunnan, China
	Mrs Valerie King (1999)	Jiujiang Teachers' College, Jiujiang 332000, Jiangxi Province, China
	Mr Jason Waller (1999)	Fuzhou Teachers' College, Fuzhou, Fujian 350011, China
NEPAL	**United Mission to Nepal**	
	Miss Christine Stone (1982)	PO Box 126, Kathmandu, Nepal
	Mr Clive M. Irvine (1984) and Mrs Susan Irvine	PO Box 126, Kathmandu, Nepal
	Mr Stephen Martin and Mrs Shirley Martin (1992)	PO Box 126, Kathmandu, Nepal
	Mr John Ross (1995)	PO Box 126, Kathmandu, Nepal
PAKISTAN	**Church of Pakistan**	
	Mr Ian A. Murray (1962) and Mrs Isabel Murray	Murree Christian School, Jhika Gali, Murree Hills, Pakistan
	Mrs Elizabeth M. McKee	Murree Christian School, Jhika Gali, Murree Hills, Pakistan
	Mr William Seaman and Mrs Catherine Seaman (1997)	Murree Christian School, Jhika Gali, Murree Hills, Pakistan
	Miss Helen F. McMillan (1981)	United Bible Training Centre, PO Box 14, Gujranwala, Pakistan
	Miss Catherine W. Nicol (1961)	St Columba Christian Girls' RTC, Barah Patthar, Sialkot 2, Pakistan
	Mr Alexander M. Sneddon (1986) and Mrs S. Marie Sneddon	Diocesan Office, Peshawar, Church of Pakistan, 1 Sir Syed Road, Peshawar 25000, Pakistan
	Rev. Paul Burgess (1994) and Mrs Cathie Burgess	Gujranwala Theological Seminary, PO Box 13, Gujranwala, Pakistan
SRI LANKA	**Presbytery of Lanka**	
	Rev. Anthony McLean Foreman (1995)	Theological College of Lanka, Pilimatalawa, Sri Lanka
THAILAND	**Church of Christ in Thailand**	
	Mr Michael D. Fucella and Mrs E. Jane Fucella (1990)	Fellowship of Sivilai, Mu 3 Ampur Sivilai, Nong Khai 43210, Thailand

MIDDLE EAST AND NORTH AFRICA

ISRAEL	[NOTE: Church Services are held in St Andrew's Scots Memorial Church, Jerusalem each Sunday at 10 am; and at Sea of Galilee Church each Sunday at 6 pm.]	
	Jerusalem	
	Vacant	St Andrew's Scots Memorial Church, PO Box 8619, Jerusalem 91086, Israel (Tel: 00 972 2 6732401/Fax: 00 972 2 673 1711)
	Mr James Aitken (1998), Pilgrim Co-ordinator	
	Ms Emma Given (1997)	Manager, St Andrew's Hospice, PO Box 8619, Jerusalem 91086, Israel
	Tiberias	
	Rev. Fred Hibbert (1996), Director and Mrs Diane Hibbert	Sea of Galilee Centre, PO Box 104, Tiberias, Israel [e-mail: scottie@rannet.com] (Tel: 00.972.6 6721165/Fax: 00 972 6 6790145)

Jaffa
Vacant, Head Teacher

Tabeetha School, PO Box 8170, 21 Yeffet Street, Jaffa, Israel
(Tel: 00 972 3 6821581/Fax: 00 972 3 6819357)
[e-mail: tabeetha@inter.net.16]

Mrs Karen Anderson (1992), Teacher	Tabeetha School
Mr Robert McLean (1995), Teacher and Mrs Sharon McLean	Tabeetha School
Mr Michael Nolan (1996) Teacher and Mrs Margaret Nolan	Tabeetha School
Ms Irene Wilson (1993) Teacher	Tabeetha School

LEBANON   Mr David Kerry (1999)

Near East School of Theology, Sourati Street, PO Box 13-5780, Chouran, Beirut, Lebanon
[e-mail: nest.lib@inco.lb]
(Tel) 00 961 1346 708)
(Fax) 00 961 1347 129)

LIST M – OVERSEAS RETIRED MISSION PARTNERS (10 or more years' service)

NAME	APP	RET	AREA	ADDRESS
Alexander, Elizabeth (Miss)	1960	1988	Kenya	Flat 22, The Dell, 6 Maryville Avenue, Giffnock, Glasgow G46 7AE
Archibald, Mary L. (Miss)	1964	1982	Nigeria/Ghana	490 Low Main Street, Wishaw ML2 7PL
Bailey, Winifred (Miss)	1949	1979	Kolhapur	22 Mardale Crescent, Edinburgh EH10 5AG
Barbour, Edith R. (Miss)	1952	1983	North India	13/11 Pratik Nagar, Yerwada, Pune 411006, Maharashta, India
Bogle, Rev. Michael M.	1936	1961	Lovedale	30 Woodburn Terrace, Edinburgh EH10 4SS
Boyle, Lexa (Miss)	1959	1992	Aden/Yemen/Sudan	7 Maxwell Grove, Glasgow G41 5JP
Buchanan, Rev. George	1931	1977	Buenos Aires/India/Bermuda	Site 46, Compartment 28, Galiano, BC Canada V0V 1PO
Burnett, Dr Fiona	1988	1998	Zambia	Cardon Farm, Broughton, by Biggar ML12 6JF
Burt, M.R.C. (Miss)	1940	1975	Kenya	22 The Loaning, Chirnside, Duns TD11
Cameron, F. (Miss)	1938	1969	Nigeria	37 Station Road, Banchory AB3 3XX
Campbell, George H.	1957	1971	Livingstonia	27 Avenue Street, Stewarton, Kilmarnock KA3 5AP
Coltart, Rev. Ian O.	1967	1985	North India	161 Kirk Road, Wishaw ML2 7BZ
Colvin, Rev. Tom and Mrs Patsy	1954	1990	Blantyre	1 Roseneath Terrace, Edinburgh EH9
Conn, A. (Mr)	1937	1960	Blantyre	90 Endbutt Lane, Great Crosby, Liverpool 23
Conacher, Marion (Miss)	1963	1993	India	41 Magdalene Drive, Edinburgh EH15 3BG
Cooper, Rev. George	1966	1986	Kenya	69 Montpelier Park, Edinburgh EH10 4WD
Cowan, Dr Betty	1969	1988	North India	2 Sunningdale Square, Kilwinning KA13 6PH

NAME	APP	RET	AREA	ADDRESS
Dabb, Dr R. Gwen	1943	1971	Blantyre	14/44 Ethel Terrace, Edinburgh EH10 5NA
Dougall, Ian C.	1960	1990	Kenya	60B Craigmillar Park, Edinburgh EH16 5PU
Drever, Dr Bryan	1962	1982	Aden/Yemen/Pakistan	188 Addison Road, King's Head, Birmingham
Dunlop, Walter T. (Mr)	1979	1994	Malawi/ Israel	50 Oxgangs Road, Edinburgh EH13 4DR
Fauchelle, Rev. Don and Mrs Margaret	1971	1979	Zambia, Malawi, Zimbabwe	Flat 3, 22 North Avenue, Devenport, Auckland 1309, New Zealand
Ferguson, John K.P. (Mr) and Mrs Margaret	1991	1999	Pakistan	12 Bencleuch Place, Bourtreehill, Irvine
Fischbacher, Dr Colin M and Mrs Sally	1977 1984	1989 1998	Malawi	11 Barclay Square, Gosforth, Newcastle-upon-Tyne NE3 2JB
Fleming, Rev. John R.	1938	1968	China/Malaya	41 Kilrymont Road, St Andrews KY16 8DA
Forrester-Paton, Rev. Colin	1946	1972	Ghana	Acharn, Glen Road, Peebles EH45 9AY
Gall, E.G. (Miss)	1940	1962	Blantyre	151 Raeburn Heights, Glenrothes KY16 1BW
Glass, Irene (Miss)	1945	1976	Delhi	3E Falcon Road West, Edinburgh EH10 4AA
Hutchison, C.M. (Mr)	1951	1972	Calabar	75 Grampian Road, Torry, Aberdeen AB1 3ED
Irvine, Dr Geoffrey C. and Mrs Dorothy	1952	1989	Kenya	Lakeside, PO Box 1356 Naivasha, Kenya
Kilgour, C. (Miss)	1948	1968	South Africa	20D Cameron Park, Edinburgh EH16 5LA
Kreuger, Dr Hendrikje	1957	1982	Western India	Rm 418, Nellestein Lopikhof 1, 1108, Amsterdam
Lamont, Rev. A. Donald	1941	1975	Kenya	36 St Clair Terrace, Edinburgh EH10 5PS
Liddell, Margaret (Miss)	1964	1980	Zambia	20 Wyvis Crescent, Conon Bridge IV7 8BZ
Lyon, Rev. D.H.S.	1952	1972	Nagpur	30 Mansfield Road, Balerno EH14 7JZ
McArthur, M G.	1956	1972	South Africa	3 Craigcrook Road, Edinburgh EH4 3NQ
McCulloch, Lesley (Mrs)	1982	1992	Malawi/Pakistan	c/o 19 North Approach Road, Kincardine FK10 4NW
McCutcheon, Agnes W.F. (Miss)	1957	1989	India	10A Hugh Murray Grove, Cambuslang, Glasgow G72 7NG
Macdonald, Rev. R.M.	1929	1968	Calabar	Pinewood Nursing Home, Leny Road, Callander FK17 8AP
McDougall, Rev. John N.	1935	1960	West Pakistan	2/58 Allendale Road, Mount Albert, Auckland 3, New Zealand
McGoff, A.W. (Miss)	1954	1974	Kolhapur	6 Mossvale Walk, Craigend, Glasgow G33 5PF
MacGregor, Rev. Margaret	1959	1994	India	Gordon Flat, 16 Learmonth Court, Edinburgh EH4 1PB
McKenzie, Rev. Robert	1938	1951	India	23 Foulis Crescent, Edinburgh EH14 5BN
McKenzie, Rev. W M	1958	1974	Zambia	Troqueer Road, Dumfries DG2 7DF
MacKinnon, E.L. (Miss)	1952	1972	Nigeria	142 Glencairn Street, Stevenston KA20 3BU
McNeel, M.S.H. (Miss)	1938	1975	Seoni	47/5 Gillespie Crescent, Edinburgh EH10 4JB
Malley, Beryl Stevenson (Miss)	1982	1992	Malawi	272/2 Craigcrook Road, Edinburgh EH4 7TF
Marshall, Rev. Fred J.	1992	1992	Bermuda	Flat 3, 31 Oswald Road, Edinburgh EH9 2HT
Millar, Rev. Margaret R.M.	1967	1996	Malawi/Zambia	
Millar, Rev. Peter and Mrs Dorothy	1976	1989	South India	The Manse, Taynuilt, Argyll PA35 1HW
Morrice, Rev Dr Charles and Mrs Margaret	1971	1998	Buenos Aires/Kenya	104 Baron's Hill Avenue, Linlithgow EH49 7JG

Name			Location	Address
Morris, Rev. Gordon C.	1948	1983	Zambia,Argentina	42 Regent Street, Edinburgh EH5 2AY
Morton, Rev. Colin	1988	1998	Israel	313 Lanark Road West, Currie, Midlothian EH14 5RS
Murison, Rev. W.G.	1951	1971	Santalia	21 Hailes Gardens, Edinburgh EH13 OJL
Nicholson, Rev. Thomas S.	1981	1995	Taiwan	Todholes, Greenlaw, Berwickshire TD11 3DS
Nicoll, J.M. (Miss)	1950	1967	Rajasthan	74 Brucefield Avenue, Dunfermline KY11 4SY
Pacitti, Rev. Stephen A.	1977	1996	Taiwan	157 Nithsdale Road, Pollokshields, Glasgow G41 5RD
Paterson, Rev. K.N.	1929	1959	Western Pakistan	Glasford, Marchmont Road, Greenlaw TD10 6YQ
Philip, Rev. David Stuart	1978	1991	Gibralter	6 St Bernard's Crescent, Edinburgh EH4 1NP
Philpot, Rev. David	1981	1995	W.C.C. Geneva	2/27 Pentland Drive, Edinburgh EH10 6PX
Rae, Rev. David and Mrs Margaret				29 Falcon Avenue, Edinburgh
Reid, Margaret I. (Miss)	1953	1989	India	26A Angle Park Terrace, Edinburgh EH11 2JT
Rennie, Rev. Alistair M.	1964	1982	Malawi	13 Tullich Terrace, Tillicoultry FK13 6RD
Rhodes, Rev. William S.	1939	1976	Malawi	22 Hamilton Place, Edinburgh EH3 5AU
Ritchie, Ishbel M. (Miss)	1954	1981	North India	8 Ross Street, Dunfermline KY12 0AN
Ritchie, Rev. J.M.	1955	1996	Eastern Himalaya	46 St James' Gardens, Penicuik EH26 9DU
Ritchie, Mary Scott (Miss)	1974	1977	Yemen	Afton Villa, 1 Afton Bridgend, New Cumnock KA18 4AX
Ross, Rev. Prof. Kenneth and Mrs Hester	1968	1991	Malawi/Israel	35 Madeira Street, Edinburgh EH6 4AJ
Rough, Mary E. (Miss)	1988	1998	Malawi	6 Giebe Street, Dumfries DG1 2LF
Russell, M.M. (Miss)	1966	1987	Blantyre	14 Hozier Street, Carluke ML8 5DW
Samuel, Lynda (Mrs)	1946	1969	Nigeria	c/o Balgownie, 1 Argyll Street, Brechin, Angus
Scott, Helen (Miss)	1974	1990	Madras	2 West Lynn, Dairy KA24 4LJ
Scott, M.A.B. (Miss)	1986	1998	Zambia	27 Woodbarn Terrace, Edinburgh EH10 4SS
Scrimgeour, Elizabeth (Miss)	1932	1966	Bengal	73 Novar Drive, Glasgow G12 9SS
Smith, Rev. W. Ewing	1946	1976	Darjeeling	8 Hardy Gardens, Bathgate EH48 1NH
Smith, M.L. (Miss)	1962	1978	Delhi	6 Fintry Mains, Dundee DD4 9HF
Smith, Dr R.B.	1956	1973	Madras	Flat G4, 21 Queen's Bay Crescent, Edinburgh EH15 2NA
Somerville, Rev. A.G.	1939	1958	Yemen	2 Orchard Park, Glenbum Road, Ardrishaig PA30 8EL
Stewart, Evelyn J. (Miss)	1942	1973	Nigeria	94 Baronald Drive, Glasgow G12 4HY
Stewart, Marion (Miss)	1946	1963	Livingstonia	Kirk Cottage, Kirkton of Skene AB32 6XX
Stone, W. Vernon, MA BD	1976	1989	Malawi/Israel	"Santis", Finlaystone Road, Kilmacolm PA13 4RE
Taylor, Rev. A.T.H.	1949	1966	Zambia	4 The Pleasance, Strathkinnes KY16 9SD
Wallace, A. Dorothy (Miss)	1938	1972	Nigeria/Jamaica	7 Bynack Place, Nethy Bridge PH25 3DU
Wilkie, Rev. James L.	1953	1991	North India	7 Comely Bank Avenue, Edinburgh EH4 1EW
Wilkinson, Rev. John	1959	1976	Zambia	70 Craigleith Hill Gardens, Edinburgh EH4 2JH
Wilson, Rev. Mark	1946	1975	Kenya	37 Kings Avenue, Longniddry EH32 0QN
Wilson, M.H. (Miss)	1953	1978	Nagpur	
	1946	1977	Nasik	7 Lady's Well, Moat Road, Annan, Dumfriesshire DG12 5AD

LIST N – PARISH ASSISTANTS and PROJECT WORKERS

NAME	APP	ADDRESS		TEL	PRES
Black, Colm	1996	27C Market Street, Musselburgh EH21 6PS	(Kaimes Lockhart Mememorial)	0131 665 3276	1
Cathcart, Paul	1998	5A Atholl Gardens, Springhall, Rutherglen Glasgow G73 5HF			
Craw, John	1998	26 Culloden Court, Culloden, Inverness IV2 7D	(East Kilbride: Claremont)	0141 630 0603	17
			(Inverness: Culloden The Barn)	01463 798753	37
Edminston, Pauline (Mrs)	1996	24 Miller Court, Dumbarton G82 2JX	(Dumbarton St Andrew's)	01229 732382	18
Falconer, A.J.	1996	59 Waldegrave Road, Carlisle	(Carlisle with Longtown)	01228 44757	7
McCorkindale, Yvonne (Mrs)	1997	11 Cochrane Place, Prestwick	(Kilmarnock: Shortlees)	01292 678993	11
MacDonald, Ian	1998	St Ninian's Centre, Crieff PH7 4BG	(Crieff and St Ninian's Centre)	01764 653766	28
Pearson, Lesley (Mrs)	1997	40 Muirwood Road, Currie, Midlothian EH14 5JN	(Edinburgh: Leith North)	0131 451 2628	1
Steven, Gordon R. BD	1997	51 Nantwich Drive, Edinburgh EH7 6RB	(Musselburgh: St Clement's & St Ninian's)	0131 669 2054	3

LIST O – READERS

1. EDINBURGH

Beasley, Ronald E.	37 Warrender Park Terrace, Edinburgh EH9 1EB	0131 229 8383
Campbell Marilyn (Mrs)	9 Sloan Street, Edinburgh EH6 8PL	0131 554 0530
Farrell, William J.	50 Ulster Crescent, Edinburgh EH8 7JS	0131 661 1026
Kerrigan, Herbert A. MA LLB QC	Airdene, 20 Edinburgh Road, Dalkeith EH22 1JY	0131 660 3007
Kinnear, M.A.	25 Thorburn Road, Edinburgh EH13 OBH	0131 441 3150
Lowe, James O.	38 Mountcastle Drive North, Edinburgh EH8 7SJ	0131 669 3885
Morrison, Peter K.	65 Balgreen Road, Edinburgh EH12 5UA	0131 337 7711
Scott, May (Miss)	34/2 Station Road, Kirkliston EH29 9BE	0131 335 3427

2. WEST LOTHIAN

Coyle, Charlotte (Mrs)	28 The Avenue, Whitburn EH47 0DA	01501 740687
Davidson, Sheila (Mrs)	12 Slamannan Road, Avonbridge, Falkirk FK1 2LW	01324 861554
Elliott, Sarah (Miss)	105 Seafield, Bathgate EH47 7AW	01506 654950
Galloway, Jane R. (Miss)	41 Broomieknowe Drive, Deans, Livingston EH54 8BY	01506 411053
Howarth, Jean (Mrs)	25 The Loan, Torphichen, Bathgate EH48 4NF	01506 630449
Notman, Jean G.S. (Miss)	31 South Loch Park, Bathgate EH48 2QZ	01506 633820
Smith, George	15 Manse Avenue, Armadale EH48 3HS	01501 732025

3. LOTHIAN

Booth, Sidney J. IEng CCME	6 Winton Court, Cockenzie, Prestonpans EH32 0JW	01875 813978
Cannon, S. Christopher MA	Briarwood, Winterfield Place, Belhaven, Dunbar EH42 1QQ	01368 864991
Gibson, C.B. Stewart	27 King's Avenue, Longniddry EH32 0QN	01875 853464
Hogg, David MA	82 Eskhill, Penicuik EH26 8DQ	01968 676350
Robb, Walter W. FVCM	10 Eskside Court, Dalkeith EH22 1JG	0131 663 3007

4. MELROSE AND PEEBLES

Butcher, John W.	"Sandal", 11 Ormiston Grove, Melrose TD6 9SR	01896 822339
Cozens, Averil (Mrs)	The Byre, Catrail Road, Galashiels TD1 1NW	01896 755498

5. DUNS

Deans, M. (Mrs) BA	The Lodge, Edrington House, Mordington, Berwick-on-Tweed TD15 1UF	01289 386222
Elphinston, Enid (Mrs)	Edrington House, Berwick-on-Tweed TD15 1UF	01289 386359
Landale, Wm.	Cranshaws House, Cranshaws, Duns TD11 3SJ	01361 890242

6. JEDBURGH

Agnew, Lt. Col. J.N. MA	Bonjedward House, Jedburgh TD8 6UE	01835 863464
Finlay, Elizabeth (Mrs)	10 Inch Park, Kelso TD5 7EQ	01573 226641
Forbes, William S.	Schoolhouse, Burnfoot, Hawick TD9 8EL	01450 372357
Hatton, Audrey (Mrs)	15 Ruberslaw Road, Hawick TD9 8PD	01450 870561
Knox, Dagmar (Mrs)	3 Stichill Road, Ednam, Kelso TD5 7QQ	01573 224883
Thomson, Robert R.	34/36 Fisher Avenue, Hawick TD9 9NB	01450 373851

7. ANNANDALE AND ESKDALE

Boncey, David	Redbrae, Beattock, Moffat DG10 9RF	01683 300326
Brown, S. Jeffrey BA	8 Ballplay Rd, Moffat DG10 9AR	01683 220475
Chisholm, Dennis A.G. MA BSc	Moss-side, Hightae, Lockerbie DG11 1JR	01387 811803
Dodds, Alan	Trinco, Battlehill, Annan DG12 6SN	01461 201235
Morton, Andrew A. BSc	19 Sherwood Park, Lockerbie DG11 2DX [e-mail: thccroft@enterprise.net]	01576 203164

8. DUMFRIES AND KIRKCUDBRIGHT

Allison, Douglas BD MEd	2 The Buchan, Castle Douglas DG7 1TH	01556 504279
Greer, Kathleen (Mrs)	10 Watling Street, Dumfries DG1 1HF	01387 256113
Ogilvie, D.W. MA FSAScot	Lingerwood, 2 Nelson Street, Dumfries DG2 9AY	01387 264267
Paterson, Dr Ronald M.	Mirkwood, Ringford, Castle Douglas DG7 2AL	01557 820202
Piggins, Janette (Mrs)	Cleugh Wood, Dalbeattie DG5 4PT	01387 780655

9. WIGTOWN AND STRANRAER

Moore, Douglas T.	9 Milton Road, Ayr KA9 1PU	01292 671352
Rankin, Stuart	Villa Cree, Cree Bridge, Minigaff, Newton Stewart	01671 403914
Robinson, J.J.	Kirwaugh, Wigtown, Newton Stewart DG8	01988 403244
Simpson, George W.	107 George Street, Whithorn, Newton Stewart DG8 8PT	01988 500242

10. AYR

Coghlan, Tony	"Hawthorns", Auchendoon, Hollybush, Ayr KA6 6HA	01242 560307
Fleming, William H.	53 Briar Grove, Ayr KA7 3PD	01292 268599
Jamieson, I.	2 Whinfield Avenue, Prestwick KA9 2BH	01242 476898
Johnstone, B.	15 Northpark Avenue, Girvan KA26 9DH	01465 712006
McNally, David BEd MEd ThDip ACP	50 Kenmore, Troon KA10 6PT	01292 312015
Murphy, I.	56 Lamont Crescent, Cumnock KA18 3DU	01290 423675
Riome, Elizabeth (Mrs)	Monkwood Mains, Minishant, Maybole KA19 8EY	01292 443440
Todd, Joy M. (Mrs) BD	15 Firth Road, Troon KA10 6TF	01292 312995
Todd, S.J.	15 Firth Road, Troon KA10 6TF	01292 312995
Wallace, D.	4 Holmston Crescent, Ayr KA7 3JJ	01292 261620

11. IRVINE AND KILMARNOCK

Bircham, James	8 Holmlea Place, Kilmarnock KA1 1UU	01563 532287
Clark, J. Michael	Brookfield, 81 Loudoun Road, Newmilns KA16 9HQ	01560 320033
Crosbie, Shona (Mrs)	4 Campbell Street, Darvel KA17 0PA	01560 322229
Findlay, Elizabeth (Mrs)	19 Keith Place, Kilmarnock KA3 7NS	01563 528084
Jamieson, John BSc(Hons) DEP AFBPSS	22 Moorfield Avenue, Kilmarnock KA1 1TS	01563 534065
McLean, Donald	1 Four Acres Drive, Kilmaurs, Kilmarnock KA3 2ND	01563 381475
MacTaggart, Elspeth (Miss)	21 Scargie Road, Kilmarnock KA3 1QR	01563 527713
Scott, William BA DipEd	6 Elgin Avenue, Stewarton KA3 3HJ	01560 484273
Storm, Iain	17 Kilwinning Road, Irvine KA12 8RR	01294 277647
Wilson, Robert L.S. MA BD	57 Woodstock Street, Kilmarnock KA1 2JH	01563 526658

12. ARDROSSAN

Allan, J.H.	Creaih Dhubh, Golf Course Road, Whiting Bay, Arran KA27 8RE	01770 700462
Barclay, Elizabeth (Mrs)	2 Jacks Road, Saltcoats KA21 5NT	01294 471855
Mills, Colin J.	Roadend Christian Guesthouse, Shiskine, Brodick, Arran KA27 8EW	01770 860448
Price, James	Dunjara, The Orchard, West Kilbride KA23 9AE	01294 822247
Stedman, John	Linden Lea, Sliddery, Brodick, Arran KA27 8PB	01770 870209

13. LANARK

Brown, Kay (Mrs)	16 Abington Road, Symington ML12 6JX	01899 308838
Grant, Alan	25 Moss-side Avenue, Carluke ML8 5UG	01555 771419
Kerr, Sheilagh I. (Mrs)	Dunvegan, 29 Wilsontown Road, Forth, Lanark ML11 8ER	01555 812214

14. PAISLEY

Campbell, Tom BA FRICS	100 Craigielea Road, Renfrew PA4 8NJ	0141 886 2503
McHugh, Jack	"Earlshaugh", Earl Place, Bridge of Weir PA11 3HA	01505 612789
Ross, Magnus M.B. BA MEd FRSA	"Craigalvie", Kilbarchan Road, Bridge of Weir, PA11 3EZ	01505 613835

15. GREENOCK

Geddes, Douglas S.	167 South Street, Greenock PA16 8TE	01475 723601
Hart, J.	41 Prospecthill Street, Greenock PA15 4DN	01475 726687
Jamieson, J.A.	148 Finnart Street, Greenock PA16 8HY	01475 729531
McFarlan, A.	65 Albert Road, Gourock PA19 1NJ	01475 634055
Marshall, Leon M.	Glenisla, Gryffe Road, Kilmacolm PA13 4BA	01505 872417

16. GLASGOW

Birchall, Edwin R.	11 Sunnybank Grove, Clarkston, Glasgow G76 7SU	0141 638 4332
Calder, William	111 Muirside Avenue, Kirkintilloch G66 3PP	0141 776 5495
Callander, Thomas M.S.	31 Dalkeith Avenue, Bishopbriggs G64 2HQ	0141 772 6955
Campbell, Jack T. BD BEd	27 Springfield Road, Bishopbriggs G64 1PJ	0141 563 5837
Clarke, Samuel	"Gola", 142 Shelley Road, Glasgow G12 0XN	0141 337 2238
Findlay, William	36 Firpark Road, Bishopbriggs G64 1SP	0141 772 7253
Gibson, James N.	153 Peveril Avenue, Glasgow G41 3SF	0141 632 4162
Horner, David J.	32 Burnside Road, Rutherglen G73 4RS	0141 634 2178
Lennie, Henry	14 Clyde Place, Cambuslang G72 7QT	0141 641 1410
Lockhart, James C.	56 Springfield Road, Bishopbriggs G64 1PN	0141 772 7852
MacColl, Duncan N.	14 Mosspark Avenue, Glasgow G52 1JX	0141 427 2395
McFarlane, Robert	25 Avenel Road, Glasgow G13 2PB	0141 954 5540
McLean, Robert	50 Pendicle Road, Bearsden G61 1EE	0141 942 1489
McLellan, Duncan	138 King's Park Avenue, Glasgow G44 4HS	0141 632 8433
Middleton, W.G.	20 Rannoch Avenue, Bishopbriggs G64 1BU	0141 772 6240
Montgomery, Hamish	13 Avon Avenue, Kessington, Bearsden G61 2PS	0141 942 3640
Nairne, Elizabeth (Mrs)	229 Southbrae Drive, Glasgow G13 1TT	0141 959 5066
Robertson, Adam	423 Amulree Street, Glasgow G32 7SS	0141 778 1563
Sands. Richard	1 Redwood Place, Lenzie	
Shirlaw, William	77 Southpark Avenue G12 8LF	0141 339 0454
Tindail, Margaret (Mrs)	23 Ashcroft Avenue, Lennoxtown, Glasgow G65 7EN	01360 310911
Williamson, John G.	34 King Edward Road, Glasgow G13 1QW	0141 959 1300
Wilson, George A.	46 Maxwell Drive, Garrowhill, Baillieston, Glasgow G69 6LS	0141 771 3862

17. HAMILTON

Chirnside, Peter	141 Kylepark Drive, Uddingston G71 7DB	01698 813769
Clemenson, Anne	25 Dempsey Road, Lochview, Bellshill ML4 2UF	01698 747032
Cruickshanks, William	63 Progress Drive, Caldercruix ML6 7PU	01236 843352
Falconer, Leslie D.	48 Fraser River Tower, East Kilbride G75 8AD	01355 230133
Haggarty, Frank	46 Glen Road, Caldercuix ML6 7PZ	01236 842182
Hawthorne, William	172 Main Street, Plains, Airdrie ML6 7JH	01236 842230
Hewitt, Samuel	3 Corrie Court, Earnock, Hamilton ML3 9XE	01698 457403
Leckie, Elizabeth	41 Church Street, Larkhall ML9 1EZ	01698 308933
McCart, Frances BD	26 St Andrew's Court, Sycamore Crescent, East Kilbride G75 9LN	01355 246939
McCleary, Isaac	16 Dalreoch Avenue, Baillieston, Glasgow	0141 236 0158

Name	Address	Telephone
McRae, James	36 Crosshill Road, Strathaven ML10 6DS	01357 520053
Queen, Leslie	60 Loch Assynt, East Kilbride G74 2OW	01355 233932
Robertson, Rowan	68 Townhead Road, Coatbridge ML5 2HU	01236 425703
Smith, Alexander	6 Coronation Street, Wishaw ML2 8LF	01698 385797
White, Ian	21 Muirhead, Stonehouse ML9 3HG	01698 792772
Wilson, William	115 Chatelherault Crescent, Low Waters Estate, Hamilton ML3 9PL	01698 421856

18. DUMBARTON

Name	Address	Telephone
Galbraith, Iain B.	Beechwood, Overtoun Road, Alexandria G83	01389 53563
Hart, R.J.M. BSc	7 Kidston Drive, Helensburgh G84 8QA	01436 72039
McFarlane, Andrew L.	9 Smugglers Way, Rhu, Helensburgh G84 8HX	01436 820058
Neville, Robert	4 Glen Drive, Helensburgh G84 9BJ	01436 71481

19. SOUTH ARGYLL

Holden, Robert	Tigh-an-Fhasgaidh, Ardrishaig PA30 8ER	01546 603327
Mathisen, Ian M.	Sanaigmore, Campbeltown PA28 6EP	01586 552645
Mitchell, James S.	4 Main Street, Port Charlotte, Islay PA48 7TX	01496 85250
Ramsay, Matthew M.	Portnastorm, Carradale, Campbeltown PA28 6SB	01583 431381
Stewart, Agnes	Lagvullich, Kilkerran Road, Campbeltown PA28	01586 552805
Stewart, John Y.S.	9 Foulis Road, Inveraray PA32 8UW	01499 302077
Wright, D. Gordon B.	Bealach Dearg, Craighouse, Jura PA60 7XS	01496 820212

20. DUNOON

Name	Address	Telephone
Cameron, Mary (Miss) BD	Ardencraig, Kames, Tighnabruaich PA21 2AG	01700 811376
Challis, John O.	Bay Villa, Strachur PA27 8DE	01369 860436

21. LORN AND MULL

Binner, Aileen	"Ailand", Connel, Argyll	01631 710264
Elwis, Michael,	Erray Farm Cottage, Tobermory, Mull PA75 6PS	01688 302331
Simpson, J.	Ardmhullean, Longsdale Road, Oban PA34 5JW	01631 562022
Taylor, Mary W. (Mrs)	Bunessan Manse, Isle of Mull, Argyll PA72	01681 700227

22. FALKIRK

Name	Address	Telephone
Duncan, Lorna (Mrs) BA	Richmond, 28 Solway Drive, Head of Muir, Denny FK5 5NS	01324 813020
Stewart, Arthur MA	29 Ben Nevis Way, Eastfield, Cumbernauld G68 9JG	01236 732532
Struthers, I.	169 The Auld Road, Cumbernauld G67 2RO	01236 733879

23. STIRLING

Clelland, Elizabeth	26 Broompark West, Menstrie FK11 7AL	01259 769426
Durie, Alastair	25 Forth Place, Stirling FK8 1UD	01786 451029
Kimmitt, Alan	111 Glasgow Road, Bannockburn, Stirling FK8	
Lamont, John	"Serendipity" Wardpark, Gartmore FK8 3RN	01360 850313
Millar, Charles	11 Catherine Road, Bannockburn, Stirling FK7 0XH	01786 811258
Tilly, Patricia	4 Innerdownie Place, Dollar FK14 7BY	01259 742094

24. DUNFERMLINE

Name	Address	Telephone
Arnott, Robert G.K.	25 Sealstrand, Dalgety Bay, Dunfermline KY11 5GH	01383 822293
Conway, Bernard	4 Centre Street, Kelty KY4 0DU	
McCaffery, Joyce (Mrs)	79 Union Street, Cowdenbeath	
Powrie-Smith, Robb	9 Westpark Gate, Saline, Dunfermline KY12 9US	01383 852084
Russell, David	143 Broad Street, Cowdenbeath KY4 9NS	01383 515019

25. KIRKCALDY

Name	Address	Telephone
Biernat, Ian	13 Westpark Avenue, Leslie, Glenrothes, Fife KY6 3BX	01592 741487
Biernat, Margaret (Mrs)	13 Westpark Avenue, Leslie, Glenrothes, Fife KY6 3BX	01592 741487

26. ST ANDREWS

Name	Address	Telephone
Allan, Angus J.	Craigmore, The Barony, Cupar KY15 5ER	01334 653369
Browning, Margaret (Miss)	4 Wellpark Terrace, Newport-on-Tay DD6 9JE	01382 542140
Elder, Morag (Mrs)	5 Provost Road, Tayport DD6	01382 552218
Hector, Gordon M. CMG CBE MA	4 Montgomery Court, 110 Hepburn Gardens, St Andrews KY16 9LT	01334 473784
Kettle, B.E. (Miss) MTheol	3 Alison Place, Greenside Place, St Andrews KY16 9TJ	01334 474967
Kinnis, Dr W.K.B.	4 Dempster Court, St Andrews KY16	01334 476959
Smith, Elspeth (Mrs)	Whinstead, Dalgairn, Cupar KY15	01334 653269

27. DUNKELD AND MEIGLE

Name	Address	Telephone
Davidson, Margaret (Mrs)	9 Woodlands Park, Blairgowrie PH10 6UW	01250 875957
Macmartin, Duncan M.	Teallach, Old Crieff Road, Aberfeldy PH15 2DG	01887 820693
Wilson, Michael	Moulin Gates Cottage, Atholl Road, Pitlochry PH16	01796 473199

28. PERTH

Name	Address	Telephone
Begg, J.	Craiglea, Addison Terrace, Crieff PH7 3AT	01764 655907
Brown, Stanley	14 Buchan Drive, Perth PH1 1NQ	01738 628818
Buchan, J.S.	47 Dunkeld Road, Perth PH1 5RP	01738 621814
Coulter, Hamish	95 Cedar Drive, Perth PH1 1RW	01738 636761
Hastings, W.P.	14 Gray Street, Perth PH2 0JJ	01738 626859
Johnstone, David	92 Duncansby Way, Perth PH1 5XF	01738 442051
Laing, John	14 Cairns Court, Crieff PH7 3SP	01764 654959
Michie, M (Mrs)	3 Loch Leven Court, Wester Balgedie, Kinross KY13 7NE	01592 840602
Packer, Joan (Miss)	11 Moredun Terrace, Perth PH2 0DA	01738 623873
Thomson, Enid (Mrs)	12 Strathray Road, Perth PH1 2LX	01738 628506
Thorburn, Susan (Mrs)	3 Daleally Cottages, St Madoes Road, Errol PH2 7QX	01821 642681
Yellowlees, Deirdre (Mrs)	Ringmill House, Gannochy Farm, Perth PH2 7JH	01738 633773

29. DUNDEE

Name	Address	Telephone
Baxter, John T.G.	2 Garten Street, Broughty Ferry, Dundee DD5 3HH	01382 739997
Bell, Dr S.	10 Victoria Street, Newport-on-Tay DD6 8DJ	01382 542315
Bowser, Charles N. MA	6 Wellpark Terrace, Newport-on-Tay DD6 8HT	01382 542157
Doig, Andrew	6 Lyndhurst Terrace, Dundee DD2 3HP	01382 610596

Johnston, Wm. — 62 Forthill Road, Broughty Ferry, Dundee DD5 3TJ — 01382 739704
Owler, Harry G. — 43 Brownhill Road, Dundee DD2 4LH — 01382 622902
Ramsay, Thomas A. — Inchcape Place, Broughty Ferry, Dundee DD5 2L — 01382 778915
Rodgers, Mary (Mrs) — 12 Balmerino Road, Dundee DD4 8RN — 01382 500291
Shepherd, E. — 34 Dalmahoy Drive, Dundee DD2 3UT — 01382 815825
Simpson, Webster — 51 Wemyss Crescent, Monifieth DD5 4RA — 01382 535218
Webster, Charles A. — 16 Bath Street, Broughty Ferry, Dundee DD5 2BY — 01382 739520
Woodley, Dr A.G. — 67 Marlee Road, Broughty Ferry, Dundee DD5 3EU — 01382 739820

30. ANGUS
Beedie, A.W. — 62 Newton Crescent, Arbroath DD11 3JZ — 01241 875001
Davidson, P.I. — 27 Dorward Road, Montrose DD10 8SB — 01674 674098
Ironside, C.T. PhD — 21 Tailyour Crescent, Montrose DD10 9BL — 01674 673959
Leslie Melville, (Hon Mrs) Ruth — Little Deuchar, Fern, Forfar DD8 3RA — 01356 650279
Nicol, Douglas C. — Edenbank, 16 New Road, Forfar DD8 2AE — 01307 463264
Stevens, P.J. — 7 Union Street, Montrose DD10 8PZ — 01674 673710
Wade, Nan (Mrs) — Lea-Rig, Charleston, Forfar DD8 1UF — 01307 840204
Wheat, M. — 16A South Esk Street, Montrose DD10 8BJ — 01674 676083

31. ABERDEEN
Dickie, John — 44 Kingsway, Bucksburn AB21 9BP — 01224 714354
Gray, Peter PhD — 165 Countesswells Road, Aberdeen AB15 7RA — 01224 318172
Sinton, George P. FIMLS — 12 North Donside Road, Bridge of Don, Aberdeen AB23 8PA — 01224 702273

32. KINCARDINE AND DEESIDE
Bell, Peter D. BA — 63 St Nicholas Drive, Banchory AB31 5YE — 01330 823661
Cameron, Ann (Mrs) — 30 Wilson Road, Banchory AB31 5UY — 01330 825953
Grant, (Prof) Raymond — Ballochbrock, Braemar, Ballater AB35 5YQ — 01337 41340
Haddow, Steven — 18 St Nicholas Drive, Banchory AB31 3YG — 01330 822057
Middleton, Capt. Robbie — 7 St Ternan's Road, Newtonhill, Kincardineshire AB39 2PF — 01569 730852
Mitchell, D. Ronald BDS — Brae House, Raemoir, Banchory AB31 4EB — 01330 823242
McCafferty, W. John — East Crossley, Netherley, Stonehaven AB39 3QY — 01569 730281
Sedgwick, Dr Sheila BA BD MEd PhD — Girnock Shiel, Glengirnock, Ballater AB35 5SS — 01339 755292
Wood, Eric R. MPS — 3 Carronhall, Stonehaven AB39 2HF — 01569 762591

33. GORDON
Hart, Elsie (Mrs) — The Knoll, Craigearn, Kennay AB51 9LN — 01467 642105
Rennie, Lyall — 5 Urydale, Inverurie AB51 3XW — 01467 624636
Robb, Margaret (Mrs) — Chrislouan, Keithhall AB51 0LN — 01651 882310
Robertson, James Y. — 1 Nicol Road, Kintore AB51 0QA — 01467 633001

34. BUCHAN
Davidson, James — 19 Great Stuart Street, Peterhead AB42 1JX — 01779 470234
Lumsden, Vera (Mrs) — 8 Queen's Crescent, Portsoy, Banff AB45 2PX — 01261 842712
McColl, John — 6 Bracoden Terrace, Gardenstown, Banff AB45 3ZF — 01261 851390
Mair, Dorothy (Miss) — 53 Dennyduff Road, Fraserburgh AB43 9LY — 01346 513879

Michie, William	Rosebank, 9 Seafield Street, Whitehills, Banff AB45 2NA	01261 861439
Noble, John	44 Henderson Park, Peterhead AB42 2WR	01779 472522
Ogston, Norman	Sunnybrae Christian Centre, Woodhead, Fyvie AB53 8LS	01651 891734
Simpson, Andrew C.	10 Wood Street, Banff AB45 1JX	01261 812538
Smith, Ian M.G. MA	Chomriach, 2 Hill Street, Cruden Bay, Peterhead AB42 0HF	01779 812698

35. MORAY

Benson, F.S.	8 Springfield Court, Forres	01309 671525
Carson, John	2 Woodside Drive, Forres IV36 0NF	01309 674541
Gerrard, Graeme	12 Peter's Road, Buckie AB56 1DL	01542 831124
MacKenzie, Stuart G.	Woodend Cottage, Blackburn, Fochabers IV32 7LN	01343 843248
Middleton, Alex	Coral Cottage, Pilmuir Road, Forres IV36 0HN	01309 676912

36. ABERNETHY

Berkeley, Dr John S.	Drumbeg, Coylumbridge, Aviemore PH22 1QU	01479 811055

37. INVERNESS

Chalmers, Malcolm	2 Strath Avenue, Inverness IV2 4LR	01463 232356
Cook, Arnett D.	128 Laurel Avenue, Inverness IV3 5RS	01463 242586
Maclean, Hamish	63 Ashton Road, Inverness IV2 3UY	01463 239030
MacLeod, John M. MBE JP	"Craigdarroch", 9 Dornie Place, Inverness IV2 4BX	01463 713542
Robertson, Hendry	"Park House", 51 Glenurquhart Road, Inverness IV3 5PB	01463 231858

38. LOCHABER

Fraser, John A.	26 Clunes Avenue, Caol, Fort William PH33 7BJ	01397 703467
Maitland, John	St Monance, Ardgour, Fort William PH33 7AA	01855 841267

39. ROSS

Finlayson, Mark	Amberlea, Evanton IV16 9UY	01349 830598
Gilbertson, Ian	Firth View, Crailrory, North Kessock IV1 1XH	01463 73538
McCredie, Frederick	Highfield, Highfield Park, Conon Bridge IV7 8AP	01349 862171
Robertson, Dr John	East Wing, Kincurdie House, Rosemarkie IV10 8SJ	01381 621388
Woodham, Maisey F. (Mrs)	Scardroy, Greenhill, Dingwall IV15 9JQ	01349 862116

40. SUTHERLAND

Betts-Brown, Andrew	54 Muirfield Road, Brora KW9 6QY	01408 621610
Burnett, Michael	16 The Meadows, Dornoch IV25 3SF	01862 810972
Garvie, John	Auchlea, Balnapolaig, Dornoch IV25 3HY	01862 811524
Gazey, Neville	5 Academy Street, Brora KW9 9QP	01408 621607
Mackay, Donald F.	The Retreat, Lillieshall Street, Helmsdale KW8 6JF	01431 821469
Stobo, May (Mrs)	Druim-an-Sgairnich, Lower Gledfield, Ardgay IV24 3BG	01863 766529

41. CAITHNESS

Duncan, Esme (Miss)	Avalon, Upper Warse, Canisbay, Wick KW1 4YD	01955 611309
Macnee, Anthea (Mrs)	The Manse, Canisbay, Wick KW1 4YH	

42. LOCHCARRON – SKYE

Name	Address	Phone
Mackenzie, Hector	53 Strath, Gairloch IV21 2DB	01445 712433
Macrae, D.E.	Nethania, 52 Strath, Gairloch IV21 2DB	01445 712235
Murray, John W.	Totescore, Kilmuir, Portree, Skye IV51	01470 522297
Ross, R. Ian	St Conal's, Inverinate, by Kyle of Lochalsh	01599 511371

43. UIST

MacAuley, John	Fernhaven, Flodabay, Isle of Harris HS3 3HA	01859 530340
MacNab, Ann (Mrs)	Druim Skillivat, Scolpaig, Lochmaddy, Isle of North Uist HS6	01876 510701
MacSween, John	5 Scott Road, Tarbert, Isle of Harris HS3 3DL	01859 502338
Morrison, Donald John	Lagnam, Brisgean 22, Kyles, Isle of Harris HS3 3BS	01859 502341
Taylor, Hamish	Tigh na Tobair, Flodabay, Isle of Harris HS3 3HA	01859 530310

44. LEWIS

Forsyth, William	1 Berisay Place, Stornoway, Isle of Lewis HS1 2TF	01851 702332
McAlpin, Robert J.G. MA FEIS	24 Upper Coll, Back, Isle of Lewis	01851 820288
Murray, Angus	4 Cearn Chilleagraidh, Stornoway, Isle of Lewis HS1 2UJ	01851 703550

45. ORKNEY

Alexander, Malcolm	Copwillo', Button Road, Stenness, Orkney KW16 3HA	01856 850444
Kent, Reginald F.	Greenfield, Stronsay KW17 2AG	01857 616351

46. SHETLAND

Christie, William C.	11 Fullaburn, Bressay, Shetland ZE2	01595 820244
Greig, Diane (Mrs)	Church of Scotland Manse, Sandwick, Shetland ZE2 9HW	01950 431244
Jamieson, Ian	Links View, Ringesta, Quendale, Shetland ZE2 9JD	01950 460477
Laidlay, Una (Mrs)	5 Bells Road, Lerwick, Shetland ZE1 0QB	01595 695147
Macdonald, Michael	8 Roebrek, Brae, Shetland ZE2	01806 522318
MacGregor, Robert	Vistavird, Brae, Shetland ZE2	

47. ENGLAND

Brockett, Alastair BSc	48 Holmeswood Park, Rawtenstall, Rossendale, Lancs BB4 6HZ	01706 221363
Green, Dr Peter	Samburu Cottage, Russells Green Road, Ninfield, East Sussex	01424 892033
Lunn, Dorothy (Miss) SRCN	14 Bellerby Drive, Ouston, Durham DH2 1TW	0191 492 0647
Mackay, Donald	90 Hallgarth Street, Elvet, Durham DH1 3AS	0191 383 2110
Twomey, Douglas G.	14 Southsea Avenue, Goring-by-Sea, Worthing BN12 4BN	
(Goodbourne, Dr David	145 Westcombe Hill, Blackheath, London SE3 7DP	0208 305 0126)

48. EUROPE

Name	Address	Phone
Sharp, James	102 Rue des Eaux-Vives, 1207 Geneva, Switzerland [e-mail:jsharp@world.scout.org]	00 41 22 786 48 47
Walker, David LLB	Vlaamse Gaaienlaan 6, 3080 Tervuren, Belgium	00 32 2 767 40 06

LIST P – CHURCH REPRESENTATIVES ON COUNCIL EDUCATION COMMITTEES

COUNCIL	NAME	ADDRESS
ABERDEEN CITY	Mr Ron Riddell	66 Hammersmith Road, Aberdeen AB10 6ND
ABERDEENSHIRE	Mr William Michie	Rosebank, Seafield Street, Whitehills, Banff AB45 2NA
ANGUS	Rev. Carleen Robertson	The Manse, 2 Kirkton Road, Newtyle PH12 8TS
ARGYLL and BUTE	Miss Alexandria Montgomery	47 Crichton Road, Craigmore, Rothesay PA20 9JT
AYRSHIRE EAST	Rev. John Paterson	33 Barrhill Road, Cumnock KA18 1PJ
AYRSHIRE NORTH	Mrs Christine Welch	6 Brodick Close, Kilwinning KA13 6KN
AYRSHIRE SOUTH	Rev. Roger M. Hollins	Smithy Cottage, Dunure, Ayr KA7 4LH
CLACKMANNAN	Rev. George T. Sherry	The Manse, Menstrie FK11 7EA
DUMFRIES and GALLOWAY	Mrs Elizabeth J.Smith	Kelterne, Rhonehouse, Castle Douglas DG7 1SZ
DUNBARTONSHIRE EAST	Mrs Barbara Jarvie	10 Birnam Crescent, Bearsden, Glasgow G61 2AU
DUNBARTONSHIRE WEST	Miss Sheila Rennie	128 Dumbuie Avenue, Dumbarton G82 2JW
DUNDEE	Mr K.D. Anderson	10 Douglas Terrace, Broughty Ferry DD5 1EA
EDINBURGH CITY	Mr Henry L. Philip	Lauder Grange, 69/2 Grange Loan, Edinburgh EH9 2EG
FALKIRK	Rev. Duncan McClements	30 Russel Street, Falkirk FK2 7HS
FIFE	Rev. John C. Duncan	21 Ramsay Crescent, Burntisland KY3 9JL
GLASGOW CITY	Rev. Andrew J. Philip	The Manse, 43 Smithycroft Road, Riddrie, Glasgow G33 2RH
HIGHLAND	Rev. Sandy Glass	Craigton, Tulloch Avenue, Dingwall IV15 9LH
INVERCLYDE	Rev. David J. MacAdam	80 Bardrainney Avenue, Port Glasgow PA14 6HP
LANARKSHIRE NORTH	Rev. James Munton	Old Monkland Manse, Coatbridge ML5 5QT
LANARKSHIRE SOUTH	Rev. Cameron McPherson	Dalserf, Larkhall ML9 3BN
LOTHIAN EAST	Rev. Cameron Mackenzie	15 West Road, Haddington EH41 3RD
LOTHIAN WEST	Rev. Gordon McCracken	5 Mansewood Crescent, Whitburn, West Lothian EH47 8HA
MIDLOTHIAN	Rev. Alistair K. Ridland	13 Weir Crescent, Dalkeith EH22 3JN
MORAY	Mrs Mhairi Dick	22 West High Street, Portgordon, Buckie AB56 2QS
ORKNEY	Mrs Jenny Deans	Kenmore, Tankerness KW17 2QT
PERTH and KINROSS	Mrs Mary Reid	The Manse, Dundee Road, Meigle PA12 8SB
RENFREWSHIRE	Mr Allan Millar	24 Duart Drive, Elderslie PA5 9NP
RENFREWSHIRE EAST	Rev. Angus Kerr	28 Waterside Road, Newton Mearns, Glasgow G77 6TJ
SCOTTISH BORDERS	Rev. Alan C.D. Cartwright	The Manse, Swinton, Duns TD11 3JS
SHETLAND	Rev. James A.M. Dowswell	82 St Olafs Street, Lerwick, Shetland ZE1 0ES
STIRLING	Rev. Moira MacCormick	8 Culbowie Crescent, Buchlyvie, Stirling FK8 3NH
WESTERN ISLES	Rev. Andrew W.F. Coghill	Manse of Crossboss, Leurbost, Lochs, Lewis HS2 9NS

LIST Q – RETIRED LAY AGENTS

Elliot, Alexander	24 Broompark View, East Calder EH53 0AD
Lamont, Donald	Old Mission House, Cul-nan-Cnoc, Portree, Isle of Skye IV51 9JD
MacDonald, Kenneth D.	40 Bayhead Street, Stornoway, Isle of Lewis
MacNaughton, Winifred H. (Mrs)	22 Newtown, Cupar KY15 4DD
Macrae, Kenneth	16 Ladysmith Street, Ullapool IV26 2UW
Scott, John W.	15 Manor Court, Forfar DD8 1BR
Shepherd, Denis	Mission House, Norby, Sandness, Shetland
Stephen, George	202 Inverugie Court, Inverugie Road, Peterhead AB42 6WL

SECTION 7

Congregational
Statistics
1998

CHURCH OF SCOTLAND STATISTICS
FOR 1998

Congregations 1,586
Communicants 641,340
Elders 44,388
Charges 1,279
Ministers serving charges 1,153
Chaplains to HM Forces 26
Students completing their courses 24

NOTES ON
CONGREGATIONAL STATISTICS

Com   Number of communicants at 31/12/98.

Eld   Number of elders at 31/12/98.

WG   Membership of The Guild including Young Woman's Group. The letter "j" beside a figure indicates that the figure is a joint figure for all the congregations making up the charge.

In98   Ordinary General Income for 1998.
Ordinary General Income consists of members' offerings, contributions from congregational organisations, regular fundraising events, income from investments, deposits, *etc*. This figure does not include extraordinary or special income, or income from special collections and fundraising for other charities.

Ass   Amount allocated to congregations for Mission and Aid Fund in 1998.

Gvn   Amount contributed by congregations to Mission and Aid Fund in 1998.
The amount shown includes contributions to allocation and voluntary extra contributions. The figures do not take into account late payments made in 1999 for 1998 but may contain late payments made in 1998 for 1997 and prior years.

[N.B. Figures may not be available for congregations which have entered into readjustment in 1998.]

3-11,   Number of young people in these age groups receiving Christian
-17   Education. The statistics are for the year 1996.

Congregation	Com	Eld	G	In98	Ass	Gvn	3-11	-17
1. EDINBURGH								
Abercorn	92	9	10	10279	350	350	–	–
Dalmeny	178	10	11	8233	312	312	–	–
Albany Deaf Church of Edinburgh	158	13	–	2546	0	0	–	–
Balerno	998	65	66	104977	22250	26480	102	15
Barclay	499	45	33	78990	21820	21820	61	16
Blackhall St Columba	1212	97	60	143461	41300	41299	117	34
Bristo Memorial Craigmillar	191	6	26	17679	0	0	10	–
Broughton St Mary's	372	40	30	46920	7980	8030	12	1
Canongate	476	49	–	59994	10380	10380	–	–
Carrick Knowe	848	44	119	58114	11600	11600	75	24
Cluny	737	71	29	94122	23844	24767	36	23
Colinton	1345	103	–	122679	33770	33518	143	82
Colinton Mains	315	20	26	31867	3080	3160	50	12
Corstorphine Craigsbank	1030	64	–	103071	20560	20560	83	45
Corstorphine Old	766	62	83	79449	20530	20780	59	13
Corstorphine St Anne's	569	59	54	71277	18260	18260	41	10
Corstorphine St Ninian's	1236	100	62	124441	34280	35486	130	22
Craigentinny St Christopher's	186	18	–	23689	0	0	–	–
Craiglockhart	623	60	47	98085	24190	24190	90	28
Craigmillar Park	369	31	42	76641	16840	17266	26	7
Cramond	1404	110	38	164854	48360	51315	76	24
Currie	1615	78	76	152047	32000	32000	81	40
Davidson's Mains	925	78	54	118692	30360	30360	83	32
Dean	268	26	27	44007	8760	8760	13	15
Drylaw	273	18	11	22913	0	0	125	—
Duddingston	918	67	61	68273	13870	13870	37	34
Fairmilehead	1151	98	42	103813	25994	14994	205	36
Gilmerton	293	11	–	15666	0	0	12	26
Gorgie	420	31	29	60363	11650	12150	25	9
Granton	459	35	–	35028	4080	4080	30	–
Greenbank	1036	94	93	161604	46130	48830	152	68
Greenside	317	27	24	49355	7850	7200	39	3
Greyfriars Tolbooth and Highland	479	45	12	80967	17560	17560	9	–
High (St Giles')	730	49	–	182947	32770	32357	–	–
Holyrood Abbey	307	32	25	117067	36400	36400	20	20
Holy Trinity	243	16	–	45253	3750	5388	31	19
Inverleith	496	42	–	66267	15920	15139	23	6
Juniper Green	478	38	–	75666	22320	23000	81	14
Kaimes Lockhart Memorial	198	14	18	15430	0	0	28	–
Kirkliston	434	37	41	42197	7320	7320	45	21
Kirk o' Field	300	39	–	37008	5950	5950	17	3
Leith North	556	52	47	64091	11910	11910	53	29
Leith St Andrew's	381	37	–	45404	8190	8190	64	8
Leith St Paul's	234	17	19	24497	3480	5800	16	26
Leith St Serf's	373	31	31	42568	4700	4730	21	4
Leith St Thomas' Junction Road	393	35	28	39172	6140	5999	–	–
Leith South	771	86	46	98501	22580	22875	41	–
Leith Wardie	724	87	90	96178	25540	30400	111	24
Liberton	1070	69	85	85408	21170	22070	57	16
Liberton Northfield	358	17	42	34603	0	0	31	4

Congregation	Com	Eld	G	In98	Ass	Gvn	3-11	-17
London Road	466	0	35	48067	8140	8140	24	6
Marchmont St Giles'	393	48	35	67903	15810	20810	47	–
Mayfield Salisbury	950	82	60	162076	48880	53449	77	30
Morningside Braid	439	61	30	44813	7710	7911	–	–
Morningside United	264	23	–	58141	9696	9696	19	–
Muirhouse St Andrew's	164	9	12	8530	0	0	44	17
Murrayfield	672	66	20	114739	38140	47745	56	33
Newhaven	301	15	51	52827	10140	10140	16	26
New Restalrig	537	23	34	74316	13500	13500	54	18
Old Kirk	221	18	–	17100	0	0	–	–
Palmerston Place	592	82	30	128551	36210	41769	36	19
Pilrig and Dalmeny Street	316	20	34	30543	7400	7400	17	22
Polwarth	403	34	30	58113	10100	10100	5	–
Portobello Old	485	48	46	40135	7350	7350	31	4
Portobello St James'	494	40	21	45850	8130	8751	27	–
Portobello St Philip's Joppa	823	71	131	125467	31470	31470	121	16
Priestfield	280	27	33	45452	8260	8260	–	–
Queensferry	885	43	94	51710	8380	8380	111	25
Ratho	273	20	24	34379	0	539	85	12
Reid Memorial	495	26	–	73521	18950	17796	29	7
Richmond Craigmillar	137	10	13	11420	0	0	18	2
St Andrew's and St George's	445	46	29	140751	27770	28370	22	10
St Andrew's Clermiston	393	25	–	37654	0	445	26	–
St Catherine's Argyle	369	30	31	91719	24960	24960	38	37
St Colm's	236	24	34	31502	3520	3520	58	2
St Cuthbert's	761	75	–	154231	39880	39920	15	4
St David's Broomhouse	225	18	–	40809	4608	4608	54	11
St George's West	257	44	–	100438	29050	29257	6	3
St John's Oxgangs	393	22	41	21062	0	500	18	–
St Margaret's	478	41	35	39679	4670	4670	60	12
St Martin's	332	15	27	22170	0	100	50	17
St Michael's	613	41	20	63884	8600	10245	33	16
St Nicholas' Sighthill	674	42	30	44244	7110	7491	40	15
St Stephen's Comely Bank	596	32	45	85482	17780	17780	82	16
Slateford Longstone	384	30	50	49965	4500	4971	24	6
Stenhouse St Aidan's	320	20	–	23546	0	340	10	11
Stockbridge	486	37	39	44617	8270	11270	12	4
Tron Moredun	190	14	–	7905	0	0	32	–
Viewforth	304	35	28	54515	13250	11105	49	–

2. WEST LOTHIAN

Congregation	Com	Eld	G	In98	Ass	Gvn	3-11	-17
Addiewell	105	4	21	8749	937	937	10	1
Longridge and Breich	102	5	–	8059	1452	1331	–	–
Stoneyburn	100	3	–	9796	525	525	–	–
Armadale	747	44	38	55721	8940	8940	60	8
Avonbridge	83	8	12	7857	890	0	8	2
Torphichen	298	22	–	25708	2150	4450	32	9
Bathgate Boghall	516	36	23	52453	9260	9260	65	21
Bathgate High	749	39	64	56742	13290	13290	34	10
Bathgate St David's	364	16	16	43417	6260	5830	9	9
Bathgate St John's	440	30	48	44740	5520	5520	48	–

Congregation	Com	Eld	G	In98	Ass	Gvn	3-11	-17
Blackburn	614	32	–	36102	4060	4060	20	1
Blackridge	155	8	17	12339	1600	1600	13	1
Harthill – St Andrew's	289	23	40	39369	6290	6290	34	6
Broxburn	582	28	57	46188	8050	8050	45	15
Fauldhouse St Andrew's	436	22	22	33842	4240	4240	18	–
Kirknewton and East Calder	597	38	24	52935	10220	10220	90	26
Kirk of Calder	896	38	32	61468	9890	10140	100	6
Linlithgow St Michael's	1688	112	69	199190	39470	41293	234	73
Linlithgow St Ninian's Craigmailen	682	64	96	59461	10800	11573	62	11
Livingston Ecumenical	854	42	13	71334	0	101	107	38
Livingston Old	557	32	–	51411	8320	8523	64	7
Pardovan, Kingscavil and Winchburgh	301	18	41	30938	0	0	12	–
Polbeth Harwood	339	36	–	25911	1294	1294	19	–
Strathbrock	463	42	25	79294	23000	23000	74	28
Uphall South	244	20	–	29383	0	0	68	–
West Kirk of Calder	367	28	41	31803	4710	4710	–	–
Whitburn – Brucefield	550	30	36	57865	10560	10580	36	32
Whitburn – South	456	39	43	52660	8460	8460	49	5

3. LOTHIAN

Congregation	Com	Eld	G	In98	Ass	Gvn	3-11	-17
Aberlady	370	35	–	21799	4580	4580	34	–
Gullane	530	39	51	41782	7270	7270	18	5
Athelstaneford	226	16	15	17725	1350	1850	–	–
Whitekirk and Tyninghame	185	19	–	24258	3060	3060	4	–
Belhaven	826	40	73	47149	6930	6930	51	8
Spott	102	7	–	8145	750	750	–	–
Bolton and Saltoun	258	17	21	18428	2485	2485	32	2
Humbie	126	10	12	14183	3080	3080	17	–
Yester	368	28	36	21329	3520	4520	–	–
Bonnyrigg	1064	69	76	70007	15160	15311	84	7
Borthwick	92	6	20	11680	1630	1630	10	3
Newtongrange	284	9	34	18706	1760	976	37	–
Cockenzie and Port Seton Chalmers Memorial	344	28	60	49832	7070	7724	–	–
Cockenzie and Port Seton Old	474	14	19	26252	1520	0	43	5
Cockpen and Carrington	353	21	42	13759	3140	3187	18	–
Lasswade	393	25	18	21761	4140	4140	20	–
Rosewell	240	15	–	10334	1237	1237	16	–
Cranstoun, Crichton and Ford	334	21	31	32679	3500	6600	45	–
Fala and Soutra	88	5	12	5481	770	0	10	4
Dalkeith St John's and King's Park	624	48	28	60533	10190	10190	59	6
Dalkeith St Nicholas Buccleuch	699	24	34	47343	6630	6630	21	4
Dirleton	298	19	23	19215	4660	4847	6	–
North Berwick Abbey	428	17	45	41411	6470	6863	28	8
Dunbar	918	49	73	45191	8680	9131	–	–
Dunglass	385	24	24	24787	0	350	18	–
Garvald and Morham	73	5	–	9050	820	820	–	–
Haddington West	678	34	60	43985	4570	6570	–	–
Gladsmuir	280	16	15	15824	3100	3100	7	–
Longniddry	486	42	54	58804	12740	14740	74	62

Congregation	Com	Eld	G	In98	Ass	Gvn	3-11	-17
Glencorse	380	11	29	23564	4330	4330	26	–
Roslin	425	9	–	22130	2600	2600	68	17
Bilston Mission	167	6	22	6118	1330	1380	–	–
Gorebridge	488	30	54	30226	3090	3090	37	5
Haddington St Mary's	893	61	–	82506	17590	17590	37	–
Howgate	41	5	7	9169	1930	1930	2	5
Penicuik South	347	24	30	68418	14180	15592	43	47
Loanhead	673	35	52	33571	4062	4187	27	–
Musselburgh Northesk	490	37	24	42467	7700	7700	–	–
Musselburgh St Andrew's High	551	49	43	37633	7060	7060	–	–
Musselburgh								
St Clement's and St Ninian's	425	39	11	26812	0	2785	–	–
Musselburgh St Michael's Inveresk	619	41	47	47974	8490	8490	–	5
Newbattle	587	39	28	35163	5001	5001	40	8
Newton	404	13	20	16334	0	0	39	–
North Berwick St Andrew Blackadder	877	54	45	66182	15590	16170	85	14
Ormiston	187	19	32	18356	1980	1980	13	3
Pencaitland	271	21	12	32735	4487	4487	39	10
Penicuik North	742	46	–	55675	10600	10600	81	27
Penicuik St Mungo's	583	36	35	45525	8020	8219	71	7
Prestonkirk	564	24	37	32997	7650	7650	18	4
Stenton	96	7	–	5675	620	620	18	18
Whittingehame	46	4	–	2558	279	279	–	–
Prestonpans – Prestongrange	469	62	28	28578	4000	4000	–	–
Tranent	457	25	50	38834	4540	4540	22	4

4. MELROSE AND PEEBLES

Congregation	Com	Eld	G	In98	Ass	Gvn	3-11	-17
Ashkirk	84	6	14	5219	900	900	–	–
Selkirk	717	28	53	50965	10400	10575	22	3
Bowden	115	12	14	17419	1560	1560	2	2
Newtown	262	14	–	19204	1700	1700	16	8
Broughton Glenholm and Kilbucho	193	17	–	11785	0	800	12	–
Skirling	95	6	–	3761	0	100	–	–
Stobo and Drumelzier	121	0	–	7184	0	1200	8	–
Tweedsmuir	47	5	–	7562	0	0	6	–
Caddonfoot	221	12	–	8708	2350	2350	9	–
Galashiels St Ninian's	662	41	45	47573	13620	13620	18	20
Carlops	76	12	–	8066	1330	1330	4	1
Kirkurd and Newlands	125	11	–	10570	880	880	30	7
West Linton – St Andrew's	293	19	–	26563	2210	2210	39	39
Channelkirk	86	6	8	6596	375	375	–	–
Lauder – Old	364	15	47	25129	2400	2400	30	–
Earlston	635	15	40	34500	2910	2910	42	6
Eddleston	150	6	–	6959	1077	1077	19	–
Peebles Old	804	58	–	60004	13070	13070	33	10
Ettrick	132	7	11	6698	0	0	19	–
Yarrow	112	12	11	9993	0	149	11	–
Galashiels Old and St Paul's	504	28	32	44574	6910	7310	33	8
Galashiels St Aidan's	588	25	26	38079	4660	4660	19	34
Galashiels St John's	323	16	–	25766	0	0	17	22
Innerleithen	526	22	–	33505	6090	6254	29	24

Congregation	Com	Eld	G	In98	Ass	Gvn	3-11	-17
Traquair	99	9	–	7871	890	1124	7	2
Walkerburn	121	7	–	12225	2450	2527	8	5
Lyne and Manor	111	9	–	15102	0	0	23	3
Maxton and Mertoun	163	12	16	15833	1590	1590	9	–
St Boswells	361	22	33	28578	4430	4430	26	25
Melrose	963	62	53	71627	17630	18523	49	–
Peebles St Andrew's Leckie	751	39	–	61804	10880	12890	45	20
Stow St Mary of Wedale and Heriot	234	17	–	28476	0	900	41	9

5. DUNS

Congregation	Com	Eld	G	In98	Ass	Gvn	3-11	-17
Ayton	228	12	–	10096	0	0	–	–
Burnmouth	45	4	–	2393	0	0	6	–
Grantshouse and Houndwood	68	1	–	3167	0	0	–	–
Reston	100	5	12	5642	0	0	20	6
Berwick on Tweed St Andrew's Wallace Green and Lowick	460	20	27	33078	4090	4140	9	–
Bonkyl and Preston	92	7	–	5553	700	700	–	–
Chirnside	447	18	32	20868	1520	1683	–	–
Edrom Allanton	91	8	–	4792	420	420	–	–
Coldingham	99	5	20	9610	750	750	–	–
Eyemouth	313	24	72	31827	4440	4440	43	14
St Abb's	19	3	–	1638	160	160	–	–
Coldstream	482	20	28	29651	4240	4240	31	11
Eccles	111	10	16	7376	640	640	7	–
Duns	489	22	51	26024	2080	2080	16	–
Fogo and Swinton	205	12	–	8806	1910	1910	11	–
Ladykirk	44	3	10	4982	760	760	–	–
Leitholm	128	8	–	9217	700	700	–	–
Whitsome	64	5	16	6049	480	480	–	–
Foulden and Mordington	106	10	9	6220	0	0	–	–
Hutton and Fishwick and Paxton	114	10	13	6431	0	0	4	–
Gordon St Michael's	109	6	j	7555	910	910	–	–
Greenlaw	195	13	22	16419	2950	2950	12	–
Legerwood	75	8	–	4936	420	420	–	–
Westruther	80	7	14j	5073	790	790	16	–
Kirk of Lammermuir	64	7	7	9079	0	61	–	–
Langton and Polwarth	124	0	26	14335	0	0	–	–

6. JEDBURGH

Congregation	Com	Eld	G	In98	Ass	Gvn	3-11	-17
Ancrum	209	12	18	17436	0	0	27	5
Lilliesleaf	159	10	14	11581	0	0	13	5
Bedrule	59	5	10	8725	160	160	10	2
Denholm	215	12	22	19395	160	160	21	–
Minto	90	5	8	8975	160	160	7	–
Cavers and Kirkton	159	10	–	7422	400	400	–	–
Hawick St Mary's and Old	701	27	48	34738	3920	3920	–	–
Crailing and Eckford	54	9	9	4188	169	569	–	–
Oxnam	101	4	20	5841	820	1415	–	–
Roxburgh	74	4	–	4467	280	280	12	–
Hawick Burnfoot	252	16	15	18713	0	0	36	8
Hawick Teviot and Roberton	487	17	21	38522	6340	6340	12	7

Congregation	Com	Eld	G	In98	Ass	Gvn	3-11	-17
Hawick Trinity	983	40	47	49451	5240	6103	51	16
Hawick Wilton	471	27	40	24204	3760	0	23	–
Teviothead	74	4	13	6144	900	900	9	–
Hobkirk and Southdean	174	14	10	8826	0	160	14	–
Jedburgh Old and Edgerston	871	28	23	42150	6550	6550	27	2
Jedburgh Trinity	289	12	30	36462	4020	5055	7	–
Kelso North and Ednam	1585	79	84	86313	14670	14981	35	–
Kelso Old and Sprouston	722	42	49	37297	6012	6132	27	4
Liddesdale	207	7	44	30360	100	205	16	3
Linton	108	5	–	5877	600	600	–	–
Morebattle and Hownam	214	11	35	16617	1987	1987	23	–
Yetholm	201	12	24	19432	2160	2160	26	–
Makerstoun and Smailholm	77	5	–	4707	0	0	–	–
Stichill, Hume and Nenthorn	81	4	12	3622	0	0	–	–

7. ANNANDALE AND ESKDALE

Congregation	Com	Eld	G	In98	Ass	Gvn	3-11	-17
Annan Old	563	45	50	54993	6870	6870	30	5
Annan St Andrew's Greenknowe Erskine	880	38	88	44388	8570	8570	32	4
Applegarth and Sibbaldbie	199	8	22	9145	1140	1140	20	12
Lochmaben	598	23	45	29024	6630	7130	27	21
Brydekirk	87	8	–	7179	0	0	–	–
Hoddam	188	12	15	10135	0	0	–	–
Canonbie	186	20	–	20679	1230	1230	25	3
Langholm, Ewes and Westerkirk	619	31	65	32842	7560	8040	35	6
Carlisle	471	32	52	56272	6910	6910	43	14
Longtown	56	8	20	5297	870	870	15	–
Dalton	134	10	9	13041	990	990	16	–
Hightae	100	6	20	10176	750	800	8	–
St Mungo	139	10	15	9344	680	680	14	–
Dornock	280	10	15	15306	0	0	–	–
Eskdalemuir	42	4	j	2573	0	0	–	–
Hutton and Corrie	125	11	10j	7991	0	0	7	–
Tundergarth	78	8	9	4503	0	0	5	–
Gretna Old, St Andrew's and Half Morton and Kirkpatrick Fleming	486	36	36	29330	1730	1450	65	11
Johnstone	142	10	–	6587	0	0	6	–
Kirkpatrick Juxta	197	8	12	11497	0	0	8	3
Kirtle – Eaglesfield	150	10	23	10138	1262	1262	10	–
Middlebie	121	9	14	6685	390	686	7	–
Waterbeck	77	5	–	3953	250	250	7	–
Lockerbie Dryfesdale	1075	48	53	40257	5640	5640	34	–
Moffat	520	37	48	41518	7080	9349	25	4
Wamphray	65	7	–	6985	660	660	–	–

8. DUMFRIES AND KIRKCUDBRIGHT

Congregation	Com	Eld	G	In98	Ass	Gvn	3-11	-17
Anwoth and Girthon	477	26	31	44142	5960	5960	6	–
Borgue	65	6	13	2840	200	200	17	–
Auchencairn and Rerrick	159	9	20	12132	990	891	11	–
Buittle and Kelton	292	24	24	19258	2940	2940	16	–
Balmaclellan and Kells	167	15	15	11063	0	0	17	5

Congregation	Com	Eld	G	In98	Ass	Gvn	3-11	-17
Carsphairn	116	10	12	7359	0	600	8	4
Dalry	214	12	35	10526	0	0	13	–
Balmaghie	161	6	25	14712	1720	1720	17	2
Tarff and Twynholm	220	18	33	22526	2225	2225	36	5
Caerlaverock	189	6	–	6592	0	0	24	–
Castle Douglas	630	33	67	36962	3657	3657	45	45
Closeburn	293	4	–	19449	590	590	25	–
Durisdeer	193	8	33	15905	1900	1900	17	–
Colvend, Southwick and Kirkbean	416	28	41	43097	5400	5441	47	21
Corsock and Kirkpatrick Durham	231	15	17	15433	1980	1980	–	–
Crossmichael and Parton	210	17	16	16933	2000	2000	12	–
Cummertrees	137	3	12	7838	355	355	–	–
Mouswald	97	8	10	7287	730	730	7	–
Ruthwell	159	9	20	8324	1680	1680	18	–
Dalbeattie	769	44	67j	40333	9480	11350	26	10
Urr	286	16	j	13481	2060	2060	25	–
Dumfries Greyfriars	486	30	35	59915	8360	8760	29	–
Dumfries Lincluden	177	13	–	14767	1510	1510	19	3
Holywood	201	10	11	11940	410	410	25	–
Dumfries Lochside	434	14	29	19949	0	0	15	–
Dumfries Maxwelltown West	803	51	51	55372	9960	9960	47	14
Dumfries St George's	529	42	51	54537	8760	9160	66	7
Dumfries St Mary's	934	55	53	50194	10140	8651	29	21
Dumfries St Michael's and South	970	45	36	43114	9000	9000	52	–
Dumfries Troqueer	580	33	27	50981	11230	11580	60	26
Dunscore	304	19	10	21202	2400	2400	14	–
Glencairn and Moniaive	242	13	11	20090	2250	2250	18	–
Kirkconnel	433	12	26	34908	4470	4670	26	4
Kirkcudbright	1208	55	51	60193	14730	15485	45	–
Kirkgunzeon	67	11	–	4241	0	0	–	–
Kirkmahoe	465	17	34	30080	930	930	30	–
Kirkmichael	118	6	24	10635	2690	2690	–	–
Tinwald	382	20	24	18098	5430	5430	52	–
Torthorwald	125	9	22	9208	790	790	–	–
Kirkpatrick – Irongray	291	18	12	18768	1600	1600	15	–
Lochrutton	124	9	16	7174	270	630	19	2
Terregles	143	11	7	2821	160	0	–	–
Lochend	65	4	10	2516	0	0	6	–
New Abbey	247	14	9	16777	0	0	16	–
Penpont Keir and Tynron	242	10	16	18634	0	0	11	–
Sanquhar St Bride's	613	28	46	38855	4870	2000	57	10
Thornhill	343	16	24	21541	570	1000	11	–

9. WIGTOWN AND STRANRAER

Congregation	Com	Eld	G	In98	Ass	Gvn	3-11	-17
Bargrennan	49	5	–	5741	1500	1720	–	–
Newton Stewart Penninghame St John's	668	52	41	51939	14730	15125	43	–
Ervie Kirkcolm	280	18	–	17895	1600	1600	26	6
Leswalt	307	14	33	18582	1500	1500	24	–
Glasserton and Isle of Whithorn	156	10	–	11215	1500	1533	7	–
Whithorn St Ninian's Priory	357	12	49	20653	2800	2800	16	–

Congregation	Com	Eld	G	In98	Ass	Gvn	3-11	-17
Inch	283	23	10	10227	2200	2200	11	2
Stranraer St Andrew's	529	31	–	33349	6700	6700	31	1
Kirkcowan	230	11	13	16846	2230	2230	13	1
Wigtown	307	14	24	27576	4300	4300	15	6
Kirkinner	179	6	15	11936	1200	1200	10	–
Sorbie	192	9	18	13355	1200	1200	14	–
Kirkmabreck	216	13	21	16426	960	960	6	–
Monigaff	519	30	19	30073	5200	5200	27	14
Kirkmaiden	261	22	25	21880	3000	3108	24	–
Stoneykirk	413	27	27	23145	2300	2300	29	–
Mochrum	332	22	56	23704	0	0	54	13
New Luce	117	9	33j	9721	1500	1500	24	–
Old Luce	378	23	j	34955	5300	5300	34	–
Portpatrick	276	12	32	17854	2700	2700	20	3
Stranraer St Ninian's	568	30	37	43345	8200	8200	52	–
Stranraer High Kirk	699	34	37	45603	8500	8500	48	–
Stranraer Old	458	26	49	39646	7300	7300	10	–

10. AYR

Congregation	Com	Eld	G	In98	Ass	Gvn	3-11	-17
Alloway	1439	80	51	143165	36240	38000	99	19
Annbank	375	21	25	32196	0	0	–	–
Arnsheen Barrhill	127	4	12	11714	0	300	8	–
Colmonell	221	15	15	17397	0	232	18	–
Auchinleck	463	27	52	45347	4753	4753	50	26
Ayr Auld Kirk of Ayr								
(St John the Baptist)	982	86	72	80241	16150	17625	19	20
Ayr Castlehill	924	54	78	70092	12600	12600	62	7
Ayr Newton-on-Ayr	581	52	50	71690	15450	15762	55	31
Ayr St Andrew's	759	68	28	72183	16450	16450	32	11
Ayr St Columba	1919	127	86	145338	34580	34580	147	17
Ayr St James'	593	34	58	45038	5780	5780	53	10
Ayr St Leonard's	562	32	46	40811	6070	6438	41	7
Ayr St Quivox	460	39	25	40887	4900	4900	45	–
Ayr Wallacetown	562	32	58	40811	6070	6438	14	17
Ballantrae	312	18	40	30201	1850	1850	22	3
Barr	97	6	15	7887	0	0	–	8
Dailly	232	12	27	11940	0	0	17	5
Catrine	288	23	50	28357	800	800	29	–
Sorn	184	16	20	24193	900	900	21	5
Coylton	380	30	–	17637	0	0	46	19
Drongan The Schaw Kirk	330	22	22	14127	0	300	33	–
Craigie	119	6	–	16404	570	570	22	–
Symington	427	23	37	57303	4200	4387	35	5
Crosshill	210	12	27	12797	500	550	20	–
Dalrymple	378	15	–	20423	1950	1950	8	–
Dalmellington	395	31	96	30189	3130	3000	45	7
Dundonald	688	50	70	46292	8290	8545	64	55
Fisherton	197	14	16	11665	1190	1190	–	–
Maybole West	320	18	32	23104	3050	3325	33	3
Girvan North (Old and St Andrew's)	1272	74	61	65368	15740	15748	83	40
Girvan South	390	21	26	21270	1790	1000	18	4

Congregation	Com	Eld	G	In98	Ass	Gvn	3-11	-17
Kirkmichael	262	0	25	21174	0	50	29	–
Straiton St Cuthbert's	179	13	16	10421	0	50	18	–
Kirkoswald	327	18	17	32663	2550	2550	43	14
Lugar	189	10	25	10042	900	900	18	12
Old Cumnock Old	455	22	58	46988	4200	4200	46	9
Mauchline	702	32	95	55170	11540	11989	93	11
Maybole Old	498	27	38	36867	5812	5895	34	2
Monkton and Prestwick North	691	53	80	56650	11160	11510	82	23
Muirkirk	296	19	32	25076	0	0	36	50
New Cumnock	742	39	53	38384	6590	6031	42	20
Ochiltree	285	20	21	19366	2600	2600	41	–
Stair	240	14	31	17085	2460	2960	29	–
Old Cumnock Crichton West	390	16	36	31748	4230	4230	20	3
Old Cumnock St Ninian's	103	17	24	8987	750	750	19	23
Patna Waterside	177	15	–	9634	0	0	25	9
Prestwick Kingcase	1315	110	90	84230	13840	14014	136	32
Prestwick St Nicholas'	908	72	89	77483	14900	15100	49	19
Prestwick South	453	35	89	60324	7840	7840	27	12
Tarbolton	636	39	45	37608	3920	4095	55	8
Troon Old	1299	72	–	105048	27450	36870	91	20
Troon Portland	812	51	58	85402	18520	19848	74	13
Troon St Meddan's	1262	124	115	130286	27050	27250	163	68

11. IRVINE AND KILMARNOCK

Congregation	Com	Eld	G	In98	Ass	Gvn	3-11	-17
Crosshouse	402	34	36	34079	450	450	56	16
Darvel	691	35	37	39070	6280	6280	41	17
Dreghorn and Springside	761	73	42	68217	11790	12290	74	6
Dunlop	469	37	40	50951	6200	6200	57	–
Fenwick	490	28	57	52159	9420	9420	32	–
Galston	935	62	80	83051	10440	10940	54	55
Hurlford	817	25	50	43109	8610	8610	30	18
Irvine Fullarton	615	39	35	76026	12010	12110	164	19
Irvine Girdle Toll	267	18	24	17646	0	0	81	9
Irvine Mure	495	26	36	70628	7960	9960	50	4
Irvine Old	729	64	31	85280	14290	14290	43	11
Irvine Relief	439	38	53	43297	600	600	36	14
Irvine St Andrew's	553	28	70	38286	6690	6690	82	34
Kilmarnock Grange	540	38	57	51504	8960	8960	29	9
Kilmarnock Henderson	899	77	70	88169	24260	24260	68	25
Kilmarnock Howard St Andrew's	534	45	58	60894	6950	6854	18	54
Kilmarnock Laigh	689	56	34	62635	18360	18360	60	8
Kilmarnock Old High Kirk	345	18	30	40407	3070	3120	17	9
Kilmarnock Riccarton	453	33	49	57834	8460	8460	32	17
Kilmarnock St Andrew's Glencairn	212	24	24	29256	700	1200	9	–
Kilmarnock St John's Onthank	327	24	30	34276	2560	1570	72	13
Kilmarnock St Kentigern's	302	31	–	41028	4450	4450	56	17
Kilmarnock St Marnock's	786	79	43	90877	18270	18270	157	50
Kilmarnock St Ninian's Bellfield	324	21	17	26608	3125	0	18	–
Kilmarnock Shortlees	182	16	24	29233	0	944	26	6
Kilmarnock West High	500	49	34	45163	9590	4590	46	13
Kilmaurs St Maur's Glencairn	407	21	25	45394	4296	4296	37	16

Congregation	Com	Eld	G	In98	Ass	Gvn	3-11	-17
Newmilns Loudoun 492	13	–	54866	11980	11980	59	20
Stewarton John Knox 440	38	46	57659	9520	9520	43	9
Stewarton St Columba's 694	47	63	43871	8990	10474	65	30

12. ARDROSSAN

Ardrossan Barony St John's 388	21	46	42539	5537	5537	38	10
Ardrossan Park 602	38	48	42166	6150	6150	88	25
Beith High 1069	88	52	62542	15090	15377	72	28
Beith Trinity 275	32	30	41301	5756	5886	30	26
Brodick 222	19	–	28496	0	537	20	–
Corrie 59	6	–	8409	0	223	8	5
Cumbrae 372	25	40	24229	0	200	24	14
Dalry St Margaret's 1164	60	35	83218	18890	19997	73	11
Dalry Trinity 381	22	34	68588	15170	15389	34	8
Fairlie 340	28	51	41828	5190	5670	32	3
Fergushill 62	3	–	5800	0	145	3	–
Kilwinning Erskine 144	11	16	24064	0	849	36	5
Kilbirnie Auld Kirk 591	43	40	31315	5440	5440	26	4
Kilbirnie St Columba's 678	46	39	44096	7010	6811	57	24
Kilmory 41	5	6	5614	0	0	7	–
Lamlash 157	15	44	23411	0	176	13	–
Kilwinning Abbey 1045	64	52	76762	14500	14500	64	29
Kilwinning Mansefield 264	17	25	23267	0	0	34	12
Largs Clark Memorial 1066	80	87	80562	21250	21250	130	104
Largs St Columba's 772	64	82	64078	15890	15890	50	1
Largs St John's 847	51	79	85583	19280	20400	64	49
Lochranza and Pirnmill 80	7	33	10805	0	0	8	–
Shiskine 73	10	–	14976	0	0	1	17
Saltcoats New Trinity 421	36	35	45249	5890	5890	40	18
Saltcoats North 533	25	26	38929	3690	3690	30	6
Saltcoats St Cuthbert's 584	59	57	66839	13800	14245	51	8
Stevenston Ardeer 420	26	45	38499	5160	5160	62	19
Stevenston High 326	28	61	53509	9740	10889	43	10
Stevenston Livingstone 412	39	44	40938	8550	8740	30	9
West Kilbride Overton 382	30	52	36709	5890	5890	26	10
West Kilbride St Andrew's 801	58	65	77387	15260	15112	56	25
Whiting Bay and Kildonan 140	14	–	29399	0	1351	24	3

13. LANARK

Biggar 858	48	61	61827	11970	12170	43	30
Black Mount 135	7	21	15959	0	32	19	14
Cairngryffe 317	22	18	23040	2437	2437	14	1
Symington 264	16	30	21044	3375	3375	24	15
Carluke Kirkton 846	33	26	75203	14200	14200	104	56
Carluke St Andrew's 453	21	33	38779	6080	8580	30	20
Carluke St John's 954	67	69	74458	16610	16610	85	32
Carnwath 451	34	32	30681	987	987	42	5
Carstairs 286	12	39	20909	2020	2186	32	–
Carstairs Junction 152	7	27	16278	1580	1655	19	–
Coalburn 207	6	20	9730	0	70	12	–
Lesmahagow Old 809	37	37	38762	5380	5700	33	5

Congregation	Com	Eld	G	In98	Ass	Gvn	3-11	-17
Crossford	215	7	12	23606	3470	3470	14	2
Kirkfieldbank	152	8	25	12737	980	980	15	–
Culter	107	6	–	9926	507	507	4	–
Libberton and Quothquan	94	10	–	10584	450	450	–	–
Douglas St Bride's	377	29	28	26198	3080	3436	39	8
Douglas Water and Rigside	99	10	17	10093	870	942	7	–
Forth St Paul's	527	35	56	33492	3570	4570	55	26
Glencaple	303	27	15	22485	300	343	16	–
Lowther	57	0	–	5973	200	243	5	–
Kirkmuirhill	339	21	65	72548	12770	13520	71	59
Lanark Greyfriars	994	59	62	59126	10100	10300	51	24
Lanark St Nicholas'	896	47	36	59899	10780	11280	52	16
Law	219	14	33	25807	0	437	41	7
Lesmahagow Abbeygreen	265	18	28	53740	7750	7750	29	27

14. PAISLEY

Congregation	Com	Eld	G	In98	Ass	Gvn	3-11	-17
Barrhead Arthurlie	486	30	35	62748	11860	11860	38	10
Barrhead Bourock	605	49	80	60085	12690	22170	85	45
Barrhead South and Levern	550	43	37	57922	11570	11570	28	16
Bishopton Erskine	887	63	19	62512	13050	13050	98	19
Bridge of Weir Freeland	495	49	32	76146	19100	19100	81	24
Bridge of Weir St Machar's Ranfurly	615	49	102	72222	16980	17180	63	40
Caldwell	295	17	19	45553	6350	6350	45	10
Elderslie Kirk	766	61	118	92380	25600	25980	–	–
Houston and Killellan	800	54	57	77437	18000	18000	327	111
Howwood	276	20	36	44846	5530	5530	36	14
Inchinnan	479	42	23	45702	6670	2707	61	–
Johnstone High	516	40	75	53193	11940	11940	37	63
Johnstone St Andrew's Trinity	312	34	58	42441	5350	5691	63	22
Johnstone St Paul's	846	79	42	69530	12670	12670	80	5
Kilbarchan East	466	40	45	45253	7550	7550	60	55
Kilbarchan West	543	46	45	66463	13550	13550	78	14
Linwood	562	41	35	50093	7220	7220	59	2
Lochwinnoch	171	10	–	23038	0	0	10	2
Neilston	811	48	50	85861	19640	23208	108	42
New Erskine	601	30	66	68085	8140	10140	62	36
Paisley Abbey	872	61	15	99680	25380	25380	43	18
Paisley Castlehead	423	33	21	43468	6890	6890	26	–
Paisley Glenburn	552	27	29	39927	5260	5260	33	–
Paisley Laigh	849	94	76	62356	12670	12670	73	19
Paisley Lylesland	549	56	73	66698	16270	16480	32	4
Paisley Martyrs'	699	65	30	62342	14040	14040	74	27
Paisley Oakshaw Trinity	1072	123	77	135539	23596	23596	105	10
Paisley St Columba's Foxbar	358	36	35	41571	3023	3468	16	50
Paisley St James'	427	39	26	50682	7870	0	25	8
Paisley St Luke's	320	31	37	45728	6460	6460	19	4
Paisley St Mark's Oldhall	853	59	137	84855	20650	20720	51	24
Paisley St Ninian's Ferguslie	86	10	17	15152	0	0	25	10
Paisley Sandyford (Thread Street)	478	32	43	53861	10170	10170	37	10
Paisley Sherwood Greenlaw	1029	100	68	104990	24440	24440	86	46
Paisley Wallneuk North	640	60	49	76128	16520	16646	39	14

Congregation	Com	Eld	G	In98	Ass	Gvn	3-11	-17
Renfrew North 769	66	50	68004	15040	13536	103	45
Renfrew Old 815	55	77	66614	14230	24170	190	16
Renfrew Trinity 497	44	83	52445	10260	10260	45	11

15. GREENOCK

Congregation	Com	Eld	G	In98	Ass	Gvn	3-11	-17
Gourock Old Gourock and Ashton 1152	84	114	114323	21820	21820	96	87
Gourock St John's 751	65	35	84197	16940	16940	78	27
Greenock Ardgowan. 710	68	39	47820	15760	15760	63	54
Greenock Cartsdyke. 400	38	25	38305	550	550	20	–
Greenock Finnart St Paul's. 394	37	28	60593	12700	12700	40	–
Greenock Mount Kirk 450	51	40	57943	7450	7450	28	37
Greenock Old West Kirk 405	37	45	66424	13580	13910	25	12
Greenock St George's North. 542	41	–	58387	9160	9160	23	46
Greenock St Luke's 919	77	59	102780	23480	23480	65	14
Greenock St Margaret's 378	36	45	41180	3200	3200	44	–
Greenock St Ninian's 294	20	23	20764	0	0	29	–
Greenock Wellpark Mid Kirk 752	46	30	49026	15980	15980	47	7
Inverkip 447	30	69	47927	8380	8380	67	19
Kilmacolm Old. 856	65	63	119425	29660	40455	89	22
Kilmacolm St Columba 655	56	32	70458	21380	21644	85	17
Langbank. 174	13	–	25812	500	571	35	–
Port Glasgow Hamilton Bardrainney 587	25	21	39841	3700	3700	46	40
Port Glasgow St Andrew's 868	73	80	75571	15680	9257	47	86
Port Glasgow St Martin's 213	14	–	17577	0	0	21	–
Skelmorlie and Wemyss Bay 433	31	–	42678	10040	11125	25	16

16. GLASGOW

Congregation	Com	Eld	G	In98	Ass	Gvn	3-11	-17
Banton 88	11	–	11403	0	0	14	1
Twechar 117	9	–	8951	0	0	8	–
Bishopbriggs Kenmure 397	24	62	54193	6200	6800	62	51
Bishopbriggs Springfield Cambridge . . . 1091	58	60	79501	17100	17115	121	53
Broom 1133	71	79	158102	36000	36340	152	52
Busby. 465	34	47	53210	11300	11300	69	7
Cadder 1101	94	71	110332	28700	29292	124	40
Campsie 371	24	29	41750	1500	1500	39	31
Chryston 876	38	27	122996	19500	21500	96	82
Eaglesham Old and Carswell 822	64	90	99570	24500	24500	114	56
Gartcosh. 186	11	25	18890	0	0	22	19
Glenboig 190	6	12	9933	0	0	48	3
Giffnock Orchardhill 629	60	64	142096	38000	38000	149	29
Giffnock South. 1021	80	50	149271	40200	42200	107	18
Giffnock The Park 421	35	–	39756	5900	5956	50	11
Greenbank 1306	108	85	197385	50000	50000	217	83
Kilsyth Anderson 544	27	50	51882	9500	9500	80	12
Kilsyth Burns and Old 719	41	60	43354	7800	7800	37	60
Kirkintilloch Hillhead 189	15	20	17710	0	0	9	5
Kirkintilloch St Columba's. 736	55	45	76083	16700	17000	99	44
Kirkintilloch St David's Memorial Park. 902	64	58	91337	21700	21700	85	32
Kirkintilloch St Mary's 805	58	78	83374	20200	20200	89	24
Lenzie Old. 512	42	–	66463	14000	14100	76	5

Congregation	Com	Eld	G	In98	Ass	Gvn	3-11	-17
Lenzie Union	1036	82	115	109956	24000	24711	87	25
Maxwell Mearns Castle	343	28	–	86158	16000	16000	49	23
Mearns	809	44	–	98624	36000	36000	38	15
Milton of Campsie	413	39	38	34184	2900	2900	86	–
Netherlee	1014	102	70	139249	40000	43063	128	22
Newton Mearns	1126	85	57	108910	33000	33000	120	37
Stamperland	518	49	30	66889	10400	12052	107	68
Stepps	429	33	15	38389	4500	4500	53	18
Thornliebank	317	11	77	40415	1000	1000	34	6
Torrance	268	16	20	36300	5000	7500	42	36
Williamwood	600	69	46	105716	23000	23000	139	51
Glasgow Anderston Kelvingrove	206	28	21	21343	500	500	13	10
Glasgow Baillieston Mure Memorial	689	41	139	74449	15500	15500	109	53
Glasgow Baillieston St Andrew's	498	38	46	56066	9500	9500	95	18
Glasgow Balshagray Victoria Park	379	43	57	68939	16300	16436	4	294
Glasgow Barlanark Greyfriars	163	20	48	26322	0	50	21	11
Glasgow Battlefield East	247	14	47	37604	2250	2354	–	13
Glasgow Blairbeth: Rodger Memorial	142	14	32	11806	0	0	8	5
Glasgow Blawarthill	275	29	57	22209	0	35	36	18
Glasgow Bridgeton St Francis in the East	130	21	13	24706	0	0	37	3
Glasgow Broomhill	738	64	113	110452	29400	29976	73	40
Glasgow Burnside	828	56	88	146740	44000	44000	110	33
Glasgow Calton Parkhead	210	15	18	17540	0	0	6	–
Glasgow Cambuslang Flemington H'side	305	18	18	26783	0	0	55	6
Glasgow Cambuslang Old	538	61	51	65383	15000	15000	62	15
Glasgow Cambuslang St Andrew's	558	46	34	73617	10100	10100	63	24
Glasgow Cambuslang Trinity St Paul's	522	28	–	61856	13500	15010	34	25
Glasgow Cardonald	644	60	107	95141	24900	24900	61	83
Glasgow Carmunnock	396	30	53	55395	8000	8000	75	–
Glasgow Carmyle	136	9	45	16350	1500	1500	13	–
Glasgow Kenmuir Mount Vernon	171	11	40	25884	3650	3650	31	19
Glasgow Carntyne Old	189	22	25	27086	5000	5050	25	8
Glasgow Eastbank	188	19	30	26561	3200	3200	14	8
Glasgow Carnwadric	183	21	36	19986	0	100	29	10
Glasgow Castlemilk East	196	13	13	21049	0	0	21	6
Glasgow Castlemilk West	185	29	50	22426	0	0	38	12
Glasgow Cathcart Old	498	49	48	51934	14000	14000	19	12
Glasgow Cathcart South	501	49	66	95234	24300	27897	48	32
Glasgow Cathedral (St Mungo's or High)	622	58	–	65685	12200	12200	11	–
Glasgow Colston Milton	207	20	–	27995	0	0	29	22
Glasgow Colston Wellpark	225	19	–	23093	0	0	28	–
Glasgow Cranhill	82	16	–	11570	0	0	30	10
Glasgow Croftfoot	467	54	42	59693	12000	15865	69	15
Glasgow Crosshill Queen's Park	169	19	–	21883	1830	4030	13	–
Glasgow Dennistoun Blackfriars	205	19	26	29620	2500	2500	22	5
Glasgow Dennistoun Central	263	31	31	44040	2300	2300	22	2
Glasgow Drumchapel Drumry St Mary's	166	12	–	12578	0	0	51	19

Congregation	Com	Eld	G	In98	Ass	Gvn	3-11	-17
Glasgow Drumchapel St Andrew's 621	61	25	56769	10800	11090	51	26
Glasgow Drumchapel St Mark's 100	11	17	11752	0	0	11	8
Glasgow Easterhouse St George's							
and St Peter's 52	9	–	4535	0	0	22	9
Glasgow Eastwood. 594	63	90	62201	10200	10200	80	26
Glasgow Fernhill and Cathkin 388	23	68	36915	4000	2600	51	5
Glasgow Gairbraid 269	19	38	32397	0	100	14	2
Glasgow Gardner Street 63	8	–	39530	3100	4350	13	9
Glasgow Garthamlock							
and Craigend East 100	11	11	10389	0	0	25	6
Glasgow Gorbals 137	19	28	23451	0	0	12	10
Glasgow Govan Old 262	30	22	34304	3320	3680	13	23
Glasgow Govanhill Trinity 203	28	50	31546	2510	2530	5	–
Glasgow High Carntyne 881	37	96	67519	15500	16363	44	24
Glasgow Hillington Park 519	40	79	66540	14500	10976	57	23
Glasgow Househillwood							
St Christopher's 129	14	30	13796	0	23	16	17
Glasgow Hyndland. 340	43	57	78490	14300	15500	22	6
Glasgow Ibrox 453	26	40	47002	7520	7520	36	33
Glasgow Jordanhill. 737	88	38	116057	33400	33400	103	39
Glasgow Kelvin Stevenson Memorial. . . . 243	43	31	38306	4010	4010	11	37
Glasgow Kelvinside Hillhead 331	27	–	58568	9300	9300	12	12
Glasgow King's Park 985	84	106	114583	33000	36275	199	63
Glasgow Kinning Park 227	22	26	37999	3550	3550	41	5
Glasgow Knightswood St Margaret's 766	41	61	61635	12800	12800	17	2
Glasgow Langside 311	51	56	45333	1000	1000	41	10
Glasgow Lansdowne 176	21	–	25824	0	0	23	4
Glasgow Linthouse St Kenneth's 193	16	30	24093	0	0	21	–
Glasgow Lochwood 83	7	15	11120	0	0	12	6
Glasgow Martyrs', The. 150	9	–	26319	0	0	12	–
Glasgow Maryhill. 274	26	26	34206	1624	1934	36	7
Glasgow Merrylea 608	71	86	82753	19500	19642	54	21
Glasgow Mosspark. 372	41	61	54713	9000	9149	18	6
Glasgow Mount Florida 422	43	78	78160	17000	17000	–	–
Glasgow New Cathcart. 310	31	45	43336	5900	6300	32	20
Glasgow New Govan 177	27	40	44232	4500	4500	25	17
Glasgow Newlands South. 885	85	65	145524	44000	48000	115	34
Glasgow North Kelvinside 103	5	34	41312	4890	5191	7	2
Glasgow Partick South 329	42	36	46567	1700	1700	34	14
Glasgow Partick Trinity 267	34	–	45583	7300	7087	37	16
Glasgow Penilee St Andrew's. 232	26	–	39088	1580	1839	27	5
Glasgow Pollokshaws. 231	24	39	34363	1750	1750	26	16
Glasgow Pollokshields 411	41	70	98419	26500	26912	18	14
Glasgow Possilpark 259	24	32	29759	500	500	107	35
Glasgow Priesthill and Nitshill. 215	20	25	26745	0	25	84	10
Glasgow Renfield St Stephen's 255	31	29	79810	9100	10300	8	3
Glasgow Ruchazie 78	8	–	10958	0	0	57	24
Glasgow Ruchill 163	21	27	36468	2300	2300	20	12
Glasgow Rutherglen Old 548	36	–	47897	10500	10586	6	–
Glasgow Rutherglen Stonelaw 558	54	92	96844	24500	24500	50	75
Glasgow Rutherglen Wardlawhill 468	41	78	50621	10200	10200	56	32

Congregation	Com	Eld	G	In98	Ass	Gvn	3-11	-17
Glasgow Rutherglen West 602	30	28	54534	8500	8500	46	12
Glasgow John Ross Memorial							
(For the Deaf) 84	7	–	8075	200	200	11	–
Glasgow St Andrew's East 229	24	38	27836	0	300	26	2
Glasgow St Columba 145	18	18	32242	2150	2150	29	12
Glasgow St David's Knightswood 828	51	65	74240	13000	13000	49	26
Glasgow St Enoch's Hogganfield 320	19	60	35717	3310	3310	36	2
Glasgow St George's Tron 593	60	–	168953	49200	49200	88	61
Glasgow St James' (Pollok) 330	30	34	42835	1000	1000	56	15
Glasgow St John's Renfield 532	63	34	89260	23800	23800	102	27
Glasgow St Luke's and St Andrew's. 123	8	17	20403	0	0	16	–
Glasgow St Margaret's Tollcross 180	9	24	24933	0	0	36	16
Glasgow St Nicholas' Cardonald 502	46	44	46219	6890	6019	41	49
Glasgow St Paul's Provanmill 74	4	–	12590	0	0	23	17
Glasgow St Rollox 143	11	18	24851	0	154	18	3
Glasgow St Thomas' Gallowgate 93	9	10	11504	0	0	11	–
Glasgow Sandyford							
Henderson Memorial 200	27	21	69244	16300	16300	10	3
Glasgow Sandyhills 440	40	70	57118	10500	10500	64	37
Glasgow Scotstoun and Whiteinch 384	45	7	58868	9000	9000	67	43
Glasgow Shawlands 705	53	53	112213	0	0	95	13
Glasgow Sherbrooke St Gilbert's 599	47	36	107365	18200	18200	46	41
Glasgow Shettleston Old 366	28	37	38733	6500	6500	31	17
Glasgow South Carntyne 166	13	10	28667	0	336	16	4
Glasgow South Shawlands 281	29	–	57884	9800	9800	45	14
Glasgow Springburn. 442	44	33	60868	10800	10800	28	19
Glasgow Strathbungo Queen's Park 335	33	46	51331	1250	1250	29	38
Glasgow Temple Anniesland 637	48	60	60412	19200	19999	46	9
Glasgow Toryglen 157	15	28	22890	0	0	26	–
Glasgow Townhead Blochairn 37	4	–	6690	0	0	34	–
Glasgow Trinity Possil							
and Henry Drummond 154	9	12	35154	500	500	20	–
Glasgow Tron St Mary's. 167	17	19	23633	0	1000	18	4
Glasgow Victoria Tollcross. 190	17	42	27536	0	1000	36	3
Glasgow Wallacewell 237	20	20	22657	0	180	26	81
Glasgow Wellington. 353	45	–	81892	18000	21181	15	22
Glasgow Yoker Old 102	8	14	11650	0	0	32	13
Glasgow Yoker St Matthew's 140	9	22	13289	0	300	–	–
17. HAMILTON							
Airdrie Broomknoll 470	48	55	48993	9560	9560	36	12
Calderbank 192	12	32	15073	2100	2100	20	–
Airdrie Clarkston 592	48	35	57630	9960	9960	95	7
Airdrie Flowerhill 866	63	60	81483	18050	18594	65	82
Airdrie High 475	36	26	37298	4810	5310	42	17
Airdrie Jackson 449	45	38	47315	11000	11000	75	7
Airdrie New Monkland 510	38	37	39723	6680	1550	56	11
Airdrie Greengairs . , ... 230	9	18	12196	1710	1710	23	6
Airdrie St Columba's 277	17	16	18212	0	0	17	–
Airdrie The New Wellwynd 916	90	54	77221	18490	18490	69	17
Bargeddie 238	16	–	48760	9800	9800	38	15

Congregation	Com	Eld	G	In98	Ass	Gvn	3-11	-17
Bellshill Macdonald Memorial	351	34	30	45265	6220	7070	19	–
Bellshill Orbiston	330	23	15	14469	2460	2645	18	–
Bellshill St Andrew's	208	20	16	21505	3700	3700	20	5
Bellshill West	933	64	52	58469	13310	13710	50	11
Blantyre Livingstone Memorial	317	19	29	34147	2460	2460	62	8
Blantyre Old	438	29	47	61720	9700	9829	38	23
Blantyre St Andrew's	336	25	30	49942	4250	4270	56	10
Bothwell	728	57	56	84240	22740	22740	81	53
Caldercruix Longriggend and Meadowfield	259	13	21	42147	5550	5709	39	3
Carfin	69	6	–	6067	950	950	2	–
Newarthill	654	25	29	47821	7890	11063	62	27
Chapelhall	340	29	42	29845	4880	4880	27	10
Chapelton	217	15	37	16840	3020	3020	31	16
Strathaven Rankin	641	59	25	64205	14670	14987	63	19
Cleland	343	14	20	27910	2800	1190	22	15
Coatbridge Blairhill–Dundyvan	513	41	39	40298	5890	8889	31	13
Coatbridge Calder	631	43	65	51870	10990	10990	38	35
Coatbridge Clifton	362	25	33	40983	4200	6759	14	26
Coatbridge Middle	461	37	54	41551	4490	4940	54	33
Coatbridge Old Monkland	420	23	55	26518	2240	3584	41	35
Coatbridge St Andrew's	902	82	60	75677	15420	15420	62	10
Coatbridge Townhead	418	27	32	39392	4160	4160	45	48
Dalserf	313	20	27	40768	6300	6300	49	11
East Kilbride Claremont	950	91	64	95222	15480	15655	114	32
East Kilbride Greenhills	292	14	40	21599	0	0	22	12
East Kilbride Moncreiff	1277	83	63	97467	16170	7549	104	26
East Kilbride Mossneuk	298	18	–	23376	0	0	93	42
East Kilbride Old	819	71	104	64677	11270	11270	–	–
East Kilbride South	457	40	44	72255	17040	17040	65	26
East Kilbride West	781	42	90	57328	11020	11020	128	16
East Kilbride Westwood	849	52	142	62481	11710	12210	68	41
Glasford	197	12	25	13839	2620	2620	19	2
Strathaven East	353	36	45	36306	6440	7447	13	3
Hamilton Burnbank	187	19	21j	22389	3580	3759	10	2
Hamilton North	227	32	30	28119	5760	5760	18	10
Hamilton Cadzow	844	69	78	78289	17230	17230	97	30
Hamilton Gilmour and Whitehill	248	26	21j	32670	4212	4357	41	19
Hamilton Hillhouse	599	47	22	70176	12660	12660	118	44
Hamilton Old	929	70	42	111719	28370	31095	50	17
Hamilton St Andrew's	406	36	64	52858	10980	11080	38	16
Hamilton St John's	710	61	76	82995	20250	18803	84	25
Hamilton South	370	30	40	38534	6480	6745	39	9
Quarter	128	11	24	15131	3170	3170	13	–
Hamilton Trinity	354	29	–	37711	3500	3500	42	22
Hamilton West	435	33	9	61216	9990	9990	38	19
Holytown	421	21	31	37196	3970	3970	29	–
Kirk o' Shotts	250	12	14	17575	0	0	14	–
Larkhall Chalmers	301	20	25	29507	4650	4855	39	5
Larkhall St Machan's	801	62	64	81730	16480	16480	–	–
Larkhall Trinity	372	27	38	42738	3360	3360	121	47

Congregation	Com	Eld	G	In98	Ass	Gvn	3-11	-17
Motherwell Crosshill 618	62	94	66896	14774	15159	56	47	
Motherwell Dalziel St Andrew's 793	79	62	81022	19630	19857	44	7	
Motherwell Manse Road 317	33	31	50534	8100	8164	53	10	
Motherwell North 344	40	40	37021	4190	4340	42	22	
Motherwell St Margaret's 419	21	41	31086	4900	0	25	35	
Motherwell St Mary's 1102	105	102	82169	18360	18272	134	79	
Motherwell South Dalziel 581	64	90	68564	14660	14895	41	46	
Newmains Bonkle 224	16	31	27755	5500	5500	124	59	
Newmains Coltness Memorial 257	23	31	36716	6010	6010	113	30	
New Stevenston – Wrangholm Kirk 226	15	32	38782	4470	5680	59	20	
Overtown. 338	0	46	30960	4640	4640	39	24	
Shotts Calderhead Erskine 713	46	48	43429	6480	6480	77	9	
Stonehouse St Ninian's 562	40	73	48442	9870	9870	65	78	
Strathaven Avendale Old and Drumclog 833	76	30	109102	22610	22610	173	77	
Strathaven West 301	21	40	40301	3040	3040	33	4	
Uddingston Burnhead 308	29	16	31184	3340	1840	36	14	
Uddingston Old 801	60	80	76074	14930	16548	59	15	
Uddingston Park 392	0	33	50795	9590	9925	64	18	
Uddingston Viewpark. 502	33	40	57286	11130	11748	86	35	
Wishaw Cambusnethan North 598	40	38	60970	9360	9360	39	30	
Wishaw Cambusnethan Old 619	54	19	61206	14421	14421	58	49	
Wishaw Chalmers 571	39	56	50643	9660	6931	–	–	
Wishaw Craigneuk and Belhaven 300	34	38	43193	9162	9162	21	8	
Wishaw Old. 444	47	47	35333	4410	4410	–	–	
Wishaw St Mark's 570	38	67	52936	8500	8500	41	9	
Wishaw Thornlie 287	31	35	33362	5360	5547	26	13	

18. DUMBARTON

Congregation	Com	Eld	G	In98	Ass	Gvn	3-11	-17
Alexandria 605	41	30	58705	13520	13520	–	–	
Arrochar. 65	2	12	4540	0	0	19	–	
Luss. 125	9	24	16946	0	0	5	–	
Baldernock. 262	18	20	41731	5320	7766	15	–	
Bearsden Killermont 861	65	87	95523	25190	26560	94	18	
Bearsden New Kilpatrick 2030	130	70	256950	78910	79160	138	51	
Bearsden North 709	72	101	91096	23190	23515	125	56	
Bearsden South. 1101	91	51	134265	30700	23886	129	49	
Bearsden Westerton Fairlie Memorial. . . . 558	48	47	81427	20390	20390	66	30	
Bonhill. 940	67	–	61690	13820	13820	83	27	
Cardross. 559	40	37	79966	20690	20690	57	37	
Clydebank Abbotsford 414	29	42	45078	7310	7310	26	7	
Clydebank Faifley 259	25	58	32360	0	0	38	8	
Clydebank Kilbowie St Andrew's 430	25	48	36635	6410	6410	66	35	
Clydebank Radnor Park 326	39	46	42078	5910	5910	12	4	
Clydebank St Cuthbert's 157	17	38	20852	0	500	18	2	
Craigrownie. 252	24	21	28876	6210	6210	35	10	
Rosneath St Modan's 250	13	26	21187	3480	3480	30	2	
Dalmuir Barclay. 399	18	92	41424	6250	6250	43	6	
Dumbarton Riverside 1021	94	92	90706	15350	15513	92	22	
Dumbarton St Andrew's. 328	31	17	33591	3400	3400	31	6	
Dumbarton West Kirk 438	36	36	44462	9108	9108	41	13	

Congregation	Com	Eld	G	In98	Ass	Gvn	3-11	-17
Duntocher	411	31	31	37552	5010	5010	76	–
Garelochhead	241	14	–	37540	3820	3928	102	18
Helensburgh Park	537	51	47	80253	16850	17110	71	12
Helensburgh St Columba	657	57	48	76188	16040	16040	78	34
Helensburgh West Kirk	752	55	71	93980	24570	24570	38	11
Jamestown	538	27	39	55794	8130	8130	23	2
Kilmaronock Gartocharn	294	12	–	31103	1510	1510	26	–
Milngavie Cairns	862	61	–	91767	27250	27250	95	47
Milngavie St Luke's	483	44	56	62020	14500	14500	68	7
Milngavie St Paul's	1228	99	110	167757	45050	51800	141	37
Old Kilpatrick Bowling	431	23	37	37527	7300	12515	49	45
Renton Trinity	360	30	–	31037	3090	3090	30	30
Rhu and Shandon	359	38	55	65820	11210	11260	47	5

19. SOUTH ARGYLL

Congregation	Com	Eld	G	In98	Ass	Gvn	3-11	-17
Ardrishaig	210	29	46	31425	3690	3903	44	11
South Knapdale	33	6	–	4712	260	260	7	–
Campbeltown Highland	522	36	31	45139	4440	4440	33	2
Campbeltown Lorne and Lowland	1042	0	62	72463	13620	13979	77	25
Craignish	35	0	–	9476	0	0	–	–
Kilninver and Kilmelford	62	6	–	6373	0	0	–	–
Cumlodden Lochfyneside and Lochgair	114	14	18	16748	0	32	22	–
Gigha and Cara	46	4	–	8766	0	0	6	–
Glassary, Kilmartin and Ford	136	9	18	24916	0	800	13	–
Glenaray and Inveraray	151	11	15	17889	0	0	15	2
Jura	46	7	–	8575	0	0	10	6
Kilarrow	120	13	17	14070	0	0	17	–
Kilmeny	58	8	9	5965	0	0	21	–
Kilberry	18	4	–	1322	0	0	–	–
Tarbert	189	20	40	27063	0	0	31	–
Kilcalmonell	86	10	19	9097	0	0	8	–
Skipness	30	4	–	6029	0	0	2	–
Kilchoman	88	3	–	8253	950	950	13	3
Portnahaven	22	3	11	3863	310	310	–	–
Kildalton and Oa	136	12	19	19210	0	600	65	3
Killean and Kilchenzie	214	14	25	24554	0	0	24	12
Lochgilphead	250	22	16	25408	0	0	59	14
North Knapdale	78	7	–	23099	0	155	12	13
Saddell and Carradale	280	16	44	26308	0	0	15	–
Southend	249	13	24	24607	0	75	56	–

20. DUNOON

Congregation	Com	Eld	G	In98	Ass	Gvn	3-11	-17
Ascog	68	6	7	8195	713	813	–	–
Rothesay Craigmore St Brendan's	154	15	8	23158	1406	1406	11	–
Dunoon Old and St Cuthbert's	445	40	50	43086	4040	4090	36	9
Dunoon St John's	305	20	32	33939	5850	5850	–	–
Sandbank	165	11	–	11750	1860	1860	18	–
Innellan	148	9	26	16479	0	1028	22	–
Inverchaolain and Toward	116	9	–	14846	0	69	5	4
Kilfinan	32	5	9	2898	570	1140	12	–

Congregation	Com	Eld	G	In98	Ass	Gvn	3-11	-17
Kyles	214	14	39	24176	390	419	14	–
Kilmodan and Colintraive	137	12	8	17983	0	250	10	–
Kilmun: (St Munn's)	124	11	19	13432	0	300	15	–
Strone and Ardentinny	154	16	16	15184	0	389	35	–
Kingarth and Kilchattan Bay	101	9	21	14732	2940	2940	6	–
Rothesay The High Kirk	351	24	44	34872	4710	4710	34	5
Kirn	430	27	30	45617	9840	9840	32	8
Lochgoilhead and Kilmorich	143	13	24	18446	0	100	14	–
North Bute	173	18	21	20446	0	132	15	–
Rothesay Trinity	558	42	67	47926	8630	8830	52	12
Strachur and Strachlachlan	174	10	24	16680	0	525	19	7

21. LORN AND MULL

Congregation	Com	Eld	G	In98	Ass	Gvn	3-11	-17
Appin	94	14	20	13689	0	130	16	–
Lismore	64	6	17	5038	0	148	11	–
Ardchattan	186	14	43	23079	0	1102	26	5
Coll	15	3	–	1760	0	0	7	–
Colonsay and Oronsay	15	2	–	3307	0	0	8	–
Kilbrandon and Kilchattan	119	11	16	18939	0	259	13	2
Connel	171	19	41	29709	0	0	52	–
Glenorchy and Innishael	94	9	–	9791	0	0	12	8
Strathfillan	58	7	–	13090	0	0	–	–
Iona	15	2	–	8122	0	200	–	–
Kilfinichen and Kilvickeon and The Ross Of Mull	38	8	–	8120	0	0	–	–
Kilchrenan and Dalavich	37	4	10	6071	0	0	2	–
Muckairn	154	16	19	19525	0	300	17	7
Kilmore and Oban	901	76	90	81438	12500	12890	71	10
Kilninian and Kilmore	41	5	12	7398	0	0	–	–
Salen and Ulva	40	6	–	8363	0	0	14	–
Tobermory	109	17	17	10255	0	100	16	–
Torosay and Kinlochspelvie	31	6	–	6834	0	400	4	4
Tiree	123	11	24	20349	0	0	24	3

22. FALKIRK

Congregation	Com	Eld	G	In98	Ass	Gvn	3-11	-17
Airth	218	15	22	31800	2780	2780	16	7
Blackbraes and Shieldhill	299	19	23	20561	0	0	19	24
Bo'ness Old	810	48	38	54657	10980	10980	50	44
Bo'ness St Andrew's	621	29	–	54355	10420	10420	50	45
Bonnybridge St Helen's	744	38	41	37715	5220	5286	29	7
Bothkennar and Carronshore	351	31	13	26838	0	0	36	–
Brightons	783	47	86	69680	11180	12160	92	45
Carriden	758	46	22	44774	6900	11890	37	11
Cumbernauld Abronhill	349	31	46	34251	0	275	92	17
Cumbernauld Condorrat	569	37	37	49146	7940	7940	64	22
Cumbernauld Kildrum	515	44	–	41715	5830	5830	38	10
Cumbernauld Old	460	30	–	43811	5300	5340	67	6
Cumbernauld St Mungo's	390	32	–	43173	4650	4650	34	8
Denny Dunipace	506	38	27	44857	6260	6260	32	10
Denny Old	544	47	26	48698	7950	7950	43	12
Denny Westpark	827	68	50	75475	14260	14260	44	38

Congregation	Com	Eld	G	In98	Ass	Gvn	3-11	-17
Falkirk Bainsford	448	24	24	39121	5220	5370	26	10
Falkirk Camelon: Irving	399	18	21	24979	0	0	31	14
Falkirk Camelon St John's	422	28	29	45704	6170	6170	61	11
Falkirk Erskine	664	63	56	68719	14290	14984	69	14
Falkirk Grahamston	638	49	45	70205	15970	15970	51	30
Falkirk Laurieston	307	22	37	32822	6790	6790	27	5
Redding and Westquarter	155	13	34	16404	2550	2550	18	10
Falkirk Old and St Modan's	1168	70	53	102688	18320	18320	82	24
Falkirk St Andrew's West	722	46	33	78086	20730	20730	40	10
Falkirk St James'	426	31	14	34255	2700	2700	50	19
Grangemouth Charing Cross and West	293	18	–	30704	2530	2530	16	2
Grangemouth Dundas	385	29	–	34533	4030	4030	19	5
Grangemouth Kerse	653	55	37	43798	6440	6440	46	45
Grangemouth Kirk of the Holy Rood	820	49	–	52725	7780	7780	62	8
Grangemouth Zetland	1005	70	77	76536	12790	12790	33	6
Haggs	342	33	21	34400	2275	2730	25	16
Larbert East	677	38	68	55794	7530	7530	44	65
Larbert Old	872	54	28	75285	18430	18430	74	74
Larbert West	650	51	42	64972	11290	11290	43	29
Muiravonside	297	26	25	29993	1300	1625	19	10
Polmont Old	601	25	33	52937	12840	12840	62	39
Slamannan	300	19	15	24262	0	0	37	–
Stenhouse and Carron	708	50	25	50785	9690	9690	56	9
23. STIRLING								
Aberfoyle	161	11	20	17950	700	7386	11	4
Port of Menteith	68	6	10	9481	1730	1730	2	–
Alloa North	323	18	24	38219	4340	4340	41	–
Alloa St Mungo's	851	63	54	62604	10800	10800	19	6
Alloa West	300	26	53	37476	6540	7717	25	4
Alva	685	47	51	47589	8490	9211	72	10
Balfron	267	21	20	42228	8670	8670	27	12
Fintry	194	14	21	18463	1400	1400	12	3
Balquhidder	105	6	–	15431	750	750	–	–
Killin and Ardeonaig	183	13	25	14248	1520	1520	–	16
Bannockburn Allan	581	37	30	41222	6270	6270	31	6
Bannockburn Ladywell	745	45	50	36061	4340	4340	25	1
Bridge of Allan Chalmers	318	30	25	41030	7975	7975	25	13
Bridge of Allan Holy Trinity	660	43	48	71730	13960	13960	60	59
Buchanan	106	10	30j	12630	1800	1800	–	–
Drymen	290	20	j	30788	2640	1831	51	10
Buchlyvie	248	18	20	22157	2325	2325	28	–
Gartmore	99	14	–	13796	1750	1750	9	–
Callander	753	42	56	74714	17610	17837	69	27
Cambusbarron The Bruce Memorial	420	24	27	28123	1840	1840	18	26
Clackmannan	830	40	40	67923	9290	9290	–	–
Cowie	220	12	12	12385	970	1159	20	–
Plean	308	11	–	11926	1190	1910	25	–
Dollar	732	50	52	90041	17620	17620	77	43
Glendevon	55	4	–	3447	640	744	–	–
Muckhart	162	13	18	17504	3990	3990	18	5

Congregation	Com	Eld	G	In98	Ass	Gvn	3-11	-17
Dunblane Cathedral	1236	85	74	148992	44660	44875	107	35
Dunblane St Blane's	479	40	50	70878	14925	15102	41	13
Fallin	269	7	–	26191	0	0	71	9
Gargunnock	277	14	–	14552	2520	2520	28	–
Kincardine-in-Menteith	139	8	–	11793	670	670	23	–
Killearn	666	50	99	73731	10000	10000	54	53
Kilmadock	336	14	27	15902	394	394	–	–
Kippen	374	22	30	30571	3450	3450	–	–
Norrieston	195	9	17	11965	630	630	22	5
Lecropt	295	22	36	33358	4190	4190	15	–
Logie	749	59	95	80939	18610	18760	62	27
Menstrie	455	29	36	50311	8500	8500	42	8
Sauchie and Coalsnaughton	1057	46	48	57727	8790	8790	62	16
Stirling Allan Park South	309	41	43	33921	4960	4960	13	12
Stirling Church of The Holy Rude	260	36	–	24783	5940	6095	4	4
Stirling North	612	42	29	50779	9030	9030	41	13
Stirling St Columba's	715	74	–	72184	14150	14535	74	30
Stirling St Mark's	407	17	15	29294	1960	1400	–	–
Stirling St Ninian's Old	836	40	–	58016	13470	13470	15	41
Stirling Viewfield	649	34	41	53960	8900	9195	38	25
Strathblane	414	29	51	43789	5800	5800	38	22
Tillicoultry	1091	69	82	73644	18960	19250	84	9
Tullibody: St Serf's	648	37	18	44374	7500	1236	–	–

24. DUNFERMLINE

Congregation	Com	Eld	G	In98	Ass	Gvn	3-11	-17
Aberdour St Fillan's	460	41	–	55659	11470	11970	34	–
Ballingry	119	14	–	10697	0	0	23	4
Beath and Cowdenbeath North	225	16	18	31508	0	160	18	6
Cairneyhill	223	20	–	18248	3050	3050	41	11
Limekilns	397	41	–	55922	12620	12620	46	13
Carnock and Oakley	253	24	25	42519	1500	1500	35	11
Cowdenbeath Trinity	471	30	32	39383	0	0	55	24
Culross and Torryburn	352	24	26	31617	2343	4218	38	24
Dalgety	674	42	40	67090	12970	13030	151	67
Dunfermline Abbey	758	55	–	83459	13750	13750	70	18
Dunfermline Gillespie Memorial	655	79	36	81679	15990	15990	68	64
Dunfermline North	238	14	–	25567	0	0	18	2
Dunfermline St Andrew's Erskine	384	25	18	26310	4680	4680	18	–
Dunfermline St Leonard's	753	44	45	56108	11530	11530	105	27
Dunfermline St Margaret's	522	56	51	45579	6270	5970	34	13
Dunfermline St Ninian's	433	28	65	27834	0	0	19	–
Dunfermline St Paul's	194	31	–	29404	2430	2430	7	8
Dunfermline Townhill	508	32	55	43819	8330	8330	43	21
Inverkeithing St John's	249	27	21	24665	2250	2543	22	14
North Queensferry	101	6	–	14736	1060	1060	21	–
Inverkeithing St Peter's	366	16	–	30547	2880	2958	30	8
Kelty	410	30	51	30849	3940	3940	25	10
Lochcraig	0	5	10	9988	0	0	7	–
Lochgelly Macainsh	438	36	–	28567	2000	2000	16	–
Lochgelly St Andrew's	430	37	30	37406	4090	4090	21	10
Rosyth	527	24	–	28854	160	160	19	3

Congregation	Com	Eld	G	In98	Ass	Gvn	3-11	-17
Saline and Blairingone	293	17	21	38837	5130	5266	43	14
Tulliallan and Kincardine	721	52	80	39594	6730	6730	55	20

25. KIRKCALDY

Auchterderran	268	18	13	17358	2690	2794	18	–
Cardenden St Fothad's	223	15	10	17438	3070	3237	16	4
Kinglassie	230	12	15	13420	2290	2443	11	–
Auchtertool	93	5	13	5439	760	760	2	–
Kirkcaldy Linktown	513	43	38	44786	8100	8406	20	2
Buckhaven	366	29	26	33667	2490	132	29	7
Burntisland	773	47	75	44236	8340	8474	68	41
Denbeath	172	9	23	7794	0	0	4	–
Methilhill	200	15	40	16220	0	200	16	–
Dysart	434	31	19	45653	7830	7830	11	–
Glenrothes Christ's Kirk	319	23	25	21933	0	0	63	23
Glenrothes St Columba's	752	27	29	55116	7210	7442	68	2
Glenrothes St Margaret's	539	40	54	48466	8230	8230	27	17
Glenrothes St Ninian's	349	37	17	43599	3200	3200	19	6
Innerleven East	324	10	25	22842	0	240	8	45
Kennoway, Windygates and Balgonie St Kenneth's	894	52	45	67959	9820	10571	50	10
Kinghorn	495	27	57	43881	6290	6290	26	8
Kirkcaldy Abbotshall	876	73	42	68540	14810	14910	34	8
Kirkcaldy Old	443	40	36	44497	8410	8410	27	16
Kirkcaldy Pathhead	674	47	66	58635	10160	10160	38	9
Kirkcaldy St Andrew's	360	27	42	43134	7190	7190	43	16
Kirkcaldy St Brycedale	564	37	52	57202	8030	8030	44	32
Kirkcaldy St John's	510	57	76	58031	8470	8590	43	8
Kirkcaldy Templehall	463	24	28	41373	4890	2000	35	76
Kirkcaldy Torbain	295	32	24	25218	0	0	–	19
Kirkcaldy Viewforth	455	21	–	32763	3750	3750	7	–
Thornton	292	10	–	18445	450	450	9	–
Leslie Trinity	460	33	62	27371	2415	2415	30	4
Leven: St Andrew's	677	39	63	49456	9430	3760	36	2
Leven Scoonie Kirk	423	28	28	42189	5290	5897	20	8
Markinch	749	33	54	45867	6890	6890	48	4
Methil	459	24	56	28916	4410	2667	17	9
Wemyss	369	19	50	20093	750	755	20	3

26. ST ANDREWS

Abdie and Dunbog	186	13	15	11181	1330	1330	11	–
Newburgh	374	18	–	19580	2253	2253	13	2
Anstruther	519	35	–	35781	4740	3555	35	15
Auchtermuchty	391	26	18	27245	3060	3060	10	11
Balmerino	213	23	15	19691	3550	6731	24	–
Wormit	315	22	73	27882	7290	7290	43	25
Boarhills and Dunino	201	9	45j	13875	2110	2110	–	j
St Andrews Martyrs'	447	36	j	34867	6810	6810	23	10j
Cameron	94	8	13	9061	2140	2140	11	12
St Andrews St Leonard's	735	53	41	77001	18760	18760	34	6
Carnbee	115	10	20	12642	1400	1400	–	–

Congregation	Com	Eld	G	In98	Ass	Gvn	3-11	-17
Pittenweem	349	20	49	24406	3460	3460	48	–
Cellardyke	422	30	48	29416	5130	5130	21	12j
Kilrenny	136	11	20	14097	2230	2230	22	j
Ceres and Springfield	564	33	50	39152	6280	6280	75	31
Crail	495	35	44	32908	6870	6870	31	–
Kingsbarns	117	10	–	11217	2230	2230	–	–
Creich, Flisk and Kilmany	162	11	19	15118	1470	1470	20	–
Monimail	188	14	–	15229	2290	2290	9	–
Cupar Old and St Michael of Tarvit	745	53	30	68624	14280	14280	53	25
Cupar St John's	852	47	78	49272	11290	11290	71	16
Dairsie	146	10	18	11299	1450	1450	14	–
Kemback	120	8	22	11437	2660	2660	5	–
Strathkinness	168	15	16	14782	2270	2270	16	–
Edenshead and Strathmiglo	363	13	30	22760	2530	2530	12	–
Elie	299	19	65	40097	11430	11430	22	10
Kilconquhar and Colinsburgh	182	15	17	17024	2990	2990	14	7
Falkland	392	18	32	30520	5800	5800	48	3
Freuchie	286	16	20	24086	4630	6228	12	–
Howe of Fife	919	43	–	48324	10060	10160	83	–
Largo and Newburn	333	18	–	29840	6840	7212	35	–
Largo: St David's	225	16	56	20437	4270	4482	26	–
Largoward	85	6	14	5662	680	680	–	–
St Monans	288	17	69	33093	5060	5060	30	–
Leuchars: St Athernase and Guardbridge	585	27	36	32111	3690	3690	35	6
Newport-on-Tay	484	41	–	55405	12180	12180	37	32
St Andrews Holy Trinity	801	28	55	36464	12360	12360	33	1
St Andrews Hope Park	1021	108	66	120501	22280	22280	56	44
Tayport	500	23	37	37341	4080	4080	44	33

27. DUNKELD AND MEIGLE

Aberfeldy	376	21	36	40927	6700	6830	52	20
Amulree and Strathbraan	27	2	–	3114	450	450	4	–
Dull and Weem	95	8	17	8442	1930	1930	9	–
Alyth	872	41	40	51382	8890	8890	58	–
Ardler Kettins and Meigle	579	27	54	35835	5540	5540	25	–
Bendochy	110	9	16	12014	1080	1080	10	5
Blairgowrie St Mary's South	386	15	30	25395	2082	16807	29	5
Blair Atholl and Struan	197	15	20	16420	0	500	14	–
Blairgowrie St Andrew's	713	36	38	51010	9660	9660	24	13
Braes of Rannoch	32	5	8	9095	0	390	–	–
Foss and Rannoch	150	13	17	13159	0	280	–	–
Caputh and Clunie	221	24	23	19599	998	1058	5	–
Kinclaven	182	18	13	16799	1560	1560	7	–
Coupar Angus: Abbey	517	34	36	36324	3518	3518	25	–
Dunkeld	494	43	46	59865	10570	12099	32	6
Fortingall and Glenlyon	59	5	–	6857	1170	1170	–	–
Kenmore and Lawers	125	7	21	17921	2220	2220	–	–
Grantully Logierait and Strathtay	177	12	18	24342	1000	1766	–	–
Kirkmichael Straloch and Glenshee	166	14	16	8238	0	0	14	–
Rattray	572	41	36	26205	4480	4480	32	–

Congregation	Com	Eld	G	In98	Ass	Gvn	3-11	-17
Pitlochry 576	59	41	50597	7890	7890	33	–
Tenandry 72	9	10	8037	1875	5125	5	–

28. PERTH

Aberdalgie and Dupplin 129	6	18	11133	0	0	8	6
Forteviot 124	7	–	9911	0	0	10	5
Abernethy and Dron 299	17	20	22275	1860	2279	16	–
Arngask 181	13	29	15083	2490	2490	30	10
Aberuthven 89	9	–	7091	0	0	3	2
Dunning 275	19	22	16389	0	150	21	–
Almondbank Tibbermore 330	15	30	15854	0	400	–	–
Ardoch 178	11	25	18590	0	1500	20	11
Blackford 102	11	–	10906	0	0	28	8
Auchterarder 879	53	59	59099	11970	11970	44	10
Auchtergaven and Moneydie 555	27	49	31656	3100	3100	35	11
Cargill Burrelton 406	20	70	26130	1240	1240	23	8
Collace 154	10	14	18220	1750	1750	12	–
Cleish 267	17	19	43248	6080	6080	26	–
Fossoway: St Serf's and Devonside 242	18	–	29411	4370	4370	37	10
Comrie and Strowan 558	31	59j	55172	9620	10339	27	2
Dundurn 59	7	j	9395	1670	1973	5	1
Crieff 1341	58	71	72712	16500	16500	52	16
Dunbarney 590	32	63	44500	8290	8290	57	13
Forgandenny 97	8	11	8676	1390	1390	7	–
Errol 458	25	20	36459	6040	6040	41	5
Kilspindie and Rait 87	5	–	6819	1000	1060	9	–
Fowlis Wester 124	7	8	13821	350	350	9	–
Madderty 115	9	17	10639	350	350	17	–
Monzie 121	11	13	14046	350	350	–	–
Gask 123	9	15	8151	0	700	10	–
Methven and Logiealmond 415	36	37	23402	0	350	39	–
Kinross 734	36	20	54673	10670	12350	97	20
Muthill 386	26	11j	23878	3380	3380	48	14
Trinity Gask and Kinkell 64	3	j	4931	540	540	–	–
Orwell 375	32	29	26115	5630	6655	41	4
Portmoak 174	0	–	16220	3070	3354	30	–
Perth Craigend Moncrieffe 270	16	–	11732	0	200	13	–
Rhynd 93	11	–	5133	0	0	3	–
Perth Craigie 806	41	54	58361	9740	10840	47	–
Perth Kinnoull 454	35	45	47275	10806	10806	30	12
Perth Letham St Mark's 860	38	38	54338	9003	9003	52	–
Perth North 1635	119	41	166863	45360	45360	143	62
Perth St Andrew's and St Stephen's 744	44	34	56219	7400	7400	–	–
Perth St John the Baptist's 966	56	–	59757	15390	13597	13	9
Perth St Leonard's-in-the-Fields							
and Trinity 674	96	32	83756	18650	18650	25	10
Perth St Matthew's 1050	84	53	73120	16620	16805	51	18
Redgorton 158	11	17	11553	1030	1030	50	–
Stanley 334	23	35	25641	4540	4540	40	–
St Madoes and Kinfauns 299	24	29	17435	0	0	11	–
St Martin's 224	12	20	9960	1337	504	15	–

Congregation	Com	Eld	G	In98	Ass	Gvn	3-11	-17
Scone New	668	45	65	48652	7150	7150	53	12
Scone Old	807	54	34	49829	10490	10490	40	24
29. DUNDEE								
Abernyte	107	9	–	9802	700	700	15	–
Inchture and Kinnaird	264	23	17	20302	3450	3450	13	–
Longforgan	302	20	26	27078	3920	3920	21	–
Auchterhouse	153	14	22	18598	2060	2530	13	–
Murroes and Tealing	341	19	37	18254	890	1180	8	12
Dundee Albany – Butterburn	234	10	9	6071	0	160	16	5
Dundee St David's North	151	10	32	12382	0	0	–	–
Dundee Balgay	656	42	33	50692	9290	9290	30	23
Dundee Barnhill St Margaret's	978	86	63	90482	21880	21880	63	8
Dundee Broughty Ferry East	635	45	40	64439	11790	11790	64	14
Dundee Broughty Ferry St Aidan's	715	51	92	61771	11190	11190	40	19
Dundee Broughty Ferry St James'	288	16	42	38396	5500	5500	31	4
Dundee Broughty Ferry St Luke's and Queen Street	594	54	65	63686	9100	9643	24	–
Dundee Broughty Ferry St Stephen's and West	419	25	–	37783	7000	7000	19	9
Dundee Camperdown	268	26	25	29164	0	200	33	4
Dundee Chalmers Ardler	305	19	26	55752	9400	9752	32	24
Dundee Clepington	594	31	24	42426	4800	4800	29	52
Dundee Craigiebank	475	17	36	37344	5970	5970	31	28
Dundee Douglas and Angus	408	20	30	20516	0	0	17	6
Dundee Downfield South	545	0	40	39210	6200	6300	46	58
Dundee – Dundee (St Mary's)	752	84	35	90403	21880	22390	15	–
Dundee Fairmuir	369	15	18	34751	1710	1936	22	27
Dundee Lochee Old and St Luke's	419	29	36	32715	1950	2450	24	12
Dundee Lochee: West	707	41	28	32082	4600	4600	41	5
Dundee Logie St John's (Cross)	426	27	26	69431	17671	17671	84	16
Dundee Mains	299	11	14	21959	0	0	44	6
Dundee Mains of Fintry	174	13	–	42616	5580	5627	17	24
Dundee Meadowside St Paul's	629	65	40	65229	13370	13670	17	15
Dundee Menzieshill	602	26	–	40188	4630	1978	76	24
Dundee Mid Craigie	56	5	–	12199	0	0	11	8
Dundee Roseangle Ryehill	422	0	30	37410	6500	5850	11	13
Dundee St Andrew's	976	80	53	60002	10360	10460	89	13
Dundee St Peter's McCheyne	561	45	25	44079	8860	8910	26	–
Dundee Steeple	390	39	17	62282	14110	15366	34	17
Dundee Stobswell	703	44	26	59414	9900	6537	32	–
Dundee Strathmartine	651	44	50	46811	6680	6680	27	24
Dundee The High Kirk	677	55	71	49079	8760	8760	57	20
Dundee Trinity	874	45	65	38271	5730	5730	43	17
Dundee Whitfield	230	12	–	8122	0	0	24	–
Fowlis and Liff	183	12	8	9786	2100	2100	13	–
Lundie and Muirhead of Liff	429	26	44	25325	3820	3874	33	10
Invergowrie	546	39	51	45389	5190	5190	22	7
Monifieth Panmure	518	42	42	37206	6810	6810	39	16
Monifieth St Rule's	847	37	64	44358	7222	7222	72	15
Monifieth South	454	22	36	34693	3600	3709	62	46

Congregation	Com	Eld	G	In98	Ass	Gvn	3-11	-17
Monikie and Newbigging............392	19	13	26814	950	950	16	9

30. ANGUS

Congregation	Com	Eld	G	In98	Ass	Gvn	3-11	-17
Aberlemno........................210	11	–	14423	1000	1000	10	–
Guthrie and Rescobie 230	8	22	14593	920	920	14	5
Airlie, Ruthven and Kingoldrum 189	13	–	8348	500	650	16	–
Glenisla..........................45	4	11j	6337	550	550	5	5
Kilry 50	7	j	8113	450	450	10	–
Lintrathen 95	5	j	5378	475	475	–	–
Arbirlot.........................301	15	–	16598	2860	3040	25	59
Carmyllie 139	8	9	14378	2931	2931	14	–
Colliston 228	11	12	14354	2510	2536	12	–
Arbroath Knox's 479	29	52	26645	5310	5360	11	–
Arbroath St Vigeans 699	42	31	46065	9410	9619	39	–
Arbroath Old and Abbey 1133	46	49	52345	10650	10650	–	–
Arbroath St Andrew's 1008	55	34	55529	9370	9370	73	15
Arbroath West Kirk 1276	101	65	64917	12410	12410	57	6
Barry...........................542	21	21	31715	2360	2360	12	–
Brechin Cathedral 1329	34	32	31752	7600	5487	8	–
Brechin Gardner Memorial 1080	33	25	40075	5650	5700	43	2
Carnoustie......................786	51	39	55547	10900	11195	33	28
Carnoustie: Panbride 861	34	–	43586	7200	7200	113	19
Dun.............................91	9	j	8886	975	975	–	–
Hillside 435	25	65j	34410	1527	1527	18	–
Dunnichen, Letham and Kirkden 555	24	23	30534	4680	3897	36	15
Eassie and Nevay...................68	7	12	6156	520	520	–	–
Newtyle.........................324	15	25	34693	2037	2842	14	–
Edzell Lethnot 487	31	63	32309	7390	7890	16	9
Fern, Careston and Menmuir 148	11	5j	12820	700	1200	11	–
Glenesk 63	7	–	5850	720	825	11	–
Farnell..........................139	10	–	5735	960	1596	14	–
Montrose St Andrew's 625	25	34	29908	4460	4541	18	–
Forfar East and Old 1700	55	71	74306	15110	15422	68	27
Forfar Lowson Memorial 1242	46	43	51247	9230	9230	35	6
Forfar St Margaret's...............1148	43	36	58889	13270	13431	33	2
Friockheim and Kinnell 248	15	22	16032	770	770	27	–
Inverkeillor and Lunan...............211	8	14	18836	2340	2540	6	–
Glamis, Inverarity and Kinettles........538	31	33	37714	3140	3140	35	10
The Glens 293	10	9	14563	0	0	10	–
Inchbrayock......................252	10	–	27976	4240	7190	36	19
Montrose Melville South 444	19	–	35469	6340	6340	12	4
Kirriemuir Old...................1072	80	40	84783	17681	17681	55	52
Kirriemuir St Andrew's 620	28	56	36607	5940	6281	24	–
Oathlaw Tannadice 196	8	j	11357	550	667	–	–
Montrose Old 870	37	57	64973	12796	13296	83	10

31. ABERDEEN

Congregation	Com	Eld	G	In98	Ass	Gvn	3-11	-17
Aberdeen Beechgrove 736	90	61	102816	27620	27620	68	30
Aberdeen Bridge of Don Oldmachar 155	9	–	28827	0	0	41	5
Aberdeen Cove 43	4	–	9421	0	0	–	–
Aberdeen Craigiebuckler 922	58	77	73568	16380	16380	56	40

Congregation	Com	Eld	G	In98	Ass	Gvn	3-11	-17
Aberdeen Denburn	489	45	27	38026	5660	5660	23	20
Aberdeen Ferryhill	620	66	34	52492	11513	11513	56	30
Aberdeen Garthdee	340	20	27	27509	0	0	55	5
Aberdeen Gilcomston South	264	25	–	67599	19690	19690	16	–
Aberdeen Greyfriars John Knox	955	45	50	43928	8000	8371	25	4
Aberdeen High Hilton	697	58	64	60705	8060	8060	30	32
Aberdeen Holburn Central	700	57	23	51458	13910	13910	18	14
Aberdeen Holburn West	730	60	29	109601	29750	25394	57	8
Aberdeen Langstane Kirk	335	25	23	26898	5241	6476	7	–
Aberdeen Mannofield	1887	120	82	141554	42140	48270	135	44
Aberdeen Mastrick	712	29	30	43209	5350	5350	16	10
Aberdeen Middlefield	259	12	–	16159	0	0	51	5
Aberdeen Nigg	188	9	–	14264	0	50	21	15
Aberdeen North of St Andrew	940	75	37	63270	13890	13890	33	3
Aberdeen Northfield	457	21	35	34449	5430	5430	16	10
Aberdeen Queen's Cross	741	66	52	113573	28910	31640	38	8
Aberdeen Rosemount	207	21	18	22555	2610	5333	2	–
Aberdeen Rubislaw	729	82	53	116382	32360	42360	68	27
Aberdeen Ruthrieston South	762	53	59	54166	9420	11041	51	29
Aberdeen Ruthrieston West	492	52	30	43524	5770	6230	16	–
Aberdeen St Columba's	497	27	–	60287	6000	6550	84	49
Aberdeen St George's Tillydrone	247	14	20	25266	440	264	19	7
Aberdeen St John's for the Deaf	117	7	–	2618	0	0	–	–
Aberdeen St Machar's Cathedral	717	49	18	75076	16450	16450	27	5
Aberdeen St Mark's	633	60	22	60496	9623	8821	22	6
Aberdeen St Mary's	619	54	27	54266	7840	7840	17	4
Aberdeen St Nicholas, Kirk of	657	51	–	56558	10810	10810	11	–
Aberdeen St Nicholas South of Kincorth	607	41	55	43145	6910	6910	34	25
Aberdeen St Ninian's	375	21	34	39489	7080	7080	31	12
Aberdeen Stockethill	183	5	–	7938	300	300	–	–
Aberdeen St Stephen's	351	30	21	46873	5790	5898	18	–
Aberdeen Summerhill	244	19	–	7675	0	100	28	22
Aberdeen Torry St Fittick's	528	29	33	35187	3390	3390	44	19
Aberdeen Woodside	510	35	46	38423	4610	4710	3	14
Bucksburn Stoneywood	751	33	50	42925	8760	8760	14	14
Cults East	342	34	31	45083	6540	250	20	–
Cults West	678	47	45	92210	20520	20520	62	9
Dyce	1516	77	55	59673	13610	14000	49	43
Kingswells	494	38	23	36801	3750	3750	36	5
Newhills	1054	44	92	75385	18800	18800	57	47
Peterculter Kelman Memorial	361	24	–	34450	5150	5150	55	13
Peterculter St Peter's	780	29	39	41745	5550	5550	30	8

32. KINCARDINE AND DEESIDE

Aberluthnott	266	12	19	11899	3037	3181	20	5
Laurencekirk	481	13	55	18116	3800	3800	28	2
Aboyne and Dinnet	585	21	55	39099	8290	8290	24	5
Arbuthnott	132	8	12	7621	1230	1240	7	–
Bervie	599	25	28	32855	4200	4200	28	4
Banchory Devenick	168	11	9	10324	1490	1490	–	–

Congregation	Com	Eld	G	In98	Ass	Gvn	3-11	-17
Maryculter and Cookney	309	21	18	20465	3400	3400	8	–
Banchory Ternan East	1312	68	52	80349	16000	19160	66	42
Banchory Ternan West	728	49	52	63347	11060	11060	78	45
Birse and Feughside	330	24	–	24297	3050	3366	24	10
Braemar	119	12	16	18193	2100	2100	14	–
Crathie	192	16	12	33483	7150	7150	6	–
Cromar	277	11	16	15198	0	0	12	–
Drumoak	264	11	29	25203	0	211	30	3
Durris	210	12	23	12519	0	0	29	5
Glenmuick	394	22	26	30299	3920	3920	–	–
Kincardine O'Neil	243	0	11	8598	0	0	8	–
Lumphanan	304	0	12	14575	0	400	20	–
Kinneff	205	9	15	8372	925	760	9	–
Stonehaven South	414	27	23	31396	5600	5600	25	5
Mearns Coastal	513	0	49	19734	0	0	28	–
Newtonhill	430	20	29	33340	850	850	33	17
Portlethen	708	22	18	47301	10760	10760	83	5
Stonehaven Dunnottar	1085	40	47	53632	9370	9370	43	18
Stonehaven Fetteresso	963	48	32	86098	18410	18410	100	34
Torphins	471	35	31	37952	3750	3750	44	7
West Mearns	666	40	77	42231	5850	5850	25	–
33. GORDON								
Alford	535	24	16	25292	3025	3025	19	–
Keig	82	3	5	2648	860	300	6	–
Tullynessle and Forbes	103	10	10	8112	700	966	14	–
Barthol Chapel	148	11	12	8571	810	810	17	2
Tarves	607	37	48	37586	4730	4730	70	33
Belhelvie	673	30	32	35424	3803	3803	53	–
Blairdaff	111	13	–	10573	925	925	8	–
Chapel of Garioch	312	20	16	24653	1860	1860	21	–
Cluny	236	13	14	17082	2020	2020	16	4
Monymusk	177	7	10	15115	970	970	29	–
Culsalmond and Rayne	285	13	11	10996	1675	675	–	–
Daviot	209	12	12	12232	1300	1300	20	2
Drumblade	139	11	10	8111	1325	1325	12	–
Huntly Strathbogie	930	44	38	47418	11520	11520	50	26
Echt	351	17	18	17236	1028	1028	18	8
Midmar	185	12	–	12237	1150	1150	11	6
Ellon	2167	102	72	105854	17860	17860	115	60
Fintray and Kinellar	217	13	18j	16407	962	1329	26	–
Keithhall	86	8	j	8917	637	637	7	–
Foveran	438	20	–	29695	2525	4754	33	4
Huntly Cairnie Glass	946	38	42	36839	4760	4760	20	–
Insch – Leslie – Premnay – Oyne	675	40	43	43025	7480	8305	50	12
Inverurie St Andrew's	2062	65	77	72122	21310	21310	67	29
Inverurie West	791	48	50	42519	5580	5580	60	19
Kemnay	678	30	–	36754	6880	6880	64	30
Kintore	879	52	48	59541	16660	21660	56	22
Leochel Cushnie and Lynturk	198	11	10j	10168	0	0	21	–
Tough	99	6	j	9732	0	400	9	3

Congregation	Com	Eld	G	In98	Ass	Gvn	3-11	-17
Meldrum and Bourtie	641	0	53	39827	5750	5750	39	8
Methlick	410	26	38	32179	2970	3100	–	–
New Machar	595	35	30	37213	5160	5160	58	8
Noth	414	18	–	18121	0	0	14	–
Skene	1673	101	77	97173	14490	14490	77	42
Udny and Pitmedden	558	30	12	41221	4540	4540	50	15
Upper Donside	538	29	–	33014	0	32	15	–

34. BUCHAN

Congregation	Com	Eld	G	In98	Ass	Gvn	3-11	-17
Aberdour	187	10	25	9937	250	250	–	–
New Pitsligo	400	16	–	20943	300	385	11	–
Auchaber United	211	15	15	9083	507	623	13	–
Auchterless	264	20	17	14682	1980	2310	21	–
Banff	1026	59	51	70524	20160	20841	52	23
King Edward	195	15	15	13654	1700	1700	11	–
Crimond	353	10	14	18329	0	0	25	16
St Fergus	212	10	18	11658	0	103	21	15
Cruden	538	38	24	43929	5720	6205	24	4
Deer	1015	36	34	38045	3520	3964	43	5
Fordyce	586	40	42	41736	7300	8276	44	8
Fraserburgh Old	1011	58	96	106355	28710	27745	204	86
Fraserburgh South	396	25	28	37074	4510	4866	59	–
Inverallochy and Rathen: East	104	10	27	12376	2440	2440	22	–
Fraserburgh West	772	47	110	50109	9590	9590	75	10
Fyvie	462	29	45	33219	8575	8675	32	3
Rothienorman	208	10	10	10809	1550	1550	10	–
Gardenstown	64	10	32	32676	3230	3230	25	–
Longside	635	36	18	35911	4120	5387	100	16
Lonmay	206	16	11	18694	1290	1290	10	30
Rathen: West	139	9	–	11082	1200	421	10	–
Macduff	987	40	55	55982	10170	13115	106	53
Marnoch	452	31	20	29326	3860	3860	54	41
Maud and Savoch	343	18	16	18283	531	708	31	2
Monquhitter and New Byth	476	28	31	26253	0	0	12	–
New Deer: St Kane's	555	23	19	34334	4900	4900	62	–
Ordiquihill and Cornhill	196	13	15	10036	247	247	16	–
Whitehills	386	25	36	24171	3160	3362	32	–
Peterhead Old	625	41	45	50201	9110	9110	82	22
Peterhead St Andrew's	655	40	37	43813	6310	6310	95	8
Peterhead Trinity	456	27	26	85081	12380	12530	28	5
Pitsligo	238	15	15	23247	2225	2558	70	2
Sandhaven	113	8	20	11979	1040	1040	21	–
Strichen	531	14	47	27074	5050	5050	18	10
Tyrie	193	9	17	10259	300	300	8	3
Turriff St Andrew's	639	24	23	36649	3340	3340	47	13
Turriff St Ninian's and Forglen	1143	57	54	55583	11460	11708	78	6

35. MORAY

Congregation	Com	Eld	G	In98	Ass	Gvn	3-11	-17
Aberlour	511	21	34	31301	4210	4210	–	–
Alves and Burghead	182	17	14	21756	0	0	53	–
Kinloss and Findhorn	122	15	17	11271	0	300	18	–

Congregation	Com	Eld	G	In98	Ass	Gvn	3-11	-17
Bellie	464	17	37	38865	12500	14500	37	10
Speymouth	265	14	30	14623	2380	2380	17	–
Birnie	257	16	20	17547	1450	1450	14	–
Pluscarden	143	13	17	14432	1475	1574	14	–
Buckie North	774	43	101	50438	10530	13294	84	9
Buckie South and West	392	29	37	34110	5070	5070	41	42
Enzie	128	15	14	9085	932	1708	17	–
Cullen and Deskford	530	37	77	5598	6320	6597	51	16
Dallas	63	5	13	8498	1280	1280	–	–
Forres St Leonard's	380	28	62	37197	4120	4276	–	–
Rafford	91	6	17	7187	1380	1380	–	–
Duffus, Spynie and Hopeman	485	44	53	44247	6400	6843	39	–
Dyke	213	0	25	19470	3460	3570	41	7
Edinkillie	98	12	–	15616	1475	1475	8	2
Elgin High	858	52	59	62376	12900	13300	67	25
Elgin St Giles'	1495	71	92	96551	22810	22810	–	–
Elgin South	287	26	22	22350	1750	2043	6	–
Findochty	79	9	19	17367	0	240	25	19
Portknockie	127	8	40	13152	0	0	22	–
Rathven	158	18	39	10580	343	543	43	–
Forres St Laurence	710	39	59	54251	9780	9960	–	–
Grange	207	8	17	10672	284	0	14	–
Rothiemay	238	13	13	10660	220	1045	8	–
Keith North, Newmill and Boharm	592	53	29	65231	10570	11020	44	15
Keith St Rufus and Botriphnie	974	49	43	47349	8180	8180	49	15
Knockando, Elchies and Archiestown	284	12	15	12203	880	880	–	–
Rothes	360	16	27	20555	3670	3670	37	–
Lossiemouth St Gerardine's High	442	25	45	43598	6610	6610	32	4
Lossiemouth St James'	403	21	41	41019	6420	6420	33	5
Mortlach and Cabrach	599	37	51	27479	0	6820	–	–
St Andrew's Lhanbryde and Urquhart	508	33	28	33934	6540	6540	49	16

36. ABERNETHY

Congregation	Com	Eld	G	In98	Ass	Gvn	3-11	-17
Abernethy	167	19	–	21564	2720	2720	39	13
Cromdale and Advie	123	7	–	10925	612	0	–	–
Alvie and Insh	82	9	–	25573	7670	7670	20	11
Boat of Garten and Kincardine	109	10	16	17840	0	0	14	12
Duthil	74	9	15	9175	0	0	12	9
Dulnain Bridge	41	6	–	8319	330	330	4	–
Grantown-on-Spey	357	22	37	33176	6470	6470	33	10
Inveraven and Glenlivet	148	7	11	9622	0	0	6	3
Kingussie	138	15	–	19488	0	0	12	15
Kirkmichael and Tomintoul	95	5	–	8681	0	0	9	–
Laggan	43	5	–	7446	0	0	4	–
Newtonmore	101	9	–	11885	0	20	9	–
Rothiemurchus and Aviemore	110	5	10	17788	0	0	11	2

37. INVERNESS

Congregation	Com	Eld	G	In98	Ass	Gvn	3-11	-17
Ardclach	44	4	–	4508	0	0	2	–
Auldearn and Dalmore	105	8	21	12862	0	0	11	–
Ardersier	87	12	18	14268	0	80	32	–

Congregation	Com	Eld	G	In98	Ass	Gvn	3-11	-17
Petty	68	8	12	10487	0	0	–	–
Cawdor	162	13	24	22115	0	0	21	–
Croy and Dalcross	73	10	23	10500	0	308	15	–
Culloden The Barn	395	32	36	53392	6960	7080	67	23
Daviot and Dunlichity	66	7	–	11510	0	0	–	–
Moy, Dalarossie and Tomatin	37	4	12	6503	0	0	16	–
Dores and Boleskine	107	8	11	14254	0	0	18	–
Inverness Crown	831	91	90	83294	21470	21470	61	37
Inverness Dalneigh and Bona	274	16	31	51533	10350	14050	43	27
Inverness East	333	35	25	92313	19790	19990	71	20
Inverness Hilton	250	16	36	39524	0	0	75	12
Inverness Kinmylies	209	13	–	26996	0	0	41	10
Inverness Ness Bank	585	57	22	59788	12870	12870	48	27
Inverness St Columba (High)	291	37	26	53403	10770	10920	23	7
Inverness St Stephen's	434	33	19	48558	9360	14360	77	25
Inverness The Old High	200	30	–	30314	7240	7240	21	13
Inverness Trinity	425	45	36	61879	11720	11720	66	9
Inverness West	321	30	–	64736	14040	16040	24	10
Kilmorack and Erchless	124	14	18	26796	0	385	16	2
Kiltarlity	54	6	7	15174	0	0	36	2
Kirkhill	86	7	17	11889	0	0	23	4
Nairn Old	1025	68	42	79008	17830	17830	52	30
Nairn St Ninian's	366	20	40	31850	4380	4380	23	2
Urquhart and Glenmoriston	154	7	11	39393	4780	4962	53	8

38. LOCHABER

Congregation	Com	Eld	G	In98	Ass	Gvn	3-11	-17
Acharacle	46	5	–	9669	0	50	–	–
Ardnamurchan	20	4	–	5400	0	0	11	–
Ardgour	50	7	16	12086	0	235	16	–
Strontian	20	4	10	8122	0	157	8	–
Arisaig and The Small Isles	58	5	18	10401	0	0	10	–
Duror	52	6	17	11979	0	0	–	–
Glencoe	76	6	18	14629	0	0	10	–
Fort Augustus	80	11	20	20106	0	0	22	–
Glengarry	41	8	11	10232	0	100	12	–
Fort William Duncansburgh	370	24	23	41874	7650	7853	27	12
Kilmonivaig	74	7	15	15923	3150	5600	5	14
Fort William MacIntosh Memorial	239	31	16	44950	6400	6400	21	12
Kilmallie	234	22	30	37874	8010	8310	41	9
Kinlochleven	92	9	25	19335	0	0	8	8
Nether Lochaber	71	5	–	10890	0	0	18	–
Mallaig St Columba and Knoydart	103	5	–	23148	0	0	25	5
Morvern	59	7	10	8712	0	0	–	–

39. ROSS

Congregation	Com	Eld	G	In98	Ass	Gvn	3-11	-17
Alness	144	15	25	33778	0	0	42	9
Avoch	34	5	14	12490	1440	1440	2	–
Fortrose and Rosemarkie	146	14	–	27675	3980	3980	30	15
Contin	69	12	–	14253	0	0	–	–
Cromarty	74	2	17	12180	0	0	24	9
Dingwall Castle Street	168	20	24	41200	5110	5310	11	13

Congregation	Com	Eld	G	In98	Ass	Gvn	3-11	-17
Dingwall St Clement's 269	27	22	41086	6200	6200	57	8
Fearn Abbey and Nigg Chapelhill 108	15	42	21339	0	0	16	–
Ferintosh 214	22	41	40039	390	1060	52	9
Fodderty and Strathpeffer 174	19	25	24908	0	749	30	21
Invergordon 257	20	23	42005	6040	6388	51	18
Killearnan 149	17	–	25776	0	700	36	4
Kilmuir and Logie Easter 81	11	15	23121	0	0	13	3
Kiltearn 92	7	7	27285	0	0	28	7
Knockbain 74	6	12	16091	0	0	19	8
Lochbroom and Ullapool 59	3	13	18856	0	0	19	8
Resolis and Urquhart 107	13	–	24589	0	0	27	13
Rosskeen 170	12	36	31026	0	507	38	11
Tain 195	16	39	43304	6600	6600	57	16
Tarbat 74	7	17	15487	0	223	11	–
Urray and Kilchrist 142	22	32	35658	0	288	34	–

40. SUTHERLAND

Altnaharra and Farr 29	3	–	8338	0	0	4	–
Assynt and Stoer 33	2	–	13493	0	0	20	14
Clyne 121	9	–	21119	0	0	18	–
Creich 51	6	–	9723	0	525	17	–
Rosehall 24	3	–	6237	0	100	–	–
Dornoch Cathedral 413	32	48	56896	10710	11482	51	17
Durness and Kinlochbervie 43	4	16	14276	0	0	11	–
Eddrachillis 18	2	–	13203	0	0	16	–
Golspie 121	20	19	33567	1952	0	13	28
Kildonan and Loth Helmsdale 39	4	19	12858	0	0	3	–
Kincardine Croick and Edderton 74	10	15	19955	0	0	–	28
Lairg 51	5	23	14730	0	116	22	4
Rogart 28	5	10	8864	0	0	3	–
Melness and Tongue 51	5	10	11613	0	0	24	1

41. CAITHNESS

Berriedale and Dunbeath 22	3	–	8681	0	0	15	–
Latheron 25	3	–	9819	0	0	10	–
Bower 36	5	11	7816	0	0	19	3
Watten 45	4	8	8010	0	0	18	–
Canisbay 48	3	18	11232	0	120	15	–
Keiss 30	2	12	8774	0	0	11	–
Dunnet 21	2	9	6221	0	0	6	–
Olrig 59	5	12	8461	0	0	29	4
Halkirk and Westerdale 88	8	21	16539	0	0	49	10
Lybster and Bruan 47	7	20	18438	0	0	27	3
Reay 38	5	10	13330	0	0	12	–
Strathy and Halladale 36	6	15	9995	0	156	13	–
Thurso St Peter's and St Andrew's 268	23	52	41697	6825	6825	59	12
Thurso West 297	31	36	40070	3500	3500	61	4
Wick Bridge Street 196	12	16	38174	1730	1730	29	15
Wick Old 286	34	43	41988	3500	3500	74	17
Wick Pultneytown and Thrumster 272	15	46	47270	7610	8010	97	21

Congregation	Com	Eld	G	In98	Ass	Gvn	3-11	-17
42. LOCHCARRON – SKYE								
Applecross, Lochcarron and Torridon	77	9	27	28269	0	150	36	3
Bracadale and Durinish	97	8	11	20908	0	280	54	23
Gairloch and Dundonnell	79	6	–	35167	4610	4610	31	–
Glenelg and Kintail	60	8	–	16852	0	410	33	15
Kilmuir and Stenscholl	72	11	–	27998	0	500	33	8
Lochalsh	123	8	26	32386	3090	3262	41	8
Portree	152	7	–	45615	4320	4720	63	7
Snizort	101	7	–	38397	450	450	39	12
Strath and Sleat	194	19	37	57664	8450	17555	72	32
43. UIST								
Barra	36	5	–	7424	0	0	11	–
Benbecula	83	12	30	26275	0	500	30	20
Bernera	21	3	–	9181	0	0	9	1
Carinish	75	9	25	29987	0	0	31	5
Kilmuir and Paible	34	9	15	20994	0	0	26	3
Lochmaddy and Trumisgarry	52	4	13	17296	0	237	15	–
Manish – Scarista	45	4	–	22722	0	0	33	–
South Uist	62	12	12	15759	0	0	9	–
Tarbert	161	15	–	57869	10790	10790	55	17
44. LEWIS								
Barvas	95	11	–	31531	1700	1700	43	15
Carloway	49	0	–	23224	0	700	19	2
Cross Ness	56	6	–	24175	0	0	17	2
Kinloch	49	10	–	21850	0	0	26	4
Knock	82	6	–	31733	0	0	36	–
Lochs-in-Bernera	37	6	–	17259	0	0	13	1
Lochs – Crossbost	19	3	–	16885	0	0	21	3
Stornoway High	292	14	–	79666	18700	18700	89	19
Stornoway Martin's Memorial	111	7	24	38336	3970	3970	36	14
Stornoway St Columba's	149	12	30	56995	10360	10360	50	26
Uig	57	8	–	16556	0	0	15	11
45. ORKNEY								
Birsay	118	13	20	12361	0	0	40	–
Harray and Sandwick	304	24	49	26166	876	876	35	15
Deerness	102	9	–	6239	890	890	13	–
Holm	155	11	14	11786	1140	1336	21	–
St Andrew's	90	11	12	8582	580	580	8	–
Eday	10	3	8	2573	0	0	–	1
Stronsay: Moncur Memorial	75	10	29	11360	0	300	12	–
Evie	59	6	–	4740	468	411	3	3
Firth	146	9	21	20846	2287	2089	19	67
Rendall	68	4	14	7983	840	840	12	4
Flotta	31	4	–	3008	0	0	8	–
Hoy and Walls	83	11	17	6325	0	0	13	–
Kirkwall East	585	45	71	51870	11770	11865	45	11
Kirkwall St Magnus Cathedral	840	79	34	70006	17270	17423	72	5

Congregation	Com	Eld	G	In98	Ass	Gvn	3-11	-17
North Ronaldsay	21	2	–	2436	0	0	–	–
Sanday	117	11	19	9462	0	0	30	4
Orphir	150	11	22	17120	1040	1240	10	6
Stenness	102	9	16	14543	883	883	12	–
Papa Westray	12	3	–	3158	0	0	6	–
Westray	76	12	26	14396	0	0	26	11
Rousay	34	4	12	3638	0	0	–	–
Shapinsay	78	8	–	7907	0	50	4	–
South Ronaldsay and Burray	235	11	14	17056	0	0	36	10
Stromness	432	26	35	37298	7030	7030	–	3
46. SHETLAND								
Burra Isle	57	5	25	7425	0	0	22	5
Tingwall	184	19	25	18029	0	0	56	6
Delting	130	9	13	18292	0	0	34	8
Nesting and Lunnasting	47	5	22	7415	0	0	–	–
Dunrossness	75	13	13	14861	0	0	27	19
Sandwick Cunningsburgh and Quarff	169	11	39	22047	0	367	27	1
Fetlar	21	3	–	1910	0	0	12	–
Yell	155	8	40	10577	0	0	18	–
Lerwick and Bressay	606	0	–	52867	10580	10580	–	–
Northmavine	96	10	–	10169	0	0	–	–
Sandsting and Aithsting	61	13	9	7333	0	0	19	4
Walls and Sandness	56	10	10	7546	0	0	12	–
Unst	141	10	28	13812	0	0	25	3
Whalsay and Skerries	263	17	20	18631	0	0	–	–
47. ENGLAND								
Corby St Andrew's	393	26	31	30954	2340	2740	22	6
Corby St Ninian's	435	28	22	39132	6660	6660	23	5
Guernsey: St Andrew's in the Grange	243	20	–	33342	5760	5760	67	4
Jersey: St Columba's	149	22	–	34071	2100	2100	45	6
Liverpool: St Andrew's	54	6	9	11931	2288	2288	–	–
London Crown Court	318	46	11	70975	17530	17530	25	–
London St Columba's	1527	69	–	211261	35600	35600	99	4
Newcastle	131	20	14	14587	2970	2970	13	–

INDEX OF MINISTERS

NOTE: Ministers who are members of a Presbytery are designated "A" if holding a parochial appointment in that Presbytery, or "B" if otherwise qualifying for membership.

"A-1, A-2" *etc* indicate the numerical order of congregations in the Presbyteries of Edinburgh, Glasgow and Hamilton.

Also included are:

(1) Ministers who have resigned their seat in Presbytery (List 6-H)
(2) Ministers who hold a Ministerial Certificate (List 6-I),
(3) Ministers serving overseas (List 6-K).
(4) Auxiliary Ministers (List 6-A)

(NB *For a List of the Diaconate see List 6-G*)

Abeledo, B.J.	Paisley 14A	Archer, N.D.C.	List 6-I
Acklam, C.	Falkirk 22B	Archibald, D.Y	Dunfermline 24B
Adams, D.G.	Dunfermline 24A	Armitage, W.L.	Edinburgh 1A-50
Adamson, H.	Irvine/K'marnock 11A	Armour, C.	St Andrews 26A
Adamson, S.	Lothian 3B	Armstrong, W.R.	Greenock 15A
Aitchison, J.W.	Aberdeen 31B	Arnott, A.D.K.	St Andrews 26A
Aitken, A.J.	Glasgow 16B	Atkins, Mrs Y.E.S.	Edinburgh 1A-78
Aitken, A.R.	Edinburgh 1B	Auld, A.G.	Edinburgh 1B
Aitken, E.D.	Stirling 23B	Auld, I.A.	Melrose/Peebles 4B
Aitken, E.R.	Edinburgh 1A-79	Austin, G.	Moray 35A
Aitken, F.R.	Ayr 10A		
Aitken, I.	Aberdeen 31A	Baigrie, R.A.	Edinburgh 1B
Alexander, D.C.	Caithness 41B	Bailey, W.G.	List 6-H
Alexander, D.N.	Paisley 14B	Baillie, D.	Annandale/Eskdale 7B
Alexander, E.J.	Glasgow 16B	Bain, B.	Perth 28A
Alexander, Miss H.	List 6-I	Bain, J.	Lanark 13A
Alexander, I.W.	Edinburgh 1B	Baird, G.W.	Hamilton 17B
Alexander, J.S.	St Andrews 26B	Baird, K.S.	Glasgow 16A-41
Alexander, W.M.	Perth 28B	Baird, W.G.G	Dunfermline 24B
Allan, A.G.	Glasgow 16B	Baker, Mrs C.	Ayr 10A
Allan, J.B.	Hamilton 17B	Balfour, T.	List 6-H
Allan, R.T.	Falkirk 22B	Ballantyne, S.	Aberdeen 31B
Allen, Miss V.L.	Angus 30A	Ballentine, Miss A.M.	W' Lothian 2A
Allen, M.A.W.	Glasgow 16A-14	Banks, J.	Ayr 10B
Allison, Mrs M.M.	Dunoon 20A	Barber, P.I.	Edinburgh 1A-29
Allison, R.N.	Paisley 14A	Barbour, R.A.	Dunkeld/Meigle 27B
Allsop, T.D.	Aberdeen 31A	Barclay, I.C.	Aberdeen 31A
Almond, D.	Annan'/Eskdale 7A	Barclay, N.W.	Falkirk 22A
Alston, W.G.	Glasgow 16A-110	Barclay, S.G.	Irvine/Kilmarnock 11A
Amed, P.	Hamilton 17A-67	Bardgett, F.D.	Dunfermline 24B
Anderson, A.F.	Edinburgh 1A-32	Barge, N.L.	Glasgow 16A-43
Anderson, C.M.	Inverness 37A	Barr, A.C	Glasgow 16B
Anderson, D.	Buchan 34A	Barr, D.	Glasgow 16B
Anderson, D.J.B.	Edinburgh 1B	Barr, G.K.	Perth 28B
Anderson, D.M.	Lochaber 38B	Barr, G.R.	Edinburgh 1A-20
Anderson, H.	Edinburgh 1B	Barr, J.	Perth 28B
Anderson, J.F.	Aberdeen 31A	Barr, T.L.	Perth 28B
Anderson, J.W.	Angus 30B	Barrett, L.	Angus 30A
Anderson, K.G.	Perth 28A	Barrie, A.	Ardrossan 12A
Anderson, R.	Glasgow 16A-55	Barrie, A.P.	Hamilton 17A-42
Anderson, R.A.	West Lothian 2A	Barrington, C.	Edinburgh 1A-3
Anderson, R.J.M.	Glasgow 16A-59	Barron, Mrs J.	Dundee 29A
Anderson, R.S.	Stirling 23B	Bartholomew, D.S.	Dum/Kirk 8A
Anderson, Mrs S.M.	Irv'/K'nock 11A	Baxendale, Mrs G.M.	Paisley 14A
Andrew, J.	Gordon 33A	Baxter, R.	Kirkcaldy 25A
Andrew, R.J.M.	Ayr 10B	Baxter, R.F	Edinburgh 1B
Andrews, J.E.	Lothian 3A	Bayne, A.L.	Edinburgh 1A-6
Andrews, J.T.	Wigtown/Stranraer 9B	Beaton, D.	Lochcarron/Skye 42A
Angus, J.A.K.	Kincard'/Deeside 32B	Beattie, J.A.	Glasgow 16B
Annand, J.M.	Annandale/Eskdale 7B	Beattie, W.	List 6-I
Arbuthnott, Mrs J.	List 6-I	Beattie, W.D.	Hamilton 17A-70
Beattie, W.G.	Hamilton 17B		
Beattie, W.G.	Kincard'/Deeside 32B		
Beautyman, P.H.	Glasgow 16B		
Beck, J.C.	Moray 35A		
Becke, J.C.	Angus 30B		
Beckett, D.M.	Edinburgh 1A-33		
Beebee, G.W.	St Andrews 26A		
Bell, C.J.G.	Caithness 41A		
Bell, D.W.	Buchan 34B		
Bell, F.R.	Dunkeld/Meigle 27B		
Bell, G.K.	Glasgow 16A-60		
Bell, I.W.	Paisley 14A		
Bell, J.L.	Glasgow 16B		
Bell. Mrs M.	Paisley 14A		
Bell, R.P.	Ayr 10A		
Bennett, A.	St Andrews 26B		
Bennett, A.G.	Melrose/Peebles 4A		
Bennett, D.K.P.	Dum'/K'cudbright 8A		
Benson, J.W.	Stirling 23B		
Benzie, I.W.	Ardrossan 12A		
Berrill, P.A.D.	Kincard'/Dee' 32A		
Bertram, T.A.	Perth 28B		
Best, E.	St Andrews 26B		
Beveridge, S.E.P.	Annan'/Eskdale 7A		
Bews, J.	St Andrews 26B		
Bicket, M.S.	Angus 30A		
Billes, R.H.	Irvine/Kilmarnock 11A		
Bird, J.W.	Ayr 10B		
Birnie, C.J.	Buchan 34B		
Birrell, Mrs I.	Perth 28A		
Birrell, J.M.	Perth 28B		
Birse, G.S.	Ayr 10A		
Birss, A.D.	Paisley 14A		
Bisset, J.M.	Glasgow 16B		
Bjarnason, S.	Abernethy 36A		
Black, A.G.	Lothian 3A		
Black, A.R.	Ardrossan 12A		
Black, A.T.	Inverness 37B		
Black, D.R.	Glasgow 16A-115		
Black, D.W.	West Lothian 2A		
Black, I.W.	Falkirk 22A		
Black, J.M.	Hamilton 17A-23		
Black, Mrs J.M.K.	List 6-I		
Black, J.S.	List 6-I		
Black, Mrs S	Glasgow 16B		
Black, W.	Ayr 10B		
Black, W.B.	Lewis 44A		
Black, W.G.	List 6-I		
Blackley, Mrs J.R.M.	Glasgow 16A-1		
Blackwood, K.T.	Dumbarton 18A		
Blaikie, J.	Buchan 34B		

Henderson, J.D.	Dunkeld/Meigle 27B	Howie, Mrs M.L.K.	Ardrossan 12A
Henderson, Miss J.M	Hamilt'n 17A-68	Howie, W.	List 6-H
Henderson, R.B.	Inverness 37B	Howieson, R.A.	St Andrews 26B
Henderson, R.J.M.	Glasgow 16A-99	Howitt, Miss J.	List 6-I
Hendrie, B.R.	Falkirk 22A	Hudson, E.V.	Dumbarton 18A
Hendrie, Mrs Y	Falkirk 22B	Hudson, H.R.	Glasgow 16A-53
Henig, G.	Buchan 34A	Hudson, J.H.	Dundee 29B
Henney, W.	St Andrews 26B	Huggett, Miss J.A.	Irv'/K'nock 11B
Henry, M.N.	Perth 28B	Hughes, C.E.	Lothian 3A
Hepburn, Miss C.A.	Stirling 23A	Hughes, D.W.	Hamilton 17A-58
Hepburn, J.L.	Edinburgh 1B	Hughes, O.T.	England 47B
Heriot, C.R.	Falkirk 22B	Huie, D.F.	Europe 48A
Herkes, Mrs M.	Dunfermline 24A	Humphris, P.M.	Dundee 29A
(Heron, A.I.C.	Europe 48)	Hunt, T.G.	Orkney 45A
Heron, J.	Hamilton 17B	Hunter, A.G.	Glasgow 16B
Herron, A.	Glasgow 16B	Hunter, G.	Glasgow 16B
Hetherington, R.M.	Paisley 14A	Hunter, G.L.	Dumbarton 18B
Hewitt, E.T.	Irv'/K'marnock 11B	Hunter, J.E.	Hamilton 17B
Hewitt, W.C.	Greenock 15A	Hunter, W.F.	Glasgow 16A-120
Hibbert, F.	Jerusalem 49A	Hurst, F.R.	Sutherland 40A
Higgins, G.K.	List 6-I	Hutcheson, J.M.	Glasgow 16B
Higham, R.D.	Lorn/Mull 21A	Hutcheson, N.M.	Dum'/K'cud 8A
Hill, A.T.	Lothian 3B	Hutchison, Mrs A.M.	Aberdeen 31B
Hill, J.W.	Edinburgh 1A-15	Hutchison, A.S.	Aberdeen 31B
Hill, R.	St Andrews 26B	Hutchison, D.S.	Aberdeen 31B
Hill, R.S.	Perth 28B	Hutchison, H.	Glasgow 16B
Hill, S.	Falkirk 22B	Hutchison, Mrs M.	Dum'/K'cud 8B
Hilsley, B.C.	Edinburgh 1A-47		
Hislop, D.T.	Glasgow 16B	Inglis, Mrs A.	Edinburgh 1A-13
Hodge, W.N.T.	Angus 30B	Inglis, C.G.	List 6-H
Hogg, T.	Lothian 3A	Inglis, D.B.C.	Buchan 34A
Hogg, W.T.	Lorn/Mull 21A	Ingram, J.R.	Dundee 29B
Holland, J.C.	Falkirk 22B	Ireland, A.	List 6-I
Holland, W.	Dum'/K'cudbright 8A	Irvine, Mrs E.H.C.	Glasgow 16B
Hollins, R.M.	Ayr 10B	Irvine, R.W.W.	Stirling 23B
Holroyd, G.	Ross 39B	Irving, D.R.	Dum'/K'cudbright 8A
Holt, J.	Kincard'/Deeside 32A	Irving, G.D.	Greenock 15A
Homewood, I.M.	Edinburgh 1A-20	Irving, W.D.	Lothian 3A
Hood, A.J.J.	List 6-I	Izett, W.A.F	Lanark 13A
Hood, D	Hamilton 17A-29		
Hood, E.C.P.	Kincard'/Dee' 32B	Jack, Mrs A.M.	Edinburgh 1A-65
Hood, Mrs E.L.	Paisley 14A	Jack, D.	Kincard'/Deeside 32A
Hood, H.S.C.	England 47A	Jack, J.A.P.	Dundee 29A
Hope, Miss E.P.	Glasgow 16B	Jack, R.	Dumbarton 18B
Hope, Mrs G.H.	Duns 5A	Jackson, Mrs C.	Dundee 29A
Horne, A.M.	Falkirk 22A	Jackson, J.	Duns 5B
Horne, D.A.	Ross 39A	Jackson, W.	Perth 28A
Horsburgh, A.G.	Stirling 23A	Jaffrey, Mrs A.	Buchan 34B
Horsburgh, G.E.	Irv'/K'marnock 11A	Jamieson, D.B.	Dundee 29A
Hosain, S.	Irv'/K'marnock 11A	Jamieson, G.D.	Dundee 29A
Hosie, J.	South Argyll 19B	Jamieson, G.T.	Stirling 23B
Houghton, Mrs C.	Angus 30A	Jamieson, Mrs H.E.	Lanark 13A
Houston, A.M.	Perth 28B	Jamieson, H.M.	Melrose/Peebles 4B
Houston, Miss E.W	Dumbarton 18A	Jamieson, J.	Stirling 23B
Houston, G.R.	Edinburgh 1B	Jamieson, R.C.	Irv'/K'marnock 11B
Houston, P.M.	Dumbarton 18B	Jarvie, J.W.	St Andrews 26A
Houston, T.C.	Glasgow 16A-48	Jarvie, T.W.	Irv'/K'marnock 11A
Houston, W.R.	Hamilton 17A-4	Jeffrey, E.W.S.	Edinburgh 1B
Howe, A.Y.	Ross 39B	Jeffrey, S.D.	Buchan 34B

Jenkins, G.F.C.	Dunfermline 24A
Jenkinson, J.J.	Falkirk 22A
Jessamine, A.L.	Dunfermline 24A
Jesson, W.J.	Wigtown/Stranraer 9B
Johnson, C.I.W.	Greenock 15A
Johnston, C.D.	List 6-K
Johnston, J.	Dum'/K'cudbright 8B
Johnston, K.L.	Ayr 10A
Johnston, Miss M.H.	Glasg' 16A-103
Johnston, R.W.M.	Glasgow 16B
Johnston, T.N.	Edinburgh 1A-66
Johnston, W.	Ardrossan 12A
Johnston, W.B.	Edinburgh 1B
Johnstone, B.	Lochaber 38A
Johnstone, D.	Glasgow 16B
Johnstone, Mrs H.G.	Edinburgh 1B
Johnstone, H.M.J.	Hamilton 17A-11
Johnstone, R.	List 6-I
Johnstone, R.	Caithness 41A
Johnstone, T.J.	Hamilton 17B
Johnstone, W.	Aberdeen 31B
Jolly, A.J.	England 47B
Jolly, J.	Glasgow 16B
Jones, Mrs A.M.	Lochaber 38A
Jones, E.G.	Glasgow 16A-133
Jones, J.D.	Glasgow 16B
Jones, J.O.	Glasgow 16A-98
Jones, P.H.	Lanark 13B
Jones, R.	Ross 39A
Jones, R.A.	Gordon 33B
Jones, W.	Angus 30B
Jones, W.A.	Edinburgh 1A-21
Jones, W.G.	Ayr 10A
Kant, E.W.	Edinburgh 1B
Kavanagh, J.A.	Glasgow 16A-32
Kay, D.	Paisley 14A
Keating, Mrs G.	Edinburgh 1A-40
Keddie, D.A.	Dumbarton 18B
Keil, A.H.	Edinburgh 1A-72
Keith, D.	Angus 30B
Kellas, D.J.	Dunoon 20A
Kellet, J.M.	Melrose/Peebles 4B
Kellock, C.	Falkirk 22B
Kelly, A.F.	List 6-I
Kelly, E.	Edinburgh 1B
Kelly, Miss I.J.M.	Greenock 15A
Kelly, T.A.D.	Glasgow 16A-83
Kelly, T.C.	Perth 28B
Kelly, W.	Dum'/K'cudbright 8A
Kennedy, D.A.	Lanark 13B
Kennedy, G.	Ayr 10A
Kennon, S.	Melrose/Peebles 4A
Kenny, Mrs C.G.	Europe 48A
Kenny, Miss E.	Dunfermline 24A
Kent, A.F.S.	Ayr 10B
Kent, R.M.	Hamilton 17A-48
Kerr, A.	Paisley 14B
Kerr, A.	Glasgow 16A-35

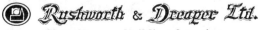

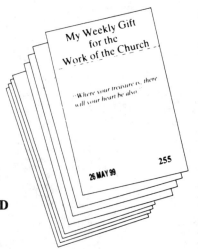

INDEX OF PLACES

NOTE: Numbers on the right of the column refer to the Presbytery in which the district lies. Names in brackets are given for ease of identification. They either refer to the name of the Parish, which may be different from that of the district, or they distinguish places with the same name.

INDEX OF SUBJECTS

INDEX OF ADVERTISERS